PROCESS MODELING, SIMULATION, AND CONTROL FOR CHEMICAL ENGINEERS

THE SERIES

ANDERSON AND WENZEL—*Introduction to Chemical Engineering*
ARIES AND NEWTON—*Chemical Engineering Cost Estimation*
BADGER AND BANCHERO—*Introduction to Chemical Engineering*
BENNETT AND MYERS—*Momentum, Heat, and Mass Transfer*
BEVERIDGE AND SCHECHTER—*Optimization: Theory and Practice*
CLARKE AND DAVIDSON—*Manual for Process Engineering Calculations*
COUGHANOWR AND KOPPEL—*Process Systems Analysis and Control*
DODGE—*Chemical Engineering Thermodynamics*
GRISWOLD—*Fuels, Combustion, and Furnaces*
GROGGINS—*Unit Processes in Organic Synthesis*
HARRIOTT—*Process Control*
HENLEY AND BIEBER—*Chemical Engineering Calculations*
JOHNSON—*Automatic Process Control*
JOHNSTONE AND THRING—*Pilot Plants, Models, and Scale-up Methods in Chemical Engineering*
KATZ, CORNELL, KOBAYASHI, POETTMANN, VARY, ELENBAAS, AND WEINAUG—*Handbook of Natural Gas Engineering*
KING—*Separation Processes*
KNUDSEN AND KATZ—*Fluid Dynamics and Heat Transfer*
LAPIDUS—*Digital Computation for Chemical Engineers*
LEVA—*Fluidization*
LEWIS, RADASCH, AND LEWIS—*Industrial Stoichiometry*
LUYBEN—*Process Modeling, Simulation, and Control for Chemical Engineers*
MANTELL—*Electrochemical Engineering*
McADAMS—*Heat Transmission*
McCABE AND SMITH, J. C.—*Unit Operations of Chemical Engineering*
MICKLEY, SHERWOOD, AND REED—*Applied Mathematics in Chemical Engineering*
NELSON—*Petroleum Refinery Engineering*
PERRY (EDITOR)—*Chemical Engineers' Handbook*
PETERS—*Elementary Chemical Engineering*
PETERS AND TIMMERHAUS—*Plant Design and Economics for Chemical Engineers*
REED AND GUBBINS—*Applied Statistical Mechanics*
REID AND SHERWOOD—*The Properties of Gases and Liquids*
SCHECHTER—*The Variational Method in Engineering*
SCHMIDT AND MARLIES—*Principles of High-polymer Theory and Practice*
SCHWEYER—*Process Engineering Economics*
SHERWOOD AND PIGFORD—*Absorption and Extraction*
SHREVE—*Chemical Process Industries*
SLATTERY—*Momentum, Energy, and Mass Transfer in Continua*
SMITH, B. D.—*Design of Equilibrium Stage Processes*
SMITH, J. M.—*Chemical Engineering Kinetics*
SMITH, J. M., AND VAN NESS—*Introduction to Chemical Engineering Thermodynamics*
TREYBAL—*Liquid Extraction*
TREYBAL—*Mass-transfer Operations*
VAN WINKLE—*Distillation*
VILBRANDT AND DRYDEN—*Chemical Engineering Plant Design*
VOLK—*Applied Statistics for Engineers*
WALAS—*Reaction Kinetics for Chemical Engineers*
WALKER, LEWIS, McADAMS, AND GILLILAND—*Principles of Chemical Engineering*
WILLIAMS AND JOHNSON—*Stoichiometry for Chemical Engineers*
WILSON AND RIES—*Principles of Chemical Engineering Thermodynamics*

Process Modeling, Simulation, and Control for Chemical Engineers

W. L. Luyben

*Associate Professor of
Chemical Engineering
Lehigh University*

McGraw-Hill Book Company

New York   St. Louis   San Francisco   Düsseldorf   Johannesburg
Kuala Lumpur   London   Mexico   Montreal   New Delhi   Panama
Rio de Janeiro   Singapore   Sydney   Toronto

PROCESS MODELING, SIMULATION, AND
CONTROL FOR CHEMICAL ENGINEERS

Library of Congress Catalog Card Number 74-173713

07-039157-2

4 5 6 7 8 9 0 K P K P 7 9 8 7 6

This book was set in Times Roman, and printed and bound by Kingsport Press, Inc. The designer was Richard Paul Kluga; the drawings were done by Reproduction Drawings Ltd. The editors were B. J. Clark and Barry Benjamin. Sally Ellyson supervised production.

*To the engineer, the scientist who
converts the feasible into the practical*

CONTENTS

Preface   *xv*
Chemical engineering references   *xviii*

Chapter 1   Introduction   *1*

1-1   Examples of the Role of Process Dynamics and Control   *1*
1-2   Objectives   *6*
1-3   Historical Background   *6*
1-4   Perspective   *7*
1-5   Motivation for Studying Process Control   *8*
1-6   General Concepts   *8*

PART ONE   MATHEMATICAL MODELS OF CHEMICAL ENGINEERING SYSTEMS

Chapter 2   Fundamentals   *15*

2-1   Introduction   *15*
    2-1.1   Uses of Mathematical Models   *15*
    2-1.2   Scope of Coverage   *16*
    2-1.3   Principles of Formulation   *16*
2-2   Fundamental Laws   *17*
    2-2.1   Continuity Equations   *18*
    2-2.2   Energy Equation   *24*
    2-2.3   Equations of Motion   *29*
    2-2.4   Transport Equations   *34*
    2-2.5   Equations of State   *35*
    2-2.6   Equilibrium   *36*
    2-2.7   Chemical Kinetics   *39*

Chapter 3   Examples of Mathematical Models of Chemical Engineering Systems   *43*

3-1   Introduction   *43*
3-2   Series of Isothermal, Constant-holdup CSTR's   *44*
3-3   CSTR's with Variable Holdups   *46*
3-4   Gas-phase, Pressurized CSTR   *47*
3-5   Nonisothermal CSTR   *49*
3-6   Single-component Vaporizer   *54*
3-7   Multicomponent Flash Drum   *58*
3-8   Batch Reactor   *62*
3-9   Reactor with Mass Transfer   *67*
3-10 Ideal Binary Distillation Column   *69*
3-11 Multicomponent Nonideal Distillation Column   *75*

PART TWO   COMPUTER SIMULATION

Chapter 4   Analog Simulation   *93*

4-1   Introduction   *93*
4-2   Basic Components   *94*
4-3   Operational Blocks   *95*
4-4   Simple Examples   *99*
4-5   More Complex Systems   *107*

Chapter 5   Digital Simulation   *121*

5-1   Numerical Methods   *123*
    5-1.1   Implicit Function Convergence   *123*
    5-1.2   Numerical Integration   *130*
5-2   Examples   *139*
    5-2.1   Three CSTR's in Series   *139*
    5-2.2   Nonisothermal CSTR   *144*
    5-2.3   Binary Distillation Column   *148*
    5-2.4   Multicomponent Distillation Column   *152*
    5-2.5   Batch Reactor   *160*

PART THREE   DYNAMICS

Chapter 6   Time-domain Dynamics   *173*

6-1   Classification and Definition   *174*
6-2   Linearization and Perturbation Variables   *177*
    6-2.1   Linearization   *177*
    6-2.2   Perturbation Variables   *180*
6-3   Responses of Simple Linear Systems   *182*
    6-3.1   First-order Linear Ordinary Differential Equation (ODE)   *182*
    6-3.2   Second-order Linear Ordinary Differential Equations with Constant Coefficients   *187*
    6-3.3   Nth-order Linear Ordinary Differential Equations with Constant Coefficients   *198*
6-4   Steady-state Techniques   *201*

Chapter 7   Laplace-domain Dynamics   *208*

7-1   Laplace-transformation Fundamentals   *209*
    7-1.1   Definition   *209*
    7-1.2   Linearity Property   *209*
7-2   Laplace Transformation of Important Functions   *210*
    7-2.1   Step Function   *210*
    7-2.2   Ramp   *210*
    7-2.3   Sine   *211*
    7-2.4   Exponential   *211*
    7-2.5   Exponential Multiplied by Time   *212*
    7-2.6   Impulse (Dirac Delta Function $\delta_{(t)}$)   *212*

7-3   Inversion of Laplace Transforms   *213*
7-4   Transfer Functions   *216*
    7-4.1   Multiplication by a Constant   *216*
    7-4.2   Differentiation with Respect to Time   *217*
    7-4.3   Integration   *218*
    7-4.4   Dead Time   *219*
7-5   Examples   *220*
7-6   Properties of Transfer Functions   *229*

Chapter 8   Frequency-domain Dynamics   *237*

8-1   Definition   *238*
8-2   Basic Theorem   *240*
8-3   Representation   *244*
    8-3.1   Nyquist Plots   *244*
    8-3.2   Bode Plots   *250*
    8-3.3   Nichols Plots   *261*
8-4   Frequency-domain Solution Techniques   *264*

Chapter 9   Process Identification   *279*

9-1   Purpose   *279*
9-2   Direct Methods   *280*
    9-2.1   Time-domain Fitting of Step Test Data   *280*
    9-2.2   Direct Sine-wave Testing   *280*
9-3   Pulse Testing   *282*
    9-3.1   Calculation of $G_{(i\omega)}$ from Pulse Test Date   *284*
    9-3.2   Digital Evaluation of Fourier Transformations   *285*
    9-3.3   Practical Tips on Pulse Testing   *291*
    9-3.4   Processes with Integration   *292*
9-4   Step Testing   *294*
9-5   Other Process Identification Methods   *295*
9-6   Relationships among Time, Laplace, and Frequency Domains   *296*
    9-6.1   Laplace to Frequency Domain   *296*
    9-6.2   Frequency to Laplace Domain   *296*
    9-6.3   Time to Laplace Domain   *298*
    9-6.4   Laplace to Time Domain   *298*
    9-6.5   Time to Frequency Domain   *298*
    9-6.6   Frequency to Time Domain   *298*

PART FOUR   FEEDBACK CONTROL

Chapter 10   Time-domain Synthesis   *305*

10-1   Control Instrumentation   *305*
    10-1.1   Sensors   *308*
    10-1.2   Transmitters   *310*
    10-1.3   Control Valves   *313*
    10-1.4   Controllers   *317*
    10-1.5   Computing Relays and Other Useful Gadgets   *321*

10-1.6   Digital Process-control Computers   *322*
10-2   Performance of Conventional Feedback Controllers   *323*
10-2.1   Specifications for Closed-loop Response   *323*
10-2.2   Load Performance   *323*
10-3   Controller Tuning   *328*
10-3.1   Rules of Thumb   *328*
10-3.2   On-line Trial and Error   *330*
10-3.3   Ziegler-Nichols Method   *331*
10-4   Control-systems Design Concepts   *332*
10-5   Nonconventional Control   *338*
10-5.1   Computed Variables   *338*
10-5.2   Nonlinear Controllers   *339*
10-5.3   Anti-Reset Windup   *341*
10-5.4   Selective Control Loops   *342*
10-5.5   Ratio Control   *344*

Chapter 11   Laplace-domain Synthesis   *352*

11-1   Stability   *352*
11-1.1   Relationship between Open-loop and Closed-loop Transfer Functions   *353*
11-1.2   Routh Stability Criterion   *355*
11-1.3   Direct Substitution for Stability Limit   *359*
11-2   Performance Specifications   *360*
11-2.1   Steady-state Performance   *360*
11-2.2   Dynamic Specifications   *362*
11-3   Root Locus Analysis and Synthesis Techniques   *363*
11-3.1   Definition   *363*
11-3.2   Construction of Root Locus Curves   *366*
11-4   Open-loop Unstable Processes   *372*
11-4.1   First-order Open-loop Unstable Process   *374*
11-4.2   Second-order Open-loop Unstable Process   *374*
11-4.3   Third-order Open-loop Unstable Process   *376*
11-5   Processes with Inverse Response   *377*
11-6   Interacting Control Systems   *380*

Chapter 12   Frequency-domain Synthesis   *389*

12-1   Nyquist Stability Criterion   *390*
12-1.1   Proof of Nyquist Stability Criterion   *390*
12-1.2   Examples   *393*
12-1.3   Representation   *402*
12-2   Specifications in the Frequency Domain   *404*
12-2.1   Phase Margin   *404*
12-2.2   Gain Margin   *407*
12-2.3   Maximum Closed-loop Log Modulus (LM)   *407*
12-3   Frequency Response of Feedback Controllers   *415*
12-3.1   Proportional Controller (P)   *415*
12-3.2   Proportional-Integral Controller (PI)   *415*

12-3.3 Proportional-Integral-Derivative Controller (PID) *415*
12-4 Examples *416*
  12-4.1 Three-CSTR System *416*
  12-4.2 First-order Lag with Dead Time *423*
  12-4.3 Open-loop Unstable Process *423*

PART FIVE FEEDFORWARD CONTROL

Chapter 13 Feedforward Control *431*

13-1 Fundamentals *431*
13-2 Typical Hardware Implementation *436*
13-3 Examples of Feedforward Controller Design for Linear Systems *437*
  13-3.1 Three-CSTR System *437*
  13-3.2 Nonisothermal CSTR *438*
  13-3.3 Distillation Column *445*
13-4 Nonlinear Feedforward Systems *446*

PART SIX SAMPLED-DATA SYSTEMS

Chapter 14 Sampling and z Transforms *455*

14-1 Introduction *455*
  14-1.1 Definition *455*
  14-1.2 Occurrence of Sampled-data Systems in Chemical Engineering *455*
14-2 Impulse Sampler *460*
14-3 Basic Sampling Theorem *464*
14-4 z Transformation *465*
  14-4.1 Definition *465*
  14-4.2 Derivation of z Transforms of Common Functions *467*
  14-4.3 Effect of Dead Time *470*
  14-4.4 z-Transform Theorems *470*
  14-4.5 Inversion *472*
14-5 Pulse Transfer Functions *477*
14-6 Hold Devices *480*
14-7 Open-loop and Closed-loop Systems *480*
  14-7.1 Open-loop Systems *481*
  14-7.2 Closed-loop Systems *485*

Chapter 15 Analysis and Synthesis of Sampled-data Control Systems *493*

15-1 Stability in the z Plane *493*
15-2 Frequency-domain Design Techniques *496*
  15-2.1 Nyquist Stability Criterion *496*
  15-2.2 Rigorous Method *497*
  15-2.3 Approximate Method *502*
15-3 z-Domain Root Locus Design Methods *504*
15-4 Bilinear-transformation Design Methods *510*

15-5 Sampled-data Controllers   *514*
    15-5.1 Physical Realizability   *515*
    15-5.2 Controller Design   *515*
    15-5.3 Approximating Continuous Elements   *518*
15-6 Minimal-prototype Sampled-data Controllers   *520*

APPENDIX

    A-1 Polynomial Root-solving Subroutine   *531*
    A-2 Instrumention Hardware   *535*

Index   *555*

PREFACE

The study of the dynamics and control of chemical engineering processes has developed over the past decade into a basic segment of a chemical engineer's education. The cause of this rapid development was the realization that process dynamic analysis and basic process-control theory are very useful parts of the practicing engineer's bag of techniques for solving practical problems. The tools that have made all this possible are analog and digital computers. These devices permit engineers to solve the complex systems of equations, called mathematical models, that describe real engineering systems.

Some ten years ago when I first began my studying and teaching in the process-control field, no text that adequately covered the subject was available for chemical engineers. Ceaglske's pioneering book (Ref. 2) covered some of the basic control theory, but it was too elementary for an in-depth course and contained almost nothing on mathematical modeling and simulation. There were, at that time, several excellent texts presenting control theory, but they were all written by and for electrical or mechanical engineers (for example, Refs. 3 and 16).

Therefore, I began to assemble a set of notes that covered the mathematical modeling of chemical engineering processes, their simulation on both analog and digital computers, and practical techniques for their control. I used these notes in graduate extension courses at the University of Delaware for four years while I worked in Du Pont's Engineering Department. Since coming to Lehigh in 1967, I have used them, with continual revisions, extensions, and modifications, in a senior-level undergraduate course and a first-year graduate course.

During the past decade a number of excellent process-control texts have appeared. Most have been devoted primarily to control theory, some at an undergraduate level (Refs. 4, 7, 9, 12, 13, 14, 17) and some at a graduate level (Refs. 6, 8, 11). Buckley (Ref. 1), Shinskey (Ref. 15), and Williams (Ref. 18) have covered some of the more practical aspects of instrumentation systems design. Some of the texts discuss analog simulation but none covers digital simulation. Very little is said about developing mathematical models.

Franks, in his pioneering book (Ref. 5) was the first to discuss mathematical modeling in detail and to present simple digital simulation techniques. Himmelblau and Bischoff (Ref. 10) and Smith et al. (Ref. 19) presented much of the same material on modeling, but at a higher level of mathematical sophistication. All these texts say little about control.

It is my conviction that the three general subjects—mathematical modeling, computer simulation, and process control—are most logically taught and meaningfully learned as an integrated subject. My course notes have therefore evolved along these lines. The enthusiastic response of my students to the unified approach has encouraged me to write this book.

I have attempted to produce a "learning" book that is written to teach, not to impress. The orientation is pointedly practical. This does not mean that mathematics has been stripped from the subject. After all, control theory is basically applied complex variables, and one of the stimulating aspects of process control is that practical answers to real industrial problems can be obtained by using reasonably sophisticated mathematical techniques.

Included in this book are those topics, tools, and techniques that I have found to be the most useful for understanding and solving practical dynamics and control problems in chemical engineering systems. My selection has naturally been a function of my own experience, but this has included both the academic world and the industrial environment in practically all engineering activities: operations, design, development, research, and consulting. The examples and problems are drawn from this experience.

My goal has been to present only useful, state-of-the-art, applications-oriented tools. Therefore, such academically stimulating but practically unimportant topics as optimal control and Liaponov stability have been excluded. In many chemical engineering systems the optimum-control strategy is obvious once the process is understood and usually involves operating at one or more constraints. State variables (matrix representation) are used only for notational convenience. Computer solution techniques for distributed systems are also not covered.

On the other hand, the newer concepts of feedforward control and sampled-data control are covered in some detail because of their increasing importance in chemical engineering systems. Likewise, digital simulation is emphasized over analog simulation because of the shift in that direction in industrial applications.

The material in this book currently forms the basis for two senior-level three-credit-hour courses at Lehigh University. During the first semester the mathematical modeling of both lumped and distributed systems is studied in detail (Part 1), and analog and digital simulation techniques for lumped systems are presented (Part 2).

During the second semester the dynamics of open-loop, uncontrolled processes is studied in the time, Laplace, and frequency domains (Part 3), and the many facets of feedback, feedforward, and sampled-data control systems are extensively explored: stability theory, single-loop and system design, tuning, and instrumentation hardware. A process-control laboratory is an integral and very important part of the second semester. Experiments include frequency response and pulse testing, on-line controller tuning, cascade control loops, and feedforward control.

It would be hopeless to attempt to acknowledge all the people who have contributed to this book. Certainly a major input of theory and inspiration came from Profs. Jack Gerster, Bob Pigford, and Dave Lamb during my graduate work at the University of Delaware. Equally important were the contributions of knowledge, encouragement, and counsel from Page Buckley of Du Pont's Engineering Department

For training in refinery operation and design I am indebted to Smokey Smolen, Bill O'Brien, Hank Anderson, Bob Millar, and Carter Conlin. For the camaraderie of fellow graduate students I particularly remember John Anderson, Pete Bouloucon, and Bob Bollinger. For training in chemical instrumentation and applied process control, I wish to thank Walt Ellingsen, Ed Fogg, Tom Vick Roy, and Rudy Pedrotti. For the inquisitiveness and the drive for simplicity and understanding that fill only young minds, I am obligated to my many students. For help and encouragement, I am grateful to my colleagues at Lehigh.

Finally, for love, faith, and encouragement I shall be eternally indebted to my wife, children, and parents.

W. L. Luyben

CHEMICAL ENGINEERING REFERENCES

1 BUCKLEY, P. S.: "Techniques of Process Control," Wiley, 1964.

2 CEAGLSKE, N. H.: "Automatic Process Control for Chemical Engineers," Wiley, 1956.

3 DEL TORO, V., and S. R. PARKER: "Principles of Control System Engineering," McGraw-Hill, 1960.

4 COUGHANOWR, D. R., and L. B. KOPPEL: "Process Systems Analysis and Control," McGraw-Hill, 1965.

5 FRANKS, R. G. E.: "Mathematical Modeling in Chemical Engineering," Wiley, 1967.

6 GOULD, L. A.: "Chemical Process Control," Addison-Wesley, 1969.

7 JOHNSON, E. F.: "Automatic Process Control," McGraw-Hill, 1967.

8 KOPPEL, L. B.: "Introduction to Control Theory," Prentice-Hall, 1968.

9 HARRIOTT, P.: "Process Control," McGraw-Hill, 1964.

10 HIMMELBLAU, D. M., and K. B. BISCHOFF: "Process Analysis and Simulation," Wiley, 1968.

11 LAPIDUS, L., and R. LUUS: "Optimal Control of Engineering Processes," Blaisdell, 1967.

12 MURRILL, P. W.: "Automatic Control of Processes," International Textbook, 1967.

13 PERLMUTTER, D. D.: "Introduction to Chemical Process Control," Wiley, 1965.

14 SHILLING, G. D.: "Process Dynamics and Control," Holt, 1963.

15 SHINSKEY, F. G.: "Process-control Systems," McGraw-Hill, 1967.

16 TRUXAL, J. G.: "Automatic Feedback Control System Synthesis," McGraw-Hill, 1955.

17 TYNER, M., and F. P. MAY: "Process Engineering Control," Ronald, 1968.

18 WILLIAMS, T. J.: "Systems Engineering for the Process Industries," McGraw-Hill, 1961.

19 SMITH, C. L., R. W. PIKE, and P. W. MURRILL: "Formulation and Optimization of Mathematical Models," International Textbook, 1970.

1

INTRODUCTION

This chapter is an introduction to process dynamics and control for those students who have had little or no contact or experience with real chemical engineering processes. The objective is to illustrate where process control fits into the picture and to indicate its relative importance in the operation, design, and development of a chemical engineering plant.

This introductory chapter is, I am sure, unnecessary for those practicing engineers who may be using this book. They are well aware of the importance of considering the dynamics of a process and of the increasingly complex and sophisticated control systems that are being used. They know that perhaps 80 percent of the time that one is "on the plant" is spent at the control panel, watching recorders and controllers. The control room is the nerve center of the plant.

1-1 EXAMPLES OF THE ROLE OF PROCESS DYNAMICS AND CONTROL

Probably the best way to illustrate what we mean by process dynamics and control is to talk about a few real examples. The first example describes a simple process where

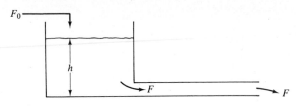

FIGURE 1-1
Gravity-flow tank.

the dynamic response, the time-dependent behavior, is important. The second example discusses a simple but reasonably typical chemical engineering plant and its conventional control system.

EXAMPLE 1-1 GRAVITY FLOW TANK

Figure 1-1 shows a tank into which an incompressible (constant-density) liquid is pumped at a variable rate F_0 (ft^3/sec); i.e., the inflow can vary with time because of changes in operations upstream. The height of liquid in the vertical cylindrical tank is h (ft). The flow rate out of the tank is F (ft^3/sec).

Now F_0, h, and F will all vary with time and are therefore functions of time t. Consequently we use the notation $F_{0(t)}$, $h_{(t)}$, and $F_{(t)}$. Liquid leaves the base of the tank via a long horizontal pipe and discharges into the top of another tank. Both tanks are open to the atmosphere.

Let us look first at the steady-state conditions. By steady state we mean, in most systems, the conditions when nothing is changing with time. Mathematically this corresponds to having all time derivatives equal to zero, or to allowing time to become very large, i.e., go to infinity. At steady state the flow out of the tank must equal the flow into the tank. In this book we will denote steady-state values of variables by an overscore or bar above the variables. Therefore at steady state in our tank system $\bar{F}_0 = \bar{F}$.

For a given $\bar{F}$, the height of liquid in the tank at steady state would also be some constant $\bar{h}$. The value of $\bar{h}$ would be that height that provides enough static pressure head at the inlet of the pipe to overcome the frictional losses of liquid flowing down the pipe. The higher the flow rate $\bar{F}$, the higher $\bar{h}$ will be.

In the steady-state design of the tank, we would naturally size the diameter of the exit line and the height of the tank so that at the maximum flow rate expected the tank would not overflow. And as any good, conservative design engineer knows, we would include in the design a 20 to 30 percent safety factor on the tank height. Since this is a book on control and instrumentation, we might also mention that a high-level

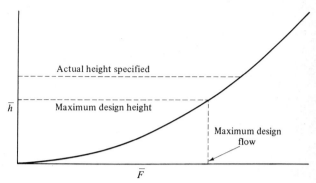

FIGURE 1-2
Steady-state height versus flow.

alarm and/or an interlock (a device to shut off the feed if the level gets too high) could be installed to guarantee that the tank would not spill over.

The design of the system would involve an economic balance between the cost of a higher tank and the cost of a bigger pipe, since the bigger the pipe diameter the lower is the liquid height. Figure 1-2 shows a curve of $\bar{h}$ versus $\bar{F}$ for a specific numerical case.

So far we have considered just the traditional steady-state design aspects of this fluid flow system. Now let us think about what would happen dynamically if we changed F_0. How will $h_{(t)}$ and $F_{(t)}$ vary with time? Obviously F eventually has to end up at the new value of F_0. We can easily determine from the steady-state design curve of Fig. 1-2 where h will go at steady state. But what path will $h_{(t)}$ and $F_{(t)}$ take to get to their new steady states?

Figure 1-3 sketches the problem. The question is which curves (1, 2, or 3) represent the actual paths that F and h will follow. Curves 1 show a very slow rise in F and h to their new steady-state values. Curves 2 show a fast rise. Curves 3 show an even faster rise *and* an overshoot; i.e., the variables go beyond the steady-state values for some time. Clearly, if the response overshoots and if the peak of the overshoot in liquid height is above the top of the tank, we would be in trouble.

Our steady-state design calculations tell us nothing about what the dynamic response of the system will be. They tell us where we will start and where we will end up but not how we get there. This kind of information is what a study of the dynamics of the system will reveal. We will return to this system later in the book to derive a mathematical model of it and to determine its dynamic response quantitatively by analog simulation.   ////

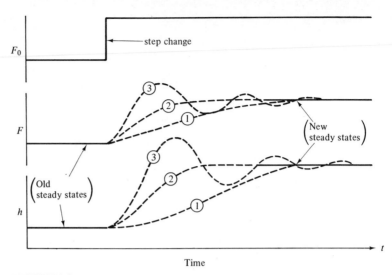

FIGURE 1-3
Possible responses of gravity-flow tank level to a step increase in flow rate into the tank.

EXAMPLE 1-2 CHEMICAL PLANT CONTROL SYSTEM For our second example let us consider the process sketched in Fig. 1-4. Two liquid feeds are pumped into a reactor in which they react to form products. The reaction is exothermic, and therefore heat must be removed from the reactor. This is accomplished by cooling water added to a jacket around the reactor. Reactor effluent is pumped through a preheater into a distillation column that splits it into two product streams.

Traditional steady-state design procedures would be used to specify the various pieces of equipment in this plant:

Fluid mechanics: pump heads; rates and power; piping sizes; column tray layout and sizing; heat-exchanger tube and shell side baffling and sizing
Heat transfer: reactor heat removal; preheater, reboiler, and condenser heat transfer area requirements
Chemical kinetics: reactor size and operating conditions (temperature, pressure, catalyst, etc.)
Thermodynamics and mass transfer: number of plates and reflux ratio; equilibrium conditions in the reactor

But how do we decide how to instrument the plant? We will spend some time exploring this important design question. In fact, this is the basic problem at which

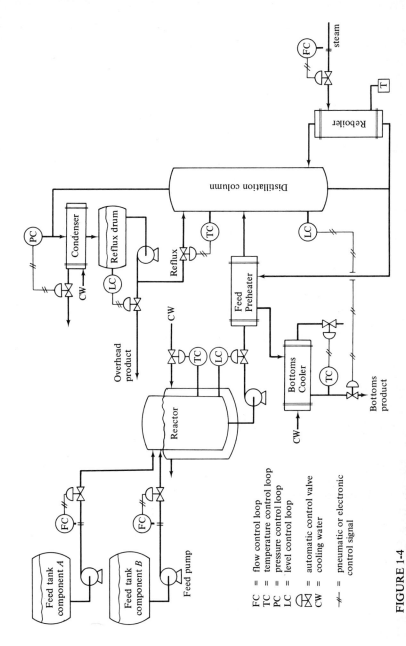

FC = flow control loop
TC = temperature control loop
PC = pressure control loop
LC = level control loop

⊠ = automatic control valve
CW = cooling water

⊣⊢ = pneumatic or electronic
     control signal

FIGURE 1-4
Typical chemical plant and control system.

this book is directed. All our studies of mathematical modeling, simulation, and control theory are aimed at understanding the dynamics of processes and control systems so that we can develop and design better plants and operate them more efficiently.

Here let us say merely that the control system shown in Fig. 1-4 is a typical conventional system. It is about the minimum that would be needed to run this plant automatically without constant operator attention. Notice that even in this simple plant with a minimum of instrumentation the total number of control loops is 10. We will find that most chemical engineering processes are multivariable.   ////

1-2 OBJECTIVES

It may be helpful to summarize briefly the objectives of our study of process dynamics and control:

1 To gain an appreciation for the dynamics, the time-dependent responses, of chemical engineering systems

2 To learn to construct realistic but reasonable mathematical models of these systems

3 To study techniques for solving the equations that make up the mathematical model

4 To become familiar with control techniques (stability theory, controller design, and systems design) and with practical, commercial control equipment (the *hardware* that goes into a real control system: sensors, transmitters, controllers, control valves, etc.)

1-3 HISTORICAL BACKGROUND

Most chemical processing plants were run essentially manually prior to the 1940s. Only the most elementary types of controllers were used. Many men were needed to keep watch on the many variables in the plant. Large tanks were employed to act as buffers or surge capacities between various units in the plant. These tanks, although sometimes quite expensive, filtered out some of the dynamic disturbances by isolating one part of the process from upsets in another part.

With increasing labor and equipment costs and with the development of more severe, higher-capacity, higher-performance equipment and processes in the 1940s and early 1950s, it became uneconomical and often impossible to run plants without automatic control devices. At this stage feedback controllers were added to the plants with little real consideration of or appreciation for the dynamics of the process itself. Rule-of-thumb guides and experience were the only design techniques.

It has been only in the last decade or so that all the dynamic analysis techniques and the control theory developed primarily by aerospace and electrical engineers have been applied to chemical engineering systems. In addition to designing better control systems, processes and plants have been developed or modified so that they are easier to control. The concept of examining the many parts of a complex plant together as a unit, with all the interactions included, and devising ways to control the entire plant is called *systems engineering*.

1-4 PERSPECTIVE

Lest I be accused of overstating the relative importance of process control to the main stream of chemical engineering, let me make it perfectly clear that the tools of dynamic analysis are but one part of the practicing engineer's bag of tools and techniques, albeit an increasingly important part. Certainly a solid foundation in the more traditional areas of thermodynamics, kinetics, unit operations, and transport phenomena is essential. In fact, such a foundation is a prerequisite to any study of process dynamics because the mathematical models that we derive are really nothing but extensions of the traditional unit operations equations to include time-dependent terms. Control engineers sometimes have a tendency to get too wrapped up in the dynamics and to forget the steady-state aspects. Keep in mind that if you cannot get the plant to work at steady state you cannot get it to work dynamically.

You should also be alert to the fact that fighting your way through this book will not in itself make you an expert in process control. You will find that a lot remains to be learned, not so much on a higher theoretical level as you might expect, but more on a practical-experience level. A sharp engineer can learn a tremendous amount about process dynamics and control that can never be put in a book, no matter how practically oriented, by climbing around a plant, talking with operators and instrument mechanics, tinkering in the instrument shop, and keeping his eyes open in the control room, both in front of and behind the instrument panel.

You may question, as you go through this book, the degree to which the dynamic analysis and controller design techniques discussed are really used in industry. At the present time 80 to 90 percent of the control loops in a plant are usually designed, installed, tuned, and operated quite successfully by simple, rule-of-thumb, experience-generated techniques. The other 10 to 20 percent of the loops are those on which the control engineer makes his money. They require more technical knowledge. Plant testing, computer simulation, and detailed controller design or process redesign may be required to achieve the desired performance. This may seem a small percentage of the total, but these critical loops often make or break the plant.

I am confident that the techniques discussed in this book will receive wider and wider application as the tools of the trade (computers and control instrumentation) become more commonly available at plant sites and, more importantly, as more young engineers with this training go to work in these plants. To quote an old Persian saying, "Dar shadr-e-kuran yek chasm koda-ast" (In a city of blind men, one eye is good).

1-5 MOTIVATION FOR STUDYING PROCESS CONTROL

Some of the motivational reasons for studying the subjects presented in this book are that they are of considerable practical importance, they are challenging, and they are fun:

1 *Important:* The control room is the major interface with the plant. Automation is increasingly common in all degrees of sophistication, from single-loop systems to computer-control systems.

2 *Interesting:* I have found, and I hope you will too, that process dynamics is fun. You will get the opportunity to use some simple and some fairly advanced mathematics to solve real plant problems. There is nothing quite like the thrill of working out a controller design on paper and then seeing it actually work on the plant, or, where a plant is having major control problems, to be able to diagnose where the problems are and to solve them by applying your knowledge of process control and your insight into the dynamics of the process. Sometimes the problem is in the process, in basic design, or in equipment malfunctioning. But sometimes it is in the control system, in basic strategy, or in hardware malfunctioning. Just your knowledge of what a given control device *should do* can be invaluable.

3 *Challenging:* You will have to draw on your knowledge of all areas of chemical engineering. You will use most of the mathematical tools available (differential equations, Laplace transforms, complex variables, numerical analysis, etc.) to solve real problems.

1-6 GENERAL CONCEPTS

I have tried to present in this book a logical development. We will begin with fundamentals and simple concepts and extend them as far as they can be gainfully extended. First we will learn to derive mathematical models of chemical engineering systems. Then we will study some of the ways to solve the resulting equations, usually ordinary differential equations. Next we will explore their open-loop (uncontrolled) dynamic behavior. Finally we will learn to design controllers that will, if we are smart enough, make the plant run automatically the way we want it to run.

Before we go into the details in the subsequent chapters, it may be worthwhile at this point to define some very broad and general concepts and some of the terminology used in dynamics and control.

1   *Dynamics:* time-dependent behavior of a process. The behavior with no controllers in the system is called the *open-loop response*.

2   *Variables:*

  a   *Input variables:* flow rates, compositions, pressures, temperatures of streams entering a process. We usually classify these inputs as *disturbances* (inputs that we cannot control and must learn to live with) and *manipulative variables* (inputs that we can change in order to control the plant).

  b   *Output variables:* flow rates, compositions, etc., of streams leaving or inside the process. Some of these outputs we will try later to control. Some will be uncontrolled.

EXAMPLE 1-3   For a distillation column, input variables might include feed rate and feed composition as disturbances, and reflux flow and heat input to the reboiler as manipulative variables. Output variables might include overhead distillate flow rate and composition, bottoms product flow rate and composition, and the composition, holdups, and flow rates of the vapor and liquid on any or all of the trays.

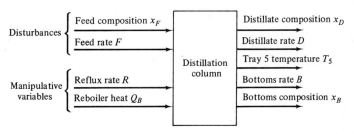

Note that one physical stream may be considered to contain many variables: its rate, its composition, its temperature, etc., that is, all its intensive and extensive properties.   ////

3   *Feedback control:* The traditional way to control a process is to measure the variable that is to be controlled, compare its value with the desired value (the set point to the controller), and feed the difference (the error) into a feed-

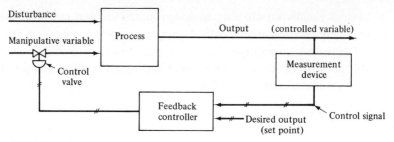

FIGURE 1-5
Feedback control.

back controller that will change a manipulative variable to drive the measured (controlled) variable back to the desired value. Information is thus "fed back" from the output variable to an input manipulative variable, as shown in Fig. 1-5.

4   *Feedforward control:* In recent years chemical engineers have made more and more use of feedforward control. The basic idea, as shown in Fig. 1-6, is to detect a disturbance as it enters the process and make an appropriate change in the manipulative variable such that the output variable is held constant (or does whatever we want it to do). Thus we begin to take corrective action as soon as a disturbance entering the system is detected instead of waiting for the disturbance to propagate all the way through the process before a correction is made.

5   *Stability:* A process is said to be *unstable* if its output becomes larger and larger. Examples are shown in Fig. 1-7. No real system ever really does this, of course, because some constraint will be met; for example, a control valve will completely open or completely shut, or a safety valve will "pop." A linear process is right at the limit of stability if it oscillates, even when undisturbed, and the amplitude of the oscillation does not decay.

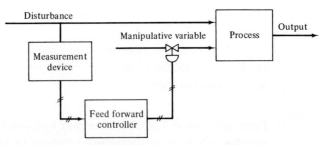

FIGURE 1-6
Feedforward control.

Most processes are *open-loop stable*, i.e., stable with no controllers on the system. An important and very interesting exception that we will study in some detail is the exothermic chemical reactor which can be open-loop *unstable*. All real processes can be made *closed-loop unstable*, i.e., unstable when a feedback controller is in the system. Thus stability is of vital concern in feedback control systems.

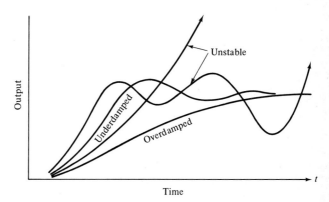

FIGURE 1-7
Stability.

PART ONE

Mathematical Models of Chemical Engineering Systems

2

FUNDAMENTALS

2-1 INTRODUCTION

2-1.1 Uses of Mathematical Models

Without doubt, the most important result of developing a mathematical model of a chemical engineering system is the understanding that is gained of what really makes the process "tick." This insight enables you to strip away from the problem the many extraneous "confusion factors" and to get to the core of the system. You can see more clearly the cause-and-effect relationships between variables.

Mathematical models can be useful in all phases of chemical engineering, from research and development to plant operations, and even in business and economic studies.

> 1 *Research and development:* determining chemical kinetic mechanisms and parameters from laboratory or pilot-plant reaction data; exploring the effects of different operating conditions for optimization studies; aiding in scale-up calculations.
>
> 2 *Design:* exploring the sizing and arrangement of processing equipment for dynamic performance; studying the interactions of various parts of the

process; evaluating alternative control strategies; simulating start-up, shut-down, and emergency situations and procedures.

3 *Plant operation:* troubleshooting control and processing problems; aiding in start-up and operator training; studying the effects of and the requirements for expansion (bottleneck-removal) projects; optimizing plant operation. It is usually much cheaper, safer, and faster to conduct the kinds of studies listed above on a mathematical model than experimentally on an operating unit. This is not to say that plant tests are not needed. As we will discuss later, they are a vital part of confirming the validity of the model and of verifying important ideas and recommendations that evolve from the model studies.

2-1.2 Scope of Coverage

We will discuss in this book only deterministic systems that can be described by ordinary or partial differential equations. Most of the emphasis will be on *lumped* systems (with one independent variable, time, described by ordinary differential equations). English units will be used exclusively, but the equations and relationships can be used with any consistent set of units.

2-1.3 Principles of Formulation

Basis The bases for mathematical models are the fundamental physical and chemical laws, such as the laws of conservation of mass, energy, and momentum. To study dynamics we will use them in their general form with time derivatives included.

Assumptions Probably the most vital role that the engineer plays in modeling is in exercising his engineering judgment as to what assumptions can be validly made. Obviously an extremely rigorous model that includes every phenomenon down to microscopic detail would be so complex that it would take a long time to develop and might be impossible to solve. An engineering compromise between a rigorous description and getting an answer that is good enough is always required. This has been called "optimum sloppiness." It involves making as many simplifying assumptions as are reasonable without "throwing out the baby with the bath water." In practice, this optimum usually corresponds to a model which is as complex as the available computing facilities will permit.

The assumptions that are made should be carefully considered and listed. They impose limitations on the model that should always be kept in mind when evaluating its predicted results.

Mathematical consistency of model Once all the equations of the mathematical model have been written, it is usually a good idea, particularly with big, complex systems of equations, to make sure that the number of variables equals the number of equations. The so-called "degrees of freedom" of the system must be zero in order to obtain a solution. If this is not true, the system is underspecified or overspecified and something is wrong with the formulation of the problem. This kind of consistency check may seem trivial, but I can testify from sad experience that it can save many hours of frustration, confusion, and wasted computer time.

Checking to see that the units of all terms in all equations are consistent is perhaps another trivial and obvious step, but one that is often forgotten. It is essential to be particularly careful of the time units of parameters in dynamic models. We will stick to "seconds" in most of our examples, but it should be remembered that many parameters are commonly on other time bases, e.g., overall heat transfer coefficients in Btu/hr-ft^2-°F.

Solution of the model equations We will concern ourselves in detail with this aspect of the model in Part 2. However, the available solution techniques and tools must be kept in mind as a mathematical model is developed. An equation without any way to solve it is, to put it in the vernacular of the farmer, about as useless as teats on a boar hog.

Verification An important but often neglected part of developing a mathematical model is proving that the model describes the real-world situation. At the design stage this sometimes cannot be done because the plant has not yet been built. However, even in this situation there are usually either similar existing plants or a pilot plant from which some experimental data can be obtained.

The design of experiments to test the validity of a model can sometimes be a real challenge and should be carefully thought out. We will talk about dynamic testing techniques, such as pulse testing, in Part 3.

2-2 FUNDAMENTAL LAWS

In this section, some fundamental laws of physics and chemistry are reviewed in their general time-dependent form, and their application to some simple chemical systems is illustrated.

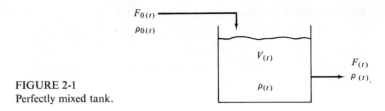

FIGURE 2-1
Perfectly mixed tank.

2-2.1 Continuity Equations

Total continuity equation (mass balance)   The principle of the conservation of mass when applied to a dynamic system says

$$\left(\begin{array}{c}\text{Mass flow}\\\text{into system}\end{array}\right) - \left(\begin{array}{c}\text{mass flow}\\\text{out of system}\end{array}\right) = \left(\begin{array}{c}\text{time rate of change}\\\text{of mass inside system}\end{array}\right) \qquad (2\text{-}1)$$

The units of this equation are mass per time. Only *one* total continuity equation can be written for one system.

The normal steady-state design equation that we are accustomed to using says "what goes in, comes out." The dynamic version of this says the same thing with the addition of the word "eventually."

The right-hand side of Eq. (2-1) will be either a partial derivative $\partial/\partial t$ or an ordinary derivative d/dt of the mass inside the system with respect to the independent variable, t.

EXAMPLE 2-1   Consider the tank of perfectly mixed liquid shown in Fig. 2-1 into which flows a liquid stream at a rate of F_0 (ft^3/sec) and a density of ρ_0 (lb$_m$/ft^3). The volumetric holdup of liquid in the tank is V (ft^3), and its density is ρ (lb$_m$/ft^3). The flow rate from the tank is F (ft^3/sec), and its density is, of course, the same as that of the tank's contents. The system for which we want to write a total continuity equation is all the liquid phase in the tank. We call this a macroscopic system, as opposed to a microscopic system, since it is of definite and finite size. The mass balance is around the whole tank, not just a small, differential element inside the tank.

$$F_0\,\rho_0 - F\rho = \text{time rate of change of } \rho V \qquad (2\text{-}2)$$

The units of this equation are (lb$_m$/sec)

$$\frac{\text{ft}^3}{\text{sec}} \times \frac{\text{lb}_m}{\text{ft}^3} - \frac{\text{ft}^3}{\text{sec}} \times \frac{\text{lb}_m}{\text{ft}^3} = \frac{(\text{ft}^3)(\text{lb}_m/\text{ft}^3)}{\text{sec}}$$

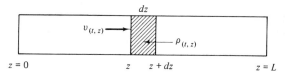

FIGURE 2-2
Flow through a pipe.

Since the liquid is perfectly mixed, the density is the same everywhere in the tank; it does not vary with radial or axial position; i.e., there are no spatial gradients in density in the tank. This is why we can use a macroscopic system. It also means that there is only one independent variable, t.

Since ρ and V are functions only of t, an ordinary derivative is used in Eq. (2-2).

$$\frac{d(\rho V)}{dt} = F_0 \rho_0 - F\rho \qquad (2\text{-}3) \qquad ////$$

EXAMPLE 2-2   Fluid is flowing through a constant-diameter cylindrical pipe sketched in Fig. 2-2. The flow is turbulent and therefore we can assume plug-flow conditions; i.e., each "slice" of liquid flows down the pipe as a unit. Therefore there are no radial gradients in velocity or any other properties. However, axial gradients can exist.

Density and velocity can change as the fluid flows along in the axial or z direction. There are now two independent variables: time t and axial position z. Density and velocity are functions of both t and z: $\rho_{(t,z)}$ and $v_{(t,z)}$. We want to apply the total continuity equation [Eq. (2-1)] to a system that consists of a small slice. The system is now a "microscopic" one. The differential element is located at an arbitrary spot z down the pipe. It is dz thick and has an area equal to the cross-sectional area of the pipe, A ft^2.

$$\textit{Time rate of change of mass inside system} = \frac{\partial}{\partial t}(A\rho\,dz) \qquad (2\text{-}4)$$

$A\,dz$ is the volume of the system; ρ is the density of the system. The units of this equation are lb$_m$/sec.

$$\textit{Mass flowing into system through boundary at } z = vA\rho \qquad (2\text{-}5)$$

Notice that the units are still lb$_m$/sec = (ft/sec)(ft^2) × (lb$_m$/ft^3).

$$\textit{Mass flowing out of system through boundary at } z + dz = vA\rho + \frac{\partial}{\partial z}(vA\rho)\,dz \qquad (2\text{-}6)$$

The above expression for the flow at $z + dz$ may be thought of as a Taylor series expansion of a function $f_{(z)}$ around z. The value of the function at a spot dz away from z is

$$f_{(z+dz)} = f_{(z)} + \left(\frac{\partial f}{\partial z}\right)_z dz + \left(\frac{\partial^2 f}{\partial z^2}\right)_z \frac{dz^2}{2!} + \cdots \qquad (2\text{-}7)$$

If dz is small the series can be truncated after the first derivative term. Letting $f_{(z)} = vA\rho$ gives Eq. (2-6).

Substituting these terms into Eq. (2-1) gives

$$\frac{\partial}{\partial t}(A \, dz \, \rho) = vA\rho - \left[vA\rho + \frac{\partial}{\partial z}(vA\rho) \, dz\right]$$

Canceling out the dz terms and assuming that A is constant yield

$$\frac{\partial \rho}{\partial t} + \frac{\partial}{\partial z}(\rho v) = 0 \qquad (2\text{-}8) \qquad ////$$

Component continuity equations (component balances)   Unlike mass, chemical components are *not* conserved. If a reaction occurs in a system, the number of moles of an individual component will increase if it is a product of the reaction or decrease if it is a reactant. Therefore the component continuity equation for the *j*th chemical species of the system says

$$\begin{pmatrix} Flow \ of \ moles \ of \ jth \\ component \ into \ system \end{pmatrix} - \begin{pmatrix} flow \ moles \ of \ jth \\ component \ out \ of \ system \end{pmatrix}$$

$$+ \begin{pmatrix} rate \ of \ formation \ of \ moles \ of \ jth \\ component \ from \ chemical \ reaction \end{pmatrix} = \begin{pmatrix} time \ rate \ of \ change \ of \ moles \\ of \ jth \ component \ inside \ system \end{pmatrix} \qquad (2\text{-}9)$$

The units of this equation are moles of *j* per unit time.

The flows in and out can be both convective (due to bulk flow) and molecular (due to diffusion). We can write one component continuity equation for *each* component in the system. If there are J components there are J component continuity equations for any one system. However, the *one* total mass-balance equation and these J component balances are not all independent, since the sum of all the moles times their respective molecular weights equals the total mass. Therefore a given system has only J independent continuity equations. We usually use the total mass-balance and $J - 1$ component balances.

EXAMPLE 2-3   Consider the same tank of perfectly mixed liquid that we used in Example 2-1 except that a chemical reaction takes place in the liquid in the tank. The system is now a CSTR (continuous stirred-tank reactor) as shown in Fig. 2-3.

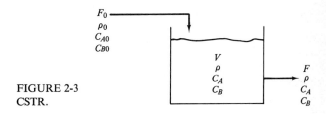

FIGURE 2-3
CSTR.

A component A reacts irreversibly and at a specific reaction rate k to form a product, component B.

$$A \xrightarrow{k} B$$

Let the concentration of component A in the inflowing or feed stream be C_{A0} (moles of A/ft^3) and in the reactor C_A. Assuming a simple first-order reaction, the rate of consumption of reactant A per unit volume will be directly proportional to the instantaneous concentration of A in the tank. Filling in the terms in Eq. (2-9) for a component balance on reactant A,

Flow of A *into system* $= F_0 C_{A0}$
Flow of A *out of system* $= F C_A$
Rate of formation of A *from reaction* $= -V k C_A$ $\diamond$† (ft^3) (1/sec) (moles A/ft^3)

(Notice the minus sign since A is consumed by the reaction.)

$$\text{\textit{Time rate of change of} A \textit{ inside tank}} = \frac{d}{dt}(V C_A)$$

Combining,

$$\frac{d}{dt}(V C_A) = F_0 C_{A0} - F C_A - V k C_A \qquad (2\text{-}10)$$

We have used an ordinary derivative since t is the only independent variable in this lumped system. The units of this component continuity equation are moles of A/sec. The left-hand side of the equation is the dynamic term. The first two terms on the right-hand side are the convective terms. The last term is the generation term. Since the system is binary (a mixture of two components, A and B), we could write another component continuity equation for component B (C_B is the moles of component B per ft^3):

$$\frac{d}{dt}(V C_B) = F_0 C_{B0} - F C_B + V k C_A$$

† We will use the symbol $\diamond$ to mean "has the units of."

Or we could use the total continuity equation [Eq. (2-3)] since C_A, C_B, and ρ are uniquely related by

$$M_A C_A + M_B C_B = \rho \qquad (2\text{-}11)$$

where M_A = molecular weight of component A, lb_m/mole
$\quad\ M_B$ = molecular weight of component B, lb_m/mole

Normally Eqs. (2-3) and (2-10) are used.   ////

EXAMPLE 2-4   Suppose we have the same macroscopic system as above except that now consecutive reactions occur. Reactant A goes to B at a specific reaction rate k_1, but B can react to form component C at a specific reaction rate k_2.

$$A \xrightarrow{\ k_1\ } B \xrightarrow{\ k_2\ } C$$

Assuming first-order reactions, the component continuity equations for components A, B, and C are

$$\frac{d}{dt}(VC_A) = F_0 C_{A0} - FC_A - Vk_1 C_A$$

$$\frac{d}{dt}(VC_B) = F_0 C_{B0} - FC_B + Vk_1 C_A - Vk_2 C_B \qquad (2\text{-}12)$$

$$\frac{d}{dt}(VC_C) = F_0 C_{C0} - FC_C + Vk_2 C_B$$

Again component concentrations are related to the density:

$$\sum_{j=A}^{C} M_j C_j = \rho \qquad (2\text{-}13)$$

Thus we could use the three component balances of Eqs. (2-12) or two of the component balances and a total mass balance like Eq. (2-3).   ////

EXAMPLE 2-5   Instead of fluid flowing down a pipe as in Example 2-2, suppose the pipe is a tubular reactor in which the same reaction A $\xrightarrow{\ k\ }$ B of Example 2-3 takes place. As a slice of material moves down the length of the reactor the concentration of reactant, C_A, decreases as A is consumed. Density ρ, velocity v, and concentration C_A can all vary with time t and axial position z. We still assume plug-flow conditions so that there are no radial gradients in velocity, density, or concentration.

The concentration of A fed to the inlet of the reactor at $z = 0$ we define as

$$C_{A(t,0)} = C_{A0(t)} \qquad (2\text{-}14)$$

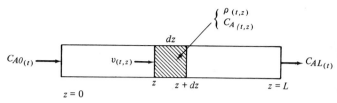

FIGURE 2-4
Tubular reactor.

The concentration of A in the reactor effluent at $z = L$ is defined as

$$C_{A(t,L)} = C_{AL(t)} \qquad (2\text{-}15)$$

We now want to apply the component continuity equation for reactant A to a small differential slice of width dz, as shown in Fig. 2-4. The inflow terms can be split into two types: bulk flow and diffusion. Diffusion can occur because of the concentration gradient in the axial direction. It is usually less important than bulk flow in most practical systems, but we will include it here to see what it contributes to the model. We will say that the diffusive flux of A, N_A (moles of A per unit time per unit area), is given by a Fick's law type of relationship

$$N_A = -\mathscr{D}_A \frac{\partial C_A}{\partial z} \qquad (2\text{-}16)$$

where $\mathscr{D}_A$ is a diffusion coefficient due to both molecular diffusion and turbulence in the fluid flow (so-called "eddy diffusivity"). $\mathscr{D}_A$ has units of ft²/sec.

Now, looking at each term in the general component continuity equation [Eq. (2-9)],

Molar flow of A into boundary at z

$$= \text{bulk flow and diffusion} = vAC_A + AN_A$$

$$\diamondsuit \frac{\text{ft}}{\text{sec}} \times \text{ft}^2 \times \frac{\text{moles A}}{\text{ft}^3} + \text{ft}^2 \times \frac{\text{moles A}}{\text{sec-ft}^2}$$

Molar flow of A into boundary at $z + dz$ $= (vAC_A + AN_A) + \dfrac{\partial}{\partial z}(vAC_A + AN_A)\,dz$

Rate of formation of A inside system $= -kC_A A\,dz$

Time rate of change of A inside system $= \dfrac{\partial}{\partial t}(A\,dz\,C_A)$

Substituting into Eq. (2-9) gives

$$A \, dz \, \frac{\partial C_A}{\partial t} = (vAC_A + AN_A) - \left[vAC_A + AN_A + \frac{\partial}{\partial z} (vAC_A + AN_A) \, dz \right] - kC_A \, dz \, A$$

$$\frac{\partial C_A}{\partial t} = - \frac{\partial}{\partial z} (vC_A + N_A) - kC_A$$

Substituting Eq. (2-16) for N_A,

$$\frac{\partial C_A}{\partial t} + \frac{\partial}{\partial z} (vC_A) + kC_A = \frac{\partial}{\partial z} \left(\mathscr{D}_A \frac{\partial C_A}{\partial z} \right) \qquad (2\text{-}17)$$

The units of the equation are moles A/sec-ft³. The terms, from left to right, are the dynamic term, the convective term, the reaction term, and the diffusion term. ////

2-2.2 Energy Equation

The first law of thermodynamics puts forward the principle of conservation of energy. Written for a general "open" system (where flow in and out of the system can occur) it is

$$\begin{pmatrix} \textit{Flow of internal, kinetic, and} \\ \textit{potential energy into system} \\ \textit{by convection or diffusion} \end{pmatrix} - \begin{pmatrix} \textit{flow of internal, kinetic, and} \\ \textit{potential energy out of system} \\ \textit{by convection or diffusion} \end{pmatrix}$$

$$+ \begin{pmatrix} \textit{heat added to system by} \\ \textit{conduction, radiation, and} \\ \textit{reaction} \end{pmatrix} - \begin{pmatrix} \textit{work done by system on} \\ \textit{surroundings (shaft work} \\ + P\bar{V} \textit{ work)} \end{pmatrix}$$

$$= \begin{pmatrix} \textit{time rate of change of internal, kinetic,} \\ \textit{and potential energy inside system} \end{pmatrix} \qquad (2\text{-}18)$$

In most chemical engineering systems the general form reduces, as we will show, to essentially an enthalpy balance. This is best illustrated by specific examples.

EXAMPLE 2-6 The CSTR system of Example 2-3 will be considered again, this time with a cooling coil inside the tank that can remove the exothermic heat of reaction, λ (Btu/mole of A reacted). We will use the normal convention that λ is negative for an exothermic reaction and positive for an endothermic reaction. The rate of heat generation due to reaction is the rate of consumption of A times λ.

$$Q_G = - \lambda V C_A k \qquad \diamondsuit \text{ Btu/sec} \qquad (2\text{-}19)$$

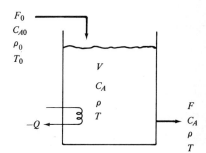

FIGURE 2-5
CSTR with heat removal.

The rate of heat removal is $-Q$ (Btu/sec). The temperature of the feed system is T_0 and the temperature in the reactor is T (°R). Writing Eq. (2-18) for this system,

$$F_0 \rho_0 (U_0 + K_0 + \Phi_0) - F\rho(U + K + \Phi) + (Q_G + Q)$$

$$- (W + FP - F_0 P_0)\frac{1}{J} = \frac{d}{dt}[(U + K + \Phi)V\rho] \qquad (2\text{-}20)$$

where U = internal energy, Btu/lb$_m$
K = kinetic energy, Btu/lb$_m$
Φ = potential energy, Btu/lb$_m$
W = shaft work done by system, ft-lb$_F$/sec
P = pressure of system, lb$_F$/ft^2
P_0 = pressure of feed stream, lb$_F$/ft^2
J = 778 ft-lb$_F$/Btu

In the system shown in Fig. 2-5 there is no shaft work, so $W = 0$. If the inlet and outlet flow velocities are not very high, the kinetic-energy term is negligible. If the elevations of the inlet and outlet flows are about the same, the potential-energy term is small. Thus Eq. (2-20) reduces to

$$\frac{d(\rho V U)}{dt} = F_0 \rho_0 U_0 - F\rho U + Q_G + Q - F\rho\left(\frac{P}{\rho}\right)\frac{1}{J} + F_0\rho_0\left(\frac{P_0}{\rho_0}\right)\frac{1}{J}$$

$$= F_0\rho_0\left(U_0 + \frac{P_0\overline{V}_0}{J}\right) - F\rho\left(U + \frac{P\overline{V}}{J}\right) + Q_G + Q \qquad (2\text{-}21)$$

where $\overline{V}$ is the specific volume (ft^3/lb$_m$), the reciprocal of the density. Enthalpy, H or h, is defined: ·

$$h \text{ or } H = U + P\overline{V}/J \qquad \diamondsuit \text{ Btu/lb}_m \qquad (2\text{-}22)$$

We will use h for the enthalpy of a liquid stream and H for the enthalpy of a vapor stream. Thus, for the CSTR, Eq. (2-21) becomes

$$\frac{d}{dt}(\rho V U) = F_0 \rho_0 h_0 - F\rho h + Q - \lambda V k C_A \qquad (2\text{-}23)$$

In many systems the $P\bar{V}$ term is negligible compared with U, and we use the time rate of change of the enthalpy of the system instead of the internal energy of the system.

$$\frac{d}{dt}(\rho V h) = F_0 \rho_0 h_0 - F\rho h + Q - \lambda V k C_A \qquad (2\text{-}24)$$

The enthalpies are functions of composition, pressure, and temperature, but primarily temperature. From thermodynamics, the heat capacities at constant pressure, C_p, and at constant volume, C_v, are

$$C_p = \left(\frac{\partial H}{\partial T}\right)_p \qquad C_v = \left(\frac{\partial U}{\partial T}\right)_v \qquad (2\text{-}25)$$

To illustrate that the energy equation is primarily influenced by temperatures, let us simplify the problem by assuming that the liquid enthalpy can be expressed as a product of absolute temperature and an average heat capacity C_p (Btu/lb$_m$-°R) that is a constant.

$$h = C_p T$$

The internal energy U is also, in general, a function of temperature, composition, and pressure. Again, for simplicity, let us assume that the liquid density is constant (so $C_p = C_v$) and the internal energy is just $C_p T$. With these simplifications Eq. (2-23) becomes

$$\rho C_p \frac{d(VT)}{dt} = \rho C_p(F_0 T_0 - FT) + Q - \lambda V k C_A \qquad (2\text{-}26)$$

Keep in mind the several simplifying assumptions made in Eq. (2-26) as opposed to the less restricted but still not completely general form in Eq. (2-23). ////

EXAMPLE 2-7 To show what form the energy equation takes for a two-phase system, consider the CSTR system shown in Fig. 2-6. Both a liquid product stream F and a vapor product stream F_v (ft^3/sec) are drawn off the vessel. The pressure in the reactor is P (lb$_F$/ft^2). Vapor and liquid volumes are V_v and V_L (ft^3). The density and temperature of the vapor phase are ρ_v and T_v. The mole fraction of A in the vapor is y. If the phases are in thermal equilibrium, the vapor and liquid temperatures are

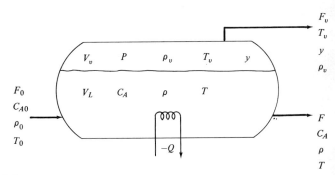

FIGURE 2-6
Two-phase CSTR with heat removal.

equal ($T = T_v$). If the phases are in phase equilibrium, the liquid and vapor composi-tions are related by Raoult's law, a relative volatility relationship, or some other vapor-liquid equilibrium relationship (see Sec. 2-2.6). The enthalpy of the vapor phase, H (Btu/lb$_m$), is in general a function of composition y, temperature T_v, and pressure P. Neglecting kinetic- and potential-energy terms and the work term, and replacing internal energies with enthalpies in the time derivative, the energy equation for the system (the vapor and liquid contents of the tank) becomes

$$\frac{d}{dt}(\rho_v V_v H + \rho V_L h) = F_0 \rho_0 h_0 - F\rho h - F_v \rho_v H + Q - \lambda V k C_A \qquad (2\text{-}27)$$

In order to express this equation explicitly in terms of temperature, let us again use a very simple form for h ($h = C_p T$) and an equally simple form for H.

$$H = C_p T + \lambda_v \qquad (2\text{-}28)$$

where λ_v is an average heat of vaporization of the mixture. In a more rigorous model λ_v could be a function of temperature T_v, composition y, and pressure P. Equation (2-27) becomes

$$\frac{d}{dt}[\rho_v V_v(C_p T + \lambda_v) + \rho V_L C_p T] = F_0 \rho_0 C_p T_0 - F\rho C_p T$$

$$- F_v \rho_v(C_p T + \lambda_v) + Q - \lambda V k C_A \qquad (2\text{-}29) \qquad ////$$

EXAMPLE 2-8   To illustrate the application of the energy equation to a microscopic system, let us return to the plug-flow tubular-reactor problem and now keep track of temperature changes as the fluid flows down the pipe. We will again assume no radial gradients in velocity, concentration, or temperature (a very poor assumption in some

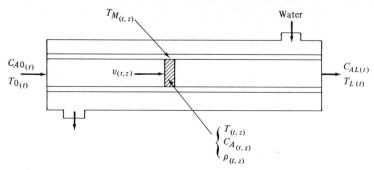

FIGURE 2-7
Jacketed tubular reactor.

strongly exothermic systems if the pipe diameter is not kept small). Suppose that the reactor has a cooling jacket around it as shown in Fig. 2-7. Heat can be transferred from the process fluid reactants and products at temperature T to the metal wall of the reactor at temperature T_M. The heat is subsequently transferred to the cooling water. For a complete description of the system we would need energy equations for the process fluid, the metal wall, and the cooling water. Here we will concern ourselves only with the process energy equation.

Looking at a little slice of the process fluid as our system, we can derive each of the terms of Eq. (2-18). Potential- and kinetic-energy terms are assumed negligible, and there is no work term. The simplified forms of the internal energy and enthalpy are assumed. Diffusive flow is assumed negligible compared with bulk flow. We will include the possibility for conduction of heat axially along the reactor due to molecular or turbulent conduction.

Flow of energy (enthalpy) into boundary at z due to bulk flow:

$$v A \rho C_p T \qquad \diamondsuit \frac{\text{ft}}{\text{sec}} \times \text{ft}^2 \times \frac{\text{lb}_\text{m}}{\text{ft}^3} \times \frac{\text{Btu}}{\text{lb}_\text{m} - {}^\circ\text{R}} \times {}^\circ\text{R} = \text{Btu/sec}$$

Flow of energy (enthalpy) out of boundary at z + dz:

$$v A \rho C_p T + \frac{\partial}{\partial z}(v A \rho C_p T)\, dz$$

Heat generated by chemical reaction $= -A\, dz\, k C_A \lambda$

Heat transferred to metal wall $= -h_T(\pi D\, dz)(T - T_M)$

where h_T = heat transfer film coefficient, Btu/ft^2-$^\circ$R-sec
       D = diameter of pipe (ft)

Heat conduction into boundary at $z = q_z A$

Heat conduction out of boundary at $z + dz = q_z A + \dfrac{\partial}{\partial z}(q_z A)\, dz$

where q_z is a heat flux in the z direction due to conduction. We will use Fourier's law to express q_z in terms of a temperature driving force:

$$q_z = -k_T \frac{\partial T}{\partial z} \qquad (2\text{-}30)$$

where k_T is an effective thermal conductivity (Btu/ft-sec-°R).

Rate of change of internal energy of system:

$$\frac{\partial}{\partial t}(\rho A\, dz\, C_p T)$$

Combining all the above gives

$$\frac{\partial}{\partial t}(\rho C_p T) + \frac{\partial}{\partial z}(v\rho C_p T) + \lambda k C_A + \frac{4h_T}{D}(T - T_M) = \frac{\partial}{\partial z}\left(k_T \frac{\partial T}{\partial z}\right) \qquad (2\text{-}31) \qquad ////$$

2-2.3 Equations of Motion

As any high school student knows, Newton's second law of motion says that force is equal to mass times acceleration for a system with constant mass M.

$$F = \frac{Ma}{g_c} \qquad (2\text{-}32)$$

where F = force, lb_F
M = mass, lb_m
a = acceleration, ft/sec^2
g_c = conversion constant needed to keep units consistent = 32.2, lb_m-ft/lb_F-sec^2

This is the basic relationship that is used in writing the equations of motion for a system. In a slightly more general form, where mass can vary with time,

$$\frac{1}{g_c}\frac{d(Mv_i)}{dt} = \sum_{j=1}^{N} F_{ji} \qquad (2\text{-}33)$$

where v_i = velocity in i direction, ft/sec
F_{ji} = jth force acting in i direction.

This says that the time rate of change of momentum in the i direction (mass times velocity in the i direction) is equal to the net sum of the forces pushing in the i direction. It can be thought of as a force balance. Or more eloquently it is called the *conservation of momentum*.

In the real world there are three directions: X, Y, and Z. Thus three force balances can be written for any system. Therefore each system has three equations of motion (plus one total mass-balance, one energy equation, and $J - 1$ component balances).

Instead of writing three equations of motion, it is often more convenient (and always more elegant) to write the three equations as one vector equation. We will not use the vector form in this book since all our examples will be simple one-dimensional force balances. There are several excellent texts[1] that cover more complex systems, particularly in the field of fluid mechanics.

EXAMPLE 2-9   The gravity-flow tank system described in Chap. 1 provides a simple example of the application of the equations of motion to a macroscopic system. Referring to Fig. 1-1, let the length of the exit line be L (ft) and its cross-sectional area be A_p (ft^2). The vertical, cylindrical tank has a cross-sectional area of A_T (ft^2).

The part of this process that is described by a force balance is the liquid flowing through the pipe. It will have a mass equal to the volume of the pipe (A_pL) times the density of the liquid, ρ. This mass of liquid will have velocity v (ft/sec) equal to the volumetric flow divided by the cross-sectional area of the pipe. Remember we have assumed plug-flow conditions and incompressible liquid, and therefore all the liquid is moving at the same velocity, more or less like a solid rod. If the flow is turbulent, this is not a bad assumption.

$$M = A_p L \rho \qquad (2\text{-}34)$$

$$v = \frac{F}{A_p} \qquad (2\text{-}35)$$

The amount of liquid in the pipe will not change with time, but if we want to change the rate of outflow, the velocity of the liquid must be changed. And to change the velocity or the momentum of the liquid we must exert a force on the liquid.

[1] R. Byron Bird, W. E. Stewart, and E. N. Lightfoot, "Transport Phenomena," Wiley, 1960.
H. Schlichting, "Boundary Layer Theory," Pergamon, 1955.
J. R. Welty, C. E. Wicks, and R. E. Wilson, "Fundamentals of Momentum, Heat and Mass Transfer," Wiley, 1969.

The direction of interest in this problem is the horizontal, since the pipe is assumed to be horizontal. The force pushing on the liquid at the left end of the pipe is the hydraulic pressure force of the liquid in the tank.

$$Hydraulic\ force = A_p \rho h \frac{g}{g_c} \qquad \diamondsuit ft^2 \times \frac{lb_m}{ft^3} \times ft \times \frac{32.2\ ft/sec^2}{32.2(lb_m - ft)/(lb_F - sec^2)} = lb_F$$

$$(2\text{-}36a)$$

g is the acceleration due to gravity and is 32.2 ft/sec² if the tank is at sea level. The static pressures at both ends of the pipe are the same, and therefore we neglect them.

The only force pushing in the opposite direction from right to left and opposing the flow is the frictional force due to the viscosity of the liquid. If the flow is turbulent, the frictional force will be proportional to the square of the velocity and the length of the pipe.

$$Frictional\ force = K_F L v^2 \qquad (2\text{-}36b)$$

where K_F is assumed to be a constant with units $lb_F/(ft^2/sec^2)$- ft.

Substituting these forces into Eq. (2-33), we get

$$\frac{1}{g_c} \frac{d}{dt}(A_p L \rho v) = A_p \rho h \frac{g}{g_c} - K_F L v^2 \qquad \diamondsuit lb_F$$

$$\frac{dv}{dt} = \frac{g}{L} h - \frac{K_F g_c}{\rho A_p} v^2 \qquad (2\text{-}37)$$

The sign of the frictional force is negative because it acts in the direction opposite the flow. We have defined left to right as the positive direction.   ////

EXAMPLE 2-10   Probably the best contemporary example of a variable-mass system would be the equations of motion for a space rocket whose mass decreases as fuel is consumed. However, to stick with chemical engineering systems, let us consider the problem sketched in Fig. 2-8. Petroleum pipelines are sometimes used for transferring several products from one location to another on a batch basis, i.e., one product at a

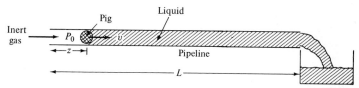

FIGURE 2-8
Pipeline and pig.

time. To reduce product contamination at the end of a batch transfer, a leather ball or "pig" that just fits the pipe is inserted in one end of the line. Inert gas is introduced behind the pig to push it through the line, thus purging the line of whatever liquid is in it.

To write a force balance on the liquid still in the pipe as it is pushed out, we must take into account the changing mass of material. Assume the pig is weightless and frictionless compared with the liquid in the line. Let z be the axial position of the pig at any time. The liquid is incompressible (density ρ) and flows in plug flow. It exerts a frictional force proportional to the square of its velocity and to the length of pipe still containing liquid.

$$\text{Frictional force} = K_F(L - z)\, v^2 \qquad \text{(2-38)}$$

The cross-sectional area of the pipe is A_p (ft^2). The mass of fluid in the pipe is $(L - z)A_p\rho$.

The pressure P_0 (lb$_F$/ft^2-gauge) of inert gas behind the pig is essentially constant all the way down the pipeline. The tank into which the liquid dumps is at atmospheric pressure. The pipeline is horizontal. A force balance in the horizontal z direction yields

$$\frac{1}{g_c}\frac{d}{dt}[\rho A_p v(L - z)] = P_0 A_p - K_F(L - z)v^2 \qquad \text{(2-39)}$$

Substituting that $v = dz/dt$ we get

$$\frac{d}{dt}\left[(L - z)\frac{dz}{dt}\right] = \frac{g_c P_0}{\rho} - \frac{g_c K_F}{\rho A_p}(L - z)\left(\frac{dz}{dt}\right)^2 \qquad \text{(2-40)} \qquad ////$$

EXAMPLE 2-11   As an example of a force balance for a microscopic system, let us look at the classic problem of the laminar flow of an incompressible, newtonian liquid in a cylindrical pipe. By "newtonian" we mean that its *shear force* (resistance that adjacent layers of fluid exhibit to flowing past each other) is proportional to the *shear rate* or the velocity gradient:

$$\tau_{rz} = -\frac{\mu}{g_c}\frac{\partial v_z}{\partial r} \qquad \text{(2-41)}$$

where τ_{rz} = shear rate (shear force per unit area) acting in z direction and perpendicular to r axis, lb$_F$/ft^2

v_z = velocity in z direction, ft/sec

$\partial v_z/\partial r$ = velocity gradient of v_z in r direction

μ = viscosity[1] of fluid, lb$_m$/ft-sec

We will pick as our system a small, doughnut-shaped element, half of which is shown in Fig. 2-9. Since the fluid is incompressible there is no radial flow of fluid, or

[1] In many industries viscosity is reported in centipoise or poise. The conversion factor is: 6.72×10^{-4} (lb$_m$/ft-sec)/centipoise.

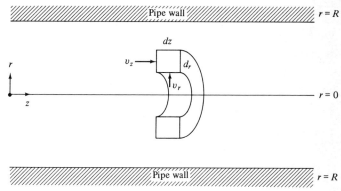

FIGURE 2-9
Laminar flow in a pipe.

$v_r = 0$. The system is symmetrical with respect to the angular coordinate (around the circumference of the pipe), and therefore we need consider only the two dimensions r and z. The forces in the z direction acting on the element are:

Forces acting left to right:

$$\text{Shear force on face at } r = \tau_{rz}(2\pi r \; dz) \qquad \diamond \; \frac{lb_F}{ft^2} \times ft^2 \qquad (2\text{-}42)$$

$$\text{Pressure force on face at } z = (2\pi r \; dr)P \qquad (2\text{-}43)$$

Forces acting right to left:

$$\text{Shear force on face at } r + dr = 2\pi r \cdot dz \; \tau_{rz} + \frac{\partial}{\partial r}(2\pi r \; dz \; \tau_{rz}) \; dr$$

$$\text{Pressure force on face at } z + dz = 2\pi r \; dr \; P + \frac{\partial}{\partial z}(2\pi r \; dr \; P) \; dz$$

$$\text{Rate of change of momentum} = \frac{1}{g_c}\frac{\partial}{\partial t}(2\pi r \; dz \; dr \; \rho v_z) \qquad (2\text{-}44)$$

Combining all the above gives

$$\frac{r\rho}{g_c}\frac{\partial v_z}{\partial t} + \frac{\partial}{\partial r}(r\tau_{rz}) + r\frac{\partial P}{\partial z} = 0 \qquad (2\text{-}45a)$$

The $\partial P/\partial z$ term, or the pressure drop per foot of pipe, will be constant if the fluid is incompressible. Let us call it $\Delta P/L$. Substituting it and Eq. (2-41) into Eq. (2-45a) gives

$$\frac{\partial v_z}{\partial t} = \frac{\mu}{\rho}\frac{1}{r}\frac{\partial}{\partial r}\left(r\frac{\partial v_z}{\partial r}\right) - \frac{g_c \Delta P}{\rho L} \qquad (2\text{-}45b) \qquad ////$$

2-2.4 Transport Equations

We have already used in the examples above most of the laws governing the transfer of energy, mass, and momentum. These transport laws all have the form of a flux (rate of transfer per unit area) being proportional to a driving force (a gradient in temperature, concentration, or velocity). The proportionality constant is a physical property of the system (like thermal conductivity, diffusivity, or viscosity).

For transport on a molecular level, the laws bear the familiar names of Fourier, Fick, and Newton.

Transfer relationships of a more macroscopic overall form are also used, for example, film coefficients and overall coefficients in heat transfer. Here the difference in the bulk properties between two locations is the driving force. The proportionality constant is an overall transfer coefficient. Table 2-1 summarizes some of the various relationships used in developing models.

Table 2-1   TRANSPORT LAWS

Quantity	Heat	Mass	Momentum
Flux	q	N_A	$g_c \tau_{rz}$
Units	Btu/sec-ft^2	moles A/sec-ft^2	$\dfrac{\text{lb}_m\text{-ft/sec}}{\text{sec-ft}^2}$
Molecular Driving force	$\dfrac{\partial T}{\partial z}$	$\dfrac{\partial C_A}{\partial z}$	$\dfrac{\partial v_z}{\partial r}$
Units	°R/ft	$\dfrac{\text{moles A/ft}^3\dagger}{\text{ft}}$	1/sec
Law	Fourier's	Fick's	Newton's
Property	Thermal conductivity k_T	Diffusivity $\mathscr{D}_A$	Viscosity μ
Units	$\dfrac{\text{Btu}}{\text{sec-ft}^2\text{-°R/ft}}$	$\dfrac{\text{moles A}}{\text{sec-ft}^2\text{-}\dfrac{\text{moles A/ft}^3}{\text{ft}}}$	$\dfrac{\text{lb}_m\text{-ft/sec}}{\text{sec-ft}^2\text{-1/sec}}$
Overall Driving force	ΔT	ΔC_A	ΔP
Units	°R	moles A/ft^3	lb$_F$/ft^2
Relationship	$q = h_T \, \Delta T$	$N_A = k_L \, \Delta C_A$	‡

† Driving forces in terms of partial pressures and mole fractions are also commonly used.
‡ The most common problem, determining pressure drops through pipes, uses friction factor correlations. $f = \dfrac{g_c \, D \, \Delta P/L}{2\rho v^2}$

2-2.5 Equations of State

To write mathematical models we need equations that tell us how the physical properties, primarily density and enthalpy, change with temperature, pressure, and composition.

$$\begin{aligned}
Liquid\ density &= \rho_L = f_{(P,T,x_i)} \\
Vapor\ density &= \rho_v = f_{(P,T,y_i)} \\
Liquid\ enthalpy &= h = f_{(P,T,x_i)} \\
Vapor\ enthalpy &= H = f_{(P,T,y_i)}
\end{aligned} \tag{2-46}$$

Occasionally these relationships have to be fairly complex to describe the system accurately. But in many cases simplification can be made without sacrificing much overall accuracy. We have already used some simple enthalpy equations in the examples of energy balances.

$$\begin{aligned}
h &= C_p T \\
H &= C_p T + \lambda_v
\end{aligned} \tag{2-47}$$

The next level of complexity would be to make the C_p's functions of temperature:

$$h = \int_{T_0}^{T} C_{p(T)}\, dT \tag{2-48}$$

A polynomial in T is often used for C_p.

$$C_{p(T)} = A_1 + A_2 T \tag{2-49}$$

Then Eq. (2-48) becomes

$$h = A_1 T + A_2 \left.\frac{T^2}{2}\right]_{T_0}^{T} = A_1(T - T_0) + \frac{A_2}{2}(T^2 - T_0{}^2)$$

$$= A_3 + A_4 T + A_5 T^2 \tag{2-50}$$

Of course, with mixtures of components the total enthalpy is needed. If heat-of-mixing effects are negligible the pure-component enthalpies can be averaged:

$$h = \frac{\sum_{j=1}^{J} x_j h_j M_j}{\sum_{j=1}^{J} x_j M_j} \tag{2-51}$$

where x_j = mole fraction of jth component
$\quad M_j$ = molecular weight of jth component, lb_m/mole
$\quad h_j$ = pure-component enthalpy of jth component, Btu/lb_m

The denominator of Eq. (2-51) is the average molecular weight of the mixture.

Liquid densities can be assumed constant in many systems unless large changes in composition and temperature occur.

Vapor densities usually cannot be considered invariant and some sort of PVT relationship is almost always required. The simplest and most often used is the perfect-gas law:

$$PV = nRT \qquad (2\text{-}52)$$

where P = absolute pressure, lb_F/ft^2
  V = volume, ft^3
  n = number of moles
  R = constant = 1,545 lb_F-ft/mole-°R
  T = absolute temperature, °R

Rearranging to get an equation for the density ρ (lb_m/ft^3) of a perfect gas with a molecular weight M (lb_m/mole), we get

$$\rho = \frac{nM}{V} = \frac{MP}{RT} \qquad (2\text{-}53)$$

2-2.6   Equilibrium

The second law of thermodynamics is the basis for the equations that tell us the conditions of a system when equilibrium conditions prevail.

Chemical equilibrium   Equilibrium occurs in a reacting system when

$$\sum_{j=1}^{J} v_j \mu_j = 0 \qquad (2\text{-}54)$$

where v_j = stoichiometric coefficient of jth component with reactants having a negative sign and products a positive sign
  μ_j = chemical potential of jth component

The usual way to work with this equation is in terms of an equilibrium constant for a reaction. For example, consider a reversible gas-phase reaction of A to form B at a specific reaction rate k_1 and B reacting back to A at a specific reaction rate k_2. The stoichiometry of the reaction is such that v_a moles of A react to form v_b moles of B.

$$v_a A \underset{k_2}{\overset{k_1}{\rightleftharpoons}} v_b B \qquad (2\text{-}55)$$

Equation (2-54) says equilibrium will occur when

$$v_b \mu_B - v_a \mu_A = 0 \qquad (2\text{-}56)$$

The chemical potentials for a perfect-gas mixture can be written[1]

$$\mu_j = \mu_j^0 + RT \ln \mathscr{P}_j \qquad (2\text{-}57)$$

[1] K. Denbigh, "Principles of Chemical Equilibrium," Cambridge, 1957.

where $\mu_j^{\,0}$ = standard chemical potential (or Gibbs free energy per mole) of jth component, which is a function of temperature only

$\mathscr{P}_j$ = partial pressure of jth component

R = perfect-gas constant

T = absolute temperature

Substituting into Eq. (2-56),

$$v_b(\mu_B^{\,0} + RT \ln \mathscr{P}_B) - v_a(\mu_A^{\,0} + RT \ln \mathscr{P}_A) = 0$$

$$RT \ln \mathscr{P}_B^{\,v_b} - RT \ln \mathscr{P}_A^{\,v_a} = v_a \mu_A^{\,0} - v_b \mu_B^{\,0}$$

$$\ln \left(\frac{\mathscr{P}_B^{\,v_b}}{\mathscr{P}_A^{\,v_a}} \right) = \frac{v_a \mu_A^{\,0} - v_b \mu_B^{\,0}}{RT} \qquad (2\text{-}58)$$

The right-hand side of this equation is a function of temperature only. The term in parentheses on the left-hand side is defined as the equilibrium constant K_p, and it tells us the equilibrium ratios of products and reactants.

$$K_p \equiv \frac{\mathscr{P}_B^{\,v_b}}{\mathscr{P}_A^{\,v_a}} \qquad (2\text{-}59)$$

Phase equilibrium Equilibrium between two phases occurs when the chemical potential of each component is the same in the two phases:

$$\mu_j^{\,I} = \mu_j^{\,II} \qquad (2\text{-}60)$$

where $\mu_j^{\,I}$ = chemical potential of jth component in phase I

$\mu_j^{\,II}$ = chemical potential of jth component in phase II

Since the vast majority of chemical engineering systems involve liquid and vapor phases, many vapor-liquid equilibrium relationships are used. They range from the very simple to the very complex. Some of the most commonly used relationships are listed below. More detailed treatments are presented in many thermodynamics texts.

Basically we need a relationship that permits us to calculate the vapor composition if we know the liquid composition, or vice versa. The most common problem is a *bubble-point* calculation: Given the pressure P of a system and the liquid composition x_j, we want to calculate the temperature of the system and the vapor composition y_j. This usually involves a trial-and-error, iterative solution because the equations can be solved explicitly only in the simplest cases.

Sometimes we know x_j and T and want to find P and y_j or we know y_j and P (or T) and want to find x_j and T (or P).

We will assume ideal vapor-phase behavior in our examples, i.e., the partial pressure of the jth component in the vapor is equal to the total pressure P times the mole fraction of the jth component in the vapor y_j (Dalton's law):

$$\mathscr{P}_j = P y_j \qquad (2\text{-}61)$$

Corrections may be required at high pressures.

1   *Raoult's law:* Liquids that obey Raoult's law are called *ideal.*

$$P = \sum_{j=1}^{J} x_j P_j^0 \qquad (2\text{-}62)$$

$$y_j = \frac{x_j P_j^0}{P} \qquad (2\text{-}63)$$

where P_j^0 is the vapor pressure of the pure jth component. Vapor pressures are functions of temperature only. This dependence is often described by

$$\ln P_j^0 = \frac{A_j}{T} + B_j \qquad (2\text{-}64)$$

2   *Relative volatility:* The relative volatility α_{ij} of component i to component j is defined:

$$\alpha_{ij} = \frac{y_i/x_i}{y_j/x_j} \qquad (2\text{-}65)$$

Relative volatilities are fairly constant in a number of systems. They are convenient and frequently used.

In a binary system the relative volatility α of the more volatile component compared with the less volatile component is

$$\alpha = \frac{y/x}{(1-y)/(1-x)}$$

Rearranging,

$$y = \frac{\alpha x}{1 + (\alpha - 1)x} \qquad (2\text{-}66)$$

3   *K values:* Equilibrium vaporization ratios or K values are widely used, particularly in the petroleum industry.

$$K_j = \frac{y_j}{x_j} \qquad (2\text{-}67)$$

The K's are functions of temperature and, to a lesser extent, composition and pressure.

4 *Activity coefficients:* For nonideal liquids, Raoult's law may be easily modified to account for the nonideality. The "fudge factors" used are called *activity coefficients.*

$$P = \sum_{j=1}^{J} x_j P_j{}^0 \gamma_j \qquad (2\text{-}68)$$

where γ_j is the activity coefficient for the jth component. The activity coefficient is equal to 1 if the component is ideal. The γ's are functions of composition, temperature, and pressure.

2-2.7 Chemical Kinetics

We will be modeling many chemical reactors, and we must be familiar with the basic relationships and terminology used in describing the kinetics (rate of reaction) of chemical reactions. For more details, consult one of the several excellent texts in this field.[1]

Arrhenius temperature dependence   The temperature dependence of a specific reaction rate, k, is usually found to be exponential:

$$k = \alpha e^{-E/RT} \qquad (2\text{-}69)$$

where k = specific reaction rate (units to be defined below)
 α = preexponential factor (units same as k), a constant
 E = activation energy (Btu/mole); shows the temperature dependence of the reaction rate, i.e., the bigger E, the faster k increases with temperature
 T = absolute temperature, °R
 R = perfect-gas constant (1.99 Btu/mole-°R)

This exponential temperature dependence represents one of the most severe nonlinearities in chemical engineering systems. Keep in mind that the "apparent" temperature dependence of a reaction may not be exponential if the reaction is mass-transfer limited, not chemical-rate limited. If both zones are encountered in the operation of the reactor, the mathematical model must obviously include both reaction-rate and mass-transfer effects.

Law of mass action   Using the conventional notation, we will define an overall reaction rate $\mathscr{R}$ as the rate of change of moles of any component per unit volume due to chemical reaction divided by that component's stoichiometric coefficient.

[1] O. Levenspiel, "Chemical Reaction Engineering," Wiley, 1962.
 J. M. Smith, "Chemical Engineering Kinetics," 2d ed., McGraw-Hill, 1970.

$$\mathscr{R} = \frac{1}{v_j V} \left(\frac{dn_j}{dt} \right)_R \qquad \diamondsuit \frac{\text{moles component } j}{\text{sec-ft}^3} \qquad (2\text{-}70)$$

The stoichiometric coefficients v_j are positive for products of the reaction and negative for reactants. Note that $\mathscr{R}$ is an intensive property and can be applied to systems of any size. For example, assume we are dealing with an irreversible reaction in which components A and B react to form components C and D.

$$v_a \, A + v_b \, B \xrightarrow{\ k\ } v_c \, C + v_d \, D$$

Then

$$\mathscr{R} = \frac{1}{-v_a V} \left(\frac{dn_A}{dt} \right)_R = \frac{1}{-v_b V} \left(\frac{dn_B}{dt} \right)_R$$

$$= \frac{1}{v_c V} \left(\frac{dn_C}{dt} \right)_R = \frac{1}{v_d V} \left(\frac{dn_D}{dt} \right)_R \qquad (2\text{-}71)$$

The law of mass action says that the overall reaction rate $\mathscr{R}$ will vary with temperature (since k is temperature-dependent) and with the concentration of reactants raised to some powers.

$$\mathscr{R} = k_{(T)} C_A{}^a C_B{}^b \qquad (2\text{-}72)$$

where C_A = concentration of component A, moles of A/ft^3
$\quad\ \ C_B$ = concentration of component B, moles of B/ft^3

The constants a and b are not, in general, equal to the stoichiometric coefficients v_a and v_b.

The reaction is said to be first order in A if $a = 1$. It is second order in A if $a = 2$. The constants a and b can be fractions.

As indicated earlier, the units of the specific reaction rate k depend on the order of the reaction. This is because the overall reaction rate $\mathscr{R}$ always has the same units. For a first-order reaction of A reacting to form B, the overall reaction rate $\mathscr{R}$ (written for component A†) would be

$$\mathscr{R} = kC_A \qquad \diamondsuit \frac{\text{moles of A}}{\text{sec-ft}^3}$$

If C_A has units of moles of A/ft^3, k must have units of 1/sec.

As indicated the overall reaction rate for the system above is second order in A,

$$\mathscr{R} = kC_A{}^2 \qquad \diamondsuit \frac{\text{moles of A}}{\text{sec-ft}^3}$$

† $\mathscr{R}$ can be applied to any component [see Eq. (2-71)].

Therefore k must have units of ft^3/sec-moles of A.

Consider the reaction A + B $\xrightarrow{k}$ C. If the overall reaction rate is first order in both A and B,

$$\mathscr{R} = kC_A C_B \qquad \diamond \quad \frac{\text{moles of A}}{\text{sec-ft}^3}$$

Therefore k must have units of ft^3/sec-moles of B.

PROBLEMS

2-1 Write the component continuity equations describing the CSTR of Example 2-3 with:
(a) Simultaneous reactions (first order, isothermal)

$$A \xrightarrow{k_1} B$$
$$A \xrightarrow{k_2} C$$

(b) Reversible (first order, isothermal)

$$A \underset{k_2}{\overset{k_1}{\rightleftharpoons}} B$$

2-2 Write the component continuity equations for a tubular reactor as in Example 2-5 with consecutive reactions occurring:

$$A \xrightarrow{k_1} B \xrightarrow{k_2} C$$

2-3 Write the component continuity equations for a perfectly mixed batch reactor (no inflow or outflow) with first-order isothermal reactions:
(a) Consecutive
(b) Simultaneous
(c) Reversible

2-4 Write the energy equation for the CSTR of Example 2-6 in which consecutive first-order reactions

$$A \xrightarrow[\lambda_1]{k_1} B \xrightarrow[\lambda_2]{k_2} C$$

occur with exothermic heats of λ_1 and λ_2.

2-5 Charlie Brown and Snoopy are sledding down a hill that is inclined θ degrees from horizontal. The total weight of Charlie, Snoopy, and the sled is M. The sled is essentially frictionless but the air resistance of the sledders is proportional to the square of their velocity. Write the equation describing their position X, relative to the top of the hill ($X = 0$). Charlie likes to "belly flop," so their initial velocity at the top of the hill is v_0.

What would happen if Snoopy jumped off the sled halfway down the hill without changing the air resistance?

2-6   An automatic bale tosser on the back of a farmer's hay baler must throw a 60-lb bale

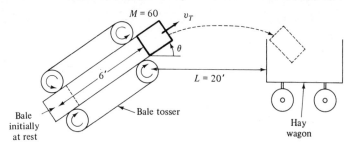

20 ft back into a wagon. If the bale leaves the tosser with a velocity v_T in a direction $\theta = 45°$ above horizontal, what must v_T be? If the tosser must accelerate the bale from a dead start to v_T in 6 ft, how much force must it exert?

What value of θ would minimize this acceleration force?

2-7   A mixture of two immiscible liquids is fed into a decanter. The heavier liquid A settles to the bottom of the tank. The lighter liquid B forms a layer on the top. The two interfaces are detected by floats and are controlled by manipulating the two flows F_A and F_B (ft³/min).

$$F_A = K_A\, h_A$$

$$F_B = K_B\, (h_A + h_B)$$

The controllers increase or decrease the flows as the levels rise or fall.

The total feed rate is w_0 (lb$_m$/min). The weight fraction of liquid A in the feed is x_A. The two densities ρ_A and ρ_B (lb$_m$/ft³) are constant.

Write the equations describing the dynamic behavior of this system.

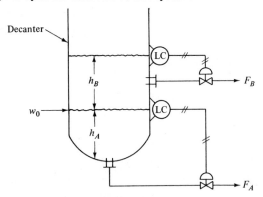

EXAMPLES OF MATHEMATICAL MODELS OF CHEMICAL ENGINEERING SYSTEMS

3-1 INTRODUCTION

Even if you were only half awake when you read the preceding chapter, you should have recognized that the equations developed in the examples constituted mathematical models or parts of mathematical models.

This chapter is devoted to more complete examples. We will start with simple systems and progress slowly to more realistic and complex processes.

It would be impossible to write mathematical models for all types of chemical engineering systems. The examples cover a number of very commonly encountered pieces of equipment: reactors of several types, distillation columns, and heat exchangers. I hope that these specific examples (or "case studies") of mathematical modeling will give you a good grasp of strategies and procedures so that you can apply them to your specific problem.

In each case we will set up all the equations required to describe the system. We will delay any discussion of solving these equations until Part 2. Our purpose at this stage is to translate the important phenomena occurring in the physical process into quantitative, mathematical equations.

3-2   SERIES OF ISOTHERMAL, CONSTANT-HOLDUP CSTR'S

The system is sketched in Fig. 3-1 and is a simple extension of the CSTR considered in Example 2-3. Product B is produced and reactant A is consumed in each of the three perfectly mixed reactors by a first-order reaction occurring in the liquid. For the moment let us assume that the temperatures and holdups (volumes) of the three tanks can be different, but both the temperatures and the liquid volumes are assumed to be constant (isothermal and constant holdup). Density is assumed constant throughout the system, which is a binary mixture of A and B.

With these assumptions in mind, we are ready to formulate our model. If the volume and density of each tank are constant, the total mass in each tank is constant. Thus the total continuity equation for the first reactor is

$$\frac{d(\rho V_1)}{dt} = \rho F_0 - \rho F_1 = 0 \qquad (3\text{-}1)$$

or

$$F_1 = F_0$$

Likewise total mass balances on tanks 2 and 3 give

$$F_3 = F_2 = F_1 = F_0 \equiv F \qquad (3\text{-}2)$$

where F is defined as the throughput (ft^3/sec).

We want to keep track of the amounts of reactant A and product B in each tank, so component continuity equations are needed. However, since the system is binary and we know the total mass of material in each tank, only one component continuity equation is required. Either B or A can be used. If we arbitrarily choose A, the equations describing the dynamic changes in the amounts of reactant A in each tank are (with units moles of A/sec)

$$V_1 \frac{dC_{A1}}{dt} = F(C_{A0} - C_{A1}) - V_1 k_1 C_{A1}$$

$$V_2 \frac{dC_{A2}}{dt} = F(C_{A1} - C_{A2}) - V_2 k_2 C_{A2} \qquad (3\text{-}3)$$

$$V_3 \frac{dC_{A3}}{dt} = F(C_{A2} - C_{A3}) - V_3 k_3 C_{A3}$$

The specific reaction rates k_n are given by the Arrhenius equation

$$k_n = \alpha e^{-E/RT_n} \qquad n = 1, 2, 3 \qquad (3\text{-}4)$$

If the temperatures in the reactors are different, the k's are different. The n refers to the stage number.

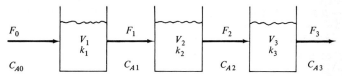

FIGURE 3-1
Series of CSTR's.

The volumes V_n can be pulled out of the time derivative because they are constant (see Sec. 3-3). The flows are all equal to F but can vary with time. An energy equation is not required because we have assumed isothermal operation.

The three first-order, nonlinear, ordinary differential equations given in Eqs. (3-3) are the mathematical model of the system. The parameters that must be known are V_1, V_2, V_3, k_1, k_2, and k_3. The variables that must be specified before these equations can be solved are F and C_{A0}. "Specified" does *not* mean that they must be constant. They can be time-variable, but they must be known or given functions of time. They are the *forcing functions*.

The initial conditions of the three concentrations (their values at time equals zero) must also be known.

Let us check the degrees of freedom of the system. There are three equations and, with the parameters and forcing functions specified, there are only three unknowns or dependent variables: C_{A1}, C_{A2}, and C_{A3}. Consequently a solution should be possible.

We will use this simple system in many subsequent parts of this book. When we use it for controller design and stability analysis, we will use an even simpler version. If the throughput F is constant and the holdups and temperatures are the same in all three tanks, Eqs. (3-3) become

$$\frac{dC_{A1}}{dt} + \left(k + \frac{1}{\tau}\right)C_{A1} = \frac{1}{\tau}C_{A0}$$

$$\frac{dC_{A2}}{dt} + \left(k + \frac{1}{\tau}\right)C_{A2} = \frac{1}{\tau}C_{A1} \qquad (3\text{-}5)$$

$$\frac{dC_{A3}}{dt} + \left(k + \frac{1}{\tau}\right)C_{A3} = \frac{1}{\tau}C_{A2}$$

where

$$\tau \equiv \frac{V}{F} \qquad \diamondsuit \frac{\text{ft}^3}{\text{ft}^3/\text{sec}} = \text{sec}$$

There is only one forcing function or input variable into the system, C_{A0}.

3-3   CSTR'S WITH VARIABLE HOLDUPS

If the previous example is modified slightly to permit the volumes in each reactor to vary with time, both total and component continuity equations are required for each reactor. To show the effects of higher-order kinetics, assume the reaction is now nth order in reactant A.

$$\frac{dV_1}{dt} = F_0 - F_1$$

$$\frac{d}{dt}(V_1 C_{A1}) = F_0 C_{A0} - F_1 C_{A1} - V_1 k_1 C_{A1}{}^n \tag{3-6}$$

$$\frac{dV_2}{dt} = F_1 - F_2$$

$$\frac{d}{dt}(V_2 C_{A2}) = F_1 C_{A1} - F_2 C_{A2} - V_2 k_2 C_{A2}{}^n \tag{3-7}$$

$$\frac{dV_3}{dt} = F_2 - F_3$$

$$\frac{d}{dt}(V_3 C_{A3}) = F_2 C_{A2} - F_3 C_{A3} - V_3 k_3 C_{A3}{}^n \tag{3-8}$$

Our mathematical model now contains six first-order, nonlinear, ordinary differential equations. Parameters that must be known are k_1, k_2, k_3, and n. Initial conditions for all the dependent variables that are to be integrated must be given: C_{A1}, C_{A2}, C_{A3}, V_1, V_2, and V_3. The forcing functions $C_{A0(t)}$ and $F_{0(t)}$ must also be given.

Let us now check the degrees of freedom of this system. There are six equations. *But* there are nine unknowns: C_{A1}, C_{A2}, C_{A3}, V_1, V_2, V_3, F_1, F_2, and F_3. Clearly this system is not sufficiently specified and a solution could not be obtained. It is *underspecified*.

What have we missed in our modeling? A good plant operator could take one look at the system and see what the problem is. We have not specified how the flows out of the tanks are to be set. Physically there would probably be control valves in the outlet lines to regulate the flows. How are these control valves to be set? A common configuration is to have the level in the tank controlled by the outflow; i.e., a level controller opens the control valve on the exit line to increase the outflow if the level in the tank increases. Or the liquid could overflow from one tank to the next.

Whatever the arrangement, there must be some hydraulic tie-in between tank volume and flow.

$$F_1 = f_{(V_1)}$$
$$F_2 = f_{(V_2)} \qquad (3\text{-}9)$$
$$F_3 = f_{(V_3)}$$

This gives the three missing equations and reduces the degrees of freedom to zero.

It might be worth noting at this point that we could have considered the flow from the third tank, F_3, as the forcing function. Then the level in tank 3 would probably be set by the flow F_2 into tank 3; and so forth back down the chain with F_0 now set by V_1. We would still have three equations.

The reactors shown in Fig. 3-1 would operate at atmospheric pressure if they were open to the atmosphere as sketched. If the reactors are not vented and if no inert blanketing is assumed, they would run at the bubble-point pressure for the specified temperature and composition. Therefore the pressures could be different in each reactor, and they would vary with time, even though temperatures are assumed constant, as the C_A's change.

3-4   GAS-PHASE, PRESSURIZED CSTR

Suppose a mixture of gases is fed into the reactor sketched in Fig. 3-2. The reactor is filled with reacting gases which are perfectly mixed. A reversible reaction occurs:

$$2A \underset{k_2}{\overset{k_1}{\rightleftharpoons}} B$$

The forward reaction is 1.5th order in A; the reverse reaction is first order in B. Note that the stoichiometric coefficient for A and the order of the reaction are not the same. The mole fraction of reactant A in the reactor is y. The pressure inside the reactor is P (lb_F/ft^2 abs). Both P and y can vary with time. The volume of the reactor V (ft^3) is constant.

We will assume an isothermal system, so the temperature T is constant. Perfect gases are also assumed. The feed stream has density ρ_0 and a mole fraction y_0 of reactant A. Its rate is F_0 (ft^3/sec).

The flow out of the reactor passes through a restriction (control valve) into another vessel which is held at a constant pressure P_D (lb_F/ft^2 abs). The outflow will

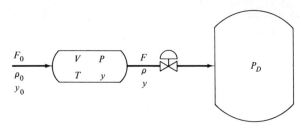

FIGURE 3-2
Gas-phase CSTR.

vary with the pressure and the composition of the reactor. Flows through control
valves are discussed in more detail in Part 3; here let us use the formula

$$F = C_V \sqrt{\frac{P - P_D}{\rho}} \qquad (3\text{-}10)$$

C_V is the valve sizing coefficient. Density varies with pressure and composition.

$$\rho = \frac{MP}{RT} = [yM_A + (1 - y)M_B]\frac{P}{RT} \qquad (3\text{-}11)$$

where M = average molecular weight
$\quad M_A$ = molecular weight of reactant A
$\quad M_B$ = molecular weight of product B

The concentration of reactant in the reactor is

$$C_A = \frac{Py}{RT} \qquad \diamondsuit \ \text{moles A/ft}^3 \qquad (3\text{-}12)$$

The overall reaction rate for the forward reaction is

$$\mathscr{R}_F = k_1(C_A)^{3/2} = -\frac{1}{2V}\left(\frac{dn_A}{dt}\right)_R$$
$$= \frac{1}{V}\left(\frac{dn_B}{dt}\right)_R \qquad (3\text{-}13)$$

The overall reaction rate for the reverse reaction is

$$\mathscr{R}_R = k_2 C_B = \frac{1}{2V}\left(\frac{dn_A}{dt}\right)_R = -\frac{1}{V}\left(\frac{dn_B}{dt}\right)_R \qquad (3\text{-}14)$$

With these fundamental relationships pinned down, we are ready to write the
total and component continuity equations.

Total continuity:

$$V \frac{d\rho}{dt} = \rho_0 F_0 - \rho F \qquad (3\text{-}15)$$

Component continuity:

$$V \frac{dC_A}{dt} = F_0 C_{A0} - F C_A - 2V k_1 C_A^{1.5} + 2V k_2 C_B \qquad (3\text{-}16)$$

The 2 in the reaction terms comes from the stoichiometric coefficient of A.

Equations (3-10) and (3-12) can be substituted into the above to express them in terms of ρ, P, and y.

$$V \frac{d\rho}{dt} = \rho_0 F_0 - \rho C_V \sqrt{\frac{P - P_D}{\rho}} \qquad (3\text{-}17)$$

$$\frac{V}{RT} \frac{d}{dt} (yP) = F_0 C_{A0} - \frac{Py}{RT} C_V \sqrt{\frac{P - P_D}{\rho}}$$
$$- 2V k_1 \left(\frac{Py}{RT}\right)^{1.5} + \frac{2V k_2 P(1 - y)}{RT} \qquad (3\text{-}18)$$

Equations (3-11), (3-17), and (3-18) are the mathematical model of this system.

The parameters that must be known are V, C_V, T, k_1, k_2, R, M_A, and M_B. The forcing functions (or inputs or independent variables) could be P_D, ρ_0, F_0, and C_{A0}. This leaves three unknowns (dependent variables): y, P, and ρ. Thus the system is properly defined.

3-5 NONISOTHERMAL CSTR

In examples studied thus far, we have shown the effects of variable holdups, variable densities, and higher-order kinetics on the total and component continuity equations. Energy equations were not needed because we assumed isothermal operations. Let us now consider a system in which temperature can change with time. An irreversible, exothermic reaction is carried out in a single perfectly mixed CSTR as shown in Fig. 3-3. The reaction is nth order in reactant A and has a heat of reaction λ (Btu/mole A reacted). Negligible heat losses and constant densities are assumed.

$$A \xrightarrow{k} B$$

To remove the heat of reaction, a cooling jacket surrounds the reactor. Cooling water is added to the jacket at a rate F_J (ft^3/sec) and an inlet temperature T_{J0} (°R). The volume of water in the jacket, V_J (ft^3), is assumed constant.

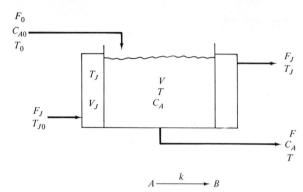

FIGURE 3-3
Nonisothermal CSTR.

CASE A The jacket water is assumed to be perfectly mixed. The mass of the metal walls is assumed negligible so that the "thermal inertia" of the metal need not be considered.

Heat transfer between the process at temperature T and the cooling water at temperature T_J is described by an overall heat transfer coefficient.

$$Q = UA_H(T - T_J) \qquad (3\text{-}19)$$

where Q = heat transfer rate, Btu/sec
$\quad U$ = overall heat transfer coefficient, Btu/sec-ft²-°R
$\qquad$ (Note: this is *not* the usual time basis for the U's reported in the literature.)
$\quad A_H$ = heat transfer area, ft²

In general the heat transfer area will vary with the holdup in the reactor.

The equations describing the system are

Reactor total continuity:

$$\frac{dV}{dt} = F_0 - F$$

Reactor component continuity:

$$\frac{d}{dt}(VC_A) = F_0 C_{A0} - FC_A - VkC_A^n$$

Reactor energy equation:

$$\rho \frac{d}{dt}(Vh) = \rho(F_0 h_0 - Fh) - \lambda VkC_A^n - UA_H(T - T_J) \qquad (3\text{-}20)$$

Jacket energy equation:

$$\rho_J V_J \frac{dh_J}{dt} = F_J \rho_J (h_{J0} - h_J) + UA_H(T - T_J) \qquad (3\text{-}21)$$

where ρ = density of process liquid, lb_m/ft^3
 ρ_J = density of cooling water, lb_m/ft^3
 h = enthalpy of process liquid, Btu/lb_m
 h_J = enthalpy of cooling water, Btu/lb_m

The assumption of constant densities makes $C_p = C_v$ and permits us to use enthalpies in the time derivatives to replace internal energies.

A hydraulic relationship between reactor holdup and the flow out of the reactor is also needed. We will assume that a level controller changes the outflow in direct proportion to the volume in the tank. The outflow increases as the volume builds up in the reactor and decreases as the volume drops. The outflow is shut off completely when the volume drops to a minimum value $V_{\min}$.

$$F = K_V (V - V_{\min}) \qquad (3\text{-}22)$$

The level controller is a proportional-only feedback controller.

Finally, we need enthalpy data to relate the h's to compositions and temperatures. Let us assume the simple forms

$$\begin{aligned} h_J &= C_J T_J \\ h &= C_p T \end{aligned} \qquad (3\text{-}23)$$

where C_J = heat capacity of cooling water, $\text{Btu/lb}_m\text{-}°\text{R}$
 C_p = heat capacity of process liquids, $\text{Btu/lb}_m\text{-}°\text{R}$

Using Eqs. (3-23) and the Arrhenius relationship for k, the five equations that describe the process are

$$\frac{dV}{dt} = F_0 - F \qquad (3\text{-}24)$$

$$\frac{d}{dt}(VC_A) = F_0 C_{A0} - FC_A - VC_A{}^n \alpha e^{-E/RT} \qquad (3\text{-}25)$$

$$\rho C_p \frac{d}{dt}(VT) = \rho C_p(F_0 T_0 - FT) - \lambda VC_A{}^n \alpha e^{-E/RT} - UA_H(T - T_J) \qquad (3\text{-}26)$$

$$\rho_J V_J C_J \frac{dT_J}{dt} = \rho_J F_J C_J(T_{J0} - T_J) + UA_H(T - T_J) \qquad (3\text{-}27)$$

$$F = K_V(V - V_{\min}) \qquad (3\text{-}28)$$

Checking the degrees of freedom, we see there are five equations and five un-knowns: V, F, C_A, T, and T_J. We must have initial conditions for these five dependent variables. The forcing functions are T_0, F_0, C_{A0}, and F_J.

The parameters that must be known are n, α, E, R, ρ, C_p, λ, U, A_H, ρ_J, V_J, C_J, T_{J0}, K_V, and $V_{\min}$. If the heat transfer area varies with the reactor holdup it would be included as another variable, but we would also have another equation: the relationship between area and holdup. If the reactor is a flat-bottomed vertical cylinder with diameter D (ft) and if the jacket is only around the outside, not around the bottom,

$$A_H = \frac{4}{D} V \qquad (3\text{-}29)$$

We have assumed the overall heat transfer coefficient U is constant. It may be a function of the coolant flow rate F_J, giving one more variable but also one more equation.

CASE B Another of the assumptions made in the above model was that the cooling water inside the jacket was perfectly mixed. In many jacketed vessels this is not a particularly good assumption. If the water flow rate is high enough so that the water temperature does not change much as it goes through the jacket, the mixing pattern makes little difference. However, if the water temperature rise is significant and if the flow is more like plug flow than a perfect mix (this would certainly be the case if a cooling coil is used inside the reactor instead of a jacket), then an average jacket temperature T_{JA}, may be used.

$$T_{JA} = \frac{T_{J0} + T_{Jex}}{2} \qquad (3\text{-}30)$$

where T_{Jex} is the outlet cooling-water temperature (°R).

The average temperature is used in the heat transfer equation and to represent the enthalpy of jacket material. Equation (3-27) would become

$$\rho_J V_J C_J \frac{dT_{JA}}{dt} = \rho_J F_J C_J (T_{J0} - T_{Jex}) + U A_H (T - T_{JA}) \qquad (3\text{-}31)$$

Equation (3-31) is integrated to obtain T_{JA} at every instant in time, and Eq. (3-30) is used to calculate T_{Jex}, also as a function of time.

Another alternative is to break up the jacket volume into a number of perfectly mixed "lumps" as shown in Fig. 3-4.

An energy equation is needed for each lump. Assuming four lumps of equal volume and heat transfer area, we get four energy equations:

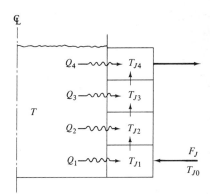

FIGURE 3-4
Lumped jacket model.

$$\tfrac{1}{4}V_J\,C_J\,\rho_J\,\frac{dT_{J1}}{dt} = F_J\,C_J\,\rho_J(T_{J0}-T_{J1}) + \tfrac{1}{4}UA_H(T-T_{J1})$$

$$\tfrac{1}{4}V_J\,C_J\,\rho_J\,\frac{dT_{J2}}{dt} = F_J\,C_J\,\rho_J(T_{J1}-T_{J2}) + \tfrac{1}{4}UA_H(T-T_{J2})$$

$$\tag{3-32}$$

$$\tfrac{1}{4}V_J\,C_J\,\rho_J\,\frac{dT_{J3}}{dt} = F_J\,C_J\,\rho_J(T_{J2}-T_{J3}) + \tfrac{1}{4}UA_H(T-T_{J3})$$

$$\tfrac{1}{4}V_J\,C_J\,\rho_J\,\frac{dT_{J4}}{dt} = F_J\,C_J\,\rho_J(T_{J3}-T_{J4}) + \tfrac{1}{4}UA_H(T-T_{J4})$$

CASE C   In some reactors, particularly high-pressure vessels or smaller-scale equipment, the mass of the metal walls and its effects on the thermal dynamics must be considered. Rigorously the energy equation for the wall should be a partial differential equation in time and radial position. A less rigorous but frequently used approximation is to "lump" the mass of the metal and use effective inside and outside film coefficients, h_i and h_o, as shown in Fig. 3-5.

The three energy equations for the process liquid, metal, and jacket cooling water are

$$\rho C_p\,\frac{d}{dt}(VT) = \rho C_p(F_0 T_0 - FT) - \lambda V C_A{}^n \alpha e^{-E/RT} - h_i A_i(T-T_M)$$

$$\rho_M C_M V_M\,\frac{dT_M}{dt} = h_i A_i(T-T_M) - h_o A_o(T_M-T_J) \qquad (3\text{-}33)$$

$$\rho_J C_J V_J\,\frac{dT_J}{dt} = \rho_J F_J C_J(T_{J0}-T_J) + h_o A_o(T_M-T_J)$$

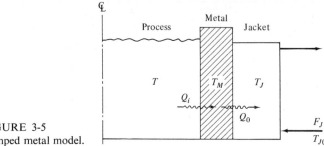

FIGURE 3-5
Lumped metal model.

where h_i = inside heat transfer coefficient, Btu/sec-ft^2-°R

    h_o = outside heat transfer coefficient, Btu/sec-ft^2-°R

    ρ_M = density of metal wall, lb$_m$/ft^3

    C_M = heat capacity of metal wall, Btu/lb$_m$-°R

    V_M = volume of metal wall, ft^3

    A_i = inside heat transfer area, ft^2

    A_o = outside heat transfer area, ft^2

    T_M = temperature of metal wall, °R

3-6 SINGLE-COMPONENT VAPORIZER[1]

Boiling systems represent some of the most interesting and important operations in chemical engineering processing and are among the most difficult to model. To describe these systems rigorously, conservation equations must be written for both the vapor and liquid phases. The basic problem is finding the rate of vaporization of material from the liquid phase into the vapor phase. The equations used to describe the boiling rate should be physically reasonable and mathematically convenient for solution.

When you write a mathematical model for one of these systems you will find that there are sufficient equations to completely specify the system, i.e., the degrees of freedom will be zero. But the way that you solve the equations, the order in which you solve them, or the way that you rearrange them can affect the stability and convergence of the solution. We will return to this question in detail in Part 2 of this book.

Consider the vaporizer sketched in Fig. 3-6. Liquid LPG (liquefied petroleum gas) is fed into a pressurized tank to hold the liquid level in the tank. We will assume the LPG is a pure single component: propane. Vaporization of mixtures of components is discussed in Sec. 3-7.

[1] R. A. Eckhart, *Ind. Eng. Chem., Process Design Dev.*, vol. 8, no. 4, p. 491, 1969.

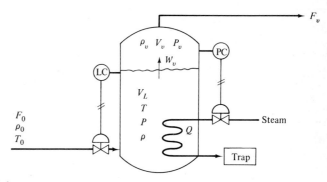

FIGURE 3-6
LPG vaporizer.

The liquid in the tank is assumed perfectly mixed. Heat is added at a rate Q (Btu/sec) to hold the desired pressure in the tank by vaporizing the liquid at a rate W_v (lb$_m$/sec). Heat losses and the mass of the tank walls are assumed negligible. Gas is drawn off the top of the tank at a rate F_v (ft^3/sec). F_v is the forcing function.

CASE A   The simplest model would neglect the dynamics of both vapor and liquid phases and relate the gas rate F_v to the heat input by

$$\rho_v F_v = \frac{Q}{H_v - h_0} \qquad (3\text{-}34)$$

where H_v = enthalpy of vapor leaving tank, Btu/lb$_m$
$\quad\quad\;\; h_0$ = enthalpy of liquid feed, Btu/lb$_m$

CASE B   A somewhat more rigorous model is obtained if we assume that the volume of the vapor phase is small enough to make its dynamics negligible. If only a few moles of liquid have to be vaporized to change the pressure in the vapor phase, we can assume that this pressure is always equal to the vapor pressure of the liquid at any temperature ($P = P_v$ and $W_v = \rho_v F_v$). An energy equation for the liquid gives the temperature (as a function of time), and the vapor-pressure relationship gives the pressure in the vaporizer.

A total continuity equation for the liquid is needed, plus the two controller equations relating pressure to heat input and liquid level to feed F_0. These feedback controller relationships will be expressed here simply as functions. In Part 4 we will discuss these functions in detail.

$$Q = f_{1(P)}$$
$$F_0 = f_{2(V_L)} \qquad (3\text{-}35)$$

An equation of state for the vapor is needed to be able to calculate density ρ_v from pressure or temperature. Knowing any one property (T, P, or ρ_v) pins down all the other properties since there is only one component. The perfect-gas law is used.

The liquid is assumed incompressible so that $C_v = C_p$ and its internal energy is $C_p T$. The enthalpy of vapor leaving the vaporizer is assumed to be of the simple form: $C_p T + \lambda_v$.

Total continuity:

$$\rho \frac{dV_L}{dt} = \rho_0 F_0 - \rho_v F_v \qquad (3\text{-}36)$$

Energy:

$$C_p \rho \frac{d}{dt}(V_L T) = \rho_0 C_p F_0 T_0 - \rho_v F_v (C_p T + \lambda_v) + Q \qquad (3\text{-}37)$$

State:

$$\rho_v = \frac{MP}{RT} \qquad (3\text{-}38)$$

Vapor-liquid equilibrium:

$$\ln P = \frac{A_1}{T} + A_2 \qquad (3\text{-}39)$$

Equations (3-35) to (3-39) give us six equations. Unknowns are Q, F_0, P, V_L, ρ_v, and T.

CASE C If the dynamics of the vapor phase cannot be neglected, total continuity and energy equations must be written for the gas in the tank. The vapor leaving the tank, $\rho_v F_v$, is no longer equal, dynamically, to the rate of vaporization, W_v.

The key problem now is to find a simple and reasonable expression for the boiling rate W_v. I have found in a number of simulations that a "mass transfer" type of equation can be conveniently employed. This kind of relationship also makes physical sense. Liquid boils because, at some temperature (and composition if more than one component is present), it exerts a vapor pressure P greater than the pressure P_v in the vapor phase above it. The driving force is this pressure differential.

$$W_v = K_{MT}(P - P_v) \qquad (3\text{-}40)$$

where K_{MT} is the pseudo "mass transfer" coefficient [$lb_m/(sec\text{-}lb_F/ft^2)$]. Naturally at equilibrium (*not* steady state) $P = P_v$. If we choose to make the assumption, as is commonly made, that the liquid and vapor are always in equilibrium, we are saying that K_{MT} is very large. When the equations are solved on a computer several values of K_{MT} can be tried to see the effects of nonequilibrium conditions.

The equations describing the system are:

LIQUID PHASE

Total continuity:

$$\rho \frac{dV_L}{dt} = \rho_0 F_0 - W_v \qquad (3\text{-}41)$$

Energy:

$$\rho \frac{d}{dt} (V_L U_L) = \rho_0 F_0 h_0 - W_v H_L + Q \qquad (3\text{-}42)$$

Vapor-liquid equilibrium:

$$P = e^{A_1/T + A_2} \qquad (3\text{-}43)$$

VAPOR PHASE

Total continuity:

$$\frac{d}{dt} (V_v \rho_v) = W_v - \rho_v F_v \qquad (3\text{-}44)$$

Energy:

$$\frac{d}{dt} (V_v \rho_v U_v) = W_v H_L - \rho_v F_v H_v \qquad (3\text{-}45)$$

State:

$$\rho_v = \frac{M P_v}{R T_v} \qquad (3\text{-}46)$$

where U_L = internal energy of liquid at temperature T, Btu/lb$_m$
H_L = enthalpy of vapor boiling off liquid, Btu/lb$_m$
U_v = internal energy of vapor at temperature T_v, Btu/lb$_m$
H_v = enthalpy of vapor phase, Btu/lb$_m$

Thermal-property data are needed to relate the enthalpies to temperatures. We would then have 10 variables: Q, F_0, V_L, W_v, T, V_v, ρ_v, T_v, P, and P_v. Counting Eqs. (3-35) and (3-40) to (3-46) we see there are only nine equations. Something is missing. A moment's reflection should generate the other relationship, a physical constraint:

$$V_L + V_v = total\ volume\ of\ tank$$

CASE D   The previous case yields a model that is about as rigorous as one can reasonably expect. A final model, not quite as rigorous but usually quite adequate, is one in which thermal equilibrium between liquid and vapor is assumed to hold at all times. More simply, the vapor and liquid temperatures are assumed equal to each other: $T = T_v$. This eliminates the need for an energy balance for the vapor phase. It probably works pretty well because the sensible heat of the vapor is usually small compared with latent-heat effects.

If the simple enthalpy relationships can be used, Eq. (3-42) becomes

$$\rho C_p \frac{d}{dt}(V_L T) = \rho_0 F_0 C_p T_0 - W_v(C_p T + \lambda_v) + Q \qquad (3\text{-}47)$$

The simpler models discussed above (such as Cases A and B) are usually good enough for continuous-flow systems where the changes in liquid and vapor holdups and temperatures are not very large. Batch systems may require the more rigorous models (Cases C and D) because of the big variations of most variables.

3-7   MULTICOMPONENT FLASH DRUM

Let us look now at vapor-liquid systems with more than one component. A liquid stream at high temperature and pressure is "flashed" into a drum, i.e., its pressure is reduced as it flows through a restriction (valve) at an inlet of the drum. This sudden expansion is irreversible and occurs at constant enthalpy. If it were a reversible expansion, entropy, not enthalpy, would be conserved. If the drum pressure is lower than the bubble-point pressure of the feed, some of it will vaporize.

Gas is drawn off the top of the drum through a control valve whose stem position is set by a pressure controller (Fig. 3-7). Liquid comes off the bottom of the tank on level control.

The pressure P_0 before the pressure letdown valve is high enough to prevent any vaporization of feed at its temperature T_0 and composition x_{0j} (mole fraction jth component). The forcing functions in this system are the feed temperature T_0, feed rate F, and feed composition x_{0j}. Adiabatic conditions (no heat losses) are assumed. The density of the liquid in the tank, ρ_L, is assumed to be a known function of temperature and composition.

$$\rho_L = f_{(x_j, T)} \qquad (3\text{-}48)$$

The density ρ_v of the vapor in the drum is a known function of temperature T, composition y_j, and pressure P. If the perfect-gas law can be used,

$$\rho_v = \frac{M_v^{av} P}{RT} \qquad (3\text{-}49)$$

where M_v^{av} is the average molecular weight of gas (lb$_m$/mole).

$$M_v^{av} = \sum_{j=1}^{J} M_j y_j \qquad (3\text{-}50)$$

where M_j is the molecular weight of the jth component.

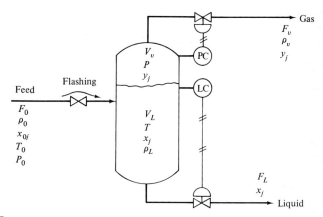

FIGURE 3-7
Flash drum.

CASE A   The simplest model of this system is one that neglects dynamics completely. Pressure is assumed constant, and the steady-state total and component continuity equations and a steady-state enthalpy balance are used. Vapor-liquid equilibrium is assumed.

Total continuity:

$$\rho_0 F_0 = \rho_v F_v + \rho_L F_L \qquad (3\text{-}51)$$

Component continuity:

$$\frac{\rho_0 F_0}{M_0^{\text{av}}} x_{0j} = \frac{\rho_v F_v}{M_v^{\text{av}}} y_j + \frac{\rho_L F_L}{M_L^{\text{av}}} x_j \qquad (3\text{-}52)$$

Vapor-liquid equilibrium:

$$y_j = f_{(x_j, T, P)} \qquad (3\text{-}53)$$

Energy equation:

$$h_0 \rho_0 F_0 = H_v \rho_v F_v + h_L \rho_L F_L \qquad (3\text{-}54)$$

Thermal properties:

$$h_0 = f_{(x_{0j}, T_0)}$$
$$h_L = f_{(x_j, T)} \qquad (3\text{-}55)$$
$$H_v = f_{(y_j, T, P)}$$

The average molecular weights M^{av} are calculated from the mole fractions in the appropriate stream [see Eq. (3-50)]. The variables in the system are $9 + 2(J - 1)$

in number: ρ_v, F_v, M_v^{av}, y_1, y_2, ..., y_{J-1}, ρ_L, F_L, M_L^{av}, x_1, x_2, ..., x_{J-1}, T, h_L and H_v. Pressure P and all the feed properties are given. There are $J - 1$ component balances [Eq. (3-52)].

There are a total of J equilibrium equations. We can say that there are J equations like Eq. (3-53). This may bother some of you. Since the sum of the y's has to add up to 1, you may feel that there are only $J - 1$ equations for the y's. But even if you think about it this way, there is still one more equation: The sum of the partial pressures has to add up to the total pressure. Thus whatever way you want to look at it, there are J equations.

		Number
Total continuity	Eq. (3-51)	1
Energy	Eq. (3-54)	1
Component continuity	Eq. (3-52)	$J - 1$
Vapor-liquid equilibrium	Eq. (3-53)	J
Densities of liquid and vapor	Eqs. (3-48) and (3-49)	2
Thermal properties for liquid and vapor	Eq. (3-55)	2
Average molecular weights	Eq. (3-50)	2
		$2J + 7$

The system is specified by the algebraic equations listed above. This is just a traditional steady-state "equilibrium-flash" calculation.[1]

CASE B Dynamics can be included in a number of ways, with varying degrees of rigor, by using models similar to those in Sec. 3-6. Let us merely indicate how a rigorous model, like Case C of Section 3-6, could be developed. Figure 3-8 shows the system schematically.

An equilibrium-flash calculation (using the same equations as in Case A above) is made at each point in time to find the vapor and liquid flow rates and properties immediately after the pressure let-down valve (the variables with the primes: F_v', F_L', y_j', x_j', ... shown in Fig. 3-8). These two streams are then fed into the vapor and liquid phases. The equations describing the two phases will be similar to Eqs. (3-40) to (3-42), and (3-44) to (3-46) with the addition of a multicomponent vapor-liquid equilibrium equation to get P and $J - 1$ component continuity equations for *each* phase. Controller equations relating V_L to F_L and P_v to F_v complete the model.

$$F_L = f_{(V_L)}$$
$$F_v = f_{(P_V)}$$
(3-56)

[1] R. G. E. Franks, "Mathematical Modeling," p. 168, Wiley, 1966.

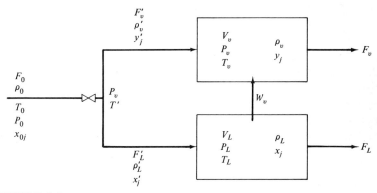

FIGURE 3-8
Dynamic flash drum.

CASE C   A more workable dynamic model can be developed if we ignore the dynamics of the vapor phase (as we did in Case B of Sec. 3-6). The vapor is assumed to be always in equilibrium with the liquid. The conservation equations are written for the liquid phase only.

Total continuity:

$$\frac{d}{dt}(V_L \rho_L) = \rho_0 F_0 - \rho_v F_v - \rho_L F_L \qquad (3\text{-}57)$$

Component continuity:

$$\frac{d}{dt}\left(\frac{V_L \rho_L x_j}{M_L{}^{\mathrm{av}}}\right) = \frac{\rho_0 F_0}{M_0{}^{\mathrm{av}}} x_{0j} - \frac{\rho_v F_v}{M_v{}^{\mathrm{av}}} y_j - \frac{\rho_L F_L}{M_L{}^{\mathrm{av}}} x_j \qquad (3\text{-}58)$$

Energy equation:

$$\frac{d}{dt}(V_L \rho_L h_L) = \rho_0 F_0 h_0 - \rho_v F_v H_v - \rho_L F_L h_L \qquad (3\text{-}59)$$

The J vapor-liquid equilibrium equations [Eq. (3-53)], the three enthalpy relationships [Eqs. (3-55)], the two density equations [Eqs. (3-48) and (3-49)], the two molecular-weight equations [Eq. (3-50)], and the feedback controller equations [Eqs. (3-56)] are all needed. The total number of equations is $2J + 9$, which equals the total number of variables: P_v, V_L, ρ_v, F_v, $M_v{}^{\mathrm{av}}$, y_1, y_2, ..., y_{J-1}, ρ_L, F_L, $M_L{}^{\mathrm{av}}$, x_1, x_2, ..., x_{J-1}, T, h_L, and H_v.

Keep in mind that all the feed properties, or forcing functions, are given: F_0, ρ_0, h_0, x_{0j}, and $M_0{}^{\mathrm{av}}$.

3-8   BATCH REACTOR

Batch processes offer some of the most interesting and challenging problems in modeling and control because of their inherent dynamic nature. Although most large-scale chemical engineering processes have traditionally been operated in a continuous fashion, many batch processes have survived, particularly batch chemical reactors, because of the intrinsic kinetic advantages of batch over continuous operation for some reactions. The recent development and application of digital process computers, with their capability to automate and optimize, may well result in a resurgence of batch processing.

Let us consider the batch reactor sketched in Fig. 3-9. Reactant is charged into the vessel. Steam is fed into the jacket to bring the reaction mass up to a desired temperature. Then cooling water is added to the jacket to remove the exothermic heat of reaction and to make the reactor temperature follow the prescribed temperature-time curve. This temperature profile is fed into the temperature controller as a set-point signal. It can be generated in a number of different function-generating devices. One of the most common is a mechanical "cam" device that has the desired profile cut onto a metal disk. As the disk rotates, a detector arms converts the position into a control signal that can be fed into the temperature controller as a set point.

First-order consecutive reactions take place in the reactor as time proceeds.

$$A \xrightarrow{\ k_1\ } B \xrightarrow{\ k_2\ } C$$

The product that we want to make is component B. If we let the reaction go on too long, too much B will react to form undesired C; that is, the yield will be low. If we stop the reaction too early, too little A will have reacted; i.e., the conversion and yield will be low. Therefore there is an optimum batch time when we should stop the reaction (by quenching it—cooling it down rapidly).[1]

There is also an optimum temperature profile. If the temperature dependence of the specific reaction rates k_1 and k_2 is the same (if their activation energies are equal), the reaction should be run at the highest possible temperature to minimize the batch time. This maximum temperature would be a limit imposed by some constraint: maximum working temperature or pressure of the equipment, further undesirable degradation or polymerization of products or reactants at very high temperatures, etc. If k_1 is more temperature-dependent than k_2, we again want to run at the highest possible temperature to favor the reaction to B. In both these cases we must be sure to stop the reaction at the right time so that too much B is not lost.

If k_1 is less temperature-dependent that k_2, the optimum temperature profile is

---

[1] K. G. Denbigh, "Chemical Reactor Theory," Cambridge, 1965.

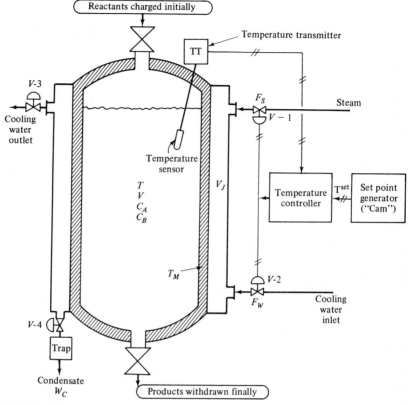

FIGURE 3-9
Batch reactor.

one that starts off at a high temperature to get the first reaction going but then drops to prevent the loss of too much B.   Figure 3-10 sketches the optimum temperature and concentration profiles. If the reaction is run longer than t_{opt}, the yield of B decreases. Also shown in Fig. 3-10 as the dashed line is an example of an actual temperature that could be achieved in a real reactor. The reaction mass must be heated up to T_{max}. We will use the optimum temperature profile as the set-point signal.

With this background, let us now derive a mathematical model for this process. We will assume that the density of the reaction liquid is constant. The total continuity equation for the reaction mass, after the reactants have been charged and the batch cycle begun, is

$$\frac{d}{dt}(\rho V) = 0 - 0 \qquad (3\text{-}60)$$

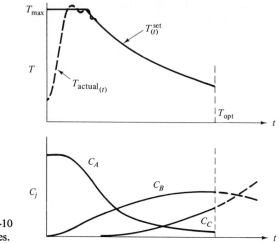

FIGURE 3-10
Batch profiles.

There is no inflow and no outflow. Since ρ is constant,

$$\frac{dV}{dt} = 0$$

Therefore the volume of liquid in the reactor is constant.

Component continuity for A:

$$V\frac{dC_A}{dt} = -Vk_1C_A \qquad (3\text{-}61)$$

Component continuity for B:

$$V\frac{dC_B}{dt} = Vk_1C_A - Vk_2C_B \qquad (3\text{-}62)$$

Kinetic equations:

$$k_1 = \alpha_1 e^{-E_1/RT}$$
$$k_2 = \alpha_2 e^{-E_2/RT} \qquad (3\text{-}63)$$

Using a lumped model for the reactor metal wall and the simple enthalpy equation $h = C_pT$, the energy equations for the reaction liquid and the metal wall are:

Energy equation, process:

$$\rho VC_p \frac{dT}{dt} = -\lambda_1 Vk_1C_A - \lambda_2 Vk_2C_B - h_i A_i(T - T_M) \qquad (3\text{-}64)$$

Energy equation, metal wall:

$$\rho_M C_M V_M \frac{dT_M}{dt} = h_i A_i(T - T_M) - h_o A_o(T_M - T_J) \qquad (3\text{-}65)$$

where λ_1 and λ_2 are the exothermic heats of reaction for the two reactions.

Notice that when the reactor is heated with steam, T_J will be bigger than T_M and T_M will be bigger than T. When cooling with water, the temperature differentials have the opposite sign. Keep in mind also that the outside film coefficient h_o is usually different for condensing steam and flowing cooling water.

This switching from heating to cooling is a pretty "tricky" operation, particularly if one is trying to heat up to T_{max} as fast as possible but cannot permit any overshoot. A commonly used system is shown in Fig. 3-9. The temperature controller keeps the steam valve (V-1) open and the water valve (V-2) shut during the heat-up. This is accomplished by using *split-ranged valves*, discussed later in Part 3. The cooling-water outlet valve (V-3) is also kept closed, and the condensate valve (V-4) is kept open. When cooling is required, the temperature controller shuts the steam valve and opens the water valve just enough to make the reactor temperature follow the set point. Valve V-3 must be opened and valve V-4 must be shut whenever cooling water is added.

We will study in detail the simulation and control of this system later in this book. Here let us simply say that there is a known relationship between the error signal E (or the temperature set point minus the reactor temperature) and the flow rates of steam F_s (ft^3/sec) and cooling water F_w (ft^3/sec):

$$\begin{aligned} F_s &= f_{1(E)} \\ F_w &= f_{2(E)} \end{aligned} \qquad (3\text{-}66)$$

To describe what is going on in the jacket we may need two different sets of equations, depending on the stage: heating or cooling. We may even need to consider a third stage: filling the jacket with cooling water. If the cooling-water flow rate is high and/or the jacket volume is small, which we will assume, the time to fill the jacket may be neglected.

Heating   During heating a total continuity equation and an energy equation for the steam vapor are needed, plus an equation of state for the steam.

Total continuity:

$$V_J \frac{d\rho_J}{dt} = F_s \rho_s - W_c \qquad (3\text{-}67)$$

where ρ_J = density of steam vapor in jacket, lb_m/ft^3
$\quad\quad V_J$ = volume of jacket, ft^3
$\quad\quad \rho_s$ = density of incoming steam, lb_m/ft^3
$\quad\quad W_c$ = rate of condensation of steam, lb_m/sec

The liquid condensate is assumed to be immediately drawn off through a steam trap.

Energy equation for steam vapor:

$$V_J \frac{d}{dt}(U_J \rho_J) = F_s \rho_s H_s - h_o A_o(T_J - T_M) - W_c h_c \quad\quad (3\text{-}68)$$

where U_J = internal energy of steam in jacket, Btu/lb_m
$\quad\quad H_s$ = enthalpy of incoming steam vapor, Btu/lb_m
$\quad\quad h_c$ = enthalpy of liquid condensate, Btu/lb_m

The internal energy changes (sensible-heat effects) can usually be neglected compared with the latent-heat effects. Thus a simple algebraic steady-state energy equation can be used:

$$W_c = \frac{h_o A_o(T_J - T_M)}{H_s - h_c} \quad\quad (3\text{-}69)$$

The equations of state for steam (or the steam tables) can be used to calculate temperature T_J and pressure P_J from density ρ_J. For example, if the perfect-gas law and a simple vapor-pressure relation can be used,

$$\rho_J = \frac{M}{RT_J} e^{A_{vp}/T_J + B_{vp}} \quad\quad (3\text{-}70)$$

where M = molecular weight of steam = 18 lb_m/mole. A_{vp} and B_{vp} are vapor-pressure constants for water. Equation (3-70) can be solved (iteratively) for T_J if ρ_J is known [from Eq. (3-67)]. Once T_J is known, P_J can be calculated from the vapor-pressure equation. It is usually necessary to know P_J in order to calculate the flow rate of steam through the inlet valve since the rate depends on the pressure drop over the valve.

If the mass of the metal surrounding the jacket is significant, an energy equation is required for it. We will assume it negligible.

Cooling During the period when cooling water is flowing through the jacket, only an energy equation for the jacket is required if we assume the water is incompressible and the water in the jacket is perfectly mixed:

$$C_J \rho_J V_J \frac{dT_J}{dt} = F_w C_J \rho_J(T_{J0} - T_J) + h_o A_o(T_M - T_J) \quad\quad (3\text{-}71)$$

where T_J = temperature of cooling water in jacket, °R

ρ_J = density of water, lb_m/ft^3

C_J = heat capacity of water, Btu/lb_m-°R

T_{J0} = inlet cooling-water temperature, °R

Checking the degrees of freedom of the system during the heating stage, we have seven variables (C_A, C_B, T, T_M, T_J, ρ_J, and W_c) and seven equations [(3-61), (3-62), (3-64), (3-65), (3-67), (3-69), and (3-70)]. During the cooling stage, we use Eq. (3-71) instead of (3-67), (3-69), and (3-70), but we have only T_J instead of T_J, ρ_J, and W_c.

3-9   REACTOR WITH MASS TRANSFER

As indicated in our earlier discussions about kinetics in Chap. 2, chemical reactors sometimes have mass-transfer limitations as well as chemical reaction-rate limitations. Mass transfer can become limiting when components must be moved from one phase into another phase, before or after reaction. As an example of the phenomenon, let us consider the gas-liquid bubble reactor sketched in Fig. 3-11.

Reactant A is fed as a gas through a distributor into the bottom of the liquid-filled reactor. A chemical reaction occurs between A and B in the liquid phase to form a liquid product C. Reactant A must dissolve into the liquid before it can react.

$$A + B \xrightarrow{k} C$$

If this rate of mass transfer of the gas A to the liquid is low, the concentration of A in the liquid will be low since it is used up by the reaction as fast as it arrives. Thus the reactor is mass-transfer-limited.

If the rate of mass transfer of the gas to the liquid is high, the reactant A concentration will build up to some value as dictated by the steady-state reaction conditions and the equilibrium solubility of A in the liquid. The reactor is chemical-rate-limited.

Notice that in the mass-transfer-limited region increasing or reducing the concentration of reactant B will make little difference in the reaction rate (or the reactor productivity) because the concentration of A in the liquid is so small. Likewise, increasing the reactor temperature will not give an exponential increase in reaction rate. The reaction rate may actually decrease with increasing temperature because of a decrease in the equilibrium solubility of A at the gas-liquid interface.

Let us try to describe some of these phenomena quantitatively. For simplicity, we will assume isothermal, constant-holdup, constant-pressure, and constant density conditions and a perfectly mixed liquid phase. The gas feed bubbles are assumed to

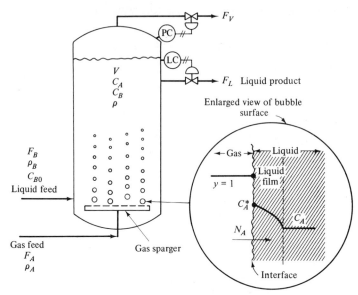

FIGURE 3-11
Gas-liquid bubble reactor.

be pure component A, which gives a constant equilibrium concentration of A at the gas-liquid interface of C_A^* (which would change if pressure and temperature were not constant). The total mass-transfer area of the bubbles is A_{MT} (ft^2) and could depend on the gas feed rate F_A. A constant-mass-transfer coefficient k_L (ft/sec) is used to give the flux of A into the liquid through the liquid film as a function of the driving force.

$$N_A = k_L(C_A^* - C_A) \qquad (3\text{-}72)$$

Mass transfer is usually limited by diffusion through the stagnant-liquid film because of the low liquid diffusivities.

We will assume the vapor-phase dynamics are negligible and that any unreacted gas is vented off the top of the reactor.

$$F_V = F_A - \frac{A_{MT} N_A M_A}{\rho_A} \qquad (3\text{-}73)$$

Component continuity for A:

$$V\frac{dC_A}{dt} = A_{MT} N_A - F_L C_A - VkC_A C_B \qquad (3\text{-}74)$$

Component continuity for B*:*

$$V \frac{dC_B}{dt} = F_B C_{B0} - F_L C_B - VkC_A C_B \qquad (3\text{-}75)$$

Total continuity:

$$\frac{d}{dt}(\rho V) = 0 = F_B \rho_B + M_A N_A A_{MT} - F_L \rho \qquad (3\text{-}76)$$

Equations (3-72) to (3-76) give us five equations. Variables are N_A, C_A, C_B, F_V, and F_L. Forcing functions are F_A, F_B, and C_{B0}.

3-10 IDEAL BINARY DISTILLATION COLUMN

Next to the ubiquitous CSTR, the distillation column is probably the most popular and important process studied in the chemical engineering literature. Distillation is used in many chemical processes for separating feed streams and for purification of final and intermediate product streams.

Most columns, in actuality, handle multicomponent feeds. But many can be approximated by binary or pseudo-binary mixtures. For this example, however, we will make several additional assumptions and idealization that are sometimes valid but more frequently are only crude approximations.

The purpose of studying this simplified case is to reduce the problem to its most elementary form so that the basic structure of the equations can be clearly seen. In the next example, a more realistic system is modeled.

We will assume a pure binary system with constant relative volatility throughout the column and perfect, 100 percent efficient (theoretical) trays; i.e., the vapor leaving the tray is in equilibrium with the liquid on the tray. This means the simple vapor-liquid equilibrium relationship can be used

$$y_n = \frac{\alpha x_n}{1 + (\alpha - 1)x_n} \qquad (3\text{-}77)$$

where x_n = liquid composition on nth tray (mole fraction of more-volatile component)

y_n = vapor composition on nth tray (mole fraction of more-volatile component)

α = relative volatility

A single feed stream is fed as a saturated liquid (at its bubble point) onto the feed tray N_s. See Fig. 3-12. Feed rate is F (moles/sec) and composition is x_F (mole fraction more-volatile component). The overhead vapor is totally condensed in a

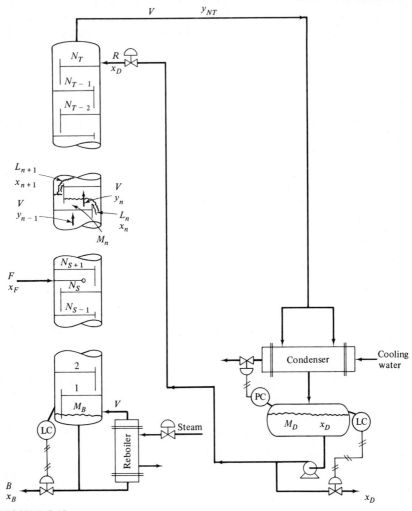

FIGURE 3-12
Binary distillation column.

condenser and flows into the reflux drum, whose holdup of liquid is M_D (moles). The contents of the drum is assumed to be perfectly mixed with composition x_D. The liquid in the drum is at its bubble point. Reflux is pumped back to the top tray (N_T) of the column at a rate R (moles/sec). Overhead distillate product is removed at a rate D (moles/sec).

We will neglect any delay time (dead time) in the vapor line from the top of the column to the reflux drum and in the reflux line back to the top tray. Notice that y_{NT} is not always equal, dynamically, to x_D. The two are equal only at steady state.

At the base of the column, liquid bottoms product is removed at a rate B (moles/sec) and with a composition x_B. Vapor boilup is generated in a thermosiphon reboiler at a rate V (moles/sec). Liquid circulates from the bottom of the column through the tubes in the vertical tube-in-shell reboiler because of the smaller density of the warmer liquid-vapor mixture in the reboiler. We will assume that the liquids in the reboiler and in the base of the column are perfectly mixed together and have the same composition x_B and a total holdup of M_B (moles). The composition of the vapor boilup is then y_B, the vapor composition in equilibrium with the liquid at x_B.

The column contains a total of N_T theoretical trays. The liquid holdup on each tray including the downcomer is M_n (moles). The liquid is assumed to be perfectly mixed with a composition x_n. The holdup of vapor is assumed negligible throughout the system. Although the vapor volume is large, the number of moles is usually small because the vapor density is so much smaller than the liquid density. This assumption breaks down, of course, in very high pressure columns.

A further assumption we will make is that of equimolal overflow. If the molar heats of vaporization of the two components are about the same, whenever a mole of vapor condenses, it vaporizes a mole of liquid. Heat losses up the column and the temperature changes from tray to tray (sensible-heat effects) are assumed negligible. These assumptions mean that the vapor and liquid rates through the stripping and rectifying sections will be constant under steady-state conditions (i.e., equimolal overflow). The "operating lines" on the familiar McCabe-Thiele diagram are straight lines.

However, we are interested here in the dynamic conditions. The assumptions above, including the negligible vapor holdup, mean that the vapor rate through all trays of the column is the same, dynamically as well as at steady-state.

$$V = V_1 = V_2 = V_3 = \cdots = V_{NT} \qquad (3\text{-}78)$$

Remember these V's are not necessarily constant. The vapor boilup can be manipulated dynamically. The mathematical effect of assuming equimolar overflow is that we do not need an energy equation for each tray. This is quite a significant simplification.

The liquid rates throughout the column will *not* be the same dynamically. They will depend on the fluid mechanics of the tray. Often a simple Francis weir formula relationship[1] is used to relate the liquid holdup on a tray to the liquid flow rate

---

[1] $F_L = 3.33l(h)^{3/2}$
where $F_L =$ liquid rate, ft^3/sec
  $l =$ length of weir, ft
  $h =$ height of liquid over weir, ft

L_n (moles/sec) over the outlet weir. A more complex relationship can be obtained from the tray hydraulic equations to include the effects of vapor rate, densities, compositions, etc. We will assume a simple functional relationship between the tray liquid holdup M_n (moles) and the liquid rate L_n (moles/sec).

$$M_n = f_{(L_n)} \qquad (3\text{-}79)$$

Finally, we will neglect the dynamics of the condenser and reboiler. In commercial-scale columns, the dynamic response of these heat exchangers is usually much faster than the response of the column itself. In some systems, however, the dynamics of this peripheral equipment is important and must be included in the model.

With all these assumptions in mind, we are ready to write the equations describing the system. Adopting the usual convention, our total continuity equations are written in terms of moles per unit time. This is kosher because no chemical reaction is assumed to occur in the column.

CONDENSER AND
REFLUX DRUM
Total continuity:

$$\frac{dM_D}{dt} = V - R - D \qquad (3\text{-}80)$$

Component continuity:

$$\frac{d}{dt}(M_D x_D) = V y_{NT} - (R + D)x_D \qquad (3\text{-}81)$$

TOP TRAY $(n = N_T)$
Total continuity:

$$\frac{dM_{NT}}{dt} = R - L_{NT} \qquad (3\text{-}82)$$

Component continuity:

$$\frac{d(M_{NT} x_{NT})}{dt} = R x_D - L_{NT} x_{NT} + V y_{NT-1} - V y_{NT} \qquad (3\text{-}83)$$

NEXT TO TOP TRAY $(n = N_T - 1)$
Total continuity:

$$\frac{dM_{NT-1}}{dt} = L_{NT} - L_{NT-1} \qquad (3\text{-}84)$$

Component continuity:

$$\frac{d}{dt}(M_{NT-1}x_{NT-1}) = L_{NT}x_{NT} - L_{NT-1}x_{NT-1} + Vy_{NT-2} - Vy_{NT-1} \qquad (3\text{-}85)$$

nth TRAY
Total continuity:

$$\frac{dM_n}{dt} = L_{n+1} - L_n \qquad (3\text{-}86)$$

Component continuity:

$$\frac{d}{dt}(M_n x_n) = L_{n+1}x_{n+1} - L_n x_n + Vy_{n-1} - Vy_n \qquad (3\text{-}87)$$

FEED TRAY $(n = N_S)$
Total continuity:

$$\frac{dM_{NS}}{dt} = L_{NS+1} - L_{NS} + F \qquad (3\text{-}88)$$

Component continuity:

$$\frac{d}{dt}(M_{NS}x_{NS}) = L_{NS+1}x_{NS+1} - L_{NS}x_{NS} + Vy_{NS-1} - Vy_{NS} + Fx_F \qquad (3\text{-}89)$$

FIRST TRAY $(n = 1)$
Total continuity:

$$\frac{dM_1}{dt} = L_2 - L_1 \qquad (3\text{-}90)$$

Component continuity:

$$\frac{d}{dt}(M_1 x_1) = L_2 x_2 - L_1 x_1 + Vy_B - Vy_1 \qquad (3\text{-}91)$$

REBOILER AND COLUMN BASE
Total continuity:

$$\frac{dM_B}{dt} = L_1 - V - B \qquad (3\text{-}92)$$

Component continuity:

$$\frac{d}{dt}(M_B x_B) = L_1 x_1 - Vy_B - Bx_B \qquad (3\text{-}93)$$

Each tray and the reboiler have equilibrium equations [Eq. (3-77)]. Each tray also has a hydraulic equation [Eq. (3-79)]. We also need two equations representing the level controllers on the column base and reflux drum shown in Fig. 3-12.

$$D = f_1(M_D)$$
$$B = f_2(M_B)$$

(3-94)

Let us now examine the degrees of freedom of the system. The feed rate F and composition x_F are assumed to be the forcing functions (or disturbances).

Number of variables:

Tray compositions (x_n and y_n)	=	$2N_T$
Tray liquid flows (L_n)	=	N_T
Tray liquid holdups (M_n)	=	N_T
Reflux drum composition (x_D)	=	1
Reflux drum flows (R and D)	=	2
Reflux drum holdup M_D	=	1
Reboiler compositions (x_B and y_B)	=	2
Reboiler flows (V and B)	=	2
Reboiler holdup (M_B)	=	1
		$4N_T + 9$

Number of equations   *Equation no.*

Tray component continuity	=	N_T	(3-87)
Tray total continuity	=	N_T	(3-86)
Equilibrium (trays plus reboiler)	=	$N_T + 1$	(3-77)
Hydraulic	=	N_T	(3-79)
Level control	=	2	(3-94)
Reflux drum component continuity	=	1	(3-81)
Total continuity	=	1	(3-80)
Reboiler component continuity	=	1	(3-93)
Total continuity	=	1	(3-92)
		$4N_T + 7$	

Therefore the system is underspecified by two equations. From a control engineering viewpoint this means there are only *two* variables that *can be* controlled (can be fixed). The two variables that must somehow be specified are reflux flow R and vapor boilup (or heat input to the reboiler). They can be held constant (an open-loop system) or they can be changed by a controller to hold some other two variables constant. In a digital simulation of this column in Part 2 we will assume two feedback controllers adjusting R and V to control overhead and bottoms compositions x_D and x_B.

$$R = f_1(x_D)$$
$$V = f_2(x_B)$$
(3-95)

3-11 MULTICOMPONENT NONIDEAL DISTILLATION COLUMN

As our pièce de résistance of mathematical-modeling examples, let us develop the equations describing a distillation column with J components, nonideal vapor-liquid equilibrium, inefficient trays, variable pressures, and nonequimolal overflow. The only assumptions that we will make are:

1 Liquid on the tray is perfectly mixed and incompressible.
2 Tray vapor holdups are negligible.
3 Vapor and liquid are in thermal equilibrium (at the same temperature) but not in phase equilibrium. A Murphree vapor-phase efficiency will be used to describe the departure from equilibrium.

$$E_{nj} = \frac{y_{nj} - y_{n-1,j}^T}{y_{nj}^* - y_{n-1,j}^T}$$
(3-96)

where y_{nj}^* = composition of vapor in phase equilibrium with liquid on nth tray with composition x_n

y_{nj} = actual vapor composition leaving nth tray

$y_{n-1,j}^T$ = actual vapor composition entering nth tray

E_{nj} = Murphree vapor efficiency for jth component on nth tray

Dynamics of the condenser and reboiler will be included. Multiple feeds, both liquid and vapor, and liquid sidestream drawoffs will be permitted. Modification of the model for vapor sidestreams is straightforward.

A general nth tray is sketched in Fig. 3-13. Nomenclature is summarized in Table 3-1.

Table 3-1 nth TRAY STREAMS

Number	Rate, moles/sec	Composition, mole fraction	Temperature, °R
1	F_n^L	x_{nj}^F	T_n^F
2	F_{n-1}^V	$y_{n-1,j}^F$	T_{n-1}^F
3	L_{n+1}	$x_{n+1,j}$	T_{n+1}
4	V_n	y_{nj}	T_n
5	V_{n-1}	$y_{n-1,j}$	T_{n-1}
6	S_n	x_{nj}	T_n
7	L_n	x_{nj}	T_n

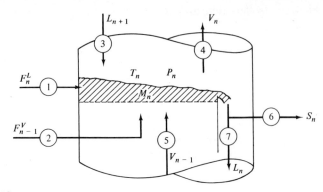

FIGURE 3-13
nth tray of multicomponent column.

The equations describing this tray are:

Total continuity equation (one per tray):

$$\frac{dM_n}{dt} = L_{n+1} + F_n^L + F_{n-1}^V + V_{n-1} - V_n - L_n - S_n \qquad (3\text{-}97)$$

Component continuity equations (J-1 per tray):

$$\frac{d}{dt}(M_n x_{nj}) = L_{n+1} x_{n+1,j} + F_n^L x_{nj}^F + F_{n-1}^V y_{n-1,j}^F$$

$$+ V_{n-1} y_{n-1,j} - V_n y_{nj} - L_n x_{nj} - S_n x_{nj} \qquad (3\text{-}98)$$

Energy (one per tray):

$$\frac{d}{dt}(M_n U_n) = L_{n+1} h_{n+1} + F_n^L h_n^F + F_{n-1}^V H_{n-1}^F$$

$$+ V_{n-1} H_{n-1} - V_n H_n - L_n h_n - S_n h_n \qquad (3\text{-}99)$$

where the internal energy U_n and enthalpies h and H all have units of Btu/mole.

Phase equilibrium (J per tray):

$$y_{nj}^* = f_{(x_{nj},\, P_n,\, T_n)} \qquad (3\text{-}100)$$

An appropriate vapor-liquid equilibrium relationship, as discussed in Sec. 2-2.6, could be used to find y_{nj}^*. Then Eq. (3-96) can be used to calculate the y_{nj} for the inefficient tray. The y_{n-1}^T would be calculated from the two vapors entering the tray: F_{n-1}^V and V_{n-1}.

THERMAL PROPERTIES

$$h_n = f(x_{nj}, T_n)$$
$$H_n = f(y_{nj}, T_n, P_n)$$
$$h_n^F = f(x_{nj}^F, T_n^F) \qquad (3\text{-}101)$$
$$H_n^F = f(y_{nj}^F, T_n^F, P_n)$$

EQUATIONS OF MOTION

Liquid:

$$L_n = f(M_n, V_n, x_{nj}, T_n, P_n) \qquad (3\text{-}102)$$

Vapor:

$$V_n = f(P_n, P_{n-1}, y_{nj}, T_n) \qquad (3\text{-}103)$$

The last equation is usually of the form

$$P_{n-1} - P_n = K_{DP} \rho_n^v V_n^2 \qquad (3\text{-}104)$$

where ρ_n^v = density of vapor on nth tray, lb_m/ft^3

K_{DP} = pressure-drop coefficient, $lb_F\text{-sec}/lb_m\text{-ft}$

The algebraic functions above [Eqs. (3-96) and (3-100) to (3-103)] could theoretic-ally be used to eliminate $2J + 3$ variables (V_n, P_n, L_n, h_n, H_n, $J - 1$ of the y_{nj}'s and $J - 1$ of the y_{nj}^*'s). Then the basic model is reduced to $J + 1$ ordinary differential equations per tray [Eqs. (3-97) to (3-99)]. We will defer any discussion of the very real practical problems of solving this large number of equations until Part 2.

The equations describing the condensing and reboiling sections of the column, shown in Fig. 3-14, are listed below. Perfect mixing is assumed in the reflux drum liquid, column base liquid, condenser vapor, and in the coolant and steam sides of the heat exchangers. The condenser is a partial condenser with both vapor and liquid products removed. The vapor is assumed to be a perfect gas and in phase equilibrium with the liquid leaving the condenser. At steady state, this liquid has the same com-position as the liquid in the reflux tank, but dynamically they may differ. Liquid and vapor holdups in the condenser itself are neglected. The pressures in the reflux drum and condenser are the same but differ from the pressure in the top of the column, P_{NT}, by the pressure drop through the overhead vapor line.

The mass of metal in the heat exchangers is lumped into M_{MC} and M_{MR} (lb_m) at temperatures T_{MC} and T_{MR} (°R).

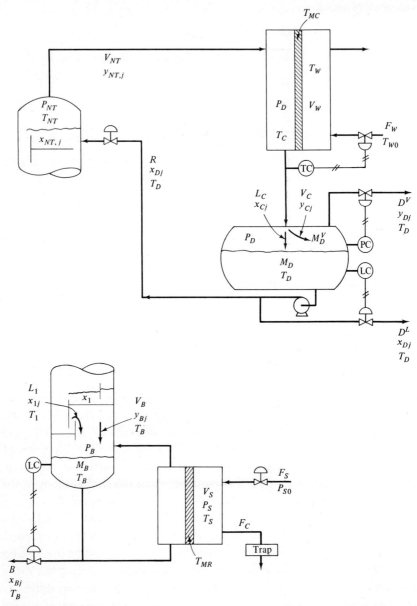

FIGURE 3-14
Condensing system and reboiler.

CONDENSER EQUATIONS

Process side (equilibrium-flash calculation):

$$V_{NT} = L_C + V_C \qquad (3\text{-}105)$$

$$V_{NT}y_{NT,\,j} = L_C x_{Cj} + V_C y_{Cj} \qquad (3\text{-}106)$$

$$P_D = P_{NT} - f(V_{NT}; y_{NT,\,j}; T_{NT}) \qquad (3\text{-}107)$$

$$Q_C = U_C A_C(T_C - T_{MC}) \qquad (3\text{-}108)$$

$$H_{NT}V_{NT} = L_C h_C + V_C H_C + Q_C \qquad (3\text{-}109)$$

$$y_{Cj} = f(x_{Cj}, P_D, T_C) \qquad (3\text{-}110)$$

Metal:

$$M_{MC} C_{MC} \frac{dT_{MC}}{dt} = U_C A_C(T_C - T_{MC}) - U_W A_W(T_{MC} - T_W) \qquad (3\text{-}111)$$

Water side:

$$V_W \rho_W C_W \frac{dT_W}{dt} = \rho_W F_W C_W(T_{WO} - T_W) + U_W A_W(T_{MC} - T_W) \qquad (3\text{-}112)$$

$$F_W = f(T_C) \qquad (3\text{-}113)$$

REFLUX DRUM EQUATIONS

Vapor phase:

$$\frac{dM_D^{\,V}}{dt} = V_C - D^V \qquad (3\text{-}114)$$

$$\frac{d}{dt}(M_D^{\,V} y_{Dj}) = V_C y_{Cj} - D^V y_{Dj} \qquad (3\text{-}115)$$

$$M_D^{\,V} = \frac{V_D^{\,V} P_D}{R T_D} \qquad (3\text{-}116)$$

$$D^V = f(P_D) \qquad (3\text{-}117)$$

where $M_D^{\,V}$ = moles of vapor in reflux drum
   $V_D^{\,V}$ = volume of vapor in reflux drum, ft^3

The volume of vapor is calculated from the total fixed volume of the system less the volume of liquid in the tank. The temperature of the gas in the reflux tank is assumed to be T_D.

Liquid phase:

$$\frac{dM_D}{dt} = L_C - D^L - R \qquad (3\text{-}118)$$

$$\frac{d}{dt}(M_D x_{Dj}) = L_C x_{Cj} - (D^L + R)x_{Dj} \qquad (3\text{-}119)$$

$$\frac{d}{dt}(M_D h_D) = h_C L_C - (D^L + R)h_D \qquad (3\text{-}120)$$

$$D^L = f_{(M_D)} \qquad (3\text{-}121)$$

REBOILER EQUATIONS

Process side:

$$\frac{dM_B}{dt} = L_1 - V_B - B \qquad (3\text{-}122)$$

$$\frac{d}{dt}(M_B x_{Bj}) = L_1 x_{1j} - V_B y_{Bj} - B x_{Bj} \qquad (3\text{-}123)$$

$$\frac{d}{dt}(M_B h_B) = L_1 h_1 - V_B H_B - B h_B + A_B U_B(T_{MR} - T_B) \qquad (3\text{-}124)$$

$$y_{Bj} = f(x_{Bj}, T_B, P_B) \qquad (3\text{-}125)$$

$$B = f_{(M_B)} \qquad (3\text{-}126)$$

Metal:

$$M_{MR} C_{MR} \frac{dT_{MR}}{dt} = U_S A_S(T_S - T_{MR}) - U_B A_B(T_{MR} - T_B) \qquad (3\text{-}127)$$

Steam side:

$$V_S \frac{d\rho_S}{dt} = F_S - F_C \qquad (3\text{-}128)$$

$$F_C = \frac{U_S A_S(T_S - T_{MR})}{\lambda_V} \qquad (3\text{-}129)$$

$$T_S = f_1(\rho_S)$$
$$P_S = f_2(\rho_S) \qquad (3\text{-}130)$$

$$F_S = C_V \sqrt{P_{S0} - P_S} \qquad (3\text{-}131)$$

PROBLEMS

3-1 A fluid of constant density ρ is pumped into a cone-shaped tank of total volume $H\pi R^2/3$. The flow out of the bottom of the tank is proportional to the square root of the height h of liquid in the tank. Derive the equations describing the system.

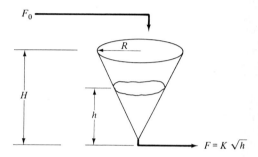

3-2 A perfect gas with molecular weight M flows at a rate W_0 (lb/min) into a cylinder through a restriction. The flow rate is proportional to the square root of the pressure drop over the restriction:

$$W_0 = K_0\sqrt{P_0 - P}$$

P is the pressure (lb_F/ft^2 abs) in the cylinder. P_0 is the constant upstream pressure. The system is isothermal. Inside the cylinder a piston is forced to the right as the pressure P builds up. A spring resists the movement of the piston with a force that is proportional to the axial displacement X of the piston.

$$F_s = K_s X$$

The piston is initially at $X = 0$ when the pressure in the cylinder is zero. The cross-sectional area of the cylinder is A (ft^2). Assume the piston has negligible mass and friction.

(*a*) Derive the equations describing the system.
(*b*) What will the steady-state piston displacement be?

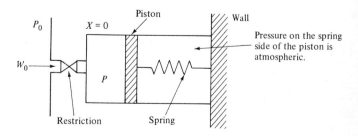

3-3 A perfectly mixed, isothermal CSTR has an outlet weir. The flow rate over the weir is proportional to the height of liquid over the weir, h_F, to the $\frac{3}{2}$ power. The weir height is h_w (ft). The cross-sectional area of the tank is A (ft^2). Assume constant density.

A first-order reaction takes place in the tank.

$$A \xrightarrow{k} B$$

Derive the equations describing the system.

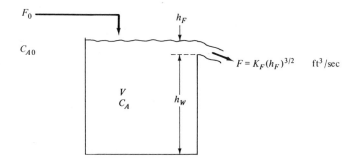

3-4 In order to ensure an adequate supply for the upcoming set-to with the Hatfields, Grandpa McCoy has begun to process a new batch of his Liquid Lightning. He begins by pumping the mash at a constant rate F_0 (ft^3/min) into an empty tank. In this tank the ethanol undergoes a first-order reaction to form a product that is the source of the high potency of McCoy's Liquid Lightning. Assuming that the concentration of ethanol in the feed, C_0 (moles/ft^3), is constant and that the operation is isothermal, derive the equations that describe how the concentration C (moles/ft^3) of ethanol in the tank and the volume V (ft^3) of liquid in the tank vary with time. Assume perfect mixing and constant density.

3-5 A rotating-metal-drum heat exchanger is half submerged in a cool stream, with its other half in a hot stream. The drum rotates at a steady angular velocity ω (radians/second). Assume T_H and T_c are constant along their respective sections of the circumference. The drum is L feet long, d feet thick, and R feet in radius. Heat transfer coefficients in the heating and cooling zones are constant (U_H and U_c). Heat capacity C_p

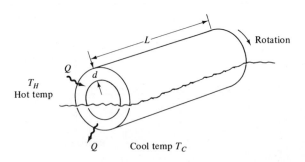

and density of the drum are constant. Neglect radial temperature gradients and assume steady-state operation.

(a) Write the equations describing the system.

(b) What are the appropriate boundary conditions?

3-6 Consider the system shown below of two stirred chemical reactors separated by a plug-flow dead time of D seconds. Assume:

> 1 Constant holdups V_1 and V_2 and throughput F
> 2 Constant density
> 3 Isothermal operation at temperatures T_1 and T_2
> 4 First-order kinetics with simultaneous reactions

$$A \xrightarrow{k_{1j}} B$$

$$A \xrightarrow{k_{2j}} C$$

NOTE: k_{ij} is the specific reaction rate for the ith reaction ($i = 1, 2$) occurring in the jth tank ($j = 1, 2$). No reaction occurs in the plug-flow section. Write the equations describing the system.

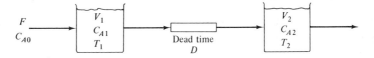

3-7 Consider the isothermal hydraulic system sketched below. A slightly compressible liquid is pumped by a constant-speed, positive-displacement pump so that W_1 lb$_m$/sec is constant. Liquid density is given by

$$\rho = \rho_0 + \beta(P - P_0)$$

where ρ_0, β, and $P_0 = $ constants
$\rho = $ liquid density, lb$_m$/ft^3
$P = $ pressure, lb$_F$/ft^2 gauge

Liquid is pumped through three resistances where the pressure drop is proportional to the square of the mass flow.

$$\Delta P = RW^2$$

A surge tank of volume V ft^3 is located between R_1 and R_2 and is liquid full. The pressure downstream of R_3 is atmospheric.

(a) Derive the differential equation that gives the pressure P (lb$_F$/ft^2 gauge) in the tank as a function of time and W_1.

(b) Find the steady-state value of tank pressure P.

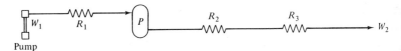

3-8 Develop the equations describing a batch distillation column during the start-up period when no product is withdrawn and the column is coming to equilibrium conditions. Reflux drum and tray holdups are *not* negligible but can be assumed constant.

Assume a binary, equimolal-overflow, constant-relative-volatility system. The initial composition on all trays and in the reflux drum is the same as the material charged to the still pot $x_B{}^0$. The amount of material charged to the still pot is $M_B{}^0$.

3-9 An ice cube is dropped into a hot, perfectly mixed, insulated cup of coffee. Develop the equations describing the dynamics of the system. List all assumptions and define all terms.

3-10 An isothermal, irreversible reaction $A \xrightarrow{k} B$ takes place in the liquid phase in a constant-volume reactor. The mixing is *not* perfect. Observation of the flow patterns indicates that a two-tank system with back mixing, as shown in the sketch below, should approximate the imperfect mixing.

Assuming F and F_R are constant, write the equations describing the system.

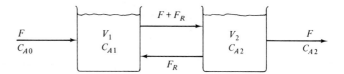

3-11 The liquid in a jacketed, nonisothermal CSTR is stirred by an agitator whose mass is significant compared with the reaction mass. The mass of the reactor wall and the mass of the jacket wall are also significant. Write the energy equations for the system.

3-12 The reaction $3A \rightarrow 2B + C$ is carried out in an isothermal semibatch reactor. Product B is the desired product. Product C is a very volatile by-product that must be vented off to prevent a pressure buildup in the reactor. Gaseous C is vented off through a condenser to force any A or B back into the reactor to prevent loss of product. Assume F_V is pure C. The reaction is first order in C_A. The relative volatilities of A and C to B are $\alpha_{AB} = 1.2$ and $\alpha_{CB} = 10$. Assume perfect gases and constant pressure. Write the equations describing the system.

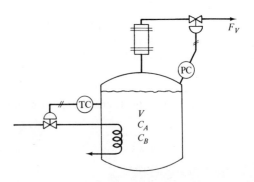

3-13 Write the equations describing a simple version of the petroleum industry's important catalytic cracking operation. There are two vessels as shown below. Component A is fed to the reactor where it reacts to form product B while depositing component C on the fluidized catalyst:

$$A \longrightarrow B + 0.1C$$

Spent catalyst is circulated to the regenerator, where air is added to burn off C.

$$C + O \longrightarrow P$$

Combustion products are vented overhead, and regenerated catalyst is returned to the reactor. Heat is added to or extracted from the regenerator at a rate Q.

Your mathematical description of the dynamic behavior of the process should be based on the following assumptions:

1 The perfect-gas law is obeyed in both vessels.
2 Constant pressure is maintained in both vessels.
3 Catalyst holdups in reactor and regenerator are constant.
4 Heat capacities of reactants and products are equal and constant in each vessel. Catalyst heat capacity is also constant.
5 Complete mixing occurs in each vessel.

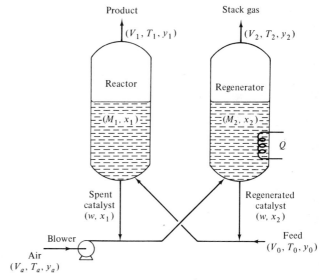

3-14 Flooded condensers are sometimes used on distillation columns. The liquid level runs up in the condenser, covering some of the tubes. Thus a variable amount of heat transfer area is available to condense the vapor. Column pressure can be controlled by changing the distillate (or reflux) drawoff rate.

Write the equations describing the dynamics of the condenser.

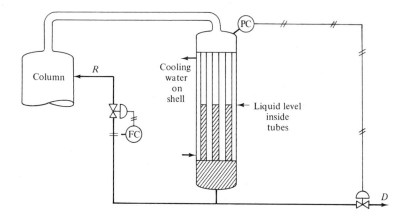

3-15 When cooling jackets and internal cooling coils do not give enough heat transfer area, a circulating cooling system is sometimes used. Process fluid from the reactor is pumped through an external heat exchanger and back into the reactor. Cooling water is added to the shell side of the heat exchanger at a rate F_W as set by the temperature controller. The circulation rate through the heat exchanger is constant. Assume that that the shell side of the exchanger can be represented by two perfectly mixed "lumps" in series and that the process fluid flows countercurrent to the water flow, also through two perfectly mixed stages.

The reaction is irreversible and first order in reactant A: $A \xrightarrow{k} B$. The contents of the tank is perfectly mixed. Neglect reactor and heat-exchanger metal.

Write the equations for the system.

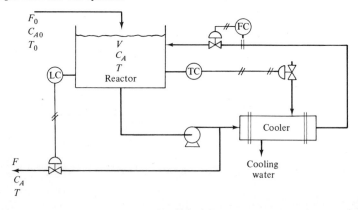

3-16   A semibatch reactor is run at constant temperature by varying the rate of addition of one of the reactants, A. The irreversible, exothermic reaction is first order in reactants A and B.

$$A + B \xrightarrow{\quad k \quad} C$$

The tank is initially filled to its 40 percent level with pure reactant B at a concentration C_{B0}. Maximum cooling-water flow is begun, and reactant A is slowly added to the perfectly stirred vessel.

Write the equations describing the system. Without solving the equations, try to sketch the profiles of F_A, C_A, and C_B with time.

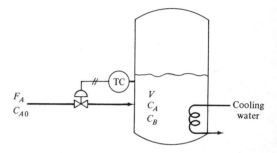

3-17   Develop a mathematical model for the three-column train of distillation columns sketched below. The feed to the first column is 400 moles/sec, containing four components A, B, C and D, each at 0.25 mole fraction. Most of the A is removed in the first column, most of the B in the second, and the third column splits between C and D. Assume constant relative volatilities throughout the system: α_A, α_B, and α_C. The condensers are total condensers. The contents of the reflux drums and reboilers are

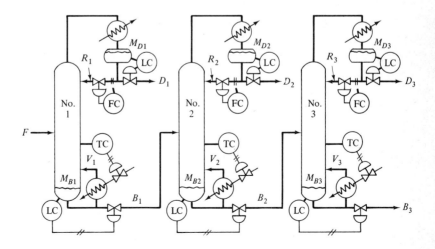

perfectly mixed. Overhead distillate products and bottoms are drawn off by level control. Reflux rates are constant. Heat inputs to the reboilers are set by temperature controllers. Assume equimolal overflow, negligible vapor holdups, and negligible reboiler and condenser dynamics. Use a linear liquid hydraulic relationship

$$L_n = \bar{L}_n + \frac{M_n - \bar{M}_n}{\beta}$$

where $\bar{L}_n$ and $\bar{M}_n$ are the initial steady-state liquid rate and holdup and β is a constant with units of seconds.

PART TWO

Computer Simulation

In the next two chapters we will study computer simulation techniques for solving some of the systems of equations we generated in the two preceding chapters. Analog techniques are discussed in Chap. 4 and digital techniques in Chap. 5.

Historically the analog computer was the device that really launched process dynamics and control in the 1950s. It permitted engineers to rapidly integrate systems of differential equations that, up to that time, were essentially unsolvable (except by very laborious manual numerical methods that took many man-days with slide rules and desk calculators). The analog is ideal for on-line studies of dynamics, controller tuning, and empirical cut-and-try control configurations. You can get a real "feel" for the process. Analog computers have the disadvantage of requiring quite a bit of time to set up the problem and get it running. They also require an electronic box per mathematical operation so that a very large number of components is required to handle complex systems with many equations.

The digital computer came into its own in the 1960s when speed and memory improvements over earlier models made numerical integration fast enough (and cheap enough) to compete with analog integration. The current status is that most studies are done digitally except for work where on-line studies are required. There are some digital systems that provide this on-line capability but most digital computers still operate batchwise.

A few simple examples are presented to illustrate the basic principles of simulation. Then more realistic and complex systems are considered to illustrate how to handle large numbers of equations.

Only solutions for ordinary differential equations are presented. To present anything more than a very superficial treatment of simulation techniques for partial differential equations would require more space than is available in this book. This subject is covered in a number of texts.[1] In practical problems, distributed systems are very often broken up into a number of "lumps" which can then be handled by ordinary differential equations.

Our discussions will be limited to only the most important and useful aspects of simulation. The techniques presented, particularly

---

[1] L. Lapidus, "Digital Computation for Chemical Engineers," McGraw-Hill, 1962. Brice Carnahan, H. R. Luther, and James D. Wilkes, "Applied Numerical Methods," Wiley, 1969.

the digital numerical techniques, will be quite simple and unsophisticated, but I have found them to work just as well for real systems as those that are more mathematically elegant. They also have the added virtues of being easy to understand and easy to program.

Some of the simple linear equations that we will simulate can, of course, be solved analytically by the methods covered in Part 3 to obtain a general solution. The nonlinear equations cannot, in general, be solved analytically, and computer simulation is usually required to get a solution. Keep in mind, however, that you must give the computer specific numerical values for parameters, initial conditions, and forcing functions. And you will get out of the computer specific numerical values for the solution (continuous voltage signals if you are using an electronic analog computer or discrete numbers if you are using a digital computer). You cannot get a general solution in terms of arbitrary, unspecified inputs, parameters, etc., as you can with an analytic solution.

Chapter 5 assumes a working knowledge of FORTRAN IV digital programming language. For those not familiar with FORTRAN programming, there are several good texts.[1]

[1] D. D. McCracken, "A Guide to FORTRAN IV Programming," Wiley, 1965.
D. Dimitry and T. Mott, "Introduction to FORTRAN IV Programming," Holt, 1966.

ANALOG SIMULATION

4-1 INTRODUCTION

As its name implies, an analog computer makes use of the fact that the equations describing some electrical devices are completely analogous to the equations describing other systems: mechanical, thermal, chemical, hydraulic, etc.

Basically all we do to simulate a process on an analog computer is to wire or patch together electronic boxes that perform the various mathematical operations that we need. The electronic gadgets do the mathematics in terms of dc voltages, usually ± 10 volts or ± 100 volts. These voltages represent the physical variables in our equations: temperatures, compositions, flows, velocities, volumes, pressures, etc.

An analog computer has boxes (or operational blocks) that add voltages, subtract voltages, integrate voltages with respect to time, multiply voltages together, divide voltages, generate arbitrary functions, etc. Let us look at some of the basic components that go into these boxes and then the operational blocks themselves. We will then be ready to wire them together to solve some real problems. For a detailed coverage of analog computers there are several texts available.[1]

---

[1] For example, C. L. Johnson, "Analog Computer Techniques," McGraw-Hill, 1956.

4-2 BASIC COMPONENTS

High-gain amplifier Practically all the mathematical operations make use of the high-gain operational amplifier shown in Fig. 4-1. It is a device that changes the sign and amplifies any voltage signal e_i fed into it. This amplification K is very large, of the order of 10^5 to 10^8. Therefore when the amplifier is hooked up with other electrical components its input voltage must effectively always be zero. If e_i is not zero, the output voltage e_o will be very large.

Another feature of the high-gain amplifier is that it draws very little current—so little that we can assume that it is zero. Thus a high-gain amplifier has two convenient features when wired up in an electric circuit: Both its input voltage and current (grid voltage and grid current) must be zero. These properties permit us to use it to add, subtract, and integrate voltages, as we show below.

Pot A *pot* or potentiometer is a resistor with a movable contact. When the contact is all the way at the top, $e_o = e_i$ or $K = 1$; when the contact is all the way at the bottom, $e_o = 0$ or $K = 0$. The bottom of the pot is usually grounded.

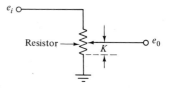

Some pots are ungrounded so that the output is K times the difference between the top and bottom voltages plus the bottom voltage.

Diode A diode is a device that conducts when the voltage input is positive but does not conduct when the voltage input is negative.

Resistors

$$R = \frac{\Delta e}{i}$$

with units of megohms $= 10^6$ ohms $= 10^6$ volts/ampere.

Capacitors

$$C = \frac{charge}{\Delta e} = \frac{\int i\, dt}{\Delta e}$$

with units of microfarads $= 10^{-6}$ farad $= 10^{-6}$ coulomb/volt $= 10^{-6}$ (ampere-sec)/ volt.

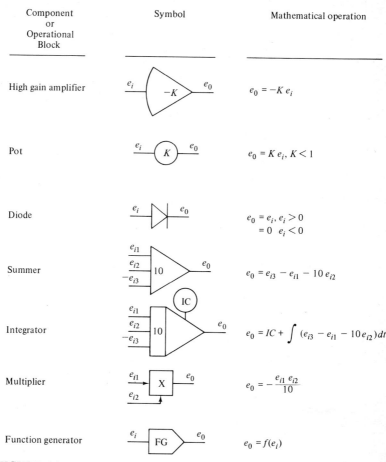

Component or Operational Block	Symbol	Mathematical operation

High gain amplifier — $e_0 = -K\,e_i$

Pot — $e_0 = K\,e_i,\ K < 1$

Diode — $e_0 = e_i,\ e_i > 0$
$\quad\ = 0\quad e_i < 0$

Summer — $e_0 = e_{i3} - e_{i1} - 10\,e_{i2}$

Integrator — $e_0 = IC + \int (e_{i3} - e_{i1} - 10\,e_{i2})\,dt$

Multiplier — $e_0 = -\dfrac{e_{i1}\,e_{i2}}{10}$

Function generator — $e_0 = f(e_i)$

FIGURE 4-1
Analog components and operational blocks.

4-3 OPERATIONAL BLOCKS

Now let us put some of these components together to perform various mathematical operations. We already know how to multiply a voltage by a number between 0 and 1 (with a pot) and by a very large number (with a high-gain amplifier).

Summer If we hook up some resistors and a high-gain amplifier as shown on the following page we get a summer. Resistors R_1, R_2, and R_3 are input resistors and R_f is the feedback resistor. From the properties of the high-gain amplifier, we know that the input or grid voltage e_g and current i_g must be zero.

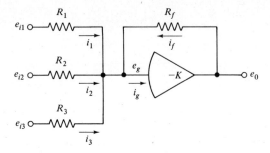

Since $e_g = 0$ $$e_o = i_f R_f \qquad (4\text{-}1)$$

Since $i_g = 0$ $$-i_f = i_1 + i_2 + i_3 \qquad (4\text{-}2)$$

Substituting for the i's gives

$$-\frac{e_o}{R_f} = \frac{e_1}{R_1} + \frac{e_2}{R_2} + \frac{e_3}{R_3}$$

$$e_o = -\frac{R_f}{R_1} e_1 - \frac{R_f}{R_2} e_2 - \frac{R_f}{R_3} e_3 \qquad (4\text{-}3)$$

If all the R's are the same, we have a summer. To subtract a voltage we merely feed it in with the opposite sign. Note that there is a sign inversion.

If the input resistors are not the same as the feedback resistor, summation and multiplication can be achieved by a constant that is greater than 1 if $R_f > R_i$. Normally two ranges of input resistors are wired into the computer to give "gains" of 10 or 1 (a 1-megohm feedback resistor with input resistors of 0.1 or 1 megohm). The summer shown in Fig. 4-1 has two gain 1's and a gain 10.

Integrator The most important operation that the analog computer does is integrate. That is precisely why it can be used to solve ordinary differential equations. An integrator can be made by simply putting a capacitor in the feedback loop around a high-gain amplifier instead of the feedback resistor.

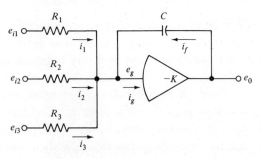

Since e_g must equal zero,

$$e_o = \frac{1}{C} \int_0^t i_f \, dt \qquad (4\text{-}4)$$

$$\frac{de_o}{dt} = \frac{1}{C} i_f \qquad (4\text{-}5)$$

Equation (4-2) still applies and so we get

$$-C \frac{de_o}{dt} = \frac{e_1}{R_1} + \frac{e_2}{R_2} + \frac{e_3}{R_3}$$

Integrating from time equals zero to time equals t gives

$$e_{o(t)} = e_{o(0)} - \frac{1}{C} \int_0^t \left(\frac{e_1}{R_1} + \frac{e_2}{R_2} + \frac{e_3}{R_3} \right) dt \qquad (4\text{-}6)$$

where $e_{o(0)}$ is the initial voltage on the capacitor.

These initial conditions (IC) are shown as the IC on the integrator in Fig. 4-1. If the initial output of the integrator is to be a specified positive voltage, the appropriate negative voltage is fed into the IC terminal on the analog patch board, usually from a pot. The units of RC are (megohms)(microfarads) = $(10^6$ volts/ampere)$[10^{-6}$ (ampere-sec)/volt] = seconds. An analog computer integrates with respect to time in seconds; i.e., time is the independent variable.

If all the R's are 1 megohm and a 1-microfarad capacitor is used, the output of an integrator will change 1 volt per second with a total input voltage of 1 volt. As was the case with summers, integrators usually have both gain 10 and gain 1 inputs.

Multipliers Multiplication is accomplished on an analog by servo multipliers or "quarter-square" multipliers.

Servo multipliers are mechanical devices in which the position of the contact or wiper arm of a potentiometer is moved by one input voltage signal. The other input voltage is connected to the top of the pot. The voltage read from the wiper arm is the product of the two input voltages divided by the voltage range of the computer.

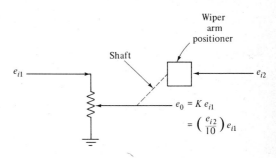

Quarter-square multipliers are electronic devices that use two function generators (see subhead below) on a printed-circuit card to square the sum and difference of the two inputs, yielding the product by the relationship

$$e_{i1}e_{i2} = \tfrac{1}{4}[(e_{i1} + e_{i2})^2 - (e_{i1} - e_{i2})^2]$$

The quarter-square card produces a current i_{qs} that is equal to $e_{i1}e_{i2}/35,500$ amperes.[1] Connecting the card to a high-gain amplifier as shown below gives a circuit whose output voltage is the desired product. Since the grid voltage and current of the amplifier must be zero,

$$i_{qs} = -i_f$$

$$\frac{e_{i1}e_{i2}}{35,500} = -\frac{e_o}{3,550}$$

Therefore

$$e_o = -\frac{e_{i1}e_{i2}}{10}$$

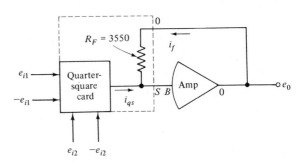

Function generators Arbitrary functions can be generated on analog computers by using "padded pots" or diode function generators. A detailed treatment of these useful gadgets is beyond the scope of this book. Consult the manufacturers' programming manuals for operating and wiring instructions.

Division Since division is merely the inverse of multiplication, the quotient of two voltages can be found by patching up either a servo or a quarter-square multiplier in the feedback loop of a high-gain amplifier.

---

[1] On the Electronic Associates TR-20 analog computer used for the examples in this text.

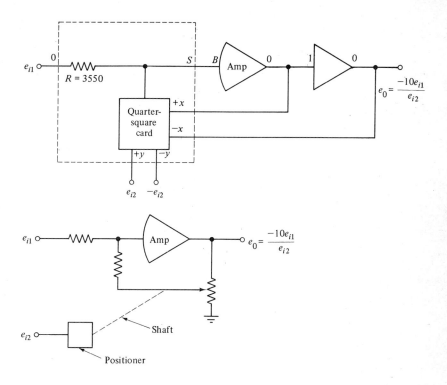

4-4 SIMPLE EXAMPLES

With the basic building blocks now available, let us show how to solve some simple ordinary differential equations.

EXAMPLE 4-1 THREE CSTR'S IN SERIES (isothermal, first order, irreversible, constant volume, and constant throughput) The equations developed in Sec. 3-2 were

$$\frac{dC_{A1}}{dt} = \frac{1}{\tau}(C_{A0} - C_{A1}) - kC_{A1}$$

$$\frac{dC_{A2}}{dt} = \frac{1}{\tau}(C_{A1} - C_{A2}) - kC_{A2} \qquad (4\text{-}7)$$

$$\frac{dC_{A3}}{dt} = \frac{1}{\tau}(C_{A2} - C_{A3}) - kC_{A3}$$

The initial conditions are

$$C_{A1(0)} = 0.4 \text{ mole of A/ft}^3$$

$$C_{A2(0)} = 0.2 \text{ mole of A/ft}^3 \qquad (4\text{-}8)$$

$$C_{A3(0)} = 0.1 \text{ mole of A/ft}^3$$

The forcing function is C_{A0}. We will assume that at time zero C_{A0} is set at 1.8 moles/ft^3 and held constant. The parameters τ and k are given.

$$\tau = 120 \text{ sec} \quad = 2 \text{ min holdup time}$$

$$k = \frac{1}{120} \text{ sec}^{-1} = 0.5 \text{ min}^{-1} \text{ rate constant} \qquad (4\text{-}9)$$

If we feed everything on the right-hand side of the first differential equation above [Eqs. (4-7)] into an integrator, we will get the integral of $-(dC_{A1}/dt)$ or just $-C_{A1}$ (as shown in step 1 in Fig. 4-2). The same holds for the other two equations. The problem is where do we get the voltages that correspond to the right-hand side of the equations. $-C_{A1}$ is available from the output of the integrator. If we run this voltage through a pot that is set at $k + 1/\tau$ we have one of the needed terms. The other term is a voltage representing C_{A0}/τ, which is just a constant $= 1.8/120 = 0.0150$ volt. This step is shown as step 2 in Fig. 4-2.

We now have C_{A1}, or the voltage signal representing C_{A1}, as a dynamic function of time. This can be fed into another integrator to get C_{A2}, and C_{A3} is obtained in the same way (step 3).

It may seem that we are now all set to patch up the computer (connect the components and operational boxes together with wires or patch cords), turn on the machine, set our pots for the correct values and let the computer begin to integrate (go into the "operate" mode). We are not quite there yet however. We still have to worry a little about voltage and time scaling.

One of the biggest disadvantages of an analog computer is that it has a limited accuracy (about 0.05 volt) and a limited range (± 10 or ± 100 volts). The latter means we must keep all voltages everywhere in the circuit less than this maximum. Thus if we want to represent a temperature of $1000°R$ we cannot let 1 volt equal $1°R$. The problem must be scaled down to keep within the voltage range available.

On the other hand, because of the accuracy limitations, voltages should be kept as high as possible. Therefore we must voltage-scale all variables to keep all voltages within these two limits. For this three-CSTR example compositions range from 1.8 moles/ft^3 at the inlet to 0.1 mole/ft^3 at the outlet. Let us assume we are working with a ± 10-volt analog computer. We could let 5 volts correspond to 1 mole/ft^3 and stay within the 10-volt limits. The easiest way to make the change of variables is to write the differential equations, forcing function, and initial conditions in terms of "$5C_{Ai}$".

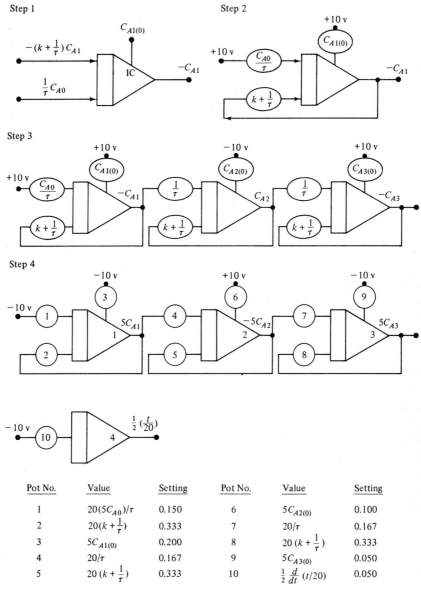

FIGURE 4-2
Analog diagrams for a three-CSTR system.

Equations (4-7) and (4-8) become

$$\frac{d(5C_{A1})}{dt} = \frac{1}{\tau}(5C_{A0} - 5C_{A1}) - k5C_{A1}$$

$$\frac{d(5C_{A2})}{dt} = \frac{1}{\tau}(5C_{A1} - 5C_{A2}) - k5C_{A2} \qquad (4\text{-}10)$$

$$\frac{d(5C_{A3})}{dt} = \frac{1}{\tau}(5C_{A2} - 5C_{A3}) - k5C_{A3}$$

$$5C_{A0} = 9 \text{ volts}$$
$$5C_{A1(0)} = 2 \text{ volts}$$
$$5C_{A2(0)} = 1 \text{ volt} \qquad (4\text{-}11)$$
$$5C_{A3(0)} = 0.5 \text{ volt}$$

Now we still have to consider the time it takes to run a problem. Remember that the analog integrates in seconds. All the equations in this three-CSTR problem have units of seconds, so we could solve the problem in real time. If all the units in the problem were in minutes, then 1 sec of computer time would equal 1 min of process time.

However, we may want to slow down the integration so that the results are easier to see, or we may want to speed it up if the integration is too slow. This "time scaling" is easily accomplished by multiplying all the derivatives (inputs to the integrators) by a number greater than 1 to speed up integration or by a number less than 1 to slow down the integration.

The easiest way to make this change of variables is to write the differential equations in terms of a multiple of the original problem time variable. In this three-CSTR problem each tank has a time constant of 120 sec. If we solve the problem in real time it will take at least $3 \times 120 = 360$ sec $= 6$ min to see what is happening in the third tank. This is a long time to wait for one run; let us speed it up by multiplying each side of Eqs. (4-10) by a factor of 20.

$$\frac{d(5C_{A1})}{d(t/20)} = \frac{20}{120}(5C_{A0} - 5C_{A1}) - \frac{20}{120}(5C_{A1})$$

$$\frac{d(5C_{A2})}{d(t/20)} = \frac{20}{120}(5C_{A1} - 5C_{A2}) - \frac{20}{120}(5C_{A2}) \qquad (4\text{-}12)$$

$$\frac{d(5C_{A3})}{d(t/20)} = \frac{20}{120}(5C_{A2} - 5C_{A3}) - \frac{20}{120}(5C_{A3})$$

We have effectively changed the independent variable to $t/20$. Each second of computer time is equal to 20 sec of process time.

If we feed a voltage of -1 volt into a gain-1 integrator with zero initial conditions, the output of the integrator will be a ramp whose voltage is equal to the independent variable $t/20$.

$$\frac{d(t/20)}{d(t/20)} = 1 \qquad (4\text{-}13)$$

Since the maximum output of any integrator is 10 volts, the integrator will overload after 10 sec (200 sec of process time). If we want to follow the dynamics of the process for a longer period of time, we simply feed less voltage into the integrator so that it will ramp up more slowly. For example, if we feed in -0.5 volt, it will take 20 sec for its output to reach the 10-volt limit. Now each volt of integrator output would correspond to 40 sec of process time.

The final time- and voltage-scaled problem is shown as step 4 in Fig. 4-2. Notice that the signs of all variables have been switched to get positive voltages for C_{A3}. The pots and integrators have been numbered.

The final equations are

$$\frac{d(5C_{A1})}{d(t/20)} = 1.50 - 0.3333(5C_{A1})$$

$$\frac{d(5C_{A2})}{d(t/20)} = 0.1667(5C_{A1}) - 0.3333(5C_{A2}) \qquad (4\text{-}14)$$

$$\frac{d(5C_{A3})}{d(t/20)} = 0.1667(5C_{A2}) - 0.3333(5C_{A3})$$

with the initial conditions given in Eqs. (4-11). Results are shown in Fig. 4-3.

If we want to plot $C_{A3(t)}$ versus time we feed the output of integrator No. 3 into the Y terminal of an X-Y plotter and the output of integrator No. 4 into the X terminal. Each volt of integrator No. 3 output corresponds to 0.2 mole/ft^3 of concentration. Each volt of integrator No. 4 output corresponds to 40 sec of process time.   ////

Some people prefer to do their voltage and time scaling by formally changing variables. For example, we could let

$$X_1 = 5C_{A1}$$
$$X_2 = 5C_{A2}$$
$$X_3 = 5C_{A3} \qquad (4\text{-}15)$$
$$\theta = \frac{t}{20}$$

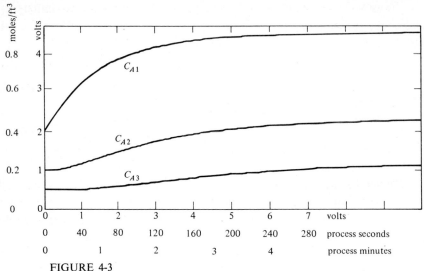

FIGURE 4-3
Analog computer results for the three-CSTR example.

and end up with the differential equations

$$\frac{dX_1}{d\theta} = 1.50 - 0.3333X_1$$

$$\frac{dX_2}{d\theta} = 0.1667X_1 - 0.3333X_2 \qquad (4\text{-}16)$$

$$\frac{dX_3}{d\theta} = 0.1667X_2 - 0.3333X_3$$

This looks neater, but in practice, when one is working on a big system, some-times trying to keep track of all the newly defined variables gets quite confusing. I have always found that keeping the problem in terms of the original variables makes it easier to relate the numbers coming out of the computer to the real physical process being modeled and simulated.

EXAMPLE 4-2   GRAVITY-FLOW TANK   The gravity-flow tank that we con-sidered in Chap. 1 and later in Example 2-9 makes a nice, simple analog simulation and will provide us with a chance to see some nonlinear operational blocks: a multiplier and function switches.

The force balance on the outlet line gave us the equation [Eq. (2-37)]

$$\frac{dv}{dt} = \frac{g}{L} h - \frac{K_F g_c}{\rho A_p} v^2 \qquad (4\text{-}17)$$

To describe the system completely a total continuity equation on the liquid in the tank is also needed.

$$A_T \frac{dh}{dt} = F_0 - F \qquad (4\text{-}18)$$

We have to pick a specific numerical case to solve these two coupled ordinary differential equations. Equation (4-17) is nonlinear because of the v^2 term. Physical dimensions, parameter values, and steady-state flow rate and liquid height are given in Table 4-1.

Equations (4-17) and (4-18), with $F_0 = \bar{F}$, become

$$\frac{dv}{dt} = 0.0107h - 0.00205v^2$$

$$(4\text{-}19)$$

$$\frac{dh}{dt} = 0.311 - 0.0624v$$

We have used the relationship $F = vA_p$. Voltage scaling is not required since both v and h are less than 10.

A useful technique for deciding if time scaling is needed before actually running the problem is to look at the magnitudes of the constant coefficients in the derivative equations. If these coefficients are much above 10, the integration will be too fast. If the coefficients are much below 0.1, the integration will be too slow. Therefore the problem should be time-scaled to keep the coefficients in the 0.1 to 10 range.

Table 4-1   GRAVITY-FLOW-TANK DATA

Pipe		
	ID = 3 ft	$\bar{F}$ = 35.1 ft³/sec (15,700 gpm)
	Area = 7.06 ft²	$\bar{h}$ = 4.72 ft
	Length = 3,000 ft	$\bar{v}$ = 4.97 ft/sec
		RE No. = 1,380,000
Tank	ID = 12 ft	Friction factor = 0.0123
	Area = 113 ft²	$K_F = 2.81 \times 10^{-2}$ lb$_F$/[(ft/sec)²-ft]
	Height = 7 ft	

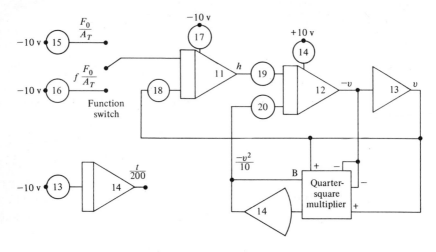

FIGURE 4-4
Gravity-flow-tank analog computer diagram.

Pot No	Variable	Pot No.	Setting $f = 1$	$f = 0.67$	$f = 0.50$
15	F_0/A_T	15	0.311	0.311	0.311
16	fF_0/A_T	16	0.311	0.207	0.156
17	$\overline{h}$	17	0.472	0.205	0.120
18	A_P/A_T	18	0.624	0.624	0.624
19	g/L	19	0.107	0.107	0.107
20	$K_F g_c/\rho A_P$	20	0.205	0.205	0.205
14	$\overline{v}$	14	0.497	0.340	0.250
13	$\frac{1}{20}\frac{d}{dt}(t/10)$	13	0.005	0.005	0.005

Looking at Eqs. (4-19) we can see that the integration rate should be increased by a factor of about 10.

$$\frac{dv}{d(t/10)} = 0.107h - 0.0205v^2$$

$$\frac{dh}{d(t/10)} = 3.11 - 0.624v \tag{4-20}$$

The analog circuit is shown in Fig. 4-4. The multiplier used to obtain v^2 is shown as a quarter-square multiplier. Two different values of the forcing function F_0 can be used by throwing the function switch one way or the other. The steady-state design value of F_0 is 35.1 ft^3/sec and is set on pot 15. Pot 16 can then be set to some fractional value of this maximum to see the effects of step disturbances in feed rate.

Results are shown in Fig. 4-5. Notice that the tank can overflow if large feed rate changes occur. ////

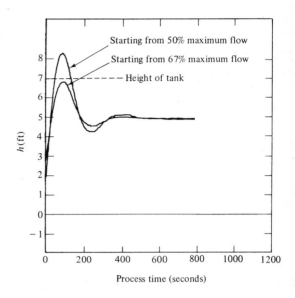

FIGURE 4-5
Gravity-flow tank.

4-5 MORE COMPLEX SYSTEMS

EXAMPLE 4-3 BINARY DISTILLATION COLUMN An analog computer
diagram for one tray of the ideal binary distillation column modeled in Sec. 3-10 is
given in Fig. 4-6. It can be seen that the equipment requirements are excessive:

	Number per tray	Total number for 20-tray column
Integrators	2	40
Multipliers	2	40
Dividers	1	20
Function generators	2	40

This shows very clearly the basic limitation of the analog computer for real
problems. A very large computer facility would be required to handle a problem with
this number of nonlinear operational blocks.

Engineers being as ingenious as they are, however, further simplifications can
be made to reduce the problem to more reasonable size. These usually include:

1 Use of a linear hydraulic relationship. This eliminates one function generator
per tray.

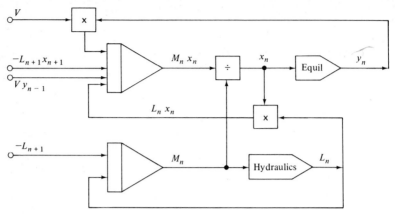

FIGURE 4-6
Analog circuit for the nth tray of a binary distillation column.

2 Use of linearized vapor-liquid equilibrium in the top and bottom sections of the column where the purities are usually fairly high. This eliminates one function generator per tray where it can be used. Normally the nonlinear vapor-liquid relationship would be retained in the middle of the column where larger composition changes occur from tray to tray.

The ultimate simplification would be to neglect flow-rate changes in V, R, and F and use linear equilibrium relationships throughout. The equations for such a 20-tray column plus reflux drum and reboiler are

$$\frac{dx_D}{dt} = \left(\frac{VK_{20}}{M_D}\right)x_{20} - \left(\frac{V}{M_D}\right)x_D$$

$$\frac{dx_{20}}{dt} = \left(\frac{R}{M_{20}}\right)x_D - \left(\frac{R+VK_{20}}{M_{20}}\right)x_{20} + \left(\frac{VK_{19}}{M_{20}}\right)x_{19}$$

$$\frac{dx_{19}}{dt} = \left(\frac{R}{M_{19}}\right)x_{20} - \left(\frac{R+VK_{19}}{M_{19}}\right)x_{19} + \left(\frac{VK_{18}}{M_{19}}\right)x_{18}$$

. . . .

$$\frac{dx_{10}}{dt} = \left(\frac{R}{M_{10}}\right)x_{11} - \left(\frac{R+F+VK_{10}}{M_{10}}\right)x_{10} + \left(\frac{VK_9}{M_{10}}\right)x_9 + \left(\frac{F}{M_{10}}\right)x_F$$

$$\frac{dx_9}{dt} = \left(\frac{R+F}{M_9}\right)x_{10} - \left(\frac{R+F+VK_9}{M_9}\right)x_9 + \left(\frac{VK_8}{M_9}\right)x_8$$

. . . .

$$\frac{dx_1}{dt} = \left(\frac{R+F}{M_1}\right)x_2 - \left(\frac{R+F+VK_1}{M_1}\right)x_1 + \left(\frac{VK_B}{M_1}\right)x_B$$

$$\frac{dx_B}{dt} = \left(\frac{R+F}{M_B}\right)x_1 - \left(\frac{B+VK_B}{M_B}\right)x_B \tag{4-21}$$

where $y_n = K_n x_n$ (4-22)

   K_n = slope of actual equilibrium curve at steady-state operating conditions for nth tray

   The analog circuit diagram is shown in Fig. 4-7. The system is completely linear, and only 22 integrators are required. However, the solution will be only approximate and only feed composition disturbances x_F can be explored.   ////

   We will return to this problem in Chap. 5 and show how simple it is to solve by digital simulation.

EXAMPLE 4-4   NONISOTHERMAL CSTR   The nonisothermal CSTR of Sec. 3-5 provides a good example of a reasonably complex nonlinear analog simulation.
   A specific numerical case must be chosen. Table 4-2 lists parameter and steady-state values. Figure 4-8 gives a simplified analog circuit diagram, showing in block-diagram form how the various operational blocks would be connected. You can see that, even for this single tank, a large number of nonlinear components are required (seven multipliers, three function generators, and two dividers).
   We will simulate a slightly simpler version of this problem. Constant holdups and flow rates will be assumed, plus first-order kinetics and constant inlet cooling-water temperature. The equations describing the system are

$$\frac{dC_A}{dt} = \left(\frac{F}{V}\right)C_{A0} - \left(\frac{F}{V}\right)C_A - C_A \alpha e^{-E/RT} \tag{4-23}$$

$$\frac{dT}{dt} = \left(\frac{F}{V}\right)T_0 - \left(\frac{F}{V}\right)T - \left(\frac{\lambda}{C_p\rho}\right)C_A \alpha e^{-E/RT} - \left(\frac{UA}{C_pV\rho}\right)(T - T_J) \tag{4-24}$$

$$\frac{dT_J}{dt} = \frac{F_J(T_{J0} - T_J)}{V_J} + \left(\frac{UA}{C_JV_J\rho_J}\right)(T - T_J) \tag{4-25}$$

$$F_J = \bar{F}_J - K_c(T^{set} - T) \tag{4-26}$$

Equation (4-26) represents a proportional controller that changes the jacket flow rate as reactor temperature varies. Forcing functions are feed concentration C_{A0} and feed temperature T_0.

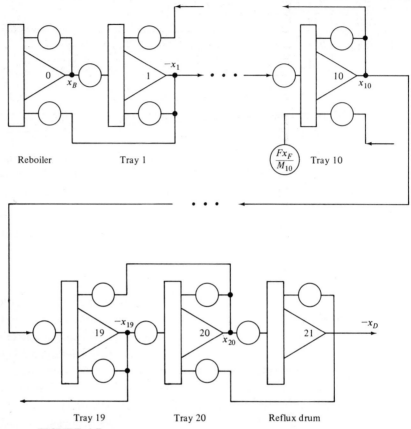

FIGURE 4-7
Analog circuit for a simplified binary distillation column with no flow-rate changes and linear equilibrium relationships.

Table 4-2   NONISOTHERMAL CSTR PARAMETER VALUES

$\bar{F} = 40$ ft³/hr	$U = 150$ Btu/(hr-ft²-°R)
$\bar{V} = 48$ ft³	$A = 250$ ft²
$\bar{C}_{A0} = 0.50$ mole/ft³	$T_{J0} = 530$°R
$\bar{C}_A = 0.245$ mole/ft³	$\bar{T}_0 = 530$°R
$\bar{T} = 600$°R	$\lambda = -30{,}000$ Btu/mole
$\bar{T}_J = 594.6$°R	$C_p = 0.75$ Btu/lb$_m$-°R
$\bar{F}_J = 49.9$ ft³/hr	$C_J = 1.0$ Btu/lb$_m$-°R
$V_J = 3.85$ ft³	$\rho = 50$ lb$_m$/ft³
$\alpha = 7.08 \times 10^{10}$ hr^{-1}	$\rho_J = 62.3$ lb$_m$/ft³
$E = 30{,}000$ Btu/mole	$K_c = 4$ (ft³/hr)/°R
$R = 1.99$ Btu/mole °R	$T^{\text{set}} = 600$°R

† Note that the time basis of all variables is hours. "Barred" quantities are steady-state variables.

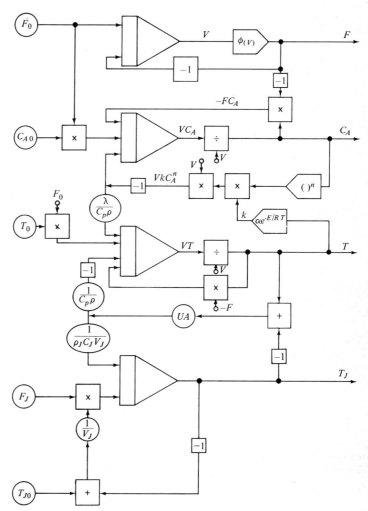

FIGURE 4-8
Computer block diagram for a nonisothermal CSTR.

Substituting the numerical values from Table 4-2 into Eq. (4-23) to (4-26) gives

$$\frac{dC_A}{dt} = 0.833C_{A0} - 0.833C_A - C_A k$$

$$\frac{dT}{dt} = 0.833T_0 - 0.833T + 800C_A k - 20.8(T - T_J)$$

$$\frac{dT_J}{dt} = 0.26F_J(530 - T_J) + 156(T - T_J)$$ (4-27)

$$F_J = 49.9 - 4(600 - T)$$

$$k = 7.08 \times 10^{10}e^{-30,000/1.99T}$$

with $C_{A(0)} = 0.245$
$T_{(0)} = 600$
$T_{J(0)} = 594.6$

The principal problem in this nonlinear simulation is the generation of the Arrhenius exponential term. Careful voltage scaling is required to avoid inaccuracy and overloading. There are several alternative methods for generating the exponential.[1] The most straightforward would be setting up a function generator, into which temperature T would be fed and out of which the specific reaction rate k would come. Another technique involves using the derivative of temperature (dT/dt), as given by the right-hand side of the second equation in Eqs. (4-27). Since

$$k = \alpha e^{-E/RT}$$

$$\frac{dk}{dt} = \alpha e^{-E/RT}\frac{d}{dt}\left(-\frac{E}{RT}\right) = \frac{kE}{RT^2}\frac{dT}{dt}$$ (4-28)

[1] R. I. Kermode and W. F. Stevens, *Can. J. Chem. Eng.*, vol. 39, p. 81, 1961.

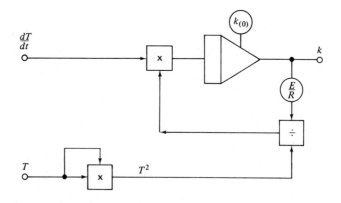

Thus the derivative of temperature is multiplied by k and divided by T squared and then the whole "mess" is integrated. Function generators are eliminated with this method but two multiplications, one division, and integration are all required.

For our example we will use a $\log x$ printed-circuit card. This card is normally used to take logarithms. It conducts a current $i_{\log}$ that is proportional to the log to the base 10 of the input voltage. Adding a high-gain amplifier at the appropriate spot permits us to find either logs or powers of 10.

$$i_{\log} = \frac{\log 10e_i}{1,000} \qquad (4\text{-}29)$$

To find logarithm to the base 10:

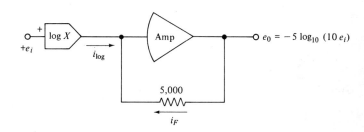

Since $i_{\log} = -i_F$,

$$\frac{\log 10e_i}{1,000} = -\frac{e_o}{5,000}$$

Therefore

$$e_o = -5 \log 10e_i \qquad (4\text{-}30)$$

To find powers of 10:

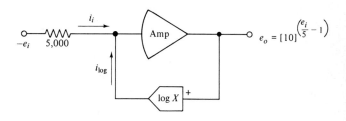

Since $i_i = -i_{\log}$,

$$\frac{-e_i}{5,000} = -\frac{\log 10e_o}{1,000}$$

$$\log 10e_o = \frac{e_i}{5}$$

$$10e_o = (10)^{e_i/5}$$

Therefore

$$e_o = (10)^{e_i/5-1} \qquad (4\text{-}31)$$

We must transform the equation for k shown in Eqs. (4-27) into some power of 10. Since the steady-state value of k is 0.86 hr^{-1}, let us voltage-scale k by a factor of 5.

$$5k = 3.54 \times 10^{11} e^{-30,000/1.99T}$$

$$\log 5k = \log 3.54 + 11 + \log (10^{0.435})^{-30,000/1.99T}$$

$$= 11.55 + \log(10)^{-6560/T} \qquad (4\text{-}32)$$

$$= 11.55 - \frac{65.6}{T/100}$$

$$5k = (10)^{11.55 - 65.6/(T/100)}$$

Equating the powers of 10 in Eqs. (4-31) and (4-32), we can solve for the input voltage e_i that must be fed into the log x card–amplifier circuit to get $5k$ out.

$$\frac{e_i}{5} - 1 = 11.55 - \frac{65.6}{T/100}$$

$$e_i = 62.75 - \frac{328}{T/100} \qquad (4\text{-}33)$$

Figure 4-9 shows the final analog circuit, including the circuit generating $5k$.

Voltage-scaling all concentrations by a factor of 10, temperatures by 0.01, and jacket flow by 0.1 converts Eqs. (4-27) to

$$\frac{d(10C_A)}{dt} = 0.833(10C_{A0}) - 0.833(10C_A) - 0.2(10C_A)(5k)$$

$$\frac{d}{dt}\left(\frac{T}{100}\right) = 0.833\left(\frac{T_0}{100}\right) - 0.833\left(\frac{T}{100}\right) + \frac{800}{500}\frac{(10C_A)(5k)}{10}$$

$$- 20.8\left(\frac{T}{100} - \frac{T_J}{100}\right)$$

$$\frac{d}{dt}\left(\frac{T_J}{100}\right) = 2.6\left(\frac{F_J}{10}\right)\left(5.3 - \frac{T_J}{100}\right) + 156\left(\frac{T - T_J}{100}\right)$$

$$\frac{F_J}{10} = 4.99 - 40\left(6 - \frac{T}{100}\right) = 40\left(\frac{T}{100}\right) - 235 \qquad (4\text{-}34)$$

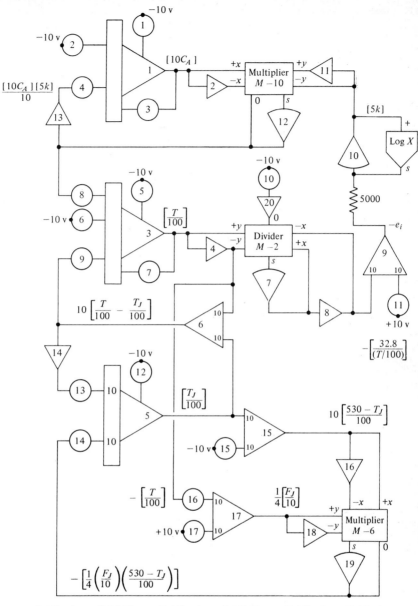

FIGURE 4-9
Analog computer diagram for a nonisothermal CSTR.

Pot Number	Pot Setting	Pot Number	Pot Setting	Pot Number	Pot Setting
1	0.245	7	0.0833	13	0.156
2	0.0416	8	0.160	14	0.104
3	0.0833	9	0.208	15	0.530
4	0.200	10	0.328	16	0.999
5	0.600	11	0.627	17	0.588
6	0.0442	12	0.595		

with the initial conditions:

$$(10C_A)_{(0)} = 2.45$$

$$\left(\frac{T}{100}\right)_{(0)} = 6.0 \qquad \text{(4-35)}$$

$$\left(\frac{T_J}{100}\right)_{(0)} = 5.95$$

Looking at the large numerical values of the coefficients in the differential equations for T and T_J, we would expect the dynamics of the system to be quite fast. Remember our units of time are hours in this problem. To slow down the rate of integration, let us time-scale by a factor of 10. Now each second of computer time will represent one-tenth of an hour or 6 min of process time.

$$\frac{d(10C_A)}{d(10t)} = 0.416 - 0.0833(10C_A) - 0.02(10C_A)(5k)$$

$$\frac{d(T/100)}{d(10t)} = 0.442 - 0.0833\left(\frac{T}{100}\right) + 0.016(10C_A)(5k) - 2.08\left(\frac{T}{100} - \frac{T_J}{100}\right)$$

$$\frac{d(T_J/100)}{d(10t)} = 0.26\left(\frac{F_J}{10}\right)\left(5.3 - \frac{T_J}{100}\right) + 15.6\left(\frac{T}{100} - \frac{T_J}{100}\right) \qquad \text{(4-36)}$$

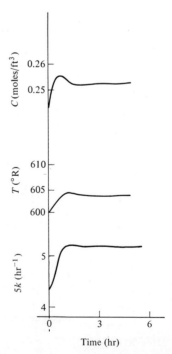

FIGURE 4-10
$+10\%\ \Delta C_{A0}$ nonisothermal CSTR.

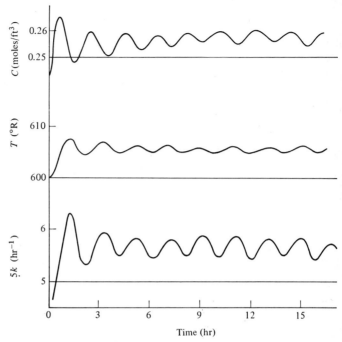

FIGURE 4-11
$+20\% \Delta C_{A0}$ nonisothermal CSTR.

Figure 4-9 shows the final circuit diagram and pot settings as simulated on a TR-20. Results for a feed composition disturbance are shown in Fig. 4-10. At time equals zero, C_{A0} was changed from its steady-state value of 0.50 moles of component A per ft³ to a value of 0.55. This instantaneous or step change in C_{A0} was accomplished by setting pot 2 to 0.0458 before switching the computer into the "operate" mode. Figure 4-11 shows the response for a step change in C_{A0} to 0.60. Note the oscillatory behavior with this feed composition. ////

PROBLEMS

4-1 Simulate on an analog computer an extension of the three-CSTR system discussed in Example 4-1 by adding a feedback controller. The controller looks at the concentration C_{A3} in the third tank and tries to hold it at a set-point value of 0.1 moles of A/ft³ by changing the inlet concentration C_{A0} in the first tank. The feedback controller is a proportional-integral type, described by the equation

$$C_{A0} = C_{AD} + 0.4 + K_c\left(E + \frac{1}{\tau_I}\int E\,dt\right)$$

where C_{AD} = disturbance variable
K_c = controller gain
E = error signal = $0.10 - C_{A3}$
τ_I = controller reset time constant
$\quad = 4$ min

The steady-state value of C_{AD} is 0.4 mole of A/ft^3. At time equals zero C_{AD} is changed instantaneously to 0.6. Plot the responses of C_{A1}, C_{A2}, and C_{A3} for several values of gain K_c: 0, 20, 30, and 40.

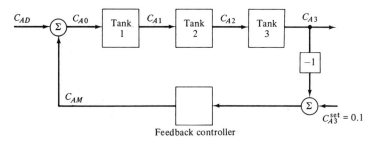

Feedback controller

4-2   The three first-order ordinary differential equations describing the three-CSTR system of Example 4-1 can be combined into one third-order ordinary differential equation. Show that for equal τ's and k's it is

$$\frac{d^3C_{A3}}{dt^3} + 3\left(\frac{1}{\tau}+k\right)\frac{d^2C_{A3}}{dt^2} + 3\left(\frac{1}{\tau}+k\right)^2\frac{dC_{A3}}{dt} + \left(\frac{1}{\tau}+k\right)^3 C_{A3} = \left(\frac{1}{\tau}\right)^3 C_{A0}$$

Simulate this third-order ordinary differential equation on an analog computer. HINT:

If you put a signal equal to $\dfrac{d^3C_{A3}}{dt^3}$ into an integrator, you will get out $-\dfrac{d^2C_{A3}}{dt^2}$.

4-3   Simulate on an analog computer the cone-shaped-tank system of Prob. 3-1. Assume a steady-state flow of 250 gpm and liquid height of 4 ft. The tank is 6 ft high and 4 ft in radius at the top. Find the response of liquid height h to both increases and decreases in feed flow F_0.

   In this simulation you will have to extract the square root of h. Since square-rooting is the inverse of squaring, you should be able to use a multiplier and a high-gain amplifier to find the square root.

4-4   Derive the equations describing an isothermal, perfectly mixed batch reactor in which first-order consecutive reactions occur:

$$A \xrightarrow{\;k_1\;} B \xrightarrow{\;k_2\;} C$$

Prepare the analog circuit diagram and solve on the computer for the dynamic changes in concentration of all species: C_A; C_B, and C_C. Use initial concentrations of

$$C_{A(0)} = 0.8 \text{ mole A/ft}^3$$

$$C_{B(0)} = C_{C(0)} = 0$$

(a) For $k_1 = k_2 = 0.5 \text{ min}^{-1}$
(b) For $k_1 = 0.5$ and $k_2 = 1.0 \text{ min}^{-1}$
(c) For $k_1 = 1.0$ and $k_2 = 0.5 \text{ min}^{-1}$

4-5 Simulate the hydraulic system of Prob. 3-7. Find the response of P in the surge vessel for a step increase and a step decrease of 25 percent in the feed flow, W_1, from its steady-state value of 5 lb_m/sec. The pressure downstream of resistance R_3 is atmospheric.

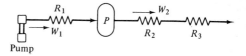

At steady-state the pressure upstream of R_3 is 1,000 psig, the pressure in the tank is 2,500 psig, and the pressure at the pump discharge is 4,500 psig. The volume of the tank is 15 ft³. Fluid density is given by

$$\rho = 75 + 0.01 \, (P - 2,500) \quad \diamondsuit \quad \text{lb}_m/\text{ft}^3$$

4-6 A centrifugal compressor is used to pump 100,000 lb_m/hr of gas from a vessel operating at a constant pressure of 75 psig, through a heat exchanger, into a cylindrical vessel 8 ft

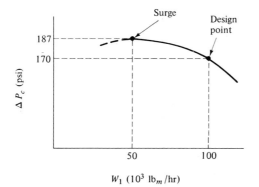

$W_1 \ (10^3 \ \text{lb}_m \ /\text{hr})$

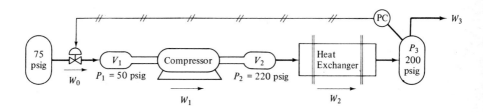

ID by 20 ft long. The performance curve for the compressor is sketched below and can be approximated by a quadratic of the form

$$P_2 - P_1 = \Delta P_c = a_0 + a_1 w_1 + a_2 w_1{}^2$$

The flow through the control valve on the suction of the compressor is given by

$$w_0 = 40,000 \ X\sqrt{75 - P_1} \quad \diamond \text{lb}_m/\text{hr}$$

where X is the stem position of the control valve (wide open at $X = 1$; shut at $X = 0$). The pressure controller is proportional-integral with the equation

$$X = 0.5 + K_c \left[(200 - P_3) + \frac{1}{\tau_I} \int (200 - P_3) \, dt \right]$$

The valve is initially half open. Steady-state initial pressures are shown in the above figure of the system. The effective "lumped" volumes at the suction and discharge of the compressor, V_1 and V_2, are 10 ft³. Pressure drop through the heat exchanger is given by

$$P_2 - P_3 = \frac{20}{10^{10}} (w_2)^2$$

Assume the gas is perfect and that the system is essentially isothermal at 100°F. Calculate the response of pressures and flows in the system to a 20 percent increase and decrease in the demand flow w_3. Try several values of the controller constants K_c and τ_I.

DIGITAL SIMULATION

The disadvantages of analog computation should now be painfully clear to those of you who actually worked through the examples and problems of Chap. 4. Setup time is lengthy because voltage scaling, time scaling, and patching are required. Many electronic components must be connected together, so the probability of errors in patching or setting pots or of component malfunction is significant. Accuracy of computed results is limited.

Digital computers practically eliminate all these problems. Scaling is not required because of the tremendous range of values that digital computers can handle (of the order of 10^{-300} to 10^{+300} on the Control Data Corporation CDC 6400 computer used in the examples in this chapter). Setup time involves writing and debugging a FORTRAN program. This usually takes much less engineering time. Once the program is working, it can be stored on cards or tape and rerun a week, a month, or a year later with little effort.

However, digital simulation is not completely without its problems. The principal difficulty arises in integration. This must be done numerically on a digital computer since the digital machine is not a continuous device but merely a very fast desk calculator. Numerical integration involves approximating continuous differential equations with discrete finite-difference equations.

The accuracy and the stability of these approximating equations must be kept in mind. Both accuracy and stability are affected by the finite-difference equation (or integration algorithm) employed. Many algorithms have been proposed in the literature. Some work better (i.e., faster and therefore more cheaply for a specified degree of accuracy) on some problems than others. Unfortunately there is no one algorithm that works best for all problems.

Over the years a number of digital programs have been developed that contain preprogrammed integration packages. In theory, these general "simulation languages"[1] relieve the engineer of knowing anything about numerical integration. They automatically monitor errors and stability and adjust the integration interval or step size to stay within some accuracy criterion. Typical examples are MIMIC, MIDAS, and LEANS.

In practice, however, these simulation languages have limited utility. In their push for generality, they usually have become inefficient. The computer execution time for a realistic engineering problem when run on one of these simulation languages is usually significantly longer than when run on a FORTRAN program written just for the specific problem.

Proponents argue, however, that the setup and programming time is reduced by using a simulation language. This may be true for the engineer who uses the computer only very occasionally and only for dynamic simulations. FORTRAN is such a universal language that essentially all engineering graduates are familiar with it. Using a simulation language requires the engineer to learn a new language and a new system. Since FORTRAN is already known and since the simple, easily programmed numerical techniques seem to work as well as the more sophisticated ones, it has been my experience that it is better for the engineer to develop his own FORTRAN program for most problems. I have yet to work with a big general-purpose program designed to do anything that does not end up wallowing in its own inefficiency.

We will begin our discussion of digital simulation by developing some of the more important and useful numerical analysis techniques. Then we will study some specific examples of the application of these techniques to practical chemical engineering systems. There are several good texts[2] devoted to numerical techniques and digital computer fundamentals and programming.

---

[1] For a good discussion of simulation languages see R. G. E. Franks, "Mathematical Modeling in Chemical Engineering," Wiley, 1966.
[2] L. Lapidus, "Digital Computation for Chemical Engineers," McGraw-Hill, 1962.
M. P. Moyle, "Introduction to Computers for Engineers," Wiley, 1967.
Brice Carnahan, H. R. Luther, and James D. Wilkes, "Applied Numerical Methods," Wiley, 1969.
Richard W. Hamming, "Introduction to Applied Numerical Analysis," McGraw-Hill, 1971.

5-1   NUMERICAL METHODS

5-1.1   Implicit Function Convergence

One common problem in digital simulation is the solution of algebraic equations. If these equations are complex or nonlinear or contain transcendental functions, analytical solutions are impossible. Therefore an iterative trial-and-error procedure of some sort must be devised. A value for the solution is guessed. It is plugged into the equation or equations to see if it satisfies them. If not, a new guess is made and the whole process is repeated until the iteration converges (one hopes) to the right value.

The key problem is to find a method for making the new guess that converges rapidly to the correct answer. There are a host of techniques. Unfortunately there is no best method for all equations. Some methods that converge very rapidly for some equations will diverge for other equations; i.e., the series of new guesses will oscillate around the correct solution with ever increasing deviations. This is one kind of numerical instability.

We will discuss only a few of the simplest and most useful methods. Fortunately, in dynamic simulations, we start out from some converged initial steady-state. At each instant in time, variables have changed very little from the values they had a short time before. Thus we are always close to the correct solution. For this reason, the simple convergence methods are usually quite adequate for dynamic simulations.

These techniques are best illustrated by a specific and important example, a vapor-liquid equilibrium calculation.

EXAMPLE 5-1   We are given the pressure P and the liquid composition x. We want to find the bubble-point temperature and the vapor composition as discussed under "Phase equilibrium" in Sec. 2-2.6. For simplicity let us assume a binary system of components 1 and 2. Component 1 is the more volatile, and the mole fraction of 1 in the liquid is x and in the vapor is y. Let us assume also that the system is ideal: Raoult's and Dalton's laws apply.

In liquid:

$$\mathscr{P}_1 = xP_1^0$$
$$\mathscr{P}_2 = (1 - x)P_2^0 \qquad (5\text{-}1)$$

In vapor:

$$\mathscr{P}_1 = yP$$
$$\mathscr{P}_2 = (1 - y)P \qquad (5\text{-}2)$$

where $\mathscr{P}_j$ = partial pressure of jth component

$P_j{}^0$ = vapor pressure of jth component which is a function of temperature T, °R

$$\ln P_1{}^0 = \frac{A_1}{T} + B_1$$

$$\ln P_2{}^0 = \frac{A_2}{T} + B_2$$

(5-3)

Equating partial pressures in liquid and vapor gives

$$P = xP_1{}^0 + (1 - x)P_2{}^0 \qquad (5\text{-}4)$$

$$y = \frac{xP_1{}^0}{P} \qquad (5\text{-}5)$$

Our convergence problem is to find the value of temperature T that will satisfy Eq. (5-4). The procedure is as follows:

1 Guess a temperature T.
2 Calculate the vapor pressures of components 1 and 2 from Eqs. (5-3).
3 Calculate a total pressure P^{calc} from Eq. (5-4).

$$P^{\text{calc}} = xP_1{}^0 + (1 - x)P_2{}^0$$

4 Compare P^{calc} with the actual total pressure given, P.
5 If P^{calc} is greater than P, the guessed temperature was too high and we must make another guess that is lower. ////

Now let us discuss several ways of making a new guess for the example above.

Interval halving This technique is quite simple but it is rock-bottom stable. It works very well in dynamic simulations because the step size can be adjusted to correspond approximately to the rate at which the variable is changing with time during the integration time step.

A fixed increment in temperature ΔT is added to or subtracted from the old guess of temperature, depending on whether P^{calc} is greater than or less than P. We keep moving in the correct direction at this fixed step size until the sign of $P - P^{\text{calc}}$ changes. This means we have crossed over the correct value of T. Then we back up halfway, i.e., we halve the increment ΔT. With each successive iteration we again halve ΔT, always moving either up or down in the appropriate direction. Figure 5-1 sketches the procedure graphically.

A digital computer program using interval halving is shown in Fig. 5-2. The program is written as a subroutine EQUIL into which known values of x and P and

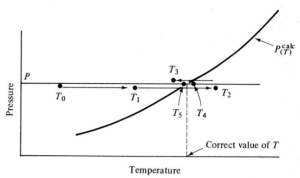

FIGURE 5-1
Interval-halving convergence.

an initial guess of T are fed. Coming back after convergence has been achieved are the correct T and the vapor composition y. The vapor-pressure constants are known and transferred to the subroutine through the COMMON statement.

The initial guess of T can be either above or below the correct value. The program will take fixed steps DT equal to one degree until it crosses the correct value of T.

```
      SUBROUTINE EQUIL1(X,P,T,Y)
      COMMON LOOP,A1,A2,B1,B2
C     INTERVAL HALVING
      DT=1.
      FLAGM=-1.
      FLAGP=-1.
      LOOP=0
100   PO1=EXP(A1/(T+460.)+B1)
      LOOP=LOOP+1
      IF(LOOP.GT.100) STOP
      PO2=EXP(A2/(T+460.)+B2)
      PCALC=X*PO1+(1.-X)*PO2
      IF(ABS(P-PCALC).LT. .001) GO TO 50
      IF(P-PCALC)10,10,1
1     IF(FLAGP.LT.0.) GO TO 2
      DT=DT/2.
2     T=T+DT
      FLAGM=1.
      GO TO 100
10    IF(FLAGM.LT.0.) GO TO 11
      DT=DT/2.
11    T=T-DT
      FLAGP=1.
      GO TO 100
50    Y=X*PO1/P
      RETURN
      END
```

FIGURE 5-2
Interval-halving convergence program.

Then interval halving begins. Clearly, the number of iterations to converge (to 0.001 psi) depends on how far the initial guess is from the correct value and the size of the initial DT.

Note the presence of a loop counter. LOOP is the number of times a new guess has been made. It is always a good idea to put these into any convergence scheme. If the system diverges instead of converging, the test for LOOP greater than 100 will stop the program.

Newton-Raphson method   This method is probably the most popular convergence method. It is somewhat more complicated since it requires the evaluation of a derivative. It also can lead to stability problems if the initial guess is poor and the functions are highly nonlinear.

Newton-Raphson amounts to using the slope of the function to extrapolate to the correct value. Using the bubble-point problem as a specific example, let us define the function $f_{(T)}$:

$$f_{(T)} = P_{(T)}^{\text{calc}} - P \qquad (5-6)$$

We want to find the value of T that makes $f_{(T)}$ equal to zero; i.e., we want to find the root of $f_{(T)}$. We guess a value of T (T_0). Then we evaluate the function at T_0, $f_{(T_0)}$. Next we evaluate the slope of the function at T_0, $f'_{(T_0)} = \left(\dfrac{df}{dT}\right)_{(T_0)}$. Then, from Fig. 5-3,

$$f'_{(T_0)} = \left(\frac{df}{dT}\right)_{(T_0)} = \frac{-f_{(T_0)}}{T_1 - T_0}$$

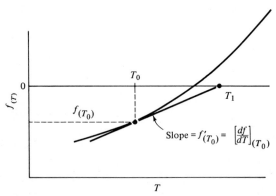

FIGURE 5-3
Graphical representation of Newton-Raphson convergence.

Solving for T_1 gives

$$T_1 = T_0 - \frac{f_{(T_0)}}{f'_{(T_0)}} \qquad (5\text{-}7)$$

T_1 in Eq. (5-7) is the new guess of temperature. If the line $f_{(T)}$ were straight we would converge to the correct solution in one iteration.

Generalizing Eq. (5-7), we get the recursive convergence algorithm:

$$T_{n+1} = T_n - \frac{f_n}{f'_n} \qquad (5\text{-}8)$$

where T_{n+1} = new guess of temperature
T_n = old guess of temperature
f_n = value of $f_{(T)}$ at $T = T_n$
f'_n = value of derivative of f, df/dT, at $T = T_n$

This technique requires the evaluation of f', the derivative of $f_{(T)}$ with respect to temperature. In our example this can be obtained analytically.

$$f_{(T)} = xe^{A_1/T + B_1} + (1 - x)e^{A_2/T + B_2} - P$$

$$f' = \frac{df}{dT} = -\frac{xA_1}{T^2} e^{A_1/T + B_1} - \frac{(1 - x)A_2}{T^2} e^{A_2/T + B_2}$$

$$= \frac{-xA_1P_1{}^0 - (1 - x)A_2P_2{}^0}{T^2} \qquad (5\text{-}9)$$

If the function were so complex that an analytical derivative could not be obtained explicitly, an approximate derivative would have to be calculated numerically [make a small change in temperature ΔT, evaluate f at $T + \Delta T$, and use $f' \simeq (f_{(T + \Delta T)} - f_{(T)})/\Delta T]$.

A digital computer program using Eqs. (5-8) and (5-9) is shown in Fig. 5-4. Note that T is in °F.

```
      SUBROUTINE EQUIL2(X,P,T,Y)
      COMMON LOOP,A1,A2,B1,B2
C     NEWTON-RAPHSON
      LOOP=0
100   PO1=EXP(A1/(T+460.)+B1)
      LOOP=LOOP+1
      IF(LOOP.GT.100) STOP
      PO2=EXP(A2/(T+460.)+B2)
      PCALC=X*PO1+(1.-X)*PO2
      IF(ABS(P-PCALC).LT. .001) GO TO 50
      F=PCALC-P
      FSLOPE=(-X*A1*PO1-(1.-X)*A2*PO2)/(T+460.)**2
      T=T-F/FSLOPE
      GO TO 100
50    Y=X*PO1/P
      RETURN
      END
```

FIGURE 5-4
Newton-Raphson convergence program.

False position This convergence technique is a combination of Newton-Raphson and interval halving. An initial guess T_0 is made, and the function $f_{(T_0)}$ is evaluated. A step is taken in the correct direction to a new temperature and $f_{(T)}$ again evaluated. If $f_{(T)}$ has not changed signs, another step is taken. Stepping is continued until some temperature T_1 is reached where $f_{(T_1)}$ differs in sign from $f_{(T_0)}$. As shown in Fig. 5-5, a new guess for temperature T_2 can be found from the geometry. From similar triangles

$$\frac{T_2 - T_0}{-f_{(T_0)}} = \frac{T_1 - T_2}{f_{(T_1)}}$$

Rearranging,

$$T_2 = T_1 - \frac{f_{(T_1)}(T_1 - T_0)}{f_{(T_1)} - f_{(T_0)}} \qquad (5\text{-}10)$$

Then $f_{(T_2)}$ is evaluated and a new guess T_3 is made, using

$$T_3 = T_2 - \frac{f_{(T_2)}(T_2 - T_1)}{f_{(T_2)} - f_{(T_1)}}$$

Generalizing, we get the recursive algorithm:

$$T_{n+1} = T_n - \frac{f_n(T_n - T_{n-1})}{f_n - f_{n-1}} \qquad (5\text{-}11)$$

Explicit convergence methods For systems of equations it is often possible to guess a value of a variable X_{guess} and then use one of the equations to solve explicitly for a new calculated value of the same variable, X_{calc}. Then the calculated value and original guess are compared and a new guess made.

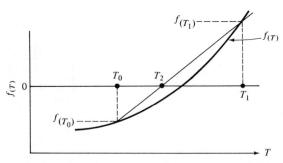

FIGURE 5-5
False-position convergence.

The new guess can be simply the calculated value (this is called *successive substitution*). Convergence may be very slow because of (1) a very slow rate of approach of X_{calc} to X_{guess} or (2) an oscillation of X_{calc} back and forth around X_{guess}. The loop can even diverge.

Therefore a convergence factor β can be used to speed up or slow down the rate at which X_{guess} is permitted to change.

$$(X_{guess})_{new} = (X_{guess})_{old} + \beta[X_{calc} - (X_{guess})_{old}] \qquad (5\text{-}12)$$

Note that letting $\beta = 1$ corresponds to successive substitution. This method is best illustrated by an example.

EXAMPLE 5-2   A countercurrent heat exchanger is an important example of a system described by equations that must be solved iteratively. Figure 5-6 shows the system. The problem is to find the steady-state outlet temperatures of the oil, T_{H2}, and cooling water, T_{C2}, and the heat transfer rate Q, given the inlet temperatures, flow rates, and heat transfer area and overall coefficient. The steady-state equations for heat transfer are

$$Q = UA(\Delta T)_{LM} \qquad (5\text{-}13)$$

$$Q = 70,000(0.5)(250 - T_{H2}) \qquad (5\text{-}14)$$

$$Q = 170.5(60)(8.33)(T_{C2} - 80) \qquad (5\text{-}15)$$

$$(\Delta T)_{LM} = \frac{(250 - T_{C2}) - (T_{H2} - 80)}{\ln\left(\dfrac{250 - T_{C2}}{T_{H2} - 80}\right)} \qquad (5\text{-}16)$$

We have four equations and four variables: Q, $(\Delta T)_{LM}$, T_{H2}, and T_{C2}. The iterative procedure we will use is:

1 Guess a value for the oil outlet temperature T_{H2}^{guess} (which must be greater than 80°F, for physical reasons).
2 Calculate Q_1 from Eq. (5-14).
3 Calculate T_{C2} from Eq. (5-15), using Q_1.
4 Calculate the log-mean-temperature driving force $(\Delta T)_{LM}$ from Eq. (5-16).
5 Calculate a new heat transfer rate Q_2 from Eq. (5-13).
6 Substitute the value of Q_2 into Eq. (5-14) to calculate a T_{H2}^{calc}.
7 Compare T_{H2}^{guess} and T_{H2}^{calc}.
8 Reguess T_{H2}^{guess}, using Eq. (5-12).

Figure 5-7 shows the successive values of T_{H2}^{guess} for different values of the convergence factor β and for several starting values of T_{H2}^{guess}.   ////

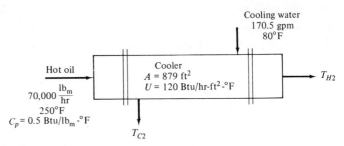

FIGURE 5-6
Countercurrent heat exchanger.

5-1.2 Numerical Integration

As discussed in the introduction to this chapter, the solution of ordinary differential equations (ODE's) on a digital computer involves numerical integration. We will present two of the simplest and most popular numerical-integration algorithms. Both are explicit, self-starting methods. There are many more sophisticated implicit, predictor-corrector techniques that are too complicated to be of much practical use.

The problems of accuracy and stability and computational efficiency (speed) will be explored empirically for one simple numerical example to illustrate the effects of integration step size and type of algorithm.

We need to study the numerical integration of only first-order ODE's. Any higher-order equations, say with Nth-order derivatives, can be reduced to N first-order equations. For example, suppose we have a third-order ODE:

$$\frac{d^3x}{dt^3} + a_2\frac{d^2x}{dt^2} + a_1\frac{dx}{dt} + a_0x = b_1y \qquad (5\text{-}17)$$

If we define the new variables

$$x_1 = x$$
$$x_2 = \frac{dx}{dt} \qquad (5\text{-}18)$$
$$x_3 = \frac{d^2x}{dt^2}$$

Eq. (5-17) becomes

$$\frac{dx_3}{dt} + a_2x_3 + a_1x_2 + a_0x_1 = b_1y$$

131

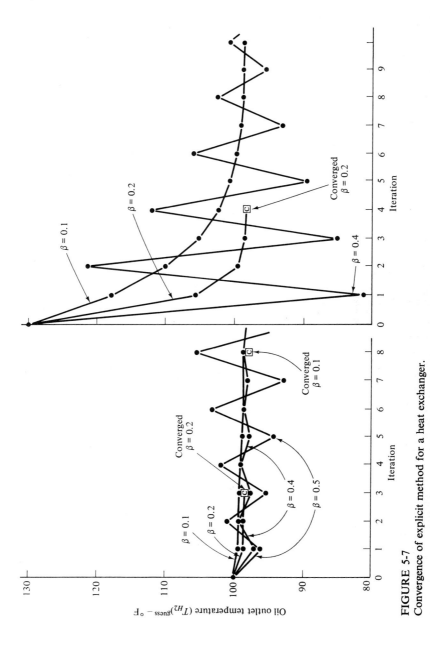

FIGURE 5-7
Convergence of explicit method for a heat exchanger.

Thus we have three first-order ODE's:

$$\frac{dx_1}{dt} = x_2$$

$$\frac{dx_2}{dt} = x_3 \qquad\qquad (5\text{-}19)$$

$$\frac{dx_3}{dt} = b_1 y - a_2 x_3 - a_1 x_2 - a_0 x_1$$

Euler   The simplest possible numerical-integration scheme is Euler (pronounced "oiler") integration, illustrated graphically in Fig. 5-8. Assume we wish to solve the ODE

$$\frac{dx}{dt} = f_{(x,t)} \qquad (5\text{-}20)$$

where f is, in general, a nonlinear function. We need to know where we are starting from; i.e., we need a known initial condition for x.

$$x_{(0)} = x_0 \qquad at\ t = 0 \qquad (5\text{-}21)$$

Now if we move forward in time by a small step Δt to $t = \Delta t$, we can get an estimate of the new value of x at $t = \Delta t$, $x_{(\Delta t)}$, from a linear extrapolation using the initial time rate of change of x. The new value of x is approximately equal to the old value of x plus the product of the derivative of x times the step size.

$$x_{(\Delta t)} = x_{(0)} + \left(\frac{dx}{dt}\right)_{t=0} \Delta t$$

$$x_1 = x_0 + f_{(x_0,0)} \Delta t$$

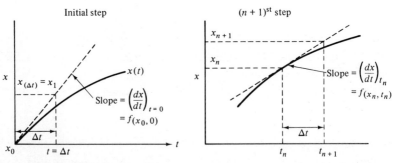

FIGURE 5-8
Graphical representation of Euler integration.

If the step size or integration interval is small enough, this estimate of $x_{(\Delta t)} \equiv x_1$ will be very close to the correct value. To step out in time another Δt, we estimate $x_{(2\Delta t)} \equiv x_2$ from

$$x_{(2\Delta t)} = x_{(\Delta t)} + \left(\frac{dx}{dt}\right)_{t=\Delta t} \Delta t$$

$$x_2 = x_1 + f_{(x_1, \Delta t)} \Delta t$$

Generalizing to the $(n+1)$st step in time,

$$x_{n+1} = x_n + f_{(x_n, t_n)} \Delta t \qquad (5\text{-}22)$$

Euler integration is clearly extremely simple to program.

If we have two simultaneous, coupled ODE's to numerically integrate,

$$\frac{dx_1}{dt} = f_{1(x_1, x_2, t)}$$

$$\frac{dx_2}{dt} = f_{2(x_1, x_2, t)} \qquad (5\text{-}23)$$

the Euler integration algorithms would be

$$x_{1, n+1} = x_{1n} + \Delta t \; f_{1(x_{1n}, x_{2n}, t_n)}$$

$$x_{2, n+1} = x_{2n} + \Delta t \; f_{2(x_{1n}, x_{2n}, t_n)} \qquad (5\text{-}24)$$

Notice that only one derivative evaluation is required per ODE at each time step.

EXAMPLE 5-3   Suppose we have a system that is described by the ODE

$$\frac{dx}{dt} = 1 - x \qquad (5\text{-}25)$$

with $x = 0$ at $t = 0$. A digital computer program using Euler integration is given in Fig. 5-9, together with the printed output. An integration step size (DELTA) of 0.05 is used. Figure 5-10 compares the computed values of x for different step sizes. The analytic solution of Eq. (5-25) is also shown, to indicate the accuracy of the method.

$$x_{(t)} = 1 - e^{-t} \qquad (5\text{-}26)$$

Fairly small steps must be taken (<0.1) if an accurate dynamic curve of $x_{(t)}$ is desired. However, very large steps can be taken (<2) and still have a stable solution, albeit inaccurate.   ////

```
C    EULER INTEGRATION OF ODE -   XDOT + X = 1.
     X=0.
     TIME=0.
     DELTA=0.05
     PRINT 1
  1  FORMAT(1H1,5X,*TIME        X         XDOT*)
100  XDOT=1.-X
     PRINT 2,TIME,X,XDOT
  2  FORMAT(1X,3F10.5)
     X=X+XDOT*DELTA
     TIME=TIME+DELTA
     IF(TIME.GT.2.) STOP
     GO TO 100
     END
```

TIME	X	XDOT
0.00000	0.00000	1.00000
.05000	.05000	.95000
.10000	.09750	.90250
.15000	.14262	.85737
.20000	.18549	.81451
.25000	.22622	.77378
.30000	.26491	.73509
.35000	.30166	.69834
.40000	.33658	.66342
.45000	.36975	.63025
.50000	.40126	.59874
.55000	.43120	.56880
.60000	.45964	.54036
.65000	.48668	.51334
.70000	.51233	.48767
.75000	.53671	.46329
.80000	.55987	.44013
.85000	.58188	.41812
.90000	.60279	.39721
.95000	.62265	.37735
1.00000	.64151	.35849
1.05000	.65944	.34056
1.10000	.67647	.32353
1.15000	.69264	.30736
1.20000	.70801	.29199
1.25000	.72261	.27739
1.30000	.73648	.26352
1.35000	.74966	.25034
1.40000	.76217	.23783
1.45000	.77406	.22594
1.50000	.78536	.21464
1.55000	.79609	.20391
1.60000	.80629	.19371
1.65000	.81597	.18403
1.70000	.82518	.17482
1.75000	.83392	.16608
1.80000	.84222	.15778
1.85000	.85011	.14989
1.90000	.85760	.14240
1.95000	.86472	.13528
2.00000	.87149	.12851

FIGURE 5-9
Euler integration program.

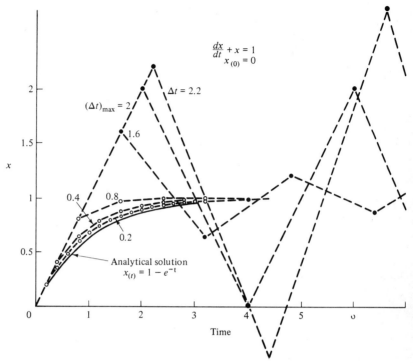

FIGURE 5-10
Effect of integration step size with Euler integration.

Runge-Kutta (fourth order)   The fourth-order Runge-Kutta is perhaps the most popular algorithm in chemical engineering. For the ODE of Eq. (5-20) the Runge-Kutta algorithm is

$$k_1 = \Delta t \, f_{(x_n, t_n)}$$
$$k_2 = \Delta t \, f_{(x_n + \frac{1}{2}k_1, t_n + \frac{1}{2}\Delta t)}$$
$$k_3 = \Delta t \, f_{(x_n + \frac{1}{2}k_2, t_n + \frac{1}{2}\Delta t)} \tag{5-27}$$
$$k_4 = \Delta t \, f_{(x_n + k_3, t_n + \Delta t)}$$
$$x_{n+1} = x_n + \tfrac{1}{6}(k_1 + 2k_2 + 2k_3 + k_4)$$

For numerically integrating two first-order ODE's

$$\frac{dx_1}{dt} = f_{1(x_1, x_2, t)}$$

$$\frac{dx_2}{dt} = f_{2(x_1, x_2, t)}$$

with fourth-order Runge-Kutta, four k's are evaluated for each ODE.

$$k_{11} = \Delta t f_{1(x_{n1},x_{n2},t_n)}$$
$$k_{12} = \Delta t f_{2(x_{n1},x_{n2},t_n)}$$
$$k_{21} = \Delta t f_{1(x_{n1}+\frac{1}{2}k_{11},x_{n2}+\frac{1}{2}k_{12},t_n+\frac{1}{2}\Delta t)}$$
$$k_{22} = \Delta t f_{2(x_{n1}+\frac{1}{2}k_{11},x_{n2}+\frac{1}{2}k_{12},t_n+\frac{1}{2}\Delta t)}$$
$$k_{31} = \Delta t f_{1(x_{n1}+\frac{1}{2}k_{21},x_{n2}+\frac{1}{2}k_{22},t_n+\frac{1}{2}\Delta t)}$$
$$k_{32} = \Delta t f_{2(x_{n1}+\frac{1}{2}k_{21},x_{n2}+\frac{1}{2}k_{22},t_n+\frac{1}{2}\Delta t)}$$
$$k_{41} = \Delta t f_{1(x_{n1}+k_{31},x_{n2}+k_{32},t_n+\Delta t)}$$
$$k_{42} = \Delta t f_{2(x_{n1}+k_{31},x_{n2}+k_{32},t_n+\Delta t)}$$

Then the new values of x_1 and x_2 are calculated:

$$x_{n+1,1} = x_{n1} + \tfrac{1}{6}(k_{11} + 2k_{21} + 2k_{31} + k_{41})$$
$$x_{n+1,2} = x_{n2} + \tfrac{1}{6}(k_{12} + 2k_{22} + 2k_{32} + k_{42})$$

Figure 5-11 gives a computer program and results for the ODE of Eq. (5-25) using fourth-order Runge-Kutta with a step size of 0.2. Figure 5-12 shows the effect of the

```
C   RUNGE-KUTTA INTEGRATION OF ODE - XDOT + X = 1.
    REAL K1,K2,K3,K4
    FD(X)=DELTA*(1.-X)
    DELTA=0.2
    TIME=0.
    X=0.
    PRINT 1
  1 FORMAT(1H1,5X,*TIME      X          K1        K2        K3        K
   14*)
100 K1=FD(X)
    K2=FD(X+K1/2.)
    K3=FD(X+K2/2.)
    K4=FD(X+K3)
    PRINT 2,TIME,X,K1,K2,K3,K4
  2 FORMAT(1X,6F10.5)
    X=X+(K1+2.*K2+2.*K3+K4)/6.
    TIME=TIME+DELTA
    IF(TIME.GT.2.) STOP
    GO TO 100
    END
```

TIME	X	K1	K2	K3	K4
0.00000	0.00000	.20000	.18000	.18200	.16360
.20000	.18127	.16375	.14737	.14901	.13394
.40000	.32968	.13406	.12066	.12200	.10967
.60000	.45118	.10976	.09879	.09988	.08979
.80000	.55067	.08987	.08088	.08178	.07351
1.00000	.63211	.07358	.06622	.06696	.06019
1.20000	.69880	.06024	.05422	.05482	.04928
1.40000	.75340	.04932	.04439	.04488	.04034
1.60000	.79810	.04038	.03634	.03675	.03303
1.80000	.83470	.03306	.02975	.03009	.02704
2.00000	.86466	.02707	.02436	.02463	.02214

FIGURE 5-11
Runge-Kutta integration program.

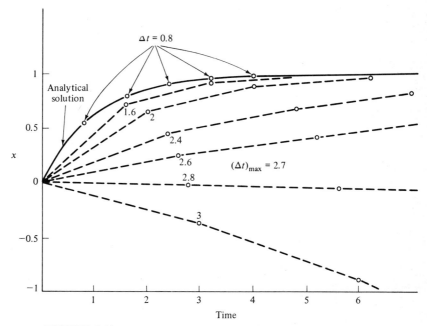

FIGURE 5-12
Effect of integration step size with fourth-order Runge-Kutta integration.

integration interval size on the computed values of x. Three-significant-figure accuracy is obtained for $\Delta t = 0.8$. The maximum stable Δt is 2.7.

Notice that four derivative evaluations are required per ODE at each time step. Thus the computer time required to run Euler with a step size of 0.05 would be about the same as the time required to run Runge-Kutta with a step size of 0.2.

We can draw some very important conclusions from the numerical results obtained in this simple example:

1 If an accurate integration is required, the fourth-order Runge-Kutta is superior to Euler. For the same computing time (with the step size used in Runge-Kutta four times that used in Euler) the Runge-Kutta is more accurate.

2 If accuracy is not required for the particular ODE being integrated, Euler is superior to Runge-Kutta. Euler is stable for step sizes that are almost as large as those for which Runge-Kutta is stable. Since Runge-Kutta requires four derivative evaluations compared with one for Euler, the Euler algorithm will run almost four times as fast.

You may wonder why we would ever be satisfied with anything less than a very accurate integration. The ODE's that make up the mathematical models of most practical chemical engineering systems usually represent a mixture of fast dynamics and slow dynamics. For example, in a distillation column the liquid flow or hydraulic dynamic response occurs fairly rapidly, of the order of a few seconds per tray. The composition dynamics, the rate of change of liquid mole fractions on the trays, is usually quite slow—minutes or even hours for big columns. Systems with this mixture of fast and slow ODE's are called *stiff* systems.

If accurate integration is specified for all the ODE's, the fast ones will require a small step size, much smaller than would be required for the slow ODE's. Therefore it is often quite acceptable to sacrifice accuracy on the fast ODE's and run at a step size for which the fast ODE's are still stable and the slow ODE's are quite accurate. This is illustrated in Fig. 5-13. Since the process is often dominated by the slow ODE's, the inaccuracy of the rapidly changing variables has little effect on the accuracy of the slowly changing variables.

Therefore my experience has been that, for most of the complex systems that chemical engineers have to live with, a simple, easily programmed Euler integration is just as good as the more complex fourth-order Runge-Kutta and very often is even better.

One final practical tip about numerical integration. Many digital simulation experts[1] advocate the use of variable step-size integration. The notion is that small steps must be taken while the process is changing rapidly, but big steps can be taken when variables are changing slowly. In terms of accuracy this is true. If, however, the fastest ODE is running at its numerical stability limit, the step size cannot be increased

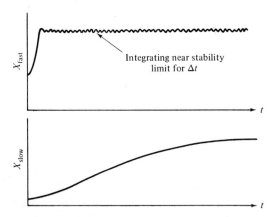

FIGURE 5-13
Responses of fast and slow ODE's.

---

[1] My favorite definition of an expert is "one who is *seldom* in doubt but *often* in error"!

no matter how slowly other variables are changing. And of course this constant checking and readjusting of step size require additional calculations at each step.

Therefore my recommended technique is to start with a very small step size[1] to get the program debugged and running. Then run a few quick empirical tests in which you keep doubling the step size. Check the accuracy of successive runs and continue increasing step size until you find the biggest Δt that gives sufficiently accurate answers and is stable.

5-2 EXAMPLES

Now that we understand some of the numerical-analysis tools, let us illustrate their application to some chemical engineering systems. We will start with two simple examples that we have already looked at on the analog computer. This should provide a good comparison of the problems and advantages of digital versus analog simulation. Then some more realistic complex systems will be simulated.

In all the programs presented the emphasis is not on programming efficiency but on easy translation of the equations and the solution logic into a workable and understandable FORTRAN program.

5-2.1 Three CSTR's in Series

EXAMPLE 5-4 The equations describing the series of three isothermal CSTR's were developed in Sec. 3-2 and simulated in Example 4-1.

$$\frac{dC_{A1}}{dt} = \frac{1}{\tau}(C_{A0} - C_{A1}) - kC_{A1}$$

$$\frac{dC_{A2}}{dt} = \frac{1}{\tau}(C_{A1} - C_{A2}) - kC_{A2} \qquad (5\text{-}28)$$

$$\frac{dC_{A3}}{dt} = \frac{1}{\tau}(C_{A2} - C_{A3}) - kC_{A3}$$

[1] Very small step sizes on some low-accuracy (few "bits") computers may lead to trouble because of roundoff errors. If the number of significant figures is low, the operation of taking differences between numbers that are about the same for small steps will be subject to considerable error. The CDC 6400 computer used for the examples in this book has approximately 14 significant figures since it is a 60-bit (binary digit) machine, and no error problems have been experienced.

Parameter values and initial conditions are

$$\tau = 2 \text{ min}$$
$$k = 0.5 \text{ min}^{-1}$$
$$C_{A1(0)} = 0.4 \text{ mole A/ft}^3$$
$$C_{A2(0)} = 0.2 \text{ mole A/ft}^3$$
$$C_{A3(0)} = 0.1 \text{ mole A/ft}^3$$

The right-hand sides of the ODE's are the functions $f_{(x,t)}$ discussed in Sec. 5-1.2. Let us call these derivatives CA1DOT, CA2DOT, and CA3DOT. At the nth step in time,

$$(\text{CA1DOT})_n = [(C_{A0})_n - (C_{A1})_n]\frac{1}{\tau} - k(C_{A1})_n$$

$$(\text{CA2DOT})_n = [(C_{A1})_n - (C_{A2})_n]\frac{1}{\tau} - k(C_{A2})_n \qquad (5\text{-}29)$$

$$(\text{CA3DOT})_n = [(C_{A2})_n - (C_{A3})_n]\frac{1}{\tau} - k(C_{A3})_n$$

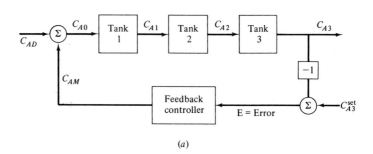

(a)

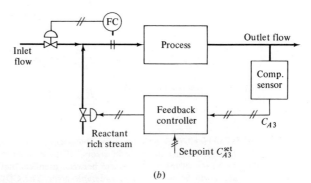

(b)

FIGURE 5-14
Closed-loop three-CSTR process. (a) Idealized system; (b) actual system.

Then to step to the new point in time, using Euler integration with a step-size DELTA,

$$(C_{A1})_{n+1} = (C_{A1})_n + DELTA(CA1DOT)_n$$
$$(C_{A2})_{n+1} = (C_{A2})_n + DELTA(CA2DOT)_n$$
$$(C_{A3})_{n+1} = (C_{A3})_n + DELTA(CA3DOT)_n \qquad (5\text{-}30)$$
$$(TIME)_{n+1} = (TIME)_n + DELTA$$

Converting these equations into a digital program is almost trivial, as shown in Fig. 5-15.

To make life a little more interesting let us include in the simulation a feedback controller (see Prob. 4-1). This gadget looks at the product concentration C_{A3} and makes adjustments in the inlet concentration to the first stage C_{A0} in order to keep C_{A3} at its desired set-point value C_{A3}^{set}. C_{AD} is a disturbance concentration and C_{AM} is a manipulative concentration that is changed by the controller. We assume that

$$C_{A0} = C_{AD} + C_{AM} \qquad (5\text{-}31)$$

```
C     THREE CSTR

C   READ DATA
   1000 READ 1,CAD,TAUI,TAU,XK,DELTA,TPRINT,XKC
        TSTOP=10.
      1 FORMAT(8F10.5)
C   SET INITIAL CONDITIONS
        CA1=.4 $ CA2=.2 $ CA3=.1
        TFLAG=0.
        TIME=0.
        ERINT=0.
        PRINT 4,CAD,XKC,TAUI
      4 FORMAT(1H1,3X,6HCAD = ,F10.5,7X,5HKC = ,F10.5,3X,7HTAUI = ,F10.5)
        PRINT 5
      5 FORMAT(4X,*TIME      CA1       CA2       CA3       CAM*)
    100 ERROR=0.1-CA3
        CAM=0.4+XKC*(ERROR+ERINT/TAUI)
        CAO=CAD+CAM
C   CHECK TIME
        IF (TIME.LT.(TFLAG-.000001)) GO TO 15
        PRINT 11,TIME,CA1,CA2,CA3,CAM
     11 FORMAT(1X,10F10.5)
        TFLAG=TFLAG+TPRINT
     15 IF(TIME.GE.TSTOP) GO TO 1000
C   CALCULATE DERIVATIVES
        CA1DOT=(CAO-CA1)/TAU-XK*CA1
        CA2DOT=(CA1-CA2)/TAU-XK*CA2
        CA3DOT=(CA2-CA3)/TAU-XK*CA3
C     EULER INTEGRATION
        TIME=TIME+DELTA
        CA1=CA1+CA1DOT*DELTA
        CA2=CA2+CA2DOT*DELTA
        CA3=CA3+CA3DOT*DELTA
        ERINT=ERINT+ERROR*DELTA
        GO TO 100
        END
```

FIGURE 5-15
Digital computer program for the three-CSTR example.

CAD =	.60000	KC =	30.00000	TAUI =	5.00000

TIME	CA1	CA2	CA3	CAM
0.00000	.40000	.20000	.10000	.40000
.20000	.41815	.20086	.10003	.39919
.40000	.43276	.20305	.10019	.39411
.60000	.44396	.20601	.10057	.38248
.80000	.45174	.20929	.10116	.36370
1.00000	.45610	.21253	.10194	.33836
1.20000	.45711	.21542	.10286	.30786
1.40000	.45500	.21773	.10385	.27410
1.60000	.45014	.21930	.10484	.23924
1.80000	.44304	.22004	.10576	.20546
2.00000	.43428	.21992	.10653	.17482
2.20000	.42454	.21897	.10712	.14907
2.40000	.41451	.21730	.10746	.12953
2.60000	.40485	.21502	.10759	.11709
2.80000	.39615	.21233	.10745	.11209
3.00000	.38892	.20939	.10709	.11437
3.20000	.38351	.20642	.10652	.12331
3.40000	.38017	.20358	.10578	.13788
3.60000	.37897	.20106	.10494	.15673
3.80000	.37983	.19898	.10404	.17832
4.00000	.38257	.19745	.10314	.20104
4.20000	.38685	.19651	.10229	.22326
4.40000	.39230	.19619	.10154	.24352
4.60000	.39846	.19647	.10092	.26056
4.80000	.40487	.19726	.10046	.27340
5.00000	.41106	.19849	.10018	.28142
5.20000	.41662	.20003	.10008	.28435
5.40000	.42120	.20175	.10015	.28226
5.60000	.42455	.20352	.10036	.27557
5.80000	.42649	.20521	.10069	.26497
6.00000	.42698	.20671	.10111	.25137
6.20000	.42604	.20791	.10158	.23583
6.40000	.42382	.20874	.10205	.21947
6.60000	.42052	.20917	.10249	.20341
6.80000	.41641	.20919	.10288	.18866
7.00000	.41180	.20880	.10317	.17612
7.20000	.40702	.20805	.10337	.16645
7.40000	.40238	.20701	.10344	.16013
7.60000	.39817	.20576	.10340	.15733
7.80000	.39464	.20438	.10324	.15803
8.00000	.39196	.20297	.10298	.16195
8.20000	.39025	.20161	.10265	.16863
8.40000	.38956	.20039	.10226	.17743
8.60000	.38987	.19938	.10183	.18764
8.80000	.39108	.19862	.10141	.19848
9.00000	.39306	.19815	.10100	.20918
9.20000	.39561	.19797	.10064	.21903
9.40000	.39853	.19807	.10034	.22740
9.60000	.40160	.19843	.10012	.23382
9.80000	.40459	.19900	.09998	.23797
10.00000	.40730	.19972	.09992	.23969

FIGURE 5-16
Printed output for the three-CSTR example.

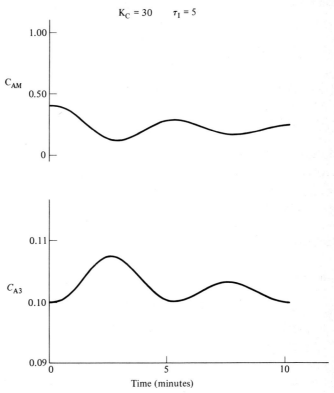

FIGURE 5-17
Plotted results for the three-CSTR example.

This is an idealization of the real physical system in which the control signal from the controller would actually move a control valve that would bleed a stream with a high concentration of reactant A into the feed stream to the process. See Fig. 5-14.

The feedback controller has proportional and integral action. It changes C_{AM} based on the magnitude of the error (the difference between the set point and C_{A3}) and the integral of the error.

$$C_{AM} = 0.4 + K_c \left(E + \frac{1}{\tau_I} \int E_{(t)} \, dt \right) \qquad (5\text{-}32)$$

where $E = C_{A3}^{\text{set}} - C_{A3}$
$\qquad K_c = feedback\ controller\ gain$
$\qquad \tau_I = feedback\ reset\ time,\ min$

To simulate Eq. (5-32) we need to numerically integrate the error to get the integral of the error term.

$$\int E_{(t)} \, dt \equiv \text{ERINT} \qquad (5\text{-}33)$$

The derivative of ERINT is just the error, since

$$\frac{d}{dt}\left(\int E_{(t)} \, dt\right) = E_{(t)} \qquad (5\text{-}34)$$

Therefore the Euler algorithm for generating ERINT is

$$(\text{ERINT})_{n+1} = (\text{ERINT})_n + \text{DELTA}(\text{ERROR})_n \qquad (5\text{-}35)$$

Figure 5-15 gives the digital computer program and Fig. 5-16 the printed output for the system for a step change in C_{AD} to 0.6 at time equals zero. Figure 5-17 is a plot of the results. An integration step size of 0.005 min was used. ////

We will return to this simple system later in Part 4 to discuss the selection of values for K_c and τ_I, that is, the "tuning" of the controller.

5-2.2   Nonisothermal CSTR

EXAMPLE 5-5   The jacketed exothermic CSTR discussed in Sec. 3-5 and simulated on the analog computer in Example 4-4 provides a good example of how much easier it is to simulate a nonlinear problem on the digital computer. We will consider a more general version than we simulated on the analog. Flows and holdups will be variable. First-order kinetics will be assumed so that we can compare the digital and analog results. It would be very easy to use any nth-order kinetics on the digital computer. A proportional level controller manipulates the liquid leaving the tank. The equations describing the system are

$$\frac{dV}{dt} = F_0 - F$$

$$\frac{d}{dt}(VC_A) = F_0 \, C_{A0} - FC_A - VkC_A$$

$$\frac{d}{dt}(VT) = F_0 \, T_0 - FT - \frac{\lambda VkC_A}{\rho C_p} - \frac{UA_H}{\rho C_p}(T - T_J) \qquad (5\text{-}36)$$

$$\frac{dT_J}{dt} = \frac{F_J(T_{J0} - T_J)}{V_J} + \frac{UA_H}{\rho_J V_J C_J}(T - T_J)$$

$$k = \alpha e^{-E/RT}$$

$$F_J = 49.9 - K_c(600 - T)$$

$$F = 40 - 10(48 - V)$$

```
C    NONISOTHERMAL CSTR
C    READ DATA
        READ 1,DELTA,TPRINT,TSTOP
 1000 READ 1,FO,CO,TO,TJO,FJO,XKC
        IF(FO.LE.0.) CALL EXIT
    1 FORMAT(8F10.5)
C  SET INITIAL CONDITIONS
        TIME=0.
        C=.245
        T=600.
        V=48.
        TJ=594.59
        VC=C*V
        VT=T*V
        TFLAG=0.
        PRINT 4,CO,TO,FO,XKC
    4 FORMAT(1H1,5HCO = ,F8.4,5X,5HTO = ,F8.2,5X,5HFO = ,F8.2,
    1 5X,5HKC = ,F8.2)
        PRINT 5
    5 FORMAT(5X,*TIME        C           T           V           F           TJ
    1 QC         FJ        5K*)
  100 XK=7.08E10*EXP(-30000./(1.99*T))
        XK5=XK*5.
        QC=150.*250.*(T-TJ)
C    PROPORTIONAL ONLY FEEDBACK CONTROLLERS
        F=40.-10.*(48.-V)
        FJ=FJO-XKC   *(600.-T)
C    CHECK TIME
   10 IF(TIME.LT.TFLAG) GO TO 15
        PRINT 11,TIME,C,T,V,F,TJ,QC,FJ,XK5
   11 FORMAT(1X,F 9.2,F 9.4,7F 9.1)
        TFLAG=TFLAG+TPRINT
   15 IF(TIME.GE.TSTOP) GO TO 1000
C  CALCULATE DERIVATIVES
        VDOT=FO-F
        VCDOT=FO*CO-F*C-V*XK*C
        VTDOT=FO*TO-F*T+(30000.*V*XK*C-QC)/(.75*50.)
        TJDOT=FJ*(TJO-TJ)/3.85+QC/240.
C  EULER INTEGRATION
        TIME=TIME+DELTA
        V=V+VDOT*DELTA
        VC=VC+VCDOT*DELTA
        VT=VT+VTDOT*DELTA
        TJ=TJ+TJDOT*DELTA
        C=VC/V
        T=VT/V
        GO TO 100
        END
```

FIGURE 5-18
Digital program for the nonisothermal CSTR example.

CO = .5500		TO = 530.00		FO = 40.00		KC = 4.00		
TIME	C	T	V	F	TJ	QC	FJ	5K
0.00	.2450	500.0	48.0	40.0	594.6	202875.0	49.9	4.3
.25	.2532	500.6	48.0	40.0	594.9	211478.4	52.1	4.4
.50	.2569	601.5	48.0	40.0	595.4	227857.6	55.8	4.6
.75	.2575	602.2	48.0	40.0	595.8	240094.6	58.5	4.7
1.00	.2570	602.5	48.0	40.0	595.9	245011.1	59.8	4.8
1.25	.2563	602.6	48.0	40.0	596.0	247302.4	60.1	4.8
1.50	.2558	602.5	48.0	40.0	595.9	246491.7	60.0	4.8
1.75	.2556	602.5	48.0	40.0	595.9	245348.3	59.7	4.8
2.00	.2556	602.4	48.0	40.0	595.9	244597.9	59.6	4.8
2.25	.2557	602.4	48.0	40.0	595.9	244303.1	59.5	4.8
2.50	.2557	602.4	48.0	40.0	595.9	244284.9	59.5	4.8
2.75	.2558	602.4	48.0	40.0	595.9	244364.9	59.5	4.8
3.00	.2558	602.4	48.0	40.0	595.9	244442.1	59.5	4.8
3.25	.2558	602.4	48.0	40.0	595.9	244484.9	59.5	4.8
3.50	.2558	602.4	48.0	40.0	595.9	244497.8	59.5	4.8
3.75	.2558	602.4	48.0	40.0	595.9	244495.4	59.5	4.8
4.00	.2558	602.4	48.0	40.0	595.9	244489.0	59.5	4.8
4.25	.2558	602.4	48.0	40.0	595.9	244484.1	59.5	4.8
4.50	.2558	602.4	48.0	40.0	595.9	244481.8	59.5	4.8
4.75	.2558	602.4	48.0	40.0	595.9	244481.4	59.5	4.8
5.00	.2558	602.4	48.0	40.0	595.9	244481.7	59.5	4.8
5.25	.2558	602.4	48.0	40.0	595.9	244482.2	59.5	4.8
5.50	.2558	602.4	48.0	40.0	595.9	244482.5	59.5	4.8
5.75	.2558	602.4	48.0	40.0	595.9	244482.6	59.5	4.8
6.00	.2558	602.4	48.0	40.0	595.9	244482.6	59.5	4.8

FIGURE 5-19
Printed output for the nonisothermal CSTR example.

Using the numerical values of parameters and initial conditions in Table 4-2, the digital program given in Fig. 5-18 is easily developed. The right-hand side of the four ODE's in Eqs. (5-36) are defined as VDOT, VCDOT, VTDOT, and TJDOT. At each instant in time, Euler integration is used to update the values of V, VC, VT, and TJ. Then C_A and T are found by dividing VC and VT by V.

Figure 5-19 gives the printed output for a 10 percent step increase in feed composition. These results are also plotted in Fig. 5-20. Feedback controller gain K_c is 4, as in the analog simulation.

Figure 5-21 shows the results for a 20 percent feed composition increase. Remember our analog simulation exhibited an oscillatory response for this disturbance. No oscillation was predicted by the digital simulation with a gain of 4. But when K_c was reduced slightly to 2.5 the oscillatory response shown in Fig. 5-21 resulted. Inaccuracy in the generation of the exponential function on the analog is the probable cause of this difference.

Figure 5-22 shows the response of the system to a change in feed rate F_0 from 40 to 50 ft^3/hr.   ////

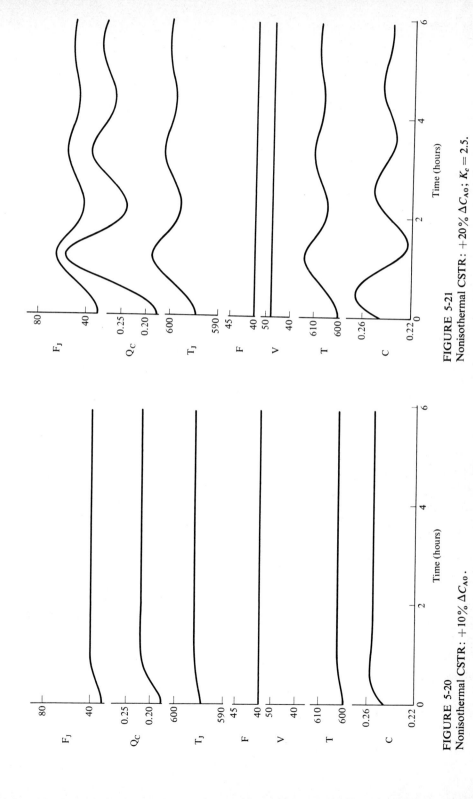

FIGURE 5-20
Nonisothermal CSTR: $+10\% \Delta C_{A0}$.

FIGURE 5-21
Nonisothermal CSTR: $+20\% \Delta C_{A0}$; $K_c = 2.5$.

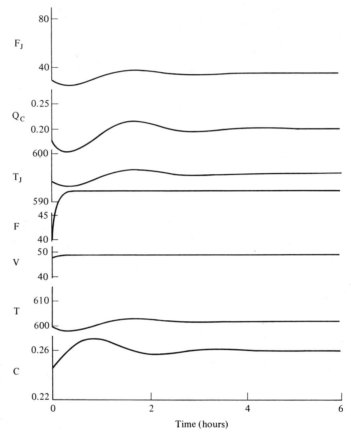

FIGURE 5-22
Nonisothermal CSTR: $+\Delta F_0$.

5-2.3 Binary Distillation Column

EXAMPLE 5-6 The digital simulation of a distillation column is fairly straight-forward. The main complication is the large number of ODE's and algebraic equations that must be solved. We will illustrate the procedure with the simplified binary distillation column for which we developed the equations in Chap. 3 (Sec. 3-10; see Fig. 3-12). Equimolal overflow, constant relative volatility, and theoretical plates are assumed. We have then two ODE's per tray (a total and a component continuity) and two algebraic equations per tray (a liquid hydraulic equation and a vapor-liquid equilibrium equation).

$$\frac{dM_n}{dt} = L_{n+1} - L_n \qquad (5\text{-}37)$$

$$\frac{d}{dt}(M_n x_n) = L_{n+1} x_{n+1} + V y_{n-1} - L_n x_n - V y_n \qquad (5\text{-}38)$$

$$y_n = \frac{\alpha x_n}{1 + (\alpha - 1)\, x_n} \qquad (5\text{-}39)$$

$$L_n = \bar{L}_n + \frac{M_n - \bar{M}_n}{\beta} \qquad (5\text{-}40)$$

We have used a simple linear relationship between the liquid holdup on a tray, M_n, and the liquid flow rate leaving the tray, L_n. β is the hydraulic constant.

Since there are many trays and all are described by Eqs. (5-37) to (5-40) (with some extra terms added at the feed tray), it is logical to use subscripted variables and to evaluate derivatives and integrate using FORTRAN "DO" loops. It also makes sense to use a SUBROUTINE or FUNCTION to find y_n, given x_n, because the same equation is used over and over again.

At any instant in time we know all holdups M_n and liquid compositions x_n. Our simulation logic is:

1 Calculate vapor compositions on all trays from Eq. (5-39).
2 Calculate all liquid flow rates from Eq. (5-40).
3 Evaluate derivatives, the right-hand sides of Eqs. (5-37) and (5-38) (MDOT and MXDOT).
4 Integrate with Euler and start again at step 1 above.

We will assume constant molar holdups in the reflux drum M_{D0} and in the column base–reboiler M_{B0}. Proportional-integral feedback controllers at both ends of the column will change reflux R and vapor-boilup V to control overhead distillate composition x_D and bottoms composition x_B at set-point values of 0.98 and 0.02, respectively.

Figure 5-23 gives the digital program, and Fig. 5-24 shows the printed output. ////

```
C     BINARY DISTILLATION COLUMN DYNAMICS
      DIMENSION XO(25),X(20),Y(20), L(20),M(20)
      DIMENSION MX(20),MDOT(20),MXDOT(20)
      REAL L,M,MO,MB,MX,MDOT,MXDOT,MDO,MO,MBO,KCD,KCB
      EQUIL(XX)=ALPHA*XX/(1.+(ALPHA-1.)*XX)
      ALPHA=2.
      READ 2,NT,NS,MDO,MBO,MO,RO,VO,FO,BETA
    2 FORMAT(2I5,7F10.5)
      READ 1,XBO,(XO(N),N=1,NT),XDO
    1 FORMAT(8F10.5)
      KCD=1000.
      KCB=1000.
      TAUDO=5.
      TAUBO=1.25
      DELTA=.005
      STOP=20.
      TPRINT=.5
 1000 READ 1,XF,F
      IF(XF.LE.0.) CALL EXIT
      PRINT 550,XF,F
  550 FORMAT(7X,*XF = *,F10.5,*   F = *,F10.2)
C   INITIAL CONDITIONS
      TIME=0.
      TFLAG=0.
      ERINTD=0.
      ERINTB=0.
      XB=XBO
      XBSET=XBO
      DO 3 N=1,NT
      X(N)=XO(N)
      M(N)=MO
      MX(N)=M(N)*X(N)
      L(N)=RO+FO
      IF(N.GT.NS)  L(N)=RO
    3 CONTINUE
      XD=XDO
      PRINT 5
    5 FORMAT(7X,*TIME       XB        X5        X10       X15       XD
     1     R         V*)
C  EVALUATE DERIVATIVES
  100 DO 20 N=1,NT
      Y(N)=EQUIL(X(N))
      L(N)=RO+FO+(M(N)-MO)/BETA
      IF(N.GT.NS)   L(N)=RO+(M(N)-MO)/BETA
   20 CONTINUE
      YB=EQUIL(XB)
C     TWO PI FEEDBACK CONTROLLERS
      ERRB=XBSET-XB
      ERRD=.98-XD
      V=VO-KCB *(ERRB+ERINTB/TAUBO)
      R=RO+KCD *(ERRD+ERINTD/TAUDO)
      D=V-R
      B= L(1)-V
      IF(R.LT.0.) GO TO 500
      IF(V.LT.0.) GO TO 500
      IF(D.LT.0.) D=0.
      IF(B.LT.0.) GO TO 500
      XBDOT=( L(1)*X(1)-V*YB-B*XB)/MBO
      MDOT(1)=L(2)-L(1)
      MXDOT(1)=V*(YB-Y(1))+ L(2)*X(2)- L(1)*X(1)
      NSM1=NS-1
      DO 102 N=2,NSM1
      MDOT(N)= L(N+1)- L(N)
  102 MXDOT(N)=V*(Y(N-1)-Y(N))+ L(N+1)*X(N+1)- L(N)*X(N)
C  FEED PLATE
      MDOT(NS)= L(NS+1)- L(NS)+F
      MXDOT(NS)=V*(Y(NS-1)-Y(NS))+ L(NS+1)*X(NS+1)- L(NS)*X(NS)+F*XF
      NSP1=NS+1
```

```
      NTM1=NT-1
      DO 103 N=NSP1,NTM1
      MDOT(N) = L(N+1)- L(N)
  103 MXDOT(N)=V*(Y(N-1)-Y(N))+ L(N+1)*X(N+1)- L(N)*X(N)
      MDOT(NT)=R- L(NT)
      MXDOT(NT)=V*(Y(NT-1)-Y(NT))+R*XD- L(NT)*X(NT)
      XDDOT=V*(Y(NT)-XD)/MDO
      IF(TIME.LT.TFLAG-.0001) GO TO 200
      PRINT 6,TIME,XB,X(5),X(10),X(15),XD,R,V
    6 FORMAT(1X,F10.2,5F10.5,2F10.2)
      TFLAG=TFLAG+TPRINT
  200 IF(TIME.GT.STOP) GO TO 500
C     EULER INTEGRATION
      TIME=TIME+DELTA
      XB=XB+DELTA*XBDOT
      DO 201 N=1,NT
      M(N)=M(N)+MDOT(N)*DELTA
      MX(N)=MX(N)+MXDOT(N)*DELTA
      X(N)=MX(N)/M(N)
      IF(X(N).LT.0.) GO TO 500
      IF(X(N).GT.1.) GO TO 500
  201 CONTINUE
      XD=XD+XDDOT*DELTA
      ERINTD=ERINTD+ERRD*DELTA
      ERINTB=ERINTB+ERRB*DELTA
      GO TO 100
  500 CONTINUE
      GO TO 1000
      END
```

FIGURE 5-23
Digital program for a binary distillation column.

XF =	.55000	F =	100.00				
TIME	XB	X5	X10	X15	XD	R	V
0.00	.02000	.18622	.47688	.74345	.98000	128.01	178.01
.50	.02014	.19570	.51310	.74940	.98000	128.01	178.16
1.00	.02107	.21174	.52426	.76049	.98010	127.91	179.31
1.50	.02217	.22038	.53026	.76847	.98034	127.64	181.06
2.00	.02275	.22209	.53229	.77217	.98061	127.33	182.65
2.50	.02268	.21881	.53141	.77222	.98076	127.11	183.69
3.00	.02212	.21287	.52879	.76993	.98077	127.02	184.10
3.50	.02132	.20639	.52560	.76672	.98065	127.07	183.99
4.00	.02051	.20104	.52282	.76381	.98047	127.19	183.55
4.50	.01987	.19777	.52109	.76196	.98030	127.32	182.98
5.00	.01950	.19679	.52057	.76142	.98018	127.42	182.47
5.50	.01939	.19756	.52106	.76198	.98014	127.45	182.14
6.00	.01950	.19956	.52209	.76315	.98016	127.41	182.02
6.50	.01972	.20162	.52320	.76438	.98022	127.33	182.08
7.00	.01995	.20314	.52400	.76525	.98029	127.24	182.25
7.50	.02012	.20380	.52434	.76557	.98034	127.15	182.43
8.00	.02019	.20362	.52422	.76537	.98036	127.09	182.56
8.50	.02016	.20289	.52381	.76484	.98035	127.07	182.61

FIGURE 5-24
Printed output from the binary distillation program.

5-2.4 Multicomponent Distillation Column

EXAMPLE 5-7 The extension of the simple ideal binary system considered in the preceding example to a multicomponent column is basically merely a question of adding more equations per tray. The general model developed in Sec. 3-11 is simulated in the digital program given in Fig. 5-25.

The specific column simulated is assumed to have the following equipment configurations and conditions:

1 There is one feed plate onto which vapor feed and liquid feed are introduced.
2 Pressure is constant on each tray but varies linearly up the column from P_B in the base to P_D at the top (psia).
3 Coolant and steam dynamics are negligible in condenser and reboiler.
4 Vapor and liquid products D_V and D_L are taken off the reflux drum and are in equilibrium. Dynamics of vapor space in reflux drum are negligible.
5 Liquid hydraulics are calculated from the Francis weir formula.
6 Volumetric holdups in the reflux drum and column base are held constant by changing bottoms product B and liquid distillate D_L.
7 Dynamic changes in internal energy on the trays are negligible compared with the latent-heat effects, so the energy equation on each tray [Eq. (3-99] is just algebraic.
8 Reflux R and heat input to the reboiler, Q_B, are constant. If desired, the program can easily be changed to use R (or D_L) to hold a temperature or a composition in the top of the column and to use Q_B to hold a temperature or a composition in the bottom of the column. There are two degrees of freedom, and so two variables can be specified.

As can be seen in Fig. 5-25, the program consists of the following sections that are essentially the same as the steps followed in the binary case:

1 Read data on the column size, components, physical properties, feeds, and initial conditions (T, x, and L).
2 Calculate initial tray holdups and the pressure profile.
3 Calculate temperatures and vapor compositions from the vapor-liquid equilibrium data, using subroutine EQUIL (Raoult's law in the example).
4 Calculate liquid and vapor enthalpies, using subroutine ENTH.
5 Calculate vapor rates on all trays, using the energy equation.
6 Evaluate all derivatives—total and component holdups.
7 Integrate.
8 Calculate new liquid rates from new holdups, using subroutine HYDRAU.
9 Go back to step 3 and repeat.

Table 5-1 gives a list of terms for input and output variables.   /////

```
C     MULTICOMPONENT DISTILLATION COLUMN DYNAMICS
      REAL MW,LO,MVB,MVD,MWA,MV,LV,M,L,MB,MD
      COMMON NJ,MW(10),DENS(10),C1(10),C2(10),C3(10),BPT(10),AVP(10),
     1 BVP(10)
      DIMENSION LV(50),L(50),P(50),XF(10),YF(10),DXD(10),YAV(10),
     1    YY(10),HL(50),HV(50),V(50),DM(50),DXM(50,10),XM(50,10),DXB(10)
      DIMENSION NAME(10)              ,T(50),XD(10),X(50,10),Y(50,10),LD(
     150),XD(10),YB(10),YD(10),XX(10),MV(50),M(50)
C.....................
C     READ COLUMN DATA
 2000 READ(5,1) NT,NS,NJ,WHS,WHR,DS,DR,WLS,WLR,MVB,MVD
    1 FORMAT (3I5,10F6.2)
      IF (NT .LE. 0) STOP
      WRITE(6,300)
  300 FORMAT(1H1,5X,*NT   NS   NJ   WHS   WHR   DS   DR   WLS   WLR
     1 MVB   MVD*)
      WRITE(6,13) NT,NS,NJ,WHS,WHR,DS,DR,WLS,WLR,MVB,MVD
C.....................
C     READ PHYSICAL PROPERTY DATA
      WRITE(6,301)
  301 FORMAT(1X,*NAME    MW        DENS   HVAP    BPT    HCAPV   HCAPL
     1 VP1    T1      VP2    T2*)
      DO 5 J=1,NJ
      READ(5,6) NAME(J),MW(J),DENS(J),HVAP(J),BPT(J),HCAPV,HCAPL,VP1,T1,VP2
     1,T2
    6 FORMAT (A6,11F5.2)
      WRITE(6,7) NAME(J),MW(J),DENS(J),HVAP,BPT(J),HCAPV,HCAPL,VP1,T1,VP
     12,T2
      AVP(J)=(T1+460.)*(T2+460.)*ALOG(VP2/VP1)/(T1-T2)
      BVP(J)=ALOG(VP2)-AVP(J)/(T2+460.)
      C2(J) = HCAPV*MW(J)
      C3(J) = HCAPL*MW(J)
    5 C1(J) =    BPT(J)*(C3(J)-C2(J)) +HVAP*MW(J)
C.....................
C     READ FEED
      READ(5,10) TFL,FL,(XF(J),J=1,NJ)
      READ(5,10) TFV,FV,(YF(J),J=1,NJ)
      WRITE(6,306)
  306 FORMAT(4X,*FL        TFL        XF1      XF2      XF3      XF4
     1    XF5*)
      WRITE(6,308) FL,TFL,(XF(J),J=1,NJ)
  308 FORMAT(1X,2F10.2,5E10.2)
      WRITE(6,307)
  307 FORMAT(4X,*FV        TFV        YF1      YF2      YF3      YF4
     1    YF5*)
      WRITE(6,308) FV,TFV,(YF(J),J=1,NJ)
      CALL ENTH(TFL,XF,YF,HLF,HVF)
    7 FORMAT(1X,A6    ,11F8.2)
    8 FORMAT(1X,2F8.2,10E10.2)
    9 FORMAT(1X,10F8.2)
   10 FORMAT (12F6.2)
   11 FORMAT(5X,2F8.2,10E10.2)
   12 FORMAT(1X,I3,1X,2F8.2,10E10.2)
   13 FORMAT(1X,3I5,5X,10F6.2)
C.....................
C     READ CONDITIONS
      READ (5,10) PD,PB,QB,R,DV,EFF
      WRITE(6,304)
  304 FORMAT(6X,*PD        PB        QB        R     DV    EFF*)
      WRITE(6,9 )PD,PB,QB,R,DV,EFF
C.....................
C     READ INITIAL CONDITIONS
      WRITE(6,305)
  305 FORMAT(4X,*N    TEMP     L        X1       X2       X3       X
     14        X5*)
```

FIGURE 5-25
Digital program for multicomponent distillation.

```
      READ (5,18 )TB,(XB(J),J=1,NJ)
      BLANK=0.
      WRITE(6,11) TB,BLANK,(XB(J),J=1,NJ)
      DO 15 N=1,NT
      READ (5,17 )T(N),LO(N),(X(N,J),J=1,NJ)
   15 WRITE(6,12)N,T(N),LO(N),(X(N,J),J=1,NJ)
      READ (5,18 )TD,(XD(J),J=1,NJ)
      WRITE(6,11 )TD,R,(XD(J),J=1,NJ)
C...................
C     CALL INITIAL HOLDUPS
      CALL MWDENS(TB,XB,MWA,DENSA)
      MB = MVB*DENSA/MWA
      DO 20 N=1,NS
      DO 21 J=1,NJ
   21 XX(J) = X(N,J)
      CALL MWDENS(T(N),XX,MWA,DENSA)
      LV(N) = LO(N) * MWA/DENSA
      L(N) = LO(N)
      HFOW = (LV(N)/(999.*WLS))**.66667
      MV(N) = (HFOW*WHS/12.)*3.1416*DS*DS/(4.*144.)
   20 M(N) = MV(N)*DENSA/MWA
      NSP1 = NS + 1
      DO 25 N=NSP1,NT
      DO 26 J=1,NJ
   26 XX(J) = X(N,J)
      CALL MWDENS(T(N),XX,MWA,DENSA)
      LV(N) = LO(N) * MWA/DENSA
      L(N) = LO(N)
      HFOW = (LV(N)/(999.*WLR))**.66667
      MV(N) = (HFOW*WHR/12.)*3.1416*DR*DR/(4.*144.)
   25 M(N) = MV(N) * DENSA/MWA
      DO 30 N=1,NT
      DO 31 J=1,NJ
      XM(N,J) = M(N)*X(N,J)
   31 CONTINUE
   30 CONTINUE
      CALL MWDENS(TD,XD,MWA,DENSA)
      MD=MVD  *DENSA/MWA
C     CALCULATE PRESSURE PROFILE
      DO 35 N=1,NT
   35 P(N)=(PB-(N*(PB-PD))/NT)
      READ(5,16) DELTA,TSTOP,TPRINT,FLPUN
      WRITE(6,37)
   37 FORMAT(1X,* DELTA      TSTOP       TPRINT*)
      WRITE(6,36) DELTA,TSTOP,TPRINT
   36 FORMAT(1X,10F10.5)
      TIME = 0.
      TFLAG = 0.
      NTM1 = NT - 1
      NSP2 = NS + 2
      NSM1 = NS - 1
C....................
C....................
  100 CONTINUE
      CALL EQUIL (TB,XB,YB,PB)
      CALL ENTH (TB,XB,YB,HLB,HVB)
      DO 105 J=1,NJ
  105 XX(J)=X(1,J)
      CALL EQUIL(T(1),XX,YY,P(1))
      DO 106 J=1,NJ
      Y(1,J)=YB(J)+EFF*(YY(J)-YB(J))
  106 YY(J)=Y(1,J)
      CALL ENTH(T(1),XX,YY,HL(1),HV(1))
      DO 110 N = 2,NS
      DO 111 J = 1,NJ
```

```
111 XX(J)=X(N,J)
    CALL EQUIL(T(N),XX,YY,P(N))
    DO 112 J = 1,NJ
    Y(N,J) =(YY(J) -Y(N-1,J))*EFF+Y(N-1,J)
112 YY(J)=Y(N,J)
    CALL ENTH (T(N),XX,YY,HL(N),HV(N))
110 CONTINUE
    DO 113 J=1,NJ
113 XX(J)=X(NSP1,J)
    CALL EQUIL(T(NSP1),XX,YY,P(NSP1))
    DO 114 J=1,NJ
    YAV(J)=(YF(J)*FV+Y(NS,J)*V(N9))/(V(NS)+FV)
    Y(NSP1,J)=(YY(J)-YAV(J))*EFF+YAV(J)
114 YY(J)=Y(NSP1,J)
    CALL ENTH(T(NSP1),XX,YY,HL(NSP1),HV(NSP1))
    DO 115 N=NSP2,NT
    DO 116 J=1,NJ
116 XX(J)=X(N,J)
    CALL EQUIL(T(N),XX,YY,P(N))
    DO 117 J=1,NJ
    Y(N,J) =(YY(J) -Y(N-1,J))*EFF+Y(N-1,J)
117 YY(J)=Y(N,J)
    CALL ENTH (T(N),XX,YY,HL(N),HV(N))
115 CONTINUE
    CALL EQUIL(TD,XD,YD,PD)
    CALL ENTH(TD,XD,YD,HLD,HVD)
C.....................
C     CALCULATE VAPOR RATES
C.....................
    VB = (QB*1000000.-L(1)*(HLB-HL(1)))/(HVB-HLB)
    B = L(1)-VB
    IF (B .LT. 0.) STOP
    V(1) = (HL(2)*L(2)+HVB*VB-HL(1)*L(1))/HV(1)
    DO 120 N = 2,NSM1
    V(N) = (HL(N+1)*L(N+1)+HV(N-1)*V(N-1)-HL(N)*L(N))/HV(N)
120 CONTINUE
    V(NS) = (HL(NSP1)*L(NSP1)+HV(NSM1)*V(NSM1)-HL(NS)*L(NS)+HLF*FL)/HV
   1(NS)
    V(NSP1) = (HL(NSP2)*L(NSP2)+HV(NS  )*V(NS  )+HVF*FV-HL(NSP1)*L(NSP
   11))/HV(NSP1)
    DO 130 N = NSP2,NTM1
130 V(N) = (HL(N+1)*L(N+1)+HV(N-1)*V(N-1)-HL(N)*L(N))/HV(N)
    V(NT) = (HLD*R+HV(NTM1)*V(NTM1)-HL(NT)*L(NT))/HV(NT)
    DL=V(NT)-DV-R
C.....................
C     EVALUATE DERIVATIVES
C.....................
    DM(1) = L(2) + VB-V(1)-L(1)
    DO 140 N = 2,NSM1
140 DM(N) = L(N+1) + V(N-1)-L(N)-V(N)
    DM(NS) = L(NSP1) + FL + V(NSM1) - L(NS) - V(NS)
    DM(NSP1) = L(NSP2) + FV + V(NS) - L(NSP1) - V(NSP1)
    DO 150 N = NSP2,NTM1
150 DM(N) = L(N+1) + V(N-1)-L(N)-V(N)
    DM(NT) = R + V(NTM1) - L(NT) - V(NT)
    DO 160 J=1,NJ
    DXB(J) = (X(1,J)*L(1)-YB(J)*VB-XB(J)*B)/MB
    DXM(1,J) = X(2,J)*L(2)+YB(J)*VB-X(1,J)*L(1)-Y(1,J)*V(1)
    DO 165 N=2,NSM1
165 DXM(N,J) = X(N+1,J)*L(N+1)+Y(N-1,J)*V(N-1)-X(N,J)*L(N)-V(N)*Y(N,J)
    DXM(NS,J) = X(NSP1,J)*L(NSP1)+Y(NSM1,J)*V(NSM1)-X(NS,J)*L(NS)-V(NS
   1)*Y(NS,J)+FL*XF(J)
    DXM(NSP1,J) = X(NSP2,J)*L(NSP2)+Y(NS,J)*V(NS)-X(NSP1,J)*L(NSP1)-V(
   1NSP1  )*Y(NSP1,J)+FV*YF(J)
    DO 170 N = NSP2,NTM1
```

FIGURE 5-25 (*Continued*)

```
  170 DXM(N,J) = X(N+1,J)*L(N+1)+Y(N-1,J)*V(N-1)-X(N,J)*L(N)-V(N)*Y(N,J)
      DXM(NT,J)= XD(J)*R+Y(NTM1,J)*V(NTM1)-X(NT,J)*L(NT)-Y(NT,J)*V(NT)
      DXD(J)=(V(NT)*Y(NT,J)-DV*YD(J)-(R+DL)*XD(J))/MD
  160 CONTINUE
      IF (TIME.GT.TSTOP) GO TO 400
      IF (TIME .LT. TFLAG) GO TO 210
      WRITE(6,201)
  201 FORMAT (5X,*TIME     T           X1          X2          X3          X4
     1     X5          L          V         M         DB*)
      WRITE(6,202) TIME,TB,(XB(J),J=1,NJ),B,VB,MB,DB
  202 FORMAT(1X,2F8.3,5E10.2,2F10.2,2F10.3)
      DO 203 N=1,NT
  203 WRITE(6,204)  N,T(N),(X(N,J),J=1,NJ),L(N),V(N),M(N)
  204 FORMAT(3X,I3,3X,F8.1,5E10.2,2F10.2,F10.3)
      WRITE(6,205) TD,(XD(J),J=1,NJ),R ,DV,MD
  205 FORMAT (9X,F8.1,5E10.2,2F10.2,F10.3)
      WRITE(6,206) (YD(J),J=1,NJ),DL
  206 FORMAT(17X,5E10.2,2F10.2)
      TFLAG = TFLAG + TPRINT
C.....................
C     INTEGRATION ALA EULER
C.....................
  210 TIME = TIME + DELTA
      DO 215 N = 1,NT
  215 M(N) = M(N) + DM(N) * DELTA
      DO 220 J = 1,NJ
      XB(J) = XB(J) + DXB(J) * DELTA
      IF (XB(J) .LT. 0.) XB(J) = 0.0
      IF (XB(J) .GT. 1.) XB(J) = 1.
      DO 225 N = 1,NT
      XM(N,J) = XM(N,J) + DXM(N,J)*DELTA
      X(N,J) = XM(N,J)/M(N)
      IF (X(N,J).GT.1.) X(N,J) = 1.
      IF (X(N,J) .LT. 0.) X(N,J) = 0.0
  225 CONTINUE
      XD(J)=XD(J)+DXD(J)*DELTA
      IF(XD(J).LT.0.) XD(J)=0.
      IF(XD(J).GT.1.) XD(J)=1.
  220 CONTINUE
C     CALC NEW LIQUID RATES
      DO 270 N=1,NS
      DO 271 J=1,NJ
  271 XX(J)=X(N,J)
      CALL HYDRAU(M(N),T(N),XX,L(N),WHS,WLS,DS)
  270 CONTINUE
      DO 273 N=NSP1,NT
      DO 275 J=1,NJ
  275 XX(J)=X(N,J)
      CALL HYDRAU(M(N),T(N),XX,L(N),WHR,WLR,DR)
  273 CONTINUE
      GO TO 100
  400 IF(FLPUN.LT.0.) GO TO 2000
   17 FORMAT (2F5.1,5E10.3)
   18 FORMAT (F10.2,5E10.3)
      WRITE(7,18) TB,(XB(J),J=1,NJ)
      DO 401 N=1,NT
  401 WRITE(7,17)T(N),L(N),(X(N,J),J=1,NJ)
      WRITE(7,18) TD,(XD(J),J=1,NJ)
      GO TO 2000
      END
```

```
      SUBROUTINE HYDRAU(M,T,X,L,WH,WL,DCOL)
      REAL M,L,MW,MWA
      COMMON NJ,MW(10),DENS(10),C1(10),C2(10),C3(10),BPT(10),AVP(10),
     1 BVP(10)
      DIMENSION X(10)
      CALL MWDENS(T,X,MWA,DENSA)
      CONST=              183.2*M*MWA/(DENSA*DCOL*DCOL)-WH/12.
      IF(CONST.LE.0.) GO TO 10
      L=DENSA*WL* 999.*((183.2*M*MWA/(DENSA*DCOL*DCOL)-WH/12.)**1.5)/MWA
      RETURN
   10 L=0.
      RETURN
      END


      SUBROUTINE ENTH(T,X,Y,HL,HV)
      COMMON NJ,MW(10),DENS(10),C1(10),C2(10),C3(10),BPT(10),AVP(10),
     1 BVP(10)
      DIMENSION X(10),Y(10)
      HL=0.0
      HV=0.0
      DO 1 J=1,NJ
      HL=HL+X(J)*C3(J)*T
      HV=HV+Y(J)*(C1(J)+C2(J)*T)
    1 CONTINUE
      RETURN
      END


      SUBROUTINE MWDENS(T,X,MWA,DENSA)
      COMMON NJ,MW(10),DENS(10),C1(10),C2(10),C3(10),BPT(10),AVP(10),
     1 BVP(10)
      DIMENSION X(10)
      REAL MW,MWA
      DENSA=0.0
      MWA=0.
      DO 1 J=1,NJ
      MWA=X(J)*MW(J)+MWA
    1 DENSA=X(J)*DENS(J) +DENSA
      RETURN
      END

      SUBROUTINE EQUIL(T,X,Y,P)
      COMMON NJ,MW(10),DENS(10),C1(10),C2(10),C3(10),BPT(10),AVP(10),
     1 BVP(10)
      DIMENSION X(10),Y(10),PO(10)
      LOOP=0
   10 LOOP=LOOP+1
      IF(LOOP.GT.50) GO TO 30
      SUMY=0.0
      DO 15 J=1,NJ
      PO(J)=EXP(BVP(J)+AVP(J)/(T+460.))
      Y(J)=PO(J)*X(J)  /P
   15 SUMY=SUMY+Y(J)
      IF(ABS(SUMY-1.).LT..00001)RETURN
      F=SUMY*P-P
      FSLOPE=0.
      TSQ=(T+460.)**2
      DO 20 J=1,NJ
   20 FSLOPE=FSLOPE-AVP(J)*X(J)*PO(J)/TSQ
      T=T-F/FSLOPE
      GO TO 10
   30 WRITE(6,21)
   21 FORMAT(1X,*TEMP LOOP*)
      STOP
      END
```

FIGURE 5-25 (*Continued*)

NT	NS	NJ	WHS	WHR	DS	DR	WLS	WLF	AVR	AVD
15	5	5	.75	1.25	72.00	72.00	48.00	48.00	10.00	10.00

NAME	MW	DENS	HVAP	PPT	HCAPV	HCAPL	VP1	T1	VP2	T2
LLK	30.00	40.00	100.00	10.00	.20	.60	14.70	10.00	50.00	30.00
LK	50.00	40.00	90.00	90.00	.40	.61	14.70	90.00	500.00	200.00
INTER	90.00	60.00	73.00	150.00	.30	.50	14.70	150.00	150.00	200.00
HK	130.00	70.00	80.00	210.00	.30	.40	14.70	210.00	150.00	300.00
HHK	300.00	90.00	80.00	360.00	.30	.40	14.70	360.00	150.00	420.00

FL	TFL	XF1	XF2	XF3	XF4	XF5
800.00	120.00	5.00E-02	6.00E-01	1.00E-02	3.00E-01	4.00E-02

FV	TFV	YF1	YF2	YF3	YF4	YF5
200.00	120.00	4.00E-01	5.30E-01	2.00E-02	5.00E-02	0.

PD	PB	QB	P	DV	EFF
19.70	21.20	5.00	400.00	200.00	.50

N	TEMP	L	X1	X2	X3	X4	X5
	201.58	0.	0.	7.25E-03	4.89E-02	8.36E-01	1.09E-01
1	154.90	740.10	9.99E-12	1.10E-01	2.40E-01	6.07E-01	4.33E-02
2	132.60	814.40	1.56E-09	2.86E-01	2.02E-01	4.77E-01	3.93E-02
3	120.20	892.00	1.82E-07	4.57E-01	1.31E-01	3.76E-01	3.59E-02
4	114.00	961.10	1.33E-05	5.72E-01	8.03E-02	3.14E-01	3.33E-02
5	108.40	986.00	7.59E-04	6.34E-01	4.96E-02	2.94E-01	3.25E-02
6	101.20	320.00	1.12E-03	8.18E-01	8.66E-02	9.42E-02	1.74E-06
7	98.20	381.90	1.29E-03	9.10E-01	4.46E-02	4.40E-02	7.76E-07
8	96.90	409.00	1.36E-03	9.53E-01	2.34E-02	2.18E-02	3.71E-07
9	96.20	423.70	1.40E-03	9.75E-01	1.24E-02	1.11E-02	1.81E-07
10	95.80	431.20	1.42E-03	9.86E-01	6.94E-03	5.62E-03	8.93E-08
11	95.50	435.20	1.43E-03	9.92E-01	3.74E-03	2.86E-03	4.40E-08
12	95.30	437.50	1.44E-03	9.95E-01	1.99E-03	1.45E-03	2.16E-08
13	95.10	438.70	1.44E-03	9.97E-01	1.04E-03	7.18E-04	1.04E-08
14	94.90	439.50	1.45E-03	9.98E-01	5.13E-04	3.42E-04	4.84E-09
15	94.20	438.60	1.75E-03	9.98E-01	2.36E-04	1.49E-04	2.05E-09
	77.20	400.00	1.74E-02	9.82E-01	8.24E-05	4.93E-05	6.59E-10

DELTA	TSTOP	TPRINT
.00003	.03000	.00500

TIME	T	X1	X2	X3	X4	X5	L	V	M	CB
0.000	201.578	0.	7.25E-03	4.89E-02	8.36E-01	1.09E-01	298.12	441.98	4.902	5.000
1	154.9	9.99E-12	1.10E-01	2.40E-01	6.07E-01	4.33E-02	740.10	516.30	2.402	
2	132.6	1.56E-09	2.86E-01	2.02E-01	4.79E-01	3.93E-02	814.40	593.76	2.554	
3	120.2	1.82E-07	4.57E-01	1.31E-01	3.76E-01	3.59E-02	892.00	651.62	2.709	
4	114.0	1.33E-05	5.72E-01	8.03E-02	3.14E-01	3.33E-02	961.10	687.30	2.840	
5	108.4	7.59E-04	6.34E-01	4.96E-02	2.84E-01	3.25E-02	986.00	821.20	2.899	
6	101.2	1.12E-03	8.18E-01	8.66E-02	9.42E-02	1.74E-05	320.00	1067.19	3.055	
7	98.2	1.29E-03	9.10E-01	4.46E-02	4.40E-02	7.76E-07	381.90	1102.35	3.280	
8	96.9	1.36E-03	9.53E-01	2.38E-02	2.18E-02	3.71E-07	409.60	1120.40	3.388	
9	96.2	1.40E-03	9.75E-01	1.24E-02	1.11E-02	1.81E-07	423.70	1129.92	3.444	
10	95.8	1.42E-03	9.86E-01	6.94E-03	5.62E-03	8.93E-08	431.20	1134.90	3.474	
11	95.5	1.43E-03	9.92E-01	3.74E-03	2.86E-03	4.40E-08	435.20	1137.77	3.490	
12	95.3	1.44E-03	9.95E-01	1.99E-03	1.45E-03	2.16E-08	437.50	1139.28	3.499	
13	95.1	1.44E-03	9.97E-01	1.04E-03	7.18E-04	1.04E-08	438.70	1140.18	3.503	
14	94.9	1.45E-03	9.98E-01	5.13E-04	3.42E-04	4.84E-09	429.90	1139.31	3.506	
15	94.2	1.75E-03	9.98E-01	2.36E-04	1.49E-04	2.05E-09	438.60	1100.76	3.506	
	77.3	1.74E-02	9.82E-01	8.24E-05	4.93E-05	5.59E-10	400.00	200.00	8.056	
		5.56E-01	4.44E-01	9.09E-07	2.69E-07	8.05E-19	500.76			

TIME	T	X1	X2	X3	X4	X5	L	V	M	CB
.005	201.784	5.83E-14	7.16E-03	4.82E-02	8.37E-01	1.08E-01	295.35	441.99	4.902	5.000
1	155.1	0.	1.09E-01	2.33E-01	6.09E-01	4.33E-02	737.34	516.78	2.400	
2	132.7	1.55E-09	2.85E-01	2.02E-01	4.74E-01	3.94E-02	811.82	594.99	2.552	
3	120.3	1.80E-07	4.56E-01	1.31E-01	3.77E-01	3.59E-02	889.77	663.61	2.709	
4	114.1	1.32E-05	5.72E-01	8.01E-02	3.15E-01	3.34E-02	958.23	689.87	2.840	
5	108.4	7.57E-04	6.33E-01	4.94E-02	2.25E-01	3.25E-02	964.42	824.01	2.899	
6	101.2	1.12E-03	8.18E-01	8.64E-02	9.45E-02	1.76E-06	318.33	1085.97	3.054	
7	98.2	1.29E-03	9.10E-01	4.44E-02	4.41E-02	7.82E-07	380.38	1113.72	3.280	
8	96.9	1.36E-03	9.53E-01	2.37E-02	2.19E-02	3.74E-07	403.07	1127.60	3.388	
9	96.2	1.40E-03	9.75E-01	1.23E-02	1.11E-02	1.83E-07	422.17	1135.27	3.444	
10	95.8	1.42E-03	9.86E-01	6.92E-03	5.64E-03	9.00E-06	429.59	1139.32	3.474	
11	95.5	1.43E-03	9.92E-01	3.73E-03	2.87E-03	4.44E-08	433.65	1141.61	3.490	
12	95.3	1.43E-03	9.95E-01	1.93E-03	1.45E-03	2.18E-08	435.99	1143.01	3.499	
13	95.1	1.44E-03	9.97E-01	1.04E-03	7.20E-04	1.05E-08	437.54	1143.94	3.504	
14	94.9	1.45E-03	9.98E-01	5.13E-04	3.43E-04	4.87E-09	438.75	1143.20	3.506	
15	94.2	1.74E-03	9.98E-01	2.35E-04	1.49E-04	2.06E-09	438.32	1104.72	3.508	
	77.3	1.74E-02	9.82E-01	8.23E-05	4.94E-05	6.64E-10	400.00	200.00	8.056	
		5.55E-01	4.44E-01	9.64E-07	2.90E-07	8.10E-18	504.72			

TIME	T	X1	X2	X3	X4	X5	L	V	M	CB
.010	201.913	0.	7.11E-03	4.77E-02	8.37E-01	1.08E-01	296.04	441.06	4.902	5.000
1	155.2	1.05E-11	1.06E-01	2.33E-01	6.10E-01	4.34E-02	737.10	515.60	2.399	
2	132.8	1.54E-09	2.84E-01	2.01E-01	4.75E-01	3.94E-02	811.62	593.73	2.552	
3	120.3	1.81E-07	4.56E-01	1.31E-01	3.77E-01	3.60E-02	869.71	662.27	2.708	

4	114.1	1.32E-05	5.72E-01	7.99E-02	3.15E-01	3.34E-02	958.24	688.41	2.840
5	108.4	7.59E-04	6.37E-01	4.93E-02	2.84E-01	3.25E-02	984.37	822.52	2.899
6	101.2	1.12E-03	8.18E-01	8.61E-02	9.48E-02	1.77E-06	718.46	1084.47	3.054
7	98.2	1.23E-03	9.10E-01	4.43E-02	4.42E-02	7.89E-07	380.35	1112.22	3.279
8	96.9	1.36E-03	9.53E-01	2.37E-02	2.20E-02	3.77E-07	408.09	1126.33	3.388
9	96.2	1.40E-03	9.75F-01	1.28E-02	1.11F-02	1.84E-07	422.21	1133.84	3.444
10	95.8	1.42E-03	9.86E-01	6.99E-03	5.66E-03	9.08E-08	429.79	1137.97	3.474
11	95.5	1.43E-03	9.92E-01	3.71E-03	2.86E-03	4.48E-08	434.04	1140.32	3.491
12	95.3	1.43E-03	9.95E-01	1.99E-03	1.45E-03	2.19E-08	436.80	1141.75	3.500
13	95.1	1.44E-03	9.97E-01	1.03E-03	7.22E-04	1.06E-08	438.25	1142.63	3.505
14	94.9	1.45E-03	9.98E-01	5.15E-04	3.44E-04	4.91E-09	438.30	1141.75	3.509
15	94.2	1.75E-03	9.98E-01	2.35E-04	1.49E-04	2.08E-09	438.53	1103.21	3.508
	77.3	1.74E-02	9.82E-01	8.17E-05	4.95E-05	6.69E-10	400.00	200.00	8.056
		5.55E-01	4.44E-01	9.61E-07	2.90E-07	8.17E-18	563.21		

FIGURE 5-25 (*Concluded*)

Table 5-1 NOMENCLATURE FOR MULTICOMPONENT DISTILLATION COLUMN

N_T	Total number of plates
N_S	Number of trays in stripping section
N_J	Total number of components
WHS, WLS, DS	Weir height and length and column diameter in stripping section (in.)
WHR, WLR, DR	Weir height and length and column diameter in rectifying section (in.)
MVB, MVD	Volumetric holdup in column base and in reflux drum (ft³)
MW	Molecular weight
HVAP	Heat of vaporization at normal boiling point (Btu/lb$_m$)
HCAPV	Heat capacity of vapor (Btu/lb$_m$-°F)
HCAPL	Heat capacity of liquid (Btu/lb$_m$-°F)
VP1	Vapor pressure (psia) at temperature T_1 (°F)
VP2	Vapor pressure (psia) at temperature T_2 (°F)
TFL, FL, XF	Liquid feed temperature (°F), flow rate (moles/hr), and composition (mole fraction)
TFV, FV, YF	Vapor feed temperature (°F), flow rate (moles/hr), and composition (mole fraction)
PD, PB	Pressures in top and bottom of column (psia)
QB	Reboiler heat input (10⁶ Btu/hr)
R	Reflux rate (moles/hr)
DV	Vapor product from reflux drum (moles/hr)
EFF	Murphree vapor-phase tray efficiency
T, LO, X	Initial conditions of temperature (°F), liquid flow rates (moles/hr), and liquid compositions for all trays
TD, TB, XD, XB	Initial conditions of temperature and compositions in reflux drum and column base
V	Vapor rates (moles/hr)
M	Molar tray holdups (moles)
MV	Volumetric tray holdups (ft³)

5-2.5 Batch Reactor

EXAMPLE 5-8 As our final digital simulation example let us simulate the batch reactor modeled in Sec. 3-8 (Fig. 3-9). Steam is initially fed into the jacket to heat the system up to temperatures at which the consecutive reactions begin. Then cooling water must be used in the jacket to remove the exothermic heats of reaction.

The output signal of the temperature controller goes to two split-range valves, a steam valve and a water valve. The instrumentation is all pneumatic, so the controller output pressure P_c goes from 3 to 15 psig. The valves will be adjusted so that the steam valve is wide open when the controller output pressure P_c is at 15 psig and is closed when $P_c = 9$ psig. The water valve will be closed at $P_c = 9$ psig and wide open at $P_c = 3$ psig. The reason for hooking up the valves in this manner is to have the correct fail-safe action in the event of an instrument air failure. The steam valve takes air pressure to open it and therefore it will fail closed. The water valve takes air to close it and therefore it will fail open.

Steam valve	closed $\longrightarrow$	open	
Fraction open X_s	0 $\longrightarrow$	1	
Controller output pressure			
P_c(psig)	3	9	15
Water valve	open $\longleftarrow$	closed	
Fraction open X_w	1 $\longleftarrow$	0	

The equations for the reaction liquid inside the tank and the vessel metal are

$$\frac{dC_A}{dt} = -k_1 C_A \qquad (5\text{-}41)$$

$$\frac{dC_B}{dt} = k_1 C_A - k_2 C_B \qquad (5\text{-}42)$$

$$\frac{dT}{dt} = \frac{-\lambda_1}{\rho C_p} k_1 C_A + \frac{-\lambda_2}{\rho C_p} k_2 C_B - \frac{Q_M}{V \rho C_p} \qquad (5\text{-}43)$$

$$Q_M = h_i A_i (T - T_M) \qquad (5\text{-}44)$$

$$\frac{dT_M}{dt} = \frac{Q_M - Q_J}{\rho_M C_M V_M} \qquad (5\text{-}45)$$

The equations for the jacket are different for the three phases of the batch.

1 With steam (35-psia supply pressure)

$$V_J \frac{d\rho_s}{dt} = w_s - w_c \qquad (5\text{-}46)$$

$$\rho_s = \frac{MP_J}{R(T_J + 460)} \qquad (5\text{-}47)$$

$$P_J = \exp\left(\frac{A_{vp}}{T_J + 460} + B_{vp}\right) \qquad (5\text{-}48)$$

$$w_s = C_{Vs} X_s \sqrt{35 - P_J} \qquad (5\text{-}49)$$

$$Q_J = -h_{os} A_o (T_J - T_M) \qquad (5\text{-}50)$$

$$w_c = -\frac{Q_J}{H_s - h_c} \qquad (5\text{-}51)$$

2 During filling with water (20-psig water header pressure)

$$A_o = \left(\frac{A_o}{V_J}\right)_{\text{total}} V_J \qquad (5\text{-}52)$$

$$\frac{dV_J}{dt} = F_{w0} \qquad (5\text{-}53)$$

$$\frac{d}{dt}(V_J T_J) = F_{w0} T_{J0} + \frac{Q_J}{\rho_J C_J} \qquad (5\text{-}54)$$

$$Q_J = h_{ow} A_o (T_M - T_J) \qquad (5\text{-}55)$$

$$F_{w0} = C_{Vw} X_w \sqrt{20} \qquad (5\text{-}56)$$

3 When jacket is full of water

$$\frac{dT_J}{dt} = \frac{F_{w0}}{V_J}(T_{J0} - T_J) + \frac{Q_J}{C_J V_J \rho_J} \qquad (5\text{-}57)$$

The system is sketched in Fig. 5-26, and numerical values of parameters are given in Table 5-2. The digital program is given in Fig. 5-27, printed output is shown in Fig. 5-28, and plotted results for a batch cycle are shown in Fig. 5-29.

The temperature transmitter has a range of 50 to 250°F, so its output pneumatic pressure signal goes from 3 psig at 50°F to 15 psig at 250°F.

$$P_{TT} = 3 + (T - 50)\frac{12}{200} \qquad (5\text{-}58)$$

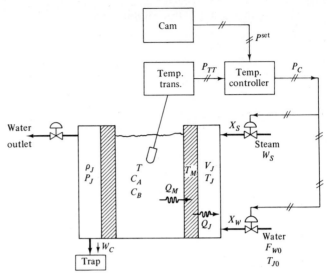

FIGURE 5-26
Batch reactor.

A proportional feedback controller is used with its output biased at 7 psig (i.e., its output pressure is 7 psig when there is zero error).

$$P_c = 7 + K_c(P^{set} - P_{TT}) \qquad (5-59)$$

The set-point signal P^{set} comes from a pneumatic function generator (a mechanical cam device is commonly used). When the process temperature gets up to 200°F the

Table 5-2 PARAMETERS FOR BATCH REACTOR

α_1	729.55 min^{-1}	V_J	18.83 ft^3
α_2	6567.6 min^{-1}	C_{Vw}	100 gpm/psi$^{1/2}$
E_1	15,000 Btu/mole	T_{J0}	80°F
E_2	20,000 Btu/mole	A_i	56.5 ft^2
A_{vp}	−8744.4°R	λ_1	−40,000 Btu/mole
B_{vp}	15.70	λ_2	−50,000 Btu/mole
C_{A0}	0.80 mole A/ft^3	C_p	1 Btu/lb$_m$-°F
T_0	80°F	V	42.5 ft^3
K_c	10	ρ	50 lb$_m$/ft^3
C_{Vs}	112 lb$_m$/min-psi$^{1/2}$	C_M	0.12 Btu/lb$_m$-°F
h_{os}	1000 Btu/hr-°F-ft^2	V_M	9.42 ft^3
h_{ow}	400 Btu/hr-°F-ft^2	ρ_M	512 lb$_m$/ft^3
h_i	160 Btu/hr-°F-ft^2	ρ_J	62.3 lb$_m$/ft^3
A_o	56.5 ft^2	C_J	1 Btu/lb$_m$-°F
$H_s - h_c$	939 Btu/lb$_m$		

```
        PROGRAM OBATCH(INPUT,OUTPUT)
        REAL K1,K2,KC
        ALPHA1=723.5488
        ALPHA2=6567.587
        AVP=-8744.4
        BVP=15.70036
        DELTA=.002
        KC=2.
        TPRINT=1.
        CA=0.8
        CB=0.
        TIME=0.
        T=80.
        TM=80.
        TJ=259.
        PJ=34.4
        DENS=18.*PJ*144./(1545.*(TJ+460.))
        PSET=12.6
        START=1.
        FWO=0.
        FULL=-1.
        VJ=0.
        VJTJ=0.
        TFLAG=0.
        CAM=-1.
        RAMP =.005
        PRINT 54
   54 FORMAT(1H1,6X,*TIME    CA      CB      XS      XW      T       TM
     1 TJ      PC      VJ      FWO     QJ      QM      PSET*)
  100 K1=ALPHA1*EXP(-15000./(1.99*(T+460.)))
        K2=ALPHA2*EXP(-20000./((T+460.)*1.99))
C    TRANSMITTER
        PTT=3.+(T-50.)*12./200.
C    CONTROLLER
        PC=7.+KC*(PSET-PTT)
        IF(PC.GT.15.) PC=15.
        IF(PC.LT.3.) PC=3.
C    VALVES
        XS=(PC-9.)/6.
        XW=(9.-PC)/6.
        IF(XS.GT.1.) XS=1.
        IF(XS.LT.0.) XS=0.
        IF(XW.GT.1.) XW=1.
        IF(XW.LT.0.) XW=0.
C    TEST FOR STEAM
        IF(START.LT.0.) GO TO 20
        IF(PJ.GE.35.) GO TO 40
        WS=XS*112.*SQRT(35.-PJ)
        GO TO 41
   40 WS=0.
   41 CONTINUE
        QJ=-1000.*56.5*(TJ-TM)/50.
        WC=-QJ/939.
        DENDOT=(WS-WC)/19.83
        DENS=DENS+DELTA*DENDOT
        FLAGP=-1.
        FLAGM=-1.
        DTJ=1.
        LOOP=0
   15 PJ=EXP(BVP+AVP/(TJ+460.))
        LOOP=LOOP+1
        IF(LOOP.GT.50)  GO TO 70
        DCALC=18.*PJ*144./(1545.*(TJ+460.))
        IF(ABS(DENS-DCALC).LT. .0011) GO TO 50
        IF(DENS.GT.DCALC) GO TO 17
        IF(FLAGM.LT.0.) GO TO 16
        DTJ=DTJ/2.
   16 TJ=TJ-DTJ
        FLAGP=1.
        GO TO 15
```

FIGURE 5-27
Digital program for batch reactor.

163

```
      70 PRINT 71
      71 FORMAT(1X,*TEMP LOOP*)
         STOP
      17 IF(FLAGP.LT.0.) GO TO 18
         DTJ=DTJ/2.
      18 TJ=TJ+DTJ
         FLAGM=1.
         GO TO 15
      20 FWO=100.*SQRT(20.)*8.33*XW/62.3
         WS=0.
         WC=0.
         DENS=0.
         PJ=0.
         XS=0.
C     TEST FOR JACKET FILLING
         IF(FULL.GT.0.) GO TO 30
         AO=VJ*56.5/18.83
         VJ=VJ+DELTA*FWO
         IF(VJ.GE. 18.83) FULL=1.
         QJ=400.*AO*(TM-TJ)/60.
         VJTJ=VJTJ+DELTA*(FWO*80.+QJ)
         IF(VJ.LE.0.) GO TO 25
         TJ=VJTJ/VJ
         GO TO 50
      25 TJ=80.
         GO TO 50
C     FULL JACKET
      30 QJ=400.*56.5*(TM-TJ)/60.
         TPRINT=2.
         DELTA=.05
         TJDOT=FWO*(80.-TJ)/18.83+QJ/(18.83*62.3)
         TJ=TJ+DELTA*TJDOT
      50 CADOT=-K1*CA
         CBDOT=K1*CA-K2*CB
         QM=160.*56.5*(T-TM)/60.
         TDOT=(K1*CA*40000.+K2*CB*50000.)/50.-QM/(42.4*50.)
         TMDOT=(QM-QJ)/(512.*.12*9.42)
C     INTEGRATION
         TIME=TIME+DELTA
         CA=CA+CADOT*DELTA
         CB=CB+CBDOT*DELTA
         T=T+TDOT*DELTA
         TM=TM+TMDOT*DELTA
         IF(T.GT.300.) STOP
         IF(T.GT.200.) START=-1.
         IF(T.GT.200.) CAM=1.
         IF(CAM.GT.0.) PSET=PSET-DELTA*RAMP
         IF(TIME.GT.200.) STOP
         IF(TIME.LT.TFLAG) GO TO 100
         PRINT 55,TIME,CA,CB,XS,XW,T,TM,TJ,PC,VJ,FWO,QJ,QM,PSET
      55 FORMAT(1X,F8.1,4F8.4,6F8.2,2E9.1,F8.4,2F8.2)
         TFLAG=TFLAG+TPRINT
         GO TO 100
         END
```

FIGURE 5-27 (*Concluded*)

TIME	CA	CB	XS	XW	T	TM	TJ	PC	VJ	FWO	QJ	QM	PSET
.0	.8000	.0000	1.0000	0.0000	80.00	80.58	251.00	15.00	0.00	0.00	-1.7E+05	0.	12.6000
1.0	.7995	.0005	1.0000	0.0000	86.29	211.97	256.00	15.00	0.00	0.00	-4.5E+04	-1.9E+04	12.6000
2.0	.7988	.0012	1.0000	0.0000	96.42	234.19	264.00	15.00	0.00	0.00	-2.3E+04	-2.1E+04	12.6000
3.0	.7979	.0021	1.0000	0.0000	105.74	238.98	266.00	15.00	0.00	0.00	-1.8E+04	-2.0E+04	12.6000
4.0	.7968	.0032	1.0000	0.0000	116.72	240.77	261.00	15.00	0.00	0.00	-2.1E+04	-1.9E+04	12.6000
5.0	.7955	.0045	1.0000	0.0000	126.35	242.55	260.00	15.00	0.00	0.00	-1.8E+04	-1.8E+04	12.6000
6.0	.7938	.0062	1.0000	0.0000	135.67	243.76	259.00	15.00	0.00	0.00	-1.8E+04	-1.6E+04	12.6000
7.0	.7917	.0087	.9731	0.0000	144.70	244.70	263.00	14.84	0.00	0.00	-1.8E+04	-1.5E+04	12.6000
8.0	.7893	.0107	.7971	0.0000	153.49	245.07	263.00	13.78	0.00	0.00	-1.6E+04	-1.4E+04	12.6000
9.0	.7864	.0136	.6248	0.0000	162.11	246.71	258.00	12.75	0.00	0.00	-1.3E+04	-1.3E+04	12.6000
10.0	.7830	.0170	.4555	0.0000	170.57	247.32	261.00	11.73	0.00	0.00	-1.1E+04	-1.2E+04	12.6000
11.0	.7790	.0209	.2481	0.0000	178.95	248.01	260.00	10.73	0.00	0.00	-1.0E+04	-1.0E+04	12.6000
12.0	.7744	.0255	.1210	0.0000	187.30	248.80	259.00	9.73	0.00	0.00	-9.6E+03	-9.3E+03	12.6000
13.0	.7691	.0308	0.0000	.0446	195.58	243.41	244.00	8.73	0.00	0.00	-5.3E+02	-7.2E+03	12.6000
14.0	.7630	.0368	0.0000	.1997	203.23	232.60	212.67	7.81	4.29	11.86	1.7E+04	-4.4E+04	12.5978
15.0	.7561	.0437	0.0000	.3367	210.39	222.91	203.17	6.98	18.86	20.14	5.1E+03	-2.0E+04	12.5927
17.0	.7404	.0591	0.0000	.5212	219.73	159.13	98.54	5.81	18.86	31.76	2.3E+04	8.9E+03	12.5827
19.0	.7237	.0755	0.0000	.5897	222.40	132.93	88.47	5.66	18.86	35.26	1.7E+04	1.3E+04	12.5727
21.0	.7069	.0928	0.0000	.6449	222.97	127.07	86.88	5.37	18.86	36.17	1.5E+04	1.4E+04	12.5627
23.0	.6905	.1077	0.0000	.6670	222.89	125.82	86.57	5.36	18.86	36.30	1.5E+04	1.5E+04	12.5527
25.0	.6745	.1231	0.0000	.6623	222.49	125.48	86.53	5.39	18.86	36.02	1.5E+04	1.5E+04	12.5427
27.0	.6591	.1370	0.0000	.5910	221.79	125.31	86.59	5.45	18.86	35.39	1.5E+04	1.5E+04	12.5327
29.0	.6442	.1520	0.0000	.5750	220.80	125.13	86.71	5.55	18.86	34.42	1.4E+04	1.4E+04	12.5227
31.0	.6298	.1535	0.0000	.5585	219.52	124.92	86.89	5.68	18.86	33.10	1.4E+04	1.4E+04	12.5127
33.0	.6162	.1784	0.0000	.5454	217.94	124.66	87.14	5.85	18.86	31.42	1.4E+04	1.4E+04	12.5027
35.0	.6032	.1905	0.0000	.4913	216.06	124.36	87.43	6.05	18.86	29.38	1.4E+04	1.4E+04	12.4927
37.0	.5908	.2019	0.0000	.4514	213.90	124.08	87.93	6.29	18.86	26.99	1.4E+04	1.4E+04	12.4827
39.0	.5792	.2127	0.0000	.4461	211.46	123.80	88.54	6.56	18.86	24.29	1.3E+04	1.3E+04	12.4727
41.0	.5683	.2227	0.0000	.3560	208.79	123.57	89.34	6.86	18.86	21.29	1.3E+04	1.3E+04	12.4627
43.0	.5581	.2321	0.0000	.3118	205.90	123.45	90.44	7.19	18.86	18.05	1.2E+04	1.2E+04	12.4527
45.0	.5485	.2408	0.0000	.2447	202.87	123.52	91.96	7.53	18.86	14.63	1.2E+04	1.2E+04	12.4427
47.0	.5396	.2489	0.0000	.1860	199.77	123.94	94.12	7.88	18.86	11.12	1.1E+04	1.1E+04	12.4327
49.0	.5313	.2565	0.0000	.1278	196.70	124.97	97.29	8.23	18.86	7.64	1.0E+04	1.1E+04	12.4227
51.0	.5235	.2635	0.0000	.0727	193.73	126.86	102.07	8.56	19.86	4.35	9.4E+03	1.0E+04	12.4127
53.0	.5160	.2701	0.0000	.0245	191.22	130.31	109.40	8.85	19.86	1.47	7.9E+03	9.2E+03	12.4027
55.0	.5093	.2763	0.0000	0.0000	189.30	136.02	119.87	9.07	18.86	0.00	6.1E+03	8.1E+03	12.3927
57.0	.5027	.2822	0.0000	0.0000	188.27	142.66	129.32	9.17	18.86	0.00	5.1E+03	6.9E+03	12.3827
59.0	.4962	.2880	0.0000	0.0000	188.11	148.67	137.24	9.17	18.86	0.00	4.3E+03	5.7E+03	12.3727
61.0	.4898	.2937	0.0000	0.0000	188.69	154.04	144.09	9.09	18.86	0.00	3.8E+03	5.2E+03	12.3627
63.0	.4833	.2994	0.0000	.0134	189.92	158.74	148.90	8.92	18.86	.80	3.7E+03	4.7E+03	12.3527
65.0	.4768	.3052	0.0000	.0479	191.48	159.03	143.62	8.71	19.86	2.86	5.7E+03	4.9E+03	12.3427
67.0	.4702	.3110	0.0000	.0729	192.54	153.55	132.54	8.56	18.86	4.36	7.9E+03	5.8E+03	12.3327
69.0	.4636	.3167	0.0000	.0773	192.60	146.63	123.49	8.53	13.86	4.66	8.7E+03	6.9E+03	12.3227
71.0	.4572	.3223	0.0000	.0645	191.74	141.82	119.38	8.61	18.86	3.86	8.5E+03	7.5E+03	12.3127
73.0	.4510	.3276	0.0000	.0411	190.40	144.13	119.94	8.75	18.86	2.46	7.6E+03	7.6E+03	12.3027
75.0	.4450	.3323	1.0000	.0169	149.03	141.42	124.45	8.90	18.86	1.01	6.4E+03	7.2E+03	12.2927
77.0	.4392	.3378	0.0000	0.0000	188.02	145.30	132.05	9.00	18.86	0.00	5.0E+03	6.5E+03	12.2827
79.0	.4336	.3426	0.0000	0.0000	147.67	150.56	139.72	9.03	18.86	0.00	4.1E+03	5.6E+03	12.2727
81.0	.4280	.3473	0.0000	.0053	188.00	155.48	145.78	8.97	18.86	.32	3.7E+03	4.9E+03	12.2627
83.0	.4225	.3520	0.0000	.0257	188.84	158.18	146.17	8.85	18.86	1.51	4.5E+03	4.6E+03	12.2527
85.0	.4169	.3567	0.0000	.0455	189.67	156.49	140.51	8.73	19.86	2.72	6.0E+03	5.0E+03	12.2427
87.0	.4114	.3615	0.0000	.0553	189.99	152.06	133.17	8.67	18.86	3.31	7.1E+03	5.7E+03	12.2327
89.0	.4059	.3659	0.0000	.0511	139.59	147.69	128.21	8.69	18.86	3.05	7.3E+03	6.3E+03	12.2227
91.0	.4006	.3703	0.0000	.0354	188.68	145.30	127.12	8.78	18.86	2.18	6.9E+03	6.5E+03	12.2127
93.0	.3954	.3746	0.0000	.0183	187.60	145.49	129.81	8.80	18.86	1.09	5.9E+03	6.4E+03	12.2027
95.0	.3904	.3787	0.0000	.0041	186.74	144.12	135.51	8.98	18.86	.25	4.8E+03	5.8E+03	12.1927
97.0	.3855	.3827	0.0000	0.0000	186.37	152.41	142.37	9.00	18.86	0.00	3.8E+03	5.1E+03	12.1827
99.0	.3807	.3865	0.0000	.0075	186.59	156.66	147.32	8.96	18.86	.44	3.5E+03	4.5E+03	12.1727
101.0	.3759	.3905	0.0000	.0232	187.23	158.62	147.31	8.86	18.86	1.39	4.2E+03	4.3E+03	12.1627
103.0	.3711	.3944	0.0000	.0386	187.83	157.13	142.55	8.77	18.86	2.71	5.5E+03	4.6E+03	12.1527
105.0	.3663	.3982	0.0000	.0452	187.97	153.42	136.51	8.73	18.86	2.70	6.4E+03	5.2E+03	12.1427
107.0	.3616	.4019	0.0000	.0402	187.54	149.83	132.56	8.76	18.86	2.40	6.5E+03	5.7E+03	12.1327
109.0	.3570	.4055	0.0000	.0270	186.71	148.04	132.12	8.84	18.86	1.61	6.0E+03	5.8E+03	12.1227
111.0	.3526	.4090	0.0000	.0120	185.79	148.64	135.16	8.93	18.86	.72	5.1E+03	5.6E+03	12.1127
113.0	.3482	.4125	0.0000	.0019	185.13	151.41	140.71	8.99	18.86	.11	4.1E+03	5.1E+03	12.1027
115.0	.3440	.4158	0.0000	.0014	184.96	155.34	146.60	8.99	18.86	.08	3.3E+03	4.5E+03	12.0927
117.0	.3398	.4190	0.0000	.0141	185.28	156.66	149.70	8.97	18.86	.66	3.4E+03	4.0E+03	12.0827
119.0	.3356	.4223	0.0000	.0257	185.85	159.34	147.99	8.85	18.86	1.54	4.2E+03	4.0E+03	12.0727
121.0	.3314	.4255	0.0000	.0370	186.24	157.07	142.86	8.78	19.86	2.21	5.3E+03	4.4E+03	12.0627
123.0	.3273	.4286	0.0000	.0386	186.14	153.49	137.75	8.77	18.86	2.31	5.9E+03	4.9E+03	12.0527
125.0	.3232	.4317	0.0000	.0304	185.55	150.68	135.29	8.82	18.86	1.82	5.8E+03	5.2E+03	12.0427
127.0	.3193	.4340	0.0000	.017.	184.71	149.91	136.33	8.90	18.86	1.01	5.1E+03	5.2E+03	12.0327
129.0	.3154	.4375	0.0000	.0048	183.94	151.45	140.46	9.00	18.86	.29	4.2E+03	4.9E+03	12.0227
131.0	.3117	.4403	0.000	0.0000	183.53	154.76	146.15	9.00	18.86	0.00	3.3E+03	4.3E+03	12.0127
133.0	.3080	.4431	0.0000	.0045	183.62	158.38	150.65	8.97	18.86	.27	2.9E+03	3.8E+03	12.0027
135.0	.3043	.4459	0.000.	.0170	184.44	160.30	151.16	8.90	18.86	1.02	3.4E+03	3.6E+03	11.9927
137.0	.3006	.4485	0.0000	.0098	184.55	159.30	147.36	8.82	18.86	1.78	4.5E+03	3.8E+03	11.9927
139.0	.2970	.4511	0.0000	.0056	184.06	156.14	142.80	8.79	18.86	2.13	5.3E+03	4.3E+03	11.9727
141.0	.2934	.4537	0.0000	.0310	184.27	152.98	138.29	8.81	18.86	1.87	5.5E+03	4.7E+03	11.9627
143.0	.2899	.4562	0.0000	.0197	183.52	151.21	137.69	8.86	18.86	1.18	5.0E+03	4.9E+03	11.9527
145.0	.2865	.4585	0.0000	.0059	182.71	151.84	140.83	8.96	18.85	.42	4.2E+03	4.7E+03	11.9427
147.0	.2832	.4610	0.0000	0.0000	182.17	154.55	146.13	9.00	18.86	0.00	3.2E+03	4.2E+03	11.9327
149.0	.2799	.4633	0.000.	.0007	182.09	158.04	151.03	9.00	18.86	.04	2.6E+03	3.6E+03	11.9227
151.0	.2766	.4655	0.0000	.0106	182.43	160.69	153.15	8.94	18.86	.64	2.8E+03	3.3E+03	11.9127
153.0	.2734	.4578	0.000.	.0238	182.92	160.73	150.70	8.86	18.86	1.43	3.7E+03	3.3E+03	11.9027
155.0	.2702	.4700	0.0000	.0323	183.17	158.14	145.51	8.81	18.86	1.93	4.7E+03	3.8E+03	11.8927
157.0	.2670	.4722	0.0000	.0313	192.93	154.69	140.97	8.81	18.86	1.87	5.2E+03	4.2E+03	11.8827
159.0	.2639	.4747	0.0000	.0216	182.28	152.36	139.40	8.87	18.86	1.29	4.9E+03	4.5E+03	11.8727
161.0	.2608	.4764	0.000.	.0037	191.47	152.24	141.40	8.95	18.86	.52	4.1E+03	4.4E+03	11.8627
163.0	.2579	.4784	0.0000	0.0000	180.83	154.39	146.18	9.00	18.86	0.00	3.1E+03	4.0E+03	11.8527

FIGURE 5-28
Printed output from the batch reactor program

165.0	.2550	.4803	0.0000	0.0000	190.62	157.64	150.93	9.01	18.86	0.00	2.5E+03	3.5E+03	11.8427
167.0	.2521	.4822	0.0000	.0054	180.83	160.60	154.28	8.97	18.86	.32	2.4E+03	3.1E+03	11.8327
169.0	.2492	.4841	0.0000	.0181	191.30	161.63	153.33	8.89	18.86	1.08	3.1E+03	3.0E+03	11.8227
171.0	.2464	.4859	0.0000	.0287	181.66	159.75	148.69	8.83	18.86	1.72	4.1E+03	3.3E+03	11.8127
173.0	.2435	.4878	0.0000	.0308	181.59	156.33	143.57	8.82	18.86	1.84	4.8E+03	3.8E+03	11.8027
175.0	.2408	.4895	0.0000	.0234	181.04	153.46	140.89	8.86	18.86	1.40	4.7E+03	4.1E+03	11.7927
177.0	.2380	.4913	0.0000	.0110	180.24	152.59	141.81	8.93	18.86	.66	4.1E+03	4.2E+03	11.7827
179.0	.2354	.4929	0.0000	0.0000	179.53	154.11	145.95	9.00	18.86	0.00	3.1E+03	3.8E+03	11.7727
181.0	.2326	.4945	0.0000	0.0000	179.19	157.09	150.60	9.02	18.86	0.00	2.5E+03	3.3E+03	11.7627
183.0	.2303	.4961	0.0000	.0008	179.26	160.02	154.43	9.00	18.86	.05	2.1E+03	2.9E+03	11.7527
185.0	.2277	.4977	0.0000	.0126	179.66	161.90	155.25	8.93	18.86	.72	2.5E+03	2.7E+03	11.7427
187.0	.2252	.4992	0.0000	.0241	180.10	161.05	151.69	8.86	18.86	1.44	3.5E+03	2.9E+03	11.7327
189.0	.2227	.5008	0.0000	.0295	180.19	157.97	146.36	8.82	18.86	1.77	4.4E+03	3.3E+03	11.7227
191.0	.2202	.5022	0.0000	.0253	179.80	154.69	142.59	8.85	18.86	1.51	4.6E+03	3.8E+03	11.7127
193.0	.2178	.5037	0.0000	.0140	179.06	153.00	142.19	8.92	18.86	.84	4.1E+03	3.9E+03	11.7027
195.0	.2154	.5051	0.0000	.0020	178.73	153.70	145.34	8.99	18.86	.12	3.2E+03	3.7E+03	11.6927
197.0	.2131	.5064	0.0000	0.0000	177.82	156.31	149.92	9.03	18.86	0.00	2.4E+03	3.3E+03	11.6827
199.0	.2108	.5078	0.0000	0.0000	177.74	159.11	153.70	9.02	18.86	0.00	2.0E+03	2.8E+03	11.6727

FIGURE 5-28 (*Concluded*)

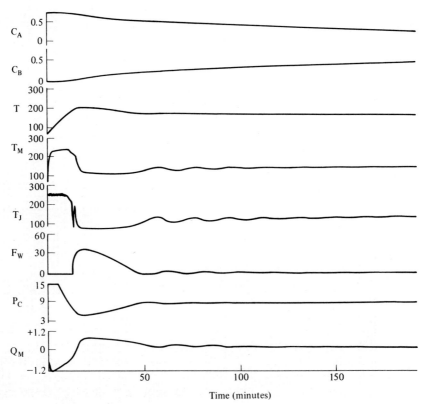

FIGURE 5-29
Plotted results for batch reactor.

P^{set} signal is ramped slowly downward in order to prevent too much loss of component B, as discussed in Sec. 3-8.

$$P^{set} = 12 - RAMP(t - t_{200}) \qquad (5\text{-}60)$$

where RAMP = rate of P^{set} change with time, psi/min

t = batch time, min

t_{200} = time when process temperature T reaches $200°F$ ////

PROBLEMS

5-1 Write an EQUIL subroutine, using false-position convergence.

5-2 Compare convergence time, using interval halving, Newton-Raphson, and false position, for an ideal, four-component vapor-liquid equilibrium system. The pure-component vapor pressures are:

Component	Vapor pressure P_j^0(psia)	
	at 150°F	at 200°F
1	25	200
2	14.7	60
3	4	14.7
4	0.5	5

Calculate the correct temperature and vapor compositions for a liquid at 75 psia with a composition

$$x_1 = 0.10$$
$$x_2 = 0.54$$
$$x_3 = 0.30$$
$$x_4 = 0.06$$

The system is ideal.

5-3 The design of ejectors requires trial and error to find the "motive" pressure P_m that, with a fixed motive flow rate of gas W_m, will suck a design flow rate W_s of suction gas from a suction pressure P_s and discharge against a higher pressure P_D. The motive gas is at 300°F and has a molecular weight of 60. Its flow rate is 5,000 lb$_m$/hr. The suction gas is at 400°F and 150 psia and has a molecular weight of 50. A suction flow of 7,000 lb$_m$/hr must be ejected into a discharge pressure of 160 psia.

Assume perfect gases and frictionless, reversible, adiabatic operation of the jet; i.e., momentum is conserved when the two streams mix in the throat and the expansions and contractions into and out of the throat are isentropic.

Find the motive pressure P_m required and the areas in the throat on the motive and suction sides, A_m and A_s (ft^2).

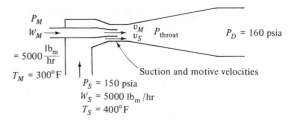

5-4 Simulate the nonisothermal CSTR of Example 5-5, using Euler and fourth-order Runge-Kutta. Vary step sizes and find the value that gives 0.1 percent accuracy for each method.

5-5 Simulate the ideal binary distillation column of Example 5-6, using Euler and fourth-order Runge-Kutta, and again compare step sizes.

5-6 Solve Prob. 4-6 by digital simulation.

5-7 Find the optimum liquid concentration of the propane-isobutane mixture in an auto-refrigerated alkylation reactor. The exothermic heat $Q_R(10^6$ Btu/hr) of the alkylation reaction is removed by vaporization of the liquid in the reactor. The vapor is compressed, condensed, and flashed into the reactor through a pressure letdown valve. The reactor must operate at 50°F, and the compressed vapors must be condensed at 110°F.

Find the liquid mole fraction x of propane that minimizes the compressor horse-power requirements for a given Q_R. Assume the compressor adiabatic efficiency is 100 percent.

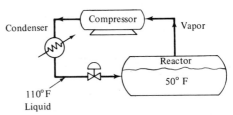

5-8 The initial start-up of an adiabatic, gas-phase packed tubular reactor makes a good example of how a distributed system can be lumped into a series of CSTR's in order to study the dynamic response. The reactor is a cylindrical vessel (3 ft ID by 20 ft long) packed with a metal packing. The packing occupies 5 percent of the total volume, provides 50 ft² of area per ft³ of total volume, weighs 400 lb$_m$/ft³, and has a heat capacity of 0.1 Btu/lb$_m$-°F. The heat transfer coefficient between the packing and the gas is 10 Btu/hr-ft²-°F.

The reaction occurring is first order: $A \xrightarrow{k} B$. A dilute mixture of reactant A in product B is fed into the reactor at y_0 mole fraction A and temperature $T_0 = 500°F$. The heat of reaction is −30,000 Btu/mole A. The specific reaction rate is $k = 4 \times 10^2$ $e^{-15,000/RT}$. Assume perfect gases with molecular weights of 40 and heat capacities equal to 0.15 Btu/lb$_m$-°F.

The pressure at the inlet of the reactor is 100 psia. The pressure drop over the reactor is 5 psi at the design superficial velocity of 1 ft/sec at inlet conditions.

Assume that this distributed system can be adequately modeled by a five-lump model of equal lengths. Inside each lump the gas temperature and composition are the same at any spatial position (perfectly mixed). The packing inside each lump is all at one temperature.

The packing and gas in each section are initially at 500°F with no reactant in the system. At time zero, y_0 is raised to 0.10 mole fraction A. Simulate the system on a digital computer and find the dynamic changes in temperatures and concentrations in all sections.

Gas "lumps"

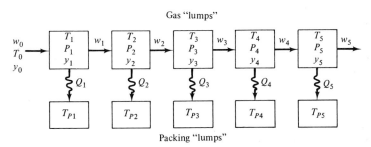

Packing "lumps"

5-9 A 6-in. ID pipe, 300 ft long, connects two process units. The liquid flows through the pipe in essentially plug-flow conditions, so the pipe acts as a pure time delay or dead time. This dead time varies with the flow rate through the pipe. From time equals zero, the flow rate is 1,000 gpm for 2 min. Then it drops to 500 gpm and holds constant for 3 min. Then it jumps to 2,000 gpm for 2 min and finally returns to 1,000 gpm. Liquid density is 50 lb_m/ft^3.

While these flow rate changes are occurring, the temperature of the fluid entering the pipe varies sinusoidally:

$$T_{in(t)} = 100 + 10 \sin \omega t$$

where T_{in} = inlet temperature, °F

$\omega = 30$ radians/minute

Write a digital program that gives the dynamic changes in the temperature of the liquid leaving the pipe, $T_{out(t)}$, for this variable dead-time process.

PART THREE

Dynamics

In the next four chapters we will study the time-dependent dynamic behavior of some simple systems, using classic analytical mathematical techniques. In the computer simulation studies of the two preceding chapters, the systems and their describing equations could be quite complex and nonlinear. In the next four chapters only systems described by linear ordinary differential equations will be considered (linearity will be defined in Chap. 6). The reason we are limited to linear systems is that practically all the analytical mathematical techniques currently available are applicable only to linear equations.

Since most chemical engineering systems are nonlinear, it might appear to be a waste of time to study methods limited to linear systems. However, linear techniques are of great practical importance, particularly for continuous processes, because the nonlinear equations describing most systems can be linearized around some steady-state operating condition. The resulting linear equations adequately describe the dynamic response of the system in some region around the steady-state conditions. The size of the region over which the linear model is valid will vary with the degree of nonlinearity of the process and the magnitude of the disturbances. In many processes the linear model can be successfully used to study dynamics and design controllers.

Complex systems can usually be broken down into a number of simple elements. We must understand the dynamics of these simple systems before we can tackle the more complex.

The systems studied in Part 3 will be, for the most part, uncontrolled. We will be examining the open-loop dynamics or the response of the system to some disturbance, having started from an initial condition, with no feedback controllers.

Our study of the dynamics of these simple linear systems will be in the time, Laplace, and frequency domains. By "time domain" we mean obtaining the dependence of the system variables on time by solving the differential equations describing the system. These dynamic functions tell us what is happening in the real world as time marches on. This is, of course, what we are primarily interested in finding out. However, as we will show in the next two parts of this book, there are very practical advantages in notation and computation in using Laplace and Fourier transformations to examine dynamics and design controllers in the Laplace and frequency domains. These useful transform techniques permit us to look at the dynamic relationships between input variables and output variables. Such input-output relationships are called *transfer functions*.

6

TIME-DOMAIN DYNAMICS

Studying the dynamics of systems in the time domain involves direct solution of differential equations. The computer simulation techniques of Part 2 are very general in the sense that they can give solutions to very complex nonlinear problems. However, they are also very specific in the sense that they provide a solution to only the particular numerical case fed into the computer.

The classic analytical techniques discussed in this chapter are limited to linear ordinary differential equations. But they yield general analytical solutions that apply for any values of parameters and initial conditions.

We will start by briefly classifying and defining types of systems and types of disturbances. Then we will learn how to linearize nonlinear equations. It is assumed that the reader has had a course in differential equations, but we will review some of the most useful solution techniques for simple ordinary differential equations. Finally we will show how useful dynamic information can sometimes be obtained from the steady-state equations alone.

6-1   CLASSIFICATION AND DEFINITION

Processes and their dynamics can be classified in several ways:

1   *Number of independent variables*
   a.   *Lumped* if time is the only independent variable and therefore described by ordinary differential equations.
   b.   *Distributed* if time and spatial variables are required; described by partial differential equations.
2   *Linearity*
   a.   *Linear* if all functions in the equations are linear functions (see Sec. 6-2).
   b.   *Nonlinear* if not linear.
3   *Stability*
   a.   *Stable* if "self-regulatory" so that variables converge to some steady state when disturbed. In analog computer jargon a stable system has *negative feedback* (feeding the output of a high-gain amplifier back into its own input stabilizes the amplifier).
   b.   *Unstable* if *positive feedback* causes the variables to go to infinity (mathematically).

   Most processes are open-loop stable. However, the exothermic stirred-tank reactor is a notable example of a process that can be open-loop unstable.

   All real processes can be made closed-loop unstable (unstable with a feedback controller in service), and therefore one of the principal objectives in feedback controller design is to avoid instability.
4   *Order*   If a system is described by one ordinary differential equation with derivatives of order N, the system is called Nth order.

$$a_N \frac{d^N x}{dt^N} + a_{N-1} \frac{d^{N-1} x}{dt^{N-1}} + \cdots + a_1 \frac{dx}{dt} + a_0 x = f_{(t)} \qquad (6\text{-}1)$$

where a_i are constants and $f_{(t)}$ is the forcing function or disturbance. Two very important special cases are for $N = 1$ and $N = 2$.

First-order:
$$a_1 \frac{dx}{dt} + a_0 x = f(t)$$

Second-order:
$$a_2 \frac{d^2 x}{dt^2} + a_1 \frac{dx}{dt} + a_0 x = f(t) \qquad (6\text{-}2)$$

The forms that we will usually employ for the above are

First-order:
$$\tau_p \frac{dx}{dt} + x = f_{(t)}$$

Second-order:
$$\tau_p^2 \frac{d^2x}{dt^2} + 2\tau_p \zeta \frac{dx}{dt} + x = f_{(t)} \qquad (6\text{-}3)$$

where τ_p = process time constant
   ζ = damping coefficient

Disturbances can also be classified and defined.

Shape (see Fig. 6-1)

1 Step: Step disturbances are functions that change instantaneously from one level to another and are thereafter constant. If the size of the step is equal to unity, the disturbance is called the *unit step function* $u_{(t)}$ defined as

$$\begin{aligned} u_{(t)} &= 1 & \text{for } t > 0 \\ u_{(t)} &= 0 & \text{for } t \le 0 \end{aligned} \qquad (6\text{-}4)$$

The response of a system to a step disturbance is called the *step response* or the *transient response*.

2 Pulse: A pulse is a function of arbitrary shape (but usually rectangular or triangular) that begins and ends at the same level. A rectangular pulse is simply the sum of one positive step function made at time zero and one negative step function made D minutes later. D is a delay time or dead time.

Rectangular pulse of height 1 *and width* $D = u_{(t)} - u_{(t-D)}$ $\qquad (6\text{-}5)$

3 Impulse: The impulse is defined as the Dirac delta function, an infinitely high pulse whose width is zero and whose area is always equal to unity. This kind of disturbance is, of course, a mathematical fiction, but we will find it a useful tool.

4 Ramp: Ramp inputs are functions that change linearly with time:

Ramp function $= Kt$ $\qquad (6\text{-}6)$

where K is a constant.

5 Sinusoidal: Pure periodic sine and cosine inputs seldom occur in real chemical engineering systems. However, the response of systems to this kind of forcing function (called the *frequency response* of the system) is of great practical importance, as we will show in Parts 3 and 4.

Location of disturbance in feedback loop   Let us now consider a process with a feedback controller in service. This closed-loop system can experience disturbances at two different spots in the feedback loop: load disturbances and set-point disturbances.

1. Step

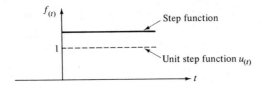

2. Pulses

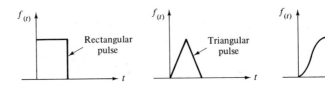

3. Impulse (Dirac delta function $\delta_{(t)}$)

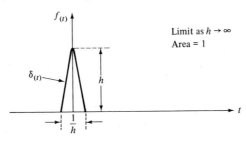

4. Ramp

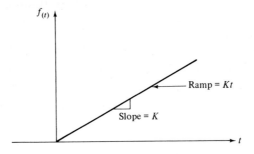

5. Sine wave

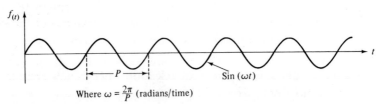

Where $\omega = \frac{2\pi}{P}$ (radians/time)

FIGURE 6-1
Disturbance shapes.

Most disturbances in chemical engineering systems are load disturbances, such as changes in throughput, feed conditions, supply steam pressure, etc. The feedback controller's function when a load disturbance occurs is to keep the controlled variable at its set point by suitable changes in the manipulative variable. The closed-loop response to a load disturbance is called the *regulator response*.

Set-point changes can also be made, particularly in batch processes and in the start-up of continuous processes. These set-point changes are just as much a disturbance to the closed-loop system as a load disturbance. Now the function of the feedback controller is to drive the controlled variable to match the set point. The closed-loop response to a set-point disturbance is called the *servo response* (from the early applications of feedback control in mechanical servomechanism tracking systems, e.g., antiaircraft gun positioning).

6-2 LINEARIZATION AND PERTURBATION VARIABLES

6-2.1 Linearization

As mentioned earlier, we must convert the rigorous nonlinear differential equations describing the system into linear differential equations if we are to be able to use the powerful linear mathematical techniques.

The first question to be answered is just what is a linear differential equation. Basically it is one that contains variables to the first power only in any one term of the equation. If square roots, squares, exponentials, products of variables, etc., appear in the equation, it is nonlinear.

Linear example:
$$a_1 \frac{dx}{dt} + a_0 x = 0$$

where a_1 and a_2 are constants or functions of time only, not of dependent variables or their derivatives.

Nonlinear examples:
$$a_1 \frac{dx}{dt} + a_0 x^{1/2} = 0$$

$$a_1 \frac{dx}{dt} + a_0(x)^2 = 0$$

$$a_1 \frac{dx}{dt} + a_0 e^x = 0$$

$$a_1 \frac{dx_1}{dt} + a_0 x_{1(t)} x_{2(t)} = 0 \qquad (6\text{-}7)$$

where x_1 and x_2 are both dependent variables.

Mathematically, a linear differential equation is one for which the following two properties hold:

1 If $x_{(t)}$ is a solution, then $cx_{(t)}$ is also a solution, where c is a constant.
2 If x_1 is a solution and x_2 is also a solution, then $x_1 + x_2$ is a solution.

Linearization is quite straightforward. All we do is take the nonlinear functions, expand them in Taylor series expansions around the steady-state operating level, and neglect all terms after the first partial derivatives.

Let us assume we have a nonlinear function f of the process variables x_1 and x_2: $f_{(x_1, x_2)}$. For example, x_1 could be mole fraction or °F or lb_m/min. We will denote the steady-state values of these variables by bars over the variables:

$$\bar{x}_1 = \text{steady-state value of } x_1$$
$$\bar{x}_2 = \text{steady-state value of } x_2$$

Now we expand the function $f_{(x_1, x_2)}$ around its steady-state value $f_{(\bar{x}_1, \bar{x}_2)}$.

$$f_{(x_1, x_2)} = f_{(\bar{x}_1, \bar{x}_2)} + \left(\frac{\partial f}{\partial x_1}\right)_{(\bar{x}_1, \bar{x}_2)} (x_1 - \bar{x}_1)$$

$$+ \left(\frac{\partial f}{\partial x_2}\right)_{(\bar{x}_1, \bar{x}_2)} (x_2 - \bar{x}_2) + \left(\frac{\partial^2 f}{\partial x_1^2}\right)_{(\bar{x}_1, \bar{x}_2)} \frac{(x_1 - \bar{x}_1)^2}{2!} + \cdots \qquad (6\text{-}8)$$

$$f_{(x_1, x_2)} \simeq f_{(\bar{x}_1, \bar{x}_2)} + \left(\frac{\partial f}{\partial x_1}\right)_{(\bar{x}_1, \bar{x}_2)} (x_1 - \bar{x}_1) + \left(\frac{\partial f}{\partial x_2}\right)_{(\bar{x}_1, \bar{x}_2)} (x_2 - \bar{x}_2) \qquad (6\text{-}9)$$

Linearization consists of truncating the series after the first partial derivatives. We are approximating the real function by a linear function. The process is sketched graphically in Fig. 6-2 for a function of a single variable. The method is best illustrated in some common examples.

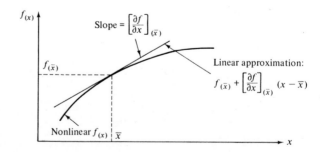

FIGURE 6-2
Linearization.

EXAMPLE 6-1 Consider the square-root dependence of flow out of a tank on the liquid height in the tank.

$$F_{(h)} = K\sqrt{h} \qquad (6\text{-}10)$$

The Taylor series expansion around the steady-state value of h, which is $\bar{h}$ in our nomenclature, is

$$F_{(h)} = F_{(\bar{h})} + \left(\frac{\partial F}{\partial h}\right)_{(\bar{h})} (h - \bar{h}) + \left(\frac{\partial^2 F}{\partial h^2}\right)_{(\bar{h})} \frac{(h - \bar{h})^2}{2!} + \cdots$$

$$\simeq F_{(\bar{h})} + \left(\frac{1}{2} K h^{-1/2}\right)_{(\bar{h})} (h - \bar{h})$$

$$F_{(h)} \simeq K\sqrt{\bar{h}} + \frac{K}{2\sqrt{\bar{h}}} (h - \bar{h}) \qquad (6\text{-}11) \qquad ////$$

EXAMPLE 6-2 The Arrhenius temperature dependence of the specific reaction rate k is a highly nonlinear function that is readily linearized.

$$k_{(T)} = \alpha e^{-E/RT} \qquad (6\text{-}12)$$

$$k_{(T)} = k_{(\bar{T})} + \left(\frac{\partial k}{\partial T}\right)_{(\bar{T})} (T - \bar{T}) + \left(\frac{\partial^2 k}{\partial T^2}\right)_{(\bar{T})} \frac{(T - \bar{T})^2}{2!} + \cdots$$

$$k_{(T)} \simeq k_{(\bar{T})} + \left(\frac{E}{RT^2} e^{-E/RT}\right)_{(\bar{T})} (T - \bar{T})$$

$$k_{(T)} \simeq \bar{k} + \frac{E\bar{k}}{R\bar{T}^2}(T - \bar{T}) \qquad (6\text{-}13)$$

where $\bar{k} \equiv k_{(\bar{T})}$. $\qquad\qquad ////$

EXAMPLE 6-3 The product of two dependent variables is a nonlinear function of the two variables.

$$f_{(C_A, F)} = C_A F$$

$$= f_{(\bar{C}_A, \bar{F})} + \left(\frac{\partial f}{\partial C_A}\right)_{(\bar{C}_A, \bar{F})} (C_A - \bar{C}_A) + \left(\frac{\partial f}{\partial F}\right)_{(\bar{C}_A, \bar{F})} (F - \bar{F})$$

$$+ \left(\frac{\partial^2 f}{\partial C_A^2}\right)_{(\bar{C}_A, \bar{F})} \frac{(C_A - \bar{C}_A)^2}{2!} + \cdots$$

Linearizing:

$$f_{(C_A, F)} \simeq f_{(\bar{C}_A, \bar{F})} + (F)_{(\bar{C}_A, \bar{F})}(C_A - \bar{C}_A) + (C_A)_{(\bar{C}_A, \bar{F})}(F - \bar{F})$$

$$C_A F \simeq \bar{C}_A \bar{F} + \bar{F}(C_A - \bar{C}_A) + \bar{C}_A(F - \bar{F}) \qquad (6\text{-}14)$$

EXAMPLE 6-4   Consider now the nonlinear ordinary differential equation for the gravity-flow tank of Example 4-2.

$$\frac{dv}{dt} = \left(\frac{g}{L}\right)h - \left(\frac{K_F g_c}{\rho A_p}\right)v^2 \qquad (6\text{-}15)$$

Linearizing the v^2 term gives

$$v^2 = \bar{v}^2 + (2\bar{v})(v - \bar{v}) \qquad (6\text{-}16)$$

Thus Eq. (6-15) becomes

$$\frac{dv}{dt} = \left(\frac{g}{L}\right)h - \left(\frac{K_F g_c}{\rho A_p}\right)[\bar{v}^2 + 2\bar{v}(v - \bar{v})] \qquad (6\text{-}17)$$

$$\frac{dv}{dt} = \left(\frac{g}{L}\right)h - \left(\frac{2\bar{v}K_F g_c}{\rho A_p}\right)v + \left(\frac{K_F g_c \bar{v}^2}{\rho A_p}\right) \qquad (6\text{-}18)$$

This equation is now linear. The terms in parentheses are constants, which depend, of course, on the steady state around which the system is linearized.   ////

EXAMPLE 6-5   The component continuity equation for an irreversible nth-order, nonisothermal reaction occurring in a constant-holdup CSTR is

$$\bar{V}\frac{dC_A}{dt} = F_0 C_{A0} - FC_A - \bar{V}C_A{}^n \alpha e^{-E/RT} \qquad (6\text{-}19)$$

Linearization gives

$$\bar{V}\frac{dC_A}{dt} = [\bar{F}_0 \bar{C}_{A0} + \bar{F}_0(C_{A0} - \bar{C}_{A0}) + \bar{C}_{A0}(F_0 - \bar{F}_0)]$$

$$- [\bar{F}\bar{C}_A + \bar{F}(C_A - \bar{C}_A) + \bar{C}_A(F - \bar{F})]$$

$$- \bar{V}\left(\bar{k}\bar{C}_A{}^n + \bar{k}n\bar{C}_A^{n-1}(C_A - \bar{C}_A) + \frac{\bar{k}\bar{C}_A{}^n E}{R\bar{T}^2}(T - \bar{T})\right)$$

$$(6\text{-}20) \qquad ////$$

6-2.2   Perturbation Variables

We will find it very useful in practically all the linear dynamics and control studies in the rest of this book to look at the changes of variables away from steady-state values instead of the absolute variables themselves. Since the total variables are functions of time, $x_{(t)}$, their departures from the steady-state values will also be functions of time, as sketched in Fig. 6-3. These departures from steady state are called *perturbations*. We will use, for the present, the symbol $x_{(t)}^p$. Thus the perturbation in x is defined:

$$x_{(t)}^p \equiv x_{(t)} - \bar{x} \qquad (6\text{-}21)$$

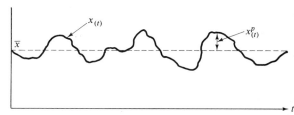

FIGURE 6-3
Perturbation variables.

The equations describing the linear system can now be expressed in terms of these perturbation variables. When this is done, two very useful results occur:

1 The terms in the ordinary differential equations with just constants in them drop out.
2 The initial conditions for the perturbation variables are all equal to zero if the starting point is the steady-state operating level.

Both of the above greatly simplify the linearized equations. For example, if the perturbations in velocity and liquid height are used in Eq. (6-17), we get

$$\frac{d}{dt}(\bar{v} + v^p_{(t)}) = \left(\frac{g}{L}\right)(\bar{h} + h^p_{(t)}) - \left(\frac{K_F g_C}{\rho A_p}\right)[\bar{v}^2 + (2\bar{v})v^p_{(t)}]$$

Since $\bar{v}$ is a constant,

$$\frac{dv^p}{dt} = \left(\frac{g}{L}\right)h^p - \left(\frac{2\bar{v}K_F g_C}{\rho A_p}\right)v^p + \left(\frac{g\bar{h}}{L} - \frac{K_F g_C \bar{v}^2}{\rho A_p}\right) \qquad (6\text{-}22)$$

Now consider Eq. (6-15) under steady-state conditions. At steady state v will be equal to $\bar{v}$, a constant, and h will be equal to $\bar{h}$, another constant.

$$\frac{d\bar{v}}{dt} = 0 = \left(\frac{g}{L}\right)\bar{h} - \left(\frac{K_F g_C}{\rho A_p}\right)\bar{v}^2 \qquad (6\text{-}23)$$

Therefore the last term in Eq. (6-22) is equal to zero. We end up with a linear ordinary differential equation with constant coefficients in terms of perturbation variables.

$$\frac{dv^p}{dt} = \left(\frac{g}{L}\right)h^p - \left(\frac{2\bar{v}K_F g_C}{\rho A_p}\right)v^p \qquad (6\text{-}24)$$

In a similar way Eq. (6-20) can be written in terms of perturbations in C_A, C_{A0}, F_0, F, and T.

$$V\frac{d}{dt}(\bar{C}_A + C_A{}^p) = (\bar{F}_0)C_{A0}{}^p + (\bar{C}_{A0})F_0{}^p - (\bar{F})C_A{}^p - (\bar{C}_A)F^p$$

$$- (\bar{V}\bar{k}n\bar{C}_A^{n-1})C_A{}^p - \left(\frac{\bar{V}k\bar{C}_A{}^nE}{R\bar{T}^2}\right)T^p + (\bar{C}_{A0}\bar{F}_0 - \bar{F}\bar{C}_A - \bar{V}\bar{k}\bar{C}_A{}^n)$$

Application of Eq. (6-19) under steady-state conditions again shows that the last term is just equal to zero.

$$V\frac{dC_A{}^p}{dt} = (\bar{F}_0)C_{A0}{}^p + (\bar{C}_{A0})F_0{}^p - (\bar{F})C_A{}^p - (\bar{C}_A)F^p$$

$$-(\bar{V}\bar{k}n\bar{C}_A^{n-1})C_A{}^p - \left(\frac{\bar{V}k\bar{C}_A{}^nE}{R\bar{T}^2}\right)T^p \qquad (6\text{-}25)$$

Since we will be using perturbation variables most of the time, we will often not bother to use the superscript p. It will be understood that whenever we write the linearized equations for the system all variables will be perturbation variables. Thus Eqs. (6-24) and (6-25) can be written

$$\frac{dv}{dt} = \left(\frac{g}{L}\right)h - \left(\frac{2\bar{v}K_F g_C}{\rho A_p}\right)v$$

$$V\frac{dC_A}{dt} = (\bar{F}_0)C_{A0} + (\bar{C}_{A0})F_0 - (\bar{F} + \bar{V}\bar{k}n\bar{C}_A^{n-1})C_A$$

$$-(\bar{C}_A)F - \left(\frac{\bar{V}k\bar{C}_A{}^nE}{R\bar{T}^2}\right)T \qquad (6\text{-}26)$$

6-3 RESPONSES OF SIMPLE LINEAR SYSTEMS

6-3.1 First-order Linear Ordinary Differential Equation (ODE)

Consider the general first-order linear ODE

$$\frac{dx}{dt} + P_{(t)}x = Q_{(t)} \qquad (6\text{-}27)$$

with a given value of x known at a fixed point in time:

$$x_{(t_0)} = x_0$$

Usually this is an initial condition where $t_0 = 0$.

Multiply both sides of Eq. (6-27) by the integrating factor $\exp\left(\int P\,dt\right)$.

$$\frac{dx}{dt}\exp\left(\int P\,dt\right) + Px\exp\left(\int P\,dt\right) = Q\exp\left(\int P\,dt\right)$$

Combining the two terms on the left-hand side of the equation above gives

$$\frac{d}{dt}\left[x\exp\left(\int P\,dt\right)\right] = Q\exp\left(\int P\,dt\right)$$

Integrating yields

$$x\exp\left(\int P\,dt\right) = \int Q\exp\left(\int P\,dt\right)dt + c_1$$

where c_1 is a constant of integration and can be evaluated by using the boundary or initial condition. Therefore the general solution of Eq. (6-27) is

$$x_{(t)} = \exp\left(-\int P\,dt\right)\left[\int Q\exp\left(\int P\,dt\right)dt + c_1\right] \qquad (6\text{-}28)$$

EXAMPLE 6-6   An isothermal, constant-holdup, constant-throughput CSTR with a first-order irreversible reaction is described by a component continuity equation that is a first-order linear ODE:

$$\frac{dC_A}{dt} + \left(\frac{F}{V} + k\right)C_A = \left(\frac{F}{V}\right)C_{A0} \qquad (6\text{-}29)$$

Let the concentrations C_{A0} and C_A be total values, not perturbations, for the present. The reactant concentration in the tank is initially zero.

$$\textit{Initial condition}: C_{A(0)} = 0$$

At time zero a step change in feed concentration is made from zero to a constant value $\bar{C}_{A0}$.

$$\textit{Forcing function}: C_{A0(t)} = \bar{C}_{A0}$$

Comparing Eqs. (6-27) and (6-29),

$$x = C_A$$

$$P = \frac{F}{V} + k$$

$$Q = \frac{F\bar{C}_{A0}}{V}$$

Therefore

$$\int P \, dt = \int \left(\frac{F}{V} + k\right) dt = \left(\frac{F}{V} + k\right)t$$

$$\exp\left(\int P \, dt\right) = e^{(F/V + k)t}$$

$$\int Q \exp\left(\int P \, dt\right) dt = \int \left(\frac{F\bar{C}_{A0}}{V}\right) e^{(F/V + k)t} \, dt = \left(\frac{F\bar{C}_{A0}}{V}\right) \frac{1}{F/V + k} e^{(F/V + k)t}$$

The solution of Eq. (6-29) is, according to Eq. (6-28),

$$C_{A(t)} = e^{-(F/V + k)t}\left[\left(\frac{F\bar{C}_{A0}}{V}\right) \frac{1}{F/V + k} e^{(F/V + k)t} + c_1\right]$$

$$= \frac{F\bar{C}_{A0}}{F + kV} + c_1 e^{-(F/V + k)t} \tag{6-30}$$

The initial condition is used to find the value of c_1.

$$C_{A(0)} = 0 = \frac{F\bar{C}_{A0}}{F + kV} + c_1(1)$$

Therefore the time-dependent response of C_A to the step disturbance in feed concentration is

$$C_{A(t)} = \frac{\bar{C}_{A0}}{1 + k\tau} [1 - e^{-(k + 1/\tau)t}] \tag{6-31}$$

where

$$\tau \equiv \frac{V}{F}$$

The response is sketched in Fig. 6-4 and is the classic first-order exponential rise to the new steady state.

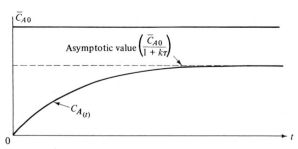

FIGURE 6-4
Step response of a first-order system.

The first thing you should always do when you get a solution is check to see if it is consistent with the initial conditions and if it is reasonable. At $t = 0$, Eq. (6-31) becomes

$$C_{A_{(t=0)}} = \frac{\bar{C}_{A0}}{1 + k\tau} (1 - 1) = 0$$

so the initial condition is satisfied.

Now look at the new steady-state value of C_A that is approached asymptotically by the exponential function. It can be found from either the solution [Eq. (6-31)], letting time t go to infinity, or from the original ODE [Eq. (6-29)], letting the time derivative dC_A/dt go to zero. Either method predicts that at steady state.

$$C_{A_{(t \to \infty)}} = \bar{C}_A = \frac{\bar{C}_{A0}}{1 + k\tau} \qquad (6\text{-}32)$$

Is this reasonable? It says that the consumption of reactant will be greater (the ratio of $\bar{C}_A$ to $\bar{C}_{A0}$ will be smaller) the bigger k and τ are. This certainly makes good physical sense. If k is zero (i.e., no reaction) the final steady-state value of $\bar{C}_A$ will equal $\bar{C}_{A0}$, as it should. Thus the steady-state predictions of the solution seem to check the real physical world.

The ratio of the steady-state value of output over input is called the steady-state *gain* of the process K_p.

$$K_p \equiv \frac{\bar{C}_A}{\bar{C}_{A0}} = \frac{1}{1 + k\tau} \qquad (6\text{-}33)$$

It will be extremely important in our dynamic studies and in controller design.

Does the solution make sense dynamically? The rate of rise will be determined by the $k + 1/\tau$ term in the exponential. The bigger this term, the faster the exponential will decay to zero. The smaller this term, the slower the decay will be. Therefore the dynamics are set by $k + 1/\tau$.

The reciprocal of this term is called the *time constant* of the process τ_p. The bigger the time constant, the slower the dynamic response will be. The solution [Eq. (6-31)] predicts that a small value of k or a big value of τ will give a large process time constant. Again, this makes good physical sense. If there is no reaction, the time constant is just equal to $\tau \equiv V/F$, the holdup time.

Before we leave this example let us put Eq. (6-29) in the form

$$\frac{1}{k + 1/\tau} \frac{dC_A}{dt} + C_A = \frac{1}{1 + k\tau} C_{A0} \qquad (6\text{-}34)$$

$$\tau_p \frac{dC_A}{dt} + C_A = K_p C_{A0} \qquad (6\text{-}35)$$

where

$$\tau_p = \frac{1}{k + 1/\tau} = \text{process time constant with units of time}$$

$$K_p = \frac{1}{1 + k\tau} = \text{process steady-state gain with units of}$$

$$\text{(moles A/ft}^3 \text{ in product)/(moles A/ft}^3 \text{ in feed)}$$

Equation (6-35) is the standard representation of a first-order ODE.

In this example we have been using total variables. If we convert Eq. (6-29) into perturbation variables, we get

$$\frac{d}{dt}(\bar{C}_A + C_A{}^p) + \left(\frac{F}{V} + k\right)(\bar{C}_A + C_A{}^p) = \left(\frac{F}{V}\right)(\bar{C}_{A0} + C_{A0}{}^p)$$

$$\frac{dC_A{}^p}{dt} + \left(\frac{F}{V} + k\right)C_A{}^p = \left(\frac{F}{V}\right)C_{A0}{}^p - \left[\left(\frac{F}{V} + k\right)\bar{C}_A - \left(\frac{F}{V}\right)\bar{C}_{A0}\right] \qquad (6\text{-}36)$$

The last term in the equation above is zero. Therefore Eq. (6-29) and (6-36) are identical, except one is in terms of total variables and the other is in terms of perturbations. Whenever the original ODE is already linear, either total or perturbation variables can be used. Initial conditions will, of course, differ by the steady-state values of all variables. ////

EXAMPLE 6-7 Suppose the feed concentration in the CSTR system considered above is ramped up with time.

$$C_{A0(t)} = Kt \qquad (6\text{-}37)$$

K is a constant. C_A is initially at zero.

Rearranging Eq. (6-35) gives

$$\frac{dC_A}{dt} + \frac{1}{\tau_p}C_A = \frac{K_p K}{\tau_p}t \qquad (6\text{-}38)$$

The solution, according to Eq. (6-28), is

$$C_{A(t)} = \exp\left(-\int\frac{1}{\tau_p}dt\right)\left[\int\frac{K_p K}{\tau_p}t\exp\left(\int\frac{1}{\tau_p}dt\right)dt + c_1\right]$$

$$= e^{-t/\tau_p}\left(\frac{K_p K}{\tau_p}\int t e^{t/\tau_p}dt + c_1\right) \qquad (6\text{-}39)$$

The integral in Eq. (6-39) can be looked up in mathematics tables or can be found by integrating by parts.

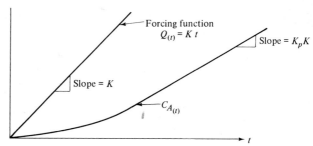

FIGURE 6-5
Ramp response of a first-order system.

Let
$$u = t \quad \text{and} \quad dv = e^{t/\tau_p} \, dt$$

Then
$$du = dt \quad v = \tau_p e^{t/\tau_p}$$

Since
$$\int u \, dv = uv - \int v \, du$$

$$\int t e^{t/\tau_p} \, dt = \tau_p \, t e^{t/\tau_p} - \int \tau_p e^{t/\tau_p} \, dt = \tau_p \, t e^{t/\tau_p} - \tau_p^2 e^{t/\tau_p} \qquad (6\text{-}40)$$

Therefore Eq. (6-39) becomes
$$C_{A(t)} = K_p K (t - \tau_p) + c_1 e^{-t/\tau_p} \qquad (6\text{-}41)$$

Using the initial condition to find c_1,
$$C_{A(0)} = 0 = K_p K(-\tau_p) + c_1$$

The final solution is
$$C_{A(t)} = K_p K \tau_p \left(\frac{t}{\tau_p} - 1 + e^{-t/\tau_p} \right) \qquad (6\text{-}42)$$

This ramp response is sketched in Fig. 6-5.   ////

6-3.2   Second-order Linear Ordinary Differential Equations with Constant Coefficients

The first-order system considered in the previous section yields well-behaved exponential responses. Second-order systems can be much more exciting since they can give an oscillatory or underdamped response.

The first-order linear equation [Eq. (6-27)] could have a time-variable coefficient;

that is, $P_{(t)}$ could be a function of time. We will consider only linear second-order ODE's that have constant coefficients (τ_p and ζ are constants).

$$\tau_p^2 \frac{d^2x}{dt^2} + 2\tau_p\zeta \frac{dx}{dt} + x = Q_{(t)} \qquad (6\text{-}43)$$

Analytical methods are available for linear ODE's with variable coefficients[1] but their solutions are usually messy infinite series. We will not consider them here.

The solution of a second-order ODE can be deduced from the solution of a first-order ODE. Equation (6-28) can be broken up into two parts:

$$x_{(t)} = \left[c_1 \exp\left(- \int P\, dt \right) \right] + \left[\exp\left(- \int P\, dt \right) \int Q \exp\left(\int P\, dt \right) dt \right] = x_c + x_p \qquad (6\text{-}44)$$

x_c is called the *complementary solution*. It is the function that satisfies the original ODE with the forcing function $Q_{(t)}$ set equal to zero (called the *homogeneous* differential equation):

$$\frac{dx}{dt} + P_{(t)}x = 0 \qquad (6\text{-}45)$$

The term x_p is called the *particular solution*. It is the function that satisfies the original ODE with a specified $Q_{(t)}$. One of the most useful properties of linear ODE's is that the total solution is the sum of the complementary solution and the particular solution.

Now we can extend the above to the second-order ODE of Eq. (6-43). First we obtain the complementary solution x_c by solving the homogeneous equation

$$\tau_p^2 \frac{d^2x}{dt^2} + 2\tau_p\zeta \frac{dx}{dt} + x = 0 \qquad (6\text{-}46)$$

Then we solve for the particular solution x_p and add the two.

Complementary solution   Since the complementary solution of the first-order ODE is an exponential, it is reasonable to guess that the complementary solution of the second-order ODE will also be of the exponential form. Let us guess that

$$x_c = c_s e^{st} \qquad (6\text{-}47)$$

where c_s and s are constants. Differentiating x_c twice gives

$$\frac{dx_c}{dt} = c_s s e^{st}$$

$$\frac{d^2 x_c}{dt^2} = c_s s^2 e^{st} \qquad (6\text{-}48)$$

[1] W. R. Marshall and R. L. Pigford, "Application of Differential Equations to Chemical Engineering Problems," University of Delaware, 1947.

Now we substitute the guessed solution and its derivatives into Eq. (6-46) to find the values of s that will make the assumed form [Eq. (6-47)] satisfy it.

$$\tau_p^2(c_s s^2 e^{st}) + 2\tau_p \zeta(c_s s e^{st}) + (c_s e^{st}) = 0$$

$$\tau_p^2 s^2 + 2\tau_p \zeta s + 1 = 0 \qquad (6\text{-}49)$$

The above equation is called the *characteristic equation* of the system. It is the system's most important dynamic feature. The values of s that satisfy Eq. (6-49) are called the *roots* of the characteristic equation (they are also called the *eigenvalues* of the system). Their values, as we will shortly show, will dictate if the system is fast or slow, stable or unstable, overdamped or underdamped.

Using the general solution for a quadratic equation, we can solve Eq. (6-49) for its roots:

$$s = \frac{-2\tau_p \zeta \pm \sqrt{(2\tau_p \zeta)^2 - 4\tau_p^2}}{2\tau_p^2} = -\frac{\zeta}{\tau_p} \pm \frac{\sqrt{\zeta^2 - 1}}{\tau_p} \qquad (6\text{-}50)$$

There are two values of s that satisfy Eq. (6-49). Therefore there are two exponentials of the form given in Eq. (6-47) that are solutions of the original homogeneous ODE [Eq. (6-46)]. The sum of these solutions is also a solution since the ODE is linear. Therefore the complementary solution is (for $s_1 \neq s_2$)

$$x_c = c_1 e^{s_1 t} + c_2 e^{s_2 t} \qquad (6\text{-}51)$$

where c_1 and c_2 are constants.

$$s_1 = -\frac{\zeta}{\tau_p} + \frac{1}{\tau_p} \sqrt{\zeta^2 - 1}$$

$$s_2 = -\frac{\zeta}{\tau_p} - \frac{1}{\tau_p} \sqrt{\zeta^2 - 1}$$

The shape of the solution curve depends strongly on the values of the physical parameter ζ, the damping coefficient. Let us now look at the various possibilities.

FOR $\zeta > 1$ (OVERDAMPED SYSTEM)   If the damping coefficient is greater than unity, the quantity inside the square root is positive. Then s_1 and s_2 will both be real numbers, and they will be different (called *distinct roots*).

EXAMPLE 6-8   Consider the ODE

$$\frac{d^2x}{dt^2} + 5\frac{dx}{dt} + 6x = 0$$

$$\left(\frac{1}{\sqrt{6}}\right)^2 \frac{d^2x}{dt^2} + 2\left(\frac{1}{\sqrt{6}}\right)\left(\frac{5}{2\sqrt{6}}\right)\frac{dx}{dt} + x = 0 \qquad (6\text{-}52)$$

Its characteristic equation is

$$s^2 + 5s + 6 = 0 \qquad (6\text{-}53)$$

$$(s + 3)(s + 2) = 0 \qquad (6\text{-}54)$$

$$\left(\frac{1}{\sqrt{6}}\right)^2 s^2 + 2\left(\frac{1}{\sqrt{6}}\right)\left(\frac{5}{2\sqrt{6}}\right)s + 1 = 0 \qquad (6\text{-}55)$$

All three of the above are completely equivalent. The time constant and damping coefficient for the system are

$$\tau_p = \frac{1}{\sqrt{6}} \qquad \zeta = \frac{5}{2\sqrt{6}}$$

The roots of the characteristic equation are obvious from Eq. (6-54), but use of Eq. (6-50) gives

$$s = -\frac{\zeta}{\tau_p} \pm \frac{1}{\tau_p}\sqrt{\zeta^2 - 1} = -\tfrac{5}{2} \pm \tfrac{1}{2}$$

$$s_1 = -2$$

$$s_2 = -3 \qquad (6\text{-}56)$$

The roots are both real, and the complementary solution is

$$x_c = c_1 e^{-2t} + c_2 e^{-3t} \qquad (6\text{-}57) \qquad ////$$

FOR $\zeta = 1$ (CRITICALLY DAMPED SYSTEM) If the damping coefficient is equal to unity, the term inside the square root of Eq. (6-50) is zero. There is only one value of s that satisfies the characteristic equation.

$$s = -\frac{1}{\tau_p} \qquad (6\text{-}58)$$

The two roots are the same and are called *repeated* roots. This is clearly seen if a value of $\zeta = 1$ is substituted into the characteristic equation [Eq. (6-49)]:

$$\tau_p^2 s^2 + 2\tau_p s + 1 = (\tau_p s + 1)(\tau_p s + 1) = 0 \qquad (6\text{-}59)$$

The complementary solution with a repeated root is

$$x_c = (c_1 + c_2 t)e^{st} = (c_1 + c_2 t)e^{-t/\tau_p} \qquad (6\text{-}60)$$

This is easily proved by substituting it into Eq. (6-46) with ζ set equal to unity.

EXAMPLE 6-9   If two CSTR's like the one considered in Example 6-6 are run in series, two first-order ODE's describe the system:

$$\frac{dC_{A1}}{dt} + \left(\frac{1}{\tau_1} + k_1\right) C_{A1} = \frac{1}{\tau_1} C_{A0}$$

$$\frac{dC_{A2}}{dt} + \left(\frac{1}{\tau_2} + k_2\right) C_{A2} = \frac{1}{\tau_2} C_{A1} \qquad (6\text{-}61)$$

Differentiating the second equation and eliminating C_{A1} give a second-order ODE:

$$\frac{d^2 C_{A2}}{dt^2} + \left(\frac{1}{\tau_1} + k_1 + \frac{1}{\tau_2} + k_2\right) \frac{dC_{A2}}{dt} + \left(\frac{1}{\tau_1} + k_1\right)\left(\frac{1}{\tau_2} + k_2\right) C_{A2} = \frac{1}{\tau_1 \tau_2} C_{A0} \qquad (6\text{-}62)$$

If temperatures and holdups are the same in both tanks, the specific reaction rates k and holdup times τ will be the same.

$$k_1 = k_2 \equiv k$$

$$\tau_1 = \tau_2 \equiv \tau$$

The characteristic equation is

$$s^2 + 2\left(\frac{1}{\tau} + k\right)s + \left(\frac{1}{\tau} + k\right)^2 = 0$$

$$\left(s + \frac{1}{\tau} + k\right)\left(s + \frac{1}{\tau} + k\right) = 0 \qquad (6\text{-}63)$$

The damping coefficient is unity and there is a real, repeated root:

$$s = -\left(\frac{1}{\tau} + k\right)$$

The complementary solution is

$$(C_{A2})_c = (c_1 + c_2 t)e^{-(k + 1/\tau)t} \qquad (6\text{-}64) \qquad ////$$

FOR $\zeta < 1$ (UNDERDAMPED SYSTEM)   Things begin to get interesting when the damping coefficient is less than 1. Now the term inside the square root in Eq. (6-50) is negative, giving an imaginary number in the roots.

$$s = -\frac{\zeta}{\tau_p} \pm \frac{1}{\tau_p}\sqrt{\zeta^2 - 1}$$

$$= -\frac{\zeta}{\tau_p} \pm i\frac{1}{\tau_p}\sqrt{1 - \zeta^2} \qquad (6\text{-}65)$$

The roots are now complex numbers with real and imaginary parts.

$$s_1 = -\frac{\zeta}{\tau_p} + i\frac{1}{\tau_p}\sqrt{1-\zeta^2}$$

$$s_2 = -\frac{\zeta}{\tau_p} - i\frac{1}{\tau_p}\sqrt{1-\zeta^2}$$

To be more specific, they are complex conjugates since they have the same real parts and their imaginary parts differ only in sign. The complementary solution is

$$x_c = c_1 e^{s_1 t} + c_2 e^{s_2 t}$$

$$= c_1 \exp\left[\left(-\frac{\zeta}{\tau_p} + i\frac{1}{\tau_p}\sqrt{1-\zeta^2}\right)t\right] + c_2 \exp\left[\left(-\frac{\zeta}{\tau_p} - i\frac{1}{\tau_p}\sqrt{1-\zeta^2}\right)t\right]$$

$$= e^{-\zeta t/\tau_p}\left[c_1 \exp\left(+\frac{i\sqrt{1-\zeta^2}}{\tau_p}t\right) + c_2 \exp\left(-\frac{i\sqrt{1-\zeta^2}}{\tau_p}t\right)\right] \tag{6-66}$$

Since

$$e^{ix} = \cos x + i\sin x \tag{6-67}$$

$$x_c = e^{-\zeta t/\tau_p}\left[c_1\left(\cos\frac{\sqrt{1-\zeta^2}}{\tau_p}t + i\sin\frac{\sqrt{1-\zeta^2}}{\tau_p}t\right)\right.$$

$$\left. + c_2\left(\cos\frac{\sqrt{1-\zeta^2}}{\tau_p}t - i\sin\frac{\sqrt{1-\zeta^2}}{\tau_p}t\right)\right]$$

$$= e^{-\zeta t/\tau_p}\left[(c_1 + c_2)\cos\frac{\sqrt{1-\zeta^2}}{\tau_p}t + i(c_1 - c_2)\sin\frac{\sqrt{1-\zeta^2}}{\tau_p}t\right] \tag{6-68}$$

The complementary solution consists of oscillating sinusoidal terms multiplied by an exponential. Thus the solution is oscillatory or undamped for $\zeta < 1$. Note that as long as the damping coefficient is positive, $\zeta > 0$, the exponential term will decay to zero as time goes to infinity. Therefore the amplitude of the oscillations will decrease to zero. This is sketched in Fig. 6-6.

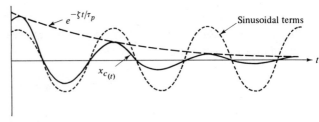

FIGURE 6-6
Complementary solution for $\zeta < 1$.

Since the solution x_c must be real, if we are describing a real physical system, the terms with the constants in Eq. (6-68) must be real. $c_1 + c_2$ and $i(c_1 - c_2)$ must both be real. This can be true only if c_1 and c_2 are complex conjugates. If z is a complex number and $\bar{z}$ is its complex conjugate,

$$z = x + iy$$

$$\bar{z} = x - iy$$

Now

$$z + \bar{z} = 2 \operatorname{Re} (z) = 2x \qquad \text{a real number}$$
$$z - \bar{z} = i\, 2 \operatorname{Im} (z) = 2yi \qquad \text{a pure imaginary number}$$
$$i(z - \bar{z}) = -2y \qquad \text{a real number}$$

Let c_1 be a complex constant:

$$c_1 = c^R + ic^I$$

Then

$$c_2 = \bar{c}_1 = c^R - ic^I$$

And the complementary solution becomes

$$x_{c(t)} = e^{-\zeta t/\tau_p}\left[(2c^R) \cos \left(\frac{\sqrt{1 - \zeta^2}}{\tau_p} t \right) - (2c^I) \sin \left(\frac{\sqrt{1 - \zeta^2}}{\tau_p} t \right) \right] \qquad (6\text{-}69)$$

EXAMPLE 6-10   Consider the ODE

$$\frac{d^2 x}{dt^2} + \frac{dx}{dt} + x = 0$$

$$\frac{d^2 x}{dt^2} + 2(0.5)\frac{dx}{dt} + x = 0 \qquad \begin{cases} \tau_p = 1 \\ \zeta = 0.5 \end{cases} \qquad (6\text{-}70)$$

Its characteristic equation is

$$s^2 + s + 1 = 0$$

Its roots are

$$s = -\frac{\zeta}{\tau_p} \pm i \frac{1}{\tau_p} \sqrt{1 - \zeta^2}$$

$$= -\tfrac{1}{2} \pm i\sqrt{1 - (\tfrac{1}{2})^2} = -\tfrac{1}{2} \pm i \frac{\sqrt{3}}{2} \qquad (6\text{-}71)$$

The complementary solution is

$$x_{c_{(t)}} = e^{-t/2}\left(2c^R \cos \frac{\sqrt{3}}{2} t - 2c^I \sin \frac{\sqrt{3}}{2} t\right) \qquad (6\text{-}72) \qquad ////$$

FOR $\zeta = 0$ (UNDAMPED SYSTEM)   The complementary solution is the same as Eq. (6-69) with the exponential term equal to unity. There is no decay of the sine and cosine terms and therefore the system will oscillate forever.

FOR $\zeta < 0$ (UNSTABLE SYSTEM)   If the damping coefficient is negative, the exponential term increases without bound as time becomes large. Thus the system is unstable.

   We have found the limit of stability of a second-order system. The roots of the characteristic equation are [from Eq. (6-65)]

$$s = -\frac{\zeta}{\tau_p} \pm i \frac{1}{\tau_p} \sqrt{1 - \zeta^2}$$

If the real part of the root $(-\zeta/\tau_p)$ is a positive number, the system is unstable.

Particular solution   Up to this point we have found only the complementary solution of the homogeneous equation

$$\tau_p^2 \frac{d^2x}{dt^2} + 2\tau_p\zeta \frac{dx}{dt} + x = 0$$

This corresponds to the solution for the unforced or undisturbed system. Now we must find the particular solutions for some specific forcing functions $Q_{(t)}$. Then the total solution will be the sum of the complementary and particular solutions.

   There are several methods for finding particular solutions. Laplace transform methods are probably the most convenient, and we will use them in the next chapter. Here we will present the *method of undetermined coefficients*. It consists of assuming a particular solution that has the same form as the forcing function. It is illustrated in the examples below.

EXAMPLE 6-11   The overdamped system of Example 6-8 is forced with a unit step function.

$$\frac{d^2x}{dt^2} + 5\frac{dx}{dt} + 6x = 1 \qquad (6\text{-}73)$$

Initial conditions are

$$x_{(0)} = 0 \qquad \left(\frac{dx}{dt}\right)_{(0)} = 0$$

The forcing function is a constant, so we assume the particular solution is also a constant:

$$x_p = c_3$$

Substituting into Eq. (6-73) gives

$$0 + 5(0) + 6(c_3) = 1$$
$$x_p = c_3 = \tfrac{1}{6} \qquad (6\text{-}74)$$

Now the total solution is [using Eq. (6-57)]

$$x = x_c + x_p = c_1 e^{-2t} + c_2 e^{-3t} + \tfrac{1}{6} \qquad (6\text{-}75)$$

The constants are evaluated from the initial conditions[1]

$$x_{(0)} = 0 = c_1 + c_2 + \tfrac{1}{6}$$
$$\left(\frac{dx}{dt}\right)_{(0)} = (-2c_1 e^{-2t} - 3c_2 e^{-3t})_{(t=0)} = -2c_1 - 3c_2 = 0$$

Therefore

$$c_1 = -\tfrac{1}{2} \qquad \text{and} \qquad c_2 = \tfrac{1}{3}$$

The final solution is

$$x_{(t)} = \tfrac{1}{3}e^{-3t} - \tfrac{1}{2}e^{-2t} + \tfrac{1}{6} \qquad (6\text{-}76) \qquad ////$$

EXAMPLE 6-12 A general underdamped second-order system is forced by a unit step function:

$$\tau_p^{\,2}\frac{d^2x}{dt^2} + 2\tau_p \zeta \frac{dx}{dt} + x = 1 \qquad (6\text{-}77)$$

Initial conditions are

$$x_{(0)} = \left(\frac{dx}{dt}\right)_{(0)} = 0$$

Since the forcing function is a constant, the particular solution is assumed to be a constant, giving

$$x_p = 1$$

---

[1] Constants are evaluated using the total solution. A common mistake is to evaluate them using only the complementary solution.

The total solution is [using the complementary solution of Eq. (6-69)]

$$x_{(t)} = 1 + e^{-\zeta t/\tau_p}\left(2c^R \cos\frac{\sqrt{1-\zeta^2}}{\tau_p}t - 2c^I \sin\frac{\sqrt{1-\zeta^2}}{\tau_p}t\right) \qquad (6\text{-}78)$$

Using the initial conditions to evaluate constants,

$$x_{(0)} = 1 + [2c^R(1) - 2c^I(0)] = 0$$

$$\frac{dx}{dt} = -\frac{\zeta}{\tau_p}e^{-\zeta t/\tau_p}\left(2c^R \cos\frac{\sqrt{1-\zeta^2}}{\tau_p}t - 2c^I \sin\frac{\sqrt{1-\zeta^2}}{\tau_p}t\right)$$

$$+ e^{-\zeta t/\tau_p}\left(-\frac{\sqrt{1-\zeta^2}}{\tau_p}2c^R \sin\frac{\sqrt{1-\zeta^2}}{\tau_p}t\right.$$

$$\left. -\frac{\sqrt{1-\zeta^2}}{\tau_p}2c^I \cos\frac{\sqrt{1-\zeta^2}}{\tau_p}t\right)$$

$$\left(\frac{dx}{dt}\right)_{(0)} = 0 = -\frac{\zeta}{\tau_p}(2c^R) + \left(-\frac{\sqrt{1-\zeta^2}}{\tau_p}2c^I\right)$$

giving
$$2c^R = -1$$

$$2c^I = \frac{\zeta}{\sqrt{1-\zeta^2}} \qquad (6\text{-}79)$$

The total solution is

$$x_{(t)} = 1 - e^{-\zeta t/\tau_p}\left[\cos\left(\frac{\sqrt{1-\zeta^2}}{\tau_p}t\right) + \frac{\zeta}{\sqrt{1-\zeta^2}}\sin\left(\frac{\sqrt{1-\zeta^2}}{\tau_p}t\right)\right] \qquad (6\text{-}80)$$

This step response is sketched in Fig. 6-7 for several values of the damping coefficient.

////

EXAMPLE 6-13   The overdamped system of Example 6-8 is now forced with a ramp input:

$$\frac{d^2x}{dt^2} + 5\frac{dx}{dt} + 6x = t \qquad (6\text{-}81)$$

Since the forcing function is the first term of a polynomial in t, we will assume that the particular solution is also a polynomial in t.

$$x_p = b_0 + b_1 t + b_2 t^2 + b_3 t^3 + \cdots \qquad (6\text{-}82)$$

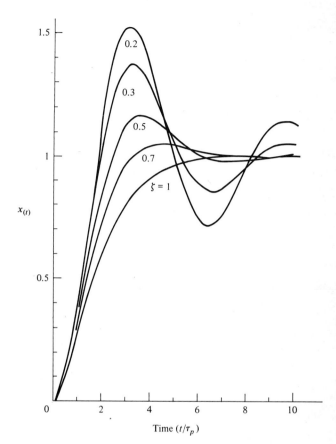

FIGURE 6-7
Step responses of a second-order underdamped system.

where the b_i are constants to be determined. Differentiating,

$$\frac{dx_p}{dt} = b_1 + 2b_2 t + 3b_3 t^2 + \cdots$$

$$\frac{d^2 x_p}{dt^2} = 2b_2 + 6b_3 t + \cdots$$

Substituting into Eq. (6-81),

$$(2b_2 + 6b_3 t + \cdots) + 5(b_1 + 2b_2 t + 3b_3 t^2 + \cdots)$$
$$+ 6(b_0 + b_1 t + b_2 t^2 + \cdots) = t$$

We now rearrange the above to group together all terms with equal powers of t.

$$\cdots + t^3(6b_3 + \cdots) + t^2(6b_2 + 15b_3 + \cdots) + t(6b_3 + 10b_2 + 6b_1)$$
$$+ (2b_2 + 5b_1 + 6b_0) = t$$

Equating like powers of t on the left- and right-hand sides of this equation gives the simultaneous equations

$$6b_3 + \cdots = 0$$
$$6b_2 + 15b_3 + \cdots = 0$$
$$6b_3 + 10b_2 + 6b_1 = 1$$
$$2b_2 + 5b_1 + 6b_0 = 0 \qquad (6\text{-}83)$$

Solving simultaneously gives

$$b_0 = -\tfrac{5}{36}$$
$$b_1 = \tfrac{1}{6}$$
$$b_2 = b_3 = \cdots = 0$$

The particular solution is

$$x_p = -\tfrac{5}{36} + \tfrac{1}{6}t \qquad (6\text{-}84)$$

The total solution is

$$x = -\tfrac{5}{36} + \tfrac{1}{6}t + c_1 e^{-2t} + c_2 e^{-3t} \qquad (6\text{-}85)$$

If the initial conditions are

$$x_{(0)} = \left(\frac{dx}{dt}\right)_{(0)} = 0$$

the constants can be evaluated:

$$\left.\begin{array}{l} x_{(0)} = 0 = -\tfrac{5}{36} + c_1 + c_2 \\[2mm] \left(\dfrac{dx}{dt}\right)_{(0)} = 0 = \tfrac{1}{6} - 2c_1 - 3c_2 \end{array}\right\} \Rightarrow \left\{\begin{array}{l} c_1 = \tfrac{1}{4} \\[2mm] c_2 = -\tfrac{1}{9} \end{array}\right. \qquad (6\text{-}86)$$

And the final solution is

$$x_{(t)} = -\tfrac{5}{36} + \tfrac{1}{6}t + \tfrac{1}{4}e^{-2t} - \tfrac{1}{9}e^{-3t} \qquad (6\text{-}87) \qquad ////$$

6-3.3   Nth-order Linear Ordinary Differential Equations with Constant Coefficients

The results obtained in the last two sections for simple first- and second-order systems can now be generalized to higher-order systems. Consider the Nth-order ODE

$$a_N \frac{d^N x}{dt^N} + a_{N-1} \frac{d^{N-1} x}{dt^{N-1}} + \cdots + a_1 \frac{dx}{dt} + a_0 x = Q_{(t)} \qquad (6\text{-}88)$$

where the a_n are constants.

The solution of this equation is the sum of a particular solution and a complementary solution:

$$x = x_p + x_c$$

The complementary solution is the sum of N exponential terms. The characteristic equation is an Nth-order polynomial:

$$a_N s^N + a_{N-1} s^{N-1} + \cdots + a_1 s + a_0 = 0 \qquad (6\text{-}89)$$

There are N roots s_i of the characteristic equation, some of which may be repeated (twice or more). Factoring Eq. (6-89) gives

$$(s - s_1)(s - s_2)(s - s_3) \cdots (s - s_{N-1})(s - s_N) = 0 \qquad (6\text{-}90)$$

where the s_i are the roots of the polynomial. The complementary solution is (for all distinct roots, i.e., no repeated roots)

$$x_{c(t)} = c_1 e^{s_1 t} + c_2 e^{s_2 t} + \ldots + c_N e^{s_N t}$$

And therefore the total solution is

$$x_{(t)} = x_{p_{(t)}} + \sum_{i=1}^{N} c_i e^{s_i t} \qquad (6\text{-}91)$$

The roots can be real or complex. But if they are complex they must appear in complex conjugate pairs. The reason for this is illustrated for a second-order system with a characteristic equation:

$$s^2 + a_1 s + a_0 = 0 \qquad (6\text{-}92)$$

Let the two roots be s_1 and s_2.

$$(s - s_1)(s - s_2) = 0$$
$$s^2 + (-s_1 - s_2)s + s_1 s_2 = 0 \qquad (6\text{-}93)$$

The coefficients a_0 and a_1 can then be expressed in terms of the roots:

$$a_0 = s_1 s_2$$
$$a_1 = -(s_1 + s_2) \qquad (6\text{-}94)$$

If Eq. (6-92) is the characteristic equation for a real physical system, the coefficients a_0 and a_1 must be real numbers.

If the roots are both real, a_0 and a_1 are certainly real. If the roots are complex, the coefficients must still be real and must also satisfy Eqs. (6-94). Complex conjugates are the only complex numbers that give real numbers when they are multiplied together *and* when added together.

$$z\bar{z} = x^2 + y^2 \qquad \text{a real number}$$
$$z + \bar{z} = 2x \qquad \text{a real number}$$

Therefore the roots s_1 and s_2 must be a complex conjugate pair if they are complex. This is exactly what we found in Eq. (6-65) of the previous section.

For example, a third-order system could have three real roots:

$$s_1 = \alpha_1$$
$$s_2 = \alpha_2$$
$$s_3 = \alpha_3 \qquad (6\text{-}95)$$

Or it could have one real root and two complex roots:

$$s_1 = \alpha_1$$
$$s_2 = \alpha_2 + i\omega_2$$
$$s_3 = \bar{s}_2 = \alpha_2 - i\omega_2 \qquad (6\text{-}96)$$

where $\qquad \alpha_i = \operatorname{Re} s_i \qquad$ and $\qquad \omega_i = \operatorname{Im} s_i$

These are the only two possibilities. The complementary solution would be either (for distinct roots):

$$x_c = c_1 e^{\alpha_1 t} + c_2 e^{\alpha_2 t} + c_3 e^{\alpha_3 t} \qquad (6\text{-}97)$$

or $\qquad x_c = c_1 e^{\alpha_1 t} + e^{\alpha_2 t}[(c_2 + c_3) \cos \omega_2 t + i(c_2 - c_3) \sin \omega_2 t] \qquad (6\text{-}98)$

where the constants c_2 and c_3 must also be complex conjugates in the latter equation, as discussed in the previous section.

If some of the roots are repeated (not distinct) the complementary solution will contain exponential terms that are multiplied by various powers of t. For example, if α_1 is a repeated root of order 2, the characteristic equation would be

$$(s - \alpha_1)^2(s - s_3)(s - s_4)\cdots(s - s_N) = 0$$

The complementary solution is

$$x_c = (c_1 + c_2 t)e^{\alpha_1 t} + \sum_{i=3}^{N} c_i e^{s_i t} \qquad (6\text{-}99)$$

If α_1 is a repeated root of order 3, the characteristic equation would be

$$(s - \alpha_1)^3(s - s_4)\cdots(s - s_N) = 0$$

and the resulting complementary solution is

$$x_c = (c_1 + c_2 t + c_3 t^2)e^{\alpha_1 t} + \sum_{i=4}^{N} c_i e^{s_i t} \qquad (6\text{-}100)$$

The stability of the system is dictated by the values of the real parts α_i of the roots. The system is stable if the real parts of *all* roots are negative, since the exponential terms go to zero as time goes to infinity. The roots of the characteristic equation can be very conveniently plotted in a two-dimensional figure (Fig. 6-8) called the "*s* plane."

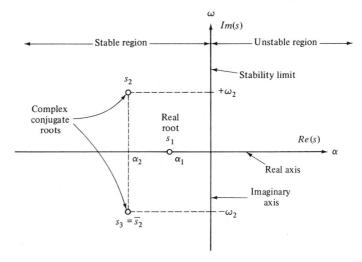

FIGURE 6-8
s-plane plot of the roots of the characteristic equation.

Let the ordinate be the imaginary part of the root ω and the abscissa be the real part of the root α. The roots of Eqs. (6-96) are shown in Fig. 6-8.

Therefore the stability criterion is:

A system is stable if all the roots of its characteristic equation lie in the left-half of the s plane.

6-4   STEADY-STATE TECHNIQUES

Sometimes useful information can be obtained about the dynamics of the system from just the steady-state equations of the system. Van Heerden[1] proposed the application of the following steady-state analysis to chemical reactors. Consider a nonisothermal CSTR described by the two nonlinear ODE's

$$\frac{d}{dt}(VC_A) = F(C_{A0} - C_A) - VC_A \alpha e^{-E/RT}$$

$$\frac{d}{dt}(VC_p \rho T) = F\rho C_p(T_0 - T) - \lambda VC_A \alpha e^{-E/RT} - UA(T - T_J) \qquad (16\text{-}101)$$

[1] C. van Heerden, *Ind. Eng. Chem.*, vol. 45, p. 1242, 1953.

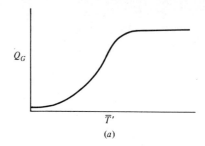

FIGURE 6-9a
Heat generation.

$\bar{T}'$

(a)

Under steady-state conditions these two equations become

$$0 = \bar{F}\bar{C}_{A0} - \bar{F}\bar{C}_A - \bar{V}\bar{C}_A \alpha e^{-E/RT} \qquad (6\text{-}102)$$

$$0 = \bar{F}C_p\rho\bar{T}_0 - \bar{F}C_p\rho\bar{T} - \lambda\bar{V}\bar{C}_A \alpha e^{-E/RT} - UA(\bar{T} - \bar{T}_J) \qquad (6\text{-}103)$$

Now let us pick a trial value of steady-state temperature $\bar{T}'$. We will see if it satisfies the two steady-state equations above. If it does, it is a bona fide steady-state temperature $\bar{T}$. Solving Eq. (6-102) for $\bar{C}_A$ gives

$$\bar{C}_A = \frac{\bar{F}\bar{C}_{A0}}{\bar{F} + \bar{V}\alpha e^{-E/R\bar{T}}} \qquad (6\text{-}104)$$

If we assume a series of values of $\bar{T}'$, the above equation gives the corresponding values of $\bar{C}_{A(T')}$. At low temperatures $\bar{C}_A$ will be essentially equal to $\bar{C}_{A0}$ since the reaction rate is low. At high temperatures $\bar{C}_A$ will approach zero since more and more of the reactant A will be used up by the reaction.

Now look at the third term in Eq. (6-103).

$$Q_G \equiv -\lambda\bar{V}\bar{C}_A \alpha e^{-E/RT} \qquad (6\text{-}105)$$

This is the "heat generation" part of the equation, i.e., the rate at which the reaction is generating exothermic heat. Figure 6-9a shows how Q_G varies with the assumed temperature $\bar{T}'$. Q_G is low at low temperatures because the reaction rate is low. Q_G increases as temperature increases, but eventually flattens out at a maximum value. The rate of heat generation cannot increase beyond the value that corresponds to complete conversion of all the reactant A in the feed stream. Another way to look at this is to realize that, although the specific reaction rate k continues to increase with temperature, the total reaction rate $(V\bar{k}\bar{C}_A)$ becomes constant because the reactant concentration $\bar{C}_A$ approaches zero.

Now we will group the other terms of Eq. (6-103) together into a "heat removal" term.

$$Q_R = UA(\bar{T} - \bar{T}_J) + \bar{F}C_p\rho(\bar{T} - \bar{T}_0) \qquad (6\text{-}106)$$

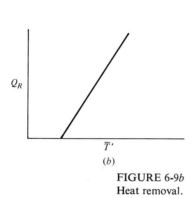

(b)

FIGURE 6-9b

Heat removal.

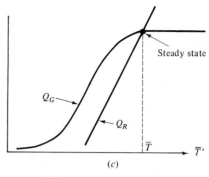

(c)

FIGURE 6-9c

Heat generation and heat removal.

The first term is the rate of heat removal by heat transfer to the cooling jacket. The second term is a sensible-heat term. The feed temperature $\bar{T}_0$ will usually be lower than the reactor temperature $\bar{T}$, and therefore heat will be soaked up in heating the feed stream up to reactor temperature. Figure 6-9b shows a plot of Q_R versus the assumed temperature $\bar{T}'$. If U, A, $\bar{F}$, C_p, $\bar{T}_0$, ρ, and $\bar{T}_J$ are all constant, Q_R is a linear function of temperature with a slope equal to $UA + \bar{F}C_p\rho$.

$$Q_R = (UA + \bar{F}C_p\rho)\bar{T} - (UA\bar{T}_J + \bar{F}C_p\rho\bar{T}_0) \qquad (6\text{-}107)$$

If Eq. (6-103) is to be satisfied at steady state, Q_G must equal Q_R. In other words, a temperature at which the Q_G and Q_R curves intersect is a steady-state temperature. Figure 6-9c shows both curves plotted together with one intersection at $\bar{T}$.

What can be concluded about the dynamics of the system from this steady-state plot? Imagine that a small disturbance causes the temperature to increase slightly above its steady-state value $\bar{T}$. At the higher temperature the heat-removal rate is greater than the heat-generation rate, according to the curves in Fig. 6-9c. Therefore the temperature will tend to be decreased toward the steady state $\bar{T}$.

If the disturbance moved the temperature down below $\bar{T}$, the heat-generation rate would be greater than the heat-removal rate. Therefore the temperature would tend to rise again to $\bar{T}$.

We can intuitively say that in order for a steady state to be stable the slope of the Q_R curve must be greater than the slope of the Q_G curve.

$$\left(\frac{dQ_R}{dT}\right)_{(T)} > \left(\frac{dQ_G}{dT}\right)_{(T)} \qquad (6\text{-}108)$$

This is a necessary but not sufficient condition for stability.

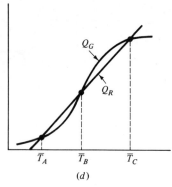

FIGURE 6-9d
Multiple steady states.

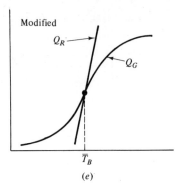

FIGURE 6-9e
Q_R curve modified to make $\overline{T}_B$ a stable
steady state.

Figure 6-9d shows another system where there are now *three* intersections of the Q_R and Q_G curves. This means that there can be three steady states. For exactly the same feed conditions and parameter values, the reactor could settle out at three different temperatures: $\overline{T}_A$, $\overline{T}_B$, or $\overline{T}_C$. The three different steady-state compositions corresponding to these steady-state temperatures would show low, medium, or high conversions (high, medium, or low concentrations of reactant A).

The possibility for multiple steady states is an intriguing notion. It can occur only in a nonlinear system.

The stability criterion of Eq. (6-108) predicts that the steady states at $\overline{T}_A$ and $\overline{T}_C$ would be stable but that the steady state at $\overline{T}_B$ would be unstable. Any little temperature disturbance would cause the reaction to "quench" down to $\overline{T}_A$ or "run away" up to conditions at $\overline{T}_C$.

If we want to run the reactor at the steady-state temperature $\overline{T}_B$, the heat-removal curve must be modified by changing system parameters (or adding a feedback controller, as we will show in the next part of this book) to make it intersect the Q_G curve at $\overline{T}_B$ with a slope greater than $(dQ_G/dT)_{(\overline{T}_B)}$ as sketched in Fig. 6-9e.

PROBLEMS

6-1 Linearize the following nonlinear functions:

(*a*) $f_{(x)} = y_{(x)} = \dfrac{\alpha x}{1 + (\alpha - 1)x}$

where α is a constant.

(*b*) $f_{(T)} = P^0{}_{(T)} = e^{A/T + B}$

where A and B are constants.

(c) $f_{(v)} = U_{(v)} = K(v)^{0.8}$

where K is a constant.

(d) $f_{(h)} = L_{(h)} = K(h)^{3/2}$

where K is a constant.

6-2 Linearize the ODE describing the conical tank modeled in Prob. 3-1 and convert to perturbation variables.

6-3 Linearize the equations describing a variable-volume CSTR similar to the one considered in Example 6-6.

6-4 Solve the ODE's:

(a) $\dfrac{d^2x}{dt^2} + 5\dfrac{dx}{dt} + 4x = 2 \qquad x_{(0)} = 0, \left(\dfrac{dx}{dt}\right)_{(0)} = 1$

(b) $\dfrac{d^2x}{dt^2} + 2\dfrac{dx}{dt} + 2x = 1 \qquad x_{(0)} = 2, \left(\dfrac{dx}{dt}\right)_{(0)} = 0$

6-5 Show that the linearized system describing the gravity-flow tank of Example 6-4 and Example 4-2 is a second-order system. Solve for the damping coefficient and the time constant in terms of the parameters of the system.

6-6 Solve the second-order ODE describing the steady-state flow of an incompressible, newtonian liquid through a pipe [the steady-state version of Eq. (2-45b)].

$$\frac{d}{dr}\left(r\frac{d\bar{v}_z}{dr}\right) = \left(\frac{\Delta Pg_c}{\mu L}\right)r$$

What are the boundary conditions?

6-7 Find the responses of general first- and second-order systems given below to the following forcing functions:

$$\tau_p\frac{dx}{dt} + x = Q_{(t)}$$

$$\tau_p{}^2\frac{d^2x}{dt^2} + 2\tau_p\zeta\frac{dx}{dt} + x = Q_{(t)} \qquad 0 < \zeta < 1$$

(a) $Q_{(t)} = \delta_{(t)}$

(HINT: Remember the impulse or Dirac delta function, when multiplied by another function $f_{(t)}$ and integrated, "sifts" out the value of the function at the argument D of the delta function:

$$\int_0^\infty f_{(t)}\,\delta_{(t-D)}\,dt = f_{(D)}$$

(b) $Q_{(t)} = \sin \omega t$

6-8 Solve for the unit step response of a general second-order system for:

(a) $\zeta = 1$

(b) $\zeta > 1$

6-9 A feedback controller is added to the CSTR of Example 6-6. The inlet concentration C_{A0} is now changed by the controller to hold C_A at its set-point value C_A^{set}.

$$C_{A0} = C_{AM} + C_{AD}$$

where C_{AD} is a disturbance composition. The controller has proportional and integral action:

$$C_{AM} = \bar{C}_{AM} + K_c\left(E + \frac{1}{\tau_I}\int E \, dt\right)$$

where
$$E = C_A^{set} - C_A$$
$$K_c, \tau_I = \text{constants}$$
$$\bar{C}_{AM} = \text{steady-state value of } C_{AM}$$

Derive the second-order equation describing the closed-loop process in terms of perturbation variables. Show that the damping coefficient is

$$\zeta = \frac{1 + k\tau + K_c}{2\sqrt{K_c \tau/\tau_I}}$$

What value of K_c will give critical damping? At what value of K_c will the system become unstable?

6-10   Combine the three first-order ODE's describing the three-CSTR system of Sec. 3-2 into one third-order ODE in terms of C_{A3}. Then solve for the response of C_{A3} to a unit step change in C_{A0}, assuming all k's and τ's are identical.

6-11   Consider the second-order underdamped system

$$\tau_p^2 \frac{d^2x}{dt^2} + 2\tau_p\zeta\frac{dx}{dt} + x = K_p Q_{(t)}$$

where K_p is the process steady-state gain and $Q_{(t)}$ is the forcing function. The unit step response of such a system can be characterized by rise time T_R, peak time T_P, settling time T_S, and peak overshoot ratio POR. T_R and T_P are defined in the sketch below. T_S is the time it takes the exponential portion of the response to decay to a given fraction F of the final steady-state value of x, x_{ss}.

$$\text{POR} \equiv \frac{x_{(T_P)} - x_{ss}}{x_{ss}}$$

Show that

(a) $$\frac{x_{(t)}}{x_{ss}} = 1 - \frac{e^{-\zeta t/\tau_p}}{\sqrt{1-\zeta^2}}\sin\left(\frac{\sqrt{1-\zeta^2}}{\tau_p}t + \phi\right)$$

where $\phi = \cos^{-1}\zeta$.

(b) $$\frac{T_R}{\tau_p} = \frac{\pi - \phi}{\sin\phi}$$

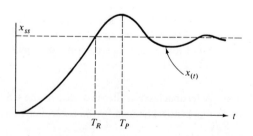

(c) $\dfrac{T_S}{\tau_p} = \dfrac{\ln\left[1/(F\sin\phi)\right]}{\cos\phi}$

(d) $POR = e^{-\pi\cot\phi}$

6-12 (a) Linearize the two ODE's given below that describe a nonisothermal CSTR with constant volume. The input variables are T_0, T_J, C_{A0}, and F.

$$V\frac{dC_A}{dt} = F(C_{A0} - C_A) - VkC_A$$

$$V\rho C_p\frac{dT}{dt} = FC_p\rho(T_0 - T) - \lambda VkC_A - UA(T - T_J)$$

where $k = \alpha e^{-E/RT}$.

(b) Convert to perturbation variables and arrange in the form

$$\frac{dC_A}{dt} = a_{11}\,C_A + a_{12}\,T + a_{13}\,C_{A0} + a_{14}\,T_0 + a_{15}\,F + a_{16}\,T_J$$

$$\frac{dT}{dt} = a_{21}\,C_A + a_{22}\,T + a_{23}\,C_{A0} + a_{24}\,T_0 + a_{25}\,F + a_{26}\,T_J$$

(c) Combine the two linear ODE's above into one second-order ODE and find the roots of the characteristic equation in terms of the a_{ij} coefficients.

6-13 The flow rate F of a manipulative stream through a control valve with equal-percentage trim is given by the following equation:

$$F = C_V\alpha^{x-1}$$

where F is flow in gpm and C_V and α are constants set by the valve size and type. The control-valve stem position x (fraction of wide open) is set by the output pressure signal P_c of a feedback controller. The valve cannot be moved instantaneously. It is approximately a first-order system:

$$\tau_V\frac{dx}{dt} + x = \frac{P_c - 3}{12}$$

The effect of the flow rate of the manipulative variable on the process temperature T is given by

$$\tau_p\frac{dT}{dt} + T = K_p F$$

Derive one linear ordinary differential equation that gives the dynamic dependence of process temperature on controller output pressure P_c.

6-14 Solve the ODE derived in Prob. 3-4 to show that the concentration C in Grandpa McCoy's batch of Liquid Lightning is

$$C_{(t)} = \frac{C_0(1 - e^{-kt})}{kt}$$

7

LAPLACE-DOMAIN DYNAMICS

As mentioned in the introduction to Part 3, the use of Laplace transformations yields some very useful simplifications in notation and computation. Laplace-transforming the linear ordinary differential equations describing our processes converts them into algebraic equations in the Laplace transform variable s. This provides a very convenient representation of system dynamics.

Most of you have probably been exposed to Laplace transforms in a mathematics course, but we will lead off this chapter with a brief review of some of the most important relationships. Then we will derive the Laplace transformations of commonly encountered functions, primarily various types of disturbances. Next we will develop the idea of transfer functions, relating input and output variables, by observing what happens to equations when they are Laplace-transformed. Finally, we will apply these techniques to some chemical engineering systems.

Keep in mind that we are always dealing with linear ODE's in the Laplace domain since Laplace transform techniques can be applied only to linear functions.

7-1 LAPLACE-TRANSFORMATION FUNDAMENTALS

7-1.1 Definition

The Laplace transformation of a function of time $f_{(t)}$ consists of "operating on" the function by multiplying it by e^{-st} and integrating with respect to time t from 0 to infinity. The operation of Laplace transforming will be indicated in this book by the notation

$$\mathscr{L}[f_{(t)}] \equiv \int_0^\infty f_{(t)} e^{-st}\, dt \qquad (7\text{-}1)$$

where $\mathscr{L}$ = Laplace transform operator

$\quad s$ = Laplace transform variable

In integrating between the definite limits of 0 and infinity we "integrate out" the time variable t and are left with a new quantity that is a function of s. We will use the notation

$$\mathscr{L}[f_{(t)}] \equiv F_{(s)} \qquad (7\text{-}2)$$

The variable s is a complex number.

Thus Laplace transformation converts functions from the time domain (where time is the independent variable) into the Laplace domain (where s is the independent variable). The advantages of using this transformation will become clear later in this chapter.

7-1.2 Linearity Property

One of the most important properties of Laplace transformation is that it is linear.

$$\mathscr{L}[f_1 + f_2] = \mathscr{L}[f_{1(t)}] + \mathscr{L}[f_{2(t)}] \qquad (7\text{-}3)$$

This property is easily proved:

$$\mathscr{L}[f_1 + f_2] \equiv \int_0^\infty (f_1 + f_2)e^{-st}\, dt$$

$$= \int_0^\infty f_1\, e^{-st}\, dt + \int_0^\infty f_2\, e^{-st}\, dt$$

$$= \mathscr{L}[f_{1(t)}] + \mathscr{L}[f_{2(t)}]$$

$$= F_{1(s)} + F_{2(s)} \qquad (7\text{-}4)$$

7-2 LAPLACE TRANSFORMATION OF IMPORTANT FUNCTIONS

Let us now apply the definition of the Laplace transformation to some important functions.

7-2.1 Step Function

Consider the function

$$f_{(t)} = Ku_{(t)} \qquad (7\text{-}5)$$

where $u_{(t)}$ is the unit step function defined in Sec. 6-1 as

$$u_{(t)} = 1 \qquad t > 0$$
$$= 0 \qquad t \leq 0 \qquad (7\text{-}6)$$

Note that the step function is just a constant (for time greater than zero).
Laplace transforming gives

$$\mathscr{L}[Ku_{(t)}] = \int_0^\infty (Ku_{(t)})e^{-st}\, dt$$

$$= K \int_0^\infty e^{-st}\, dt$$

since $u_{(t)}$ is just equal to unity over the range of integration.

$$\mathscr{L}[Ku_{(t)}] = -\frac{K}{s} e^{-st} \bigg]_{t=0}^{t=\infty} = -\frac{K}{s}(0 - 1)$$

$$= \frac{K}{s} \qquad (7\text{-}7)$$

Therefore the Laplace transformation of a step function (or a constant) of magnitude K is simply $K(1/s)$.

7-2.2 Ramp

Let

$$f_{(t)} = Kt \qquad (7\text{-}8)$$

Then the Laplace transformation is

$$\mathscr{L}[Kt] = \int_0^\infty Kte^{-st}\, dt$$

Integrating by parts:

Let

$$u = t \qquad dv = e^{-st}\, dt$$

Then

$$du = dt \qquad v = -\frac{1}{s} e^{-st}$$

Since

$$\int_0^\infty u \, dv = uv \Big]_0^\infty - \int_0^\infty v \, du \qquad (7\text{-}9)$$

$$K \int_0^\infty t e^{-st} \, dt = -\frac{Kt}{s} e^{-st} \Big]_{t=0}^{t=\infty} + \int_0^\infty \frac{K}{s} e^{-st} \, dt$$

$$= (0 - 0) - \frac{K}{s^2} e^{-st} \Big]_{t=0}^{t=\infty}$$

Therefore

$$\mathscr{L}[Kt] = K\left(\frac{1}{s^2}\right) \qquad (7\text{-}10)$$

7-2.3   Sine

$$f_{(t)} = \sin \omega t \qquad (7\text{-}11)$$

where ω = frequency (radians/time).

$$\mathscr{L}[\sin \omega t] = \int_0^\infty (\sin \omega t) \, e^{-st} \, dt$$

Using

$$\sin \omega t = \frac{e^{i\omega t} - e^{-i\omega t}}{2i} \qquad (7\text{-}12)$$

$$\mathscr{L}[\sin \omega t] = \int_0^\infty \frac{1}{2i} (e^{-(s-i\omega)t} - e^{-(s+i\omega)t}) \, dt$$

$$= \frac{1}{2i} \left[\frac{-e^{-(s-i\omega)t}}{s - i\omega} + \frac{e^{-(s+i\omega)t}}{s + i\omega} \right]_{t=0}^{t=\infty}$$

$$= \frac{1}{2i} \left(\frac{1}{s - i\omega} - \frac{1}{s + i\omega} \right)$$

Therefore

$$\mathscr{L}[\sin \omega t] = \frac{\omega}{s^2 + \omega^2} \qquad (7\text{-}13)$$

7-2.4   Exponential

$$f_{(t)} = e^{-at} \qquad (7\text{-}14)$$

$$\mathscr{L}[e^{-at}] = \int_0^\infty (e^{-at}) e^{-st} \, dt = \int_0^\infty e^{-(s+a)t} \, dt$$

$$= \frac{-1}{s + a} e^{-(s+a)t} \Big]_{t=0}^{t=\infty}$$

Therefore

$$\mathscr{L}[e^{-at}] = \frac{1}{s + a} \qquad (7\text{-}15)$$

7-2.5   Exponential Multiplied by Time

$$f_{(t)} = te^{-at} \qquad (7\text{-}16)$$

$$\mathscr{L}[te^{-at}] = \int_0^\infty (te^{-at})e^{-st}\, dt = \int_0^\infty te^{-(s+a)t}\, dt$$

Integrating by parts

$$u = t \qquad dv = e^{-(s+a)t}\, dt$$

$$du = dt \qquad v = -\frac{1}{s+a}e^{-(s+a)t}$$

$$\int_0^\infty te^{-(s+a)t}\, dt = \frac{-te^{-(s+a)t}}{s+a}\bigg]_{t=0}^{t=\infty} + \int_0^\infty \frac{e^{-(s+a)t}}{s+a}\, dt$$

$$= (0 - 0) - \frac{1}{(s+a)^2}e^{-(s+a)t}\bigg]_{t=0}^{t=\infty}$$

Therefore

$$\mathscr{L}[te^{-at}] = \frac{1}{(s+a)^2} \qquad (7\text{-}17)$$

Equation (7-17) can be generalized to give

$$\mathscr{L}[t^n e^{-at}] = \frac{n!}{(s+a)^{n+1}} \qquad (7\text{-}18)$$

7-2.6   Impulse (Dirac Delta Function $\delta_{(t)}$)

The impulse function is an infinitely high spike that has zero width and an area of one. One way to define $\delta_{(t)}$ is to call it the derivative of the unit step function.

$$\delta_{(t)} = \frac{d}{dt}u_{(t)} \qquad (7\text{-}19)$$

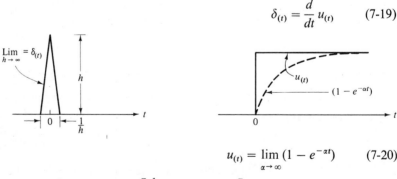

Now

$$u_{(t)} = \lim_{\alpha \to \infty}(1 - e^{-\alpha t}) \qquad (7\text{-}20)$$

Therefore

$$\mathscr{L}[\delta_{(t)}] = \mathscr{L}\left[\frac{d}{dt}\lim_{\alpha \to \infty}(1 - e^{-\alpha t})\right]$$

$$= \lim_{\alpha \to \infty}\mathscr{L}\left[\frac{d}{dt}(1 - e^{-\alpha t})\right] = \lim_{\alpha \to \infty}\mathscr{L}[\alpha e^{-\alpha t}]$$

Using Eq. (7-15) gives

$$\lim_{\alpha \to \infty} \mathscr{L}[\alpha e^{-\alpha t}] = \lim_{\alpha \to \infty} \frac{\alpha}{s + \alpha} = \lim_{\alpha \to \infty} \frac{1}{1 + s/\alpha}$$

Therefore

$$\mathscr{L}[\delta_{(t)}] = 1 \qquad (7\text{-}21)$$

7-3   INVERSION OF LAPLACE TRANSFORMS

After transforming equations into the Laplace domain and solving for output variables as functions of s, we frequently want to transform back into the time domain. This operation is called *inversion* or *inverse Laplace transformation*. We will use the notation

$$\mathscr{L}^{-1}[F_{(s)}] = f_{(t)} \qquad (7\text{-}22)$$

There are several ways to invert functions of s into functions of t. Since s is a complex number, a contour integration in the complex s plane can be used:[1]

$$f_{(t)} = \frac{1}{2\pi i} \int_{\alpha - i\infty}^{\alpha + i\infty} e^{st} F_{(s)} \, ds \qquad (7\text{-}23)$$

Another method is simply to look up the function in mathematics tables.

The most common inversion method is called *partial fractions expansion*. The function to be inverted, $F_{(s)}$, is merely rearranged into a series of simple functions:

$$F_{(s)} = F_{1(s)} + F_{2(s)} + \cdots + F_{N(s)} \qquad (7\text{-}24)$$

Then each term is inverted (usually by inspection). The total time-dependent function is the sum of the simple time-dependent functions [Eq. (7-3)]:

$$f_{(t)} = \mathscr{L}^{-1}[F_{1(s)}] + \mathscr{L}^{-1}[F_{2(s)}] + \cdots + \mathscr{L}^{-1}[F_{N(s)}]$$
$$= f_{1(t)} + f_{2(t)} + \cdots + f_{N(t)} \qquad (7\text{-}25)$$

As we will shortly find out, the $F_{(s)}$'s normally appear as ratios of polynomials in s.

$$F_{(s)} = \frac{Z_{(s)}}{P_{(s)}} \qquad (7\text{-}26)$$

where $Z_{(s)} = M$th-order polynomial in s

$\quad\ \ P_{(s)} = N$th-order polynomial in s

---

[1] R. V. Churchill, "Operational Mathematics," McGraw-Hill, 1958.
J. Irving and N. Mullineaux, "Mathematics in Physics and Engineering," Academic, 1959.

Factoring the denominator into its roots gives

$$F_{(s)} = \frac{Z_{(s)}}{(s - p_1)(s - p_2) \cdots (s - p_N)} \qquad (7\text{-}27)$$

where the p_i are the roots of the polynomial $P_{(s)}$, which may be distinct or repeated.

If all the p_i are different (i.e., distinct roots), we can express $F_{(s)}$ as a sum of N terms:

$$F_{(s)} = \frac{A}{s - p_1} + \frac{B}{s - p_2} + \cdots + \frac{W}{s - p_N} \qquad (7\text{-}28)$$

The numerators of each of the terms in Eq. (7-28) can be evaluated as shown below and then each term is inverted.

$$A = \lim_{s \to p_1} [(s - p_1) F_{(s)}]$$

$$B = \lim_{s \to p_2} [(s - p_2) F_{(s)}]$$

$$\cdots \cdots \cdots \cdots \cdots \cdots$$

$$W = \lim_{s \to p_N} [(s - p_N) F_{(s)}] \qquad (7\text{-}29)$$

EXAMPLE 7-1   Given the $F_{(s)}$ below, find its inverse $f_{(t)}$ by partial fractions expansion.

$$F_{(s)} = \frac{K_p \bar{C}_{A0}}{s(\tau_p s + 1)} \qquad (7\text{-}30)$$

$$F_{(s)} = \frac{\bar{C}_{A0} K_p / \tau_p}{s(s + 1/\tau_p)} = \frac{A}{s} + \frac{B}{s + 1/\tau_p}$$

The roots of the denominator are 0 and $-1/\tau_p$.

$$A = \lim_{s \to 0} [s F_{(s)}] = \lim_{s \to 0} \frac{K_p \bar{C}_{A0}}{\tau_p s + 1} = K_p \bar{C}_{A0}$$

$$B = \lim_{s \to -1/\tau_p} \left[\left(s + \frac{1}{\tau_p} \right) F_{(s)} \right] = \lim_{s \to -1/\tau_p} \frac{K_p \bar{C}_{A0} / \tau_p}{s} = -K_p \bar{C}_{A0}$$

Therefore

$$F_{(s)} = K_p \bar{C}_{A0} \left[\frac{1}{s} - \frac{1}{s + 1/\tau_p} \right] \qquad (7\text{-}31)$$

The two simple functions in Eq. (7-31) can be inverted by using Eqs. (7-7) and (7-15).

$$f_{(t)} = K_p \bar{C}_{A0} (1 - e^{-t/\tau_p}) \qquad (7\text{-}32) \qquad ////$$

If there are some repeated roots in the denominator of Eq. (7-27), we must expand $F_{(s)}$ as a sum of N terms:

$$F_{(s)} = \frac{Z_{(s)}}{(s - p_1)^2(s - p_3) \cdots (s - p_N)} \qquad (7\text{-}33)$$

$$F_{(s)} = \frac{A}{(s - p_1)^2} + \frac{B}{s - p_1} + \frac{C}{s - p_3} + \cdots + \frac{W}{s - p_N} \qquad (7\text{-}34)$$

The above is for a repeated root of order 2. If the root is repeated three times (or order 3) the expansion would be

$$F_{(s)} = \frac{Z_{(s)}}{(s - p_1)^3(s - p_4) \cdots (s - p_N)} \qquad (7\text{-}35)$$

$$F_{(s)} = \frac{A}{(s - p_1)^3} + \frac{B}{(s - p_1)^2} + \frac{C}{s - p_1} + \cdots + \frac{W}{s - p_N} \qquad (7\text{-}36)$$

The numerators of the terms in Eq. (7-34) are found from the relationships given below. These are easily proved by merely carrying out the indicated operations on Eq. (7-34).

$$A = \lim_{s \to p_1} [(s - p_1)^2 F_{(s)}]$$

$$B = \lim_{s \to p_1} \left\{ \frac{d}{ds} [(s - p_1)^2 F_{(s)}] \right\}$$

$$C = \lim_{s \to p_3} [(s - p_3) F_{(s)}] \qquad (7\text{-}37)$$

To find the C numerator term in Eq. (7-36) a second derivative with respect to s would have to be taken. Generalizing to the mth term A_m of an Nth order root at p_1,

$$A_m = \lim_{s \to p_1} \left[\frac{d^{m-1}}{ds^{m-1}} \left((s - p_1)^N F_{(s)} \right) \right] \frac{1}{(m - 1)!}$$

$$(7\text{-}38)$$

EXAMPLE 7-2   Given the $F_{(s)}$ below, find its inverse.

$$F_{(s)} = \frac{K_p}{s(\tau_p s + 1)^2}$$

$$= \frac{K_p/\tau_p^2}{s(s + 1/\tau_p)^2} = \frac{A}{s} + \frac{B}{(s + 1/\tau_p)^2} + \frac{C}{s + 1/\tau_p}$$

$$A = \lim_{s \to 0} \frac{K_p}{(\tau_p s + 1)^2} = K_p$$

$$B = \lim_{s \to -1/\tau_p} \frac{K_p/\tau_p^2}{s} = -\frac{K_p}{\tau_p}$$

$$C = \lim_{s \to -1/\tau_p} \left[\frac{d}{ds}\left(\frac{K_p/\tau_p^2}{s} \right) \right] = \lim_{s \to -1/\tau_p} \frac{-K_p/\tau_p^2}{s^2} = -K_p$$

Therefore
$$F_{(s)} = K_p\left[\frac{1}{s} - \frac{1/\tau_p}{(s + 1/\tau_p)^2} - \frac{1}{s + 1/\tau_p} \right] \tag{7-39}$$

Therefore
$$f_{(t)} = K_p\left(1 - \frac{t}{\tau_p}e^{-t/\tau_p} - e^{-t/\tau_p} \right) \tag{7-40} \quad ////$$

7-4 TRANSFER FUNCTIONS

Let us now see what happens when we Laplace-transform algebraic equations, ordinary differential equations, and integral equations relating two variables. $x_{(t)}$ will be the output variable or the dependent variable. $Q_{(t)}$ will be the input variable or forcing function.

7-4.1 Multiplication by a Constant

Consider the algebraic equation

$$x_{(t)} = KQ_{(t)} \tag{7-41}$$

Laplace-transforming both sides of the equation gives

$$\int_0^\infty x_{(t)}e^{-st}\, dt = K \int_0^\infty Q_{(t)}e^{-st}\, dt$$

$$X_{(s)} = KQ_{(s)} \tag{7-42}$$

where $X_{(s)}$ and $Q_{(s)}$ are the Laplace transforms of $x_{(t)}$ and $Q_{(t)}$. Note that $Q_{(t)}$ is an arbitrary function of time. We have not specified at this point the exact form of the input. Comparing Eqs. (7-41) and (7-42) shows that the input and output variables are related in the Laplace domain in exactly the same way as they are related in the time domain.

Equation (7-42) can be put into transfer-function form by finding the output-input ratio:

$$\frac{X_{(s)}}{Q_{(s)}} = K \tag{7-43}$$

For any input $Q_{(s)}$ the output $X_{(s)}$ is found simply by multiplying $Q_{(s)}$ by the constant K. Thus the transfer function relating $X_{(s)}$ and $Q_{(s)}$ is a constant or a "gain." We can represent this in block-diagram form:

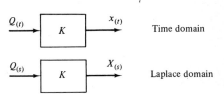

7-4.2 Differentiation with Respect to Time

Consider what happens when the time derivative of a function $x_{(t)}$ is Laplace-transformed.

$$\mathcal{L}\left[\frac{dx}{dt}\right] = \int_0^\infty \left(\frac{dx}{dt}\right) e^{-st}\, dt \qquad (7\text{-}44)$$

Integrating by parts gives

$$u = e^{-st} \qquad\qquad dv = \frac{dx}{dt}\, dt$$

$$du = -se^{-st}\, dt \qquad v = x$$

Therefore
$$\int_0^\infty \left(\frac{dx}{dt}\right) e^{-st}\, dt = xe^{-st}\Big]_{t=0}^{t=\infty} + \int_0^\infty sxe^{-st}\, dt$$

$$= 0 - x_{(t=0)} + s\int_0^\infty x_{(t)}e^{-st}\, dt$$

The integral is, by definition, just the Laplace transformation of $x_{(t)}$, which we call $X_{(s)}$.

$$\mathcal{L}\left[\frac{dx}{dt}\right] = sX_{(s)} - x_{(t=0)} \qquad (7\text{-}45)$$

This result is the most useful of all the Laplace transformations. It says that the operation of differentiation in the time domain is replaced by multiplication by s in the Laplace domain, minus an initial condition. This is where perturbation variables become so useful. If the initial condition is the steady-state operating level, all the initial conditions like $x_{(t=0)}$ are equal to zero. Then simple multiplication by s is equivalent to differentiation. In block-diagram form an ideal derivative unit or a perfect differentiator can be shown as

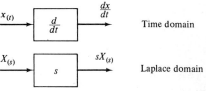

The same procedure, applied to a second-order derivative, gives the following:

$$\mathcal{L}\left[\frac{d^2x}{dt^2}\right] = s^2 X_{(s)} - sx_{(t=0)} - \left(\frac{dx}{dt}\right)_{(t=0)} \qquad (7\text{-}46)$$

Thus differentiating twice is equivalent to multiplying twice by s, if all initial conditions are zero.

The above can be generalized to say that an Nth order derivative with respect to time is simply replaced by an s^N in going from the time to the Laplace domain. Thus an ordinary differential equation will Laplace-transformed into a polynomial in s.

$$a_N \frac{d^N x}{dt^N} + a_{N-1} \frac{d^{N-1}x}{dt^{N-1}} + \cdots + a_1 \frac{dx}{dt} + a_0 x = Q_{(t)} \qquad (7\text{-}47)$$

$$a_N s^N X_{(s)} + a_{N-1} s^{N-1} X_{(s)} + \cdots + a_1 s X_{(s)} + a_0 X_{(s)} = Q_{(s)} \qquad (7\text{-}48)$$

$$(a_N s^N + a_{N-1}s^{N-1} + \cdots + a_1 s + a_0) X_{(s)} = Q_{(s)} \qquad (7\text{-}49)$$

Notice that the polynomial in Eq. (7-49) looks exactly like the characteristic equation discussed in Chapter 6. We will return to this not-accidental similarity in the next section.

7-4.3 Integration

Laplace-transforming the integral of a function $x_{(t)}$ gives

$$\mathcal{L}\left[\int x_{(t)} \, dt\right] = \int_0^\infty \left(\int x_{(t)} \, dt\right) e^{-st} \, dt$$

Integrating by parts,

$$u = \int x \, dt \qquad dv = e^{-st} \, dt$$

$$du = x \, dt \qquad v = -\frac{1}{s} e^{-st}$$

$$\int_0^\infty \left(\int x \, dt\right) e^{-st} \, dt = \frac{-e^{-st} \int x \, dt}{s} \bigg]_{t=0}^{t=\infty} + \frac{1}{s} \int_0^\infty x_{(t)} e^{-st} \, dt$$

Therefore

$$\mathcal{L}\left[\int x_{(t)} \, dt\right] = \frac{1}{s} X_{(s)} + \frac{1}{s}\left(\int x \, dt\right)_{(t=0)} \qquad (7\text{-}50)$$

The operation of integration is equivalent to division by s in the Laplace domain, using zero initial conditions. Thus integration is the inverse of differentiation.

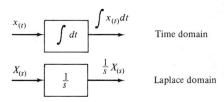

The $1/s$ is an operator or a transfer function showing what operation is performed on the input signal. This is a completely different idea than the simple Laplace transformation of a function. Remember, the Laplace transform of the unit step function was also equal to $1/s$. But this is the Laplace transformation of a function. The $1/s$ operator discussed above is a *transfer* function, not a function.

7-4.4 Dead Time

Delay time, transportation lag, or dead time is frequently encountered in chemical engineering systems since we did not earn our reputation as underpaid plumbers for nothing!

Suppose a process stream is flowing through a pipe in essentially plug flow and that it takes D minutes for any individual element of fluid to flow from the entrance to the exit of the pipe. Then the pipe represents a dead-time element.

If a certain dynamic variable $f_{(t)}$, such as temperature or composition, enters the front end of the pipe, it will emerge from the other end D minutes later with exactly the same shape, as shown in Fig. 7-1.

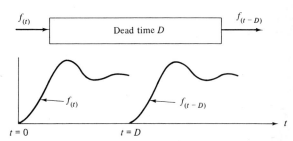

FIGURE 7-1
Effect of a dead-time element.

Let us see what happens when we Laplace-transform a function $f_{(t-D)}$ that has been delayed by a dead time. Laplace transformation is defined in Eq. (7-1).

$$\mathcal{L}[f_{(t)}] = \int_0^\infty f_{(t)} e^{-st}\, dt = F_{(s)} \qquad (7\text{-}51)$$

The variable t in the above equation is just a "dummy variable" of integration. It is integrated out, leaving a function of only s. Thus we can write Eq. (7-51) in a completely equivalent mathematical form:

$$F_{(s)} = \int_0^\infty f_{(y)}\, e^{-sy}\, dy \qquad (7\text{-}52)$$

where y is now the dummy variable of integration. Now let $y = t - D$.

$$F_{(s)} = \int_0^\infty f_{(t-D)}\, e^{-s(t-D)}\, d(t-D)$$

$$= e^{Ds} \int_0^\infty f_{(t-D)}\, e^{-st}\, dt$$

$$= e^{Ds}\, \mathcal{L}[f_{(t-D)}] \qquad (7\text{-}53)$$

Therefore
$$\mathcal{L}[f_{(t-D)}] = e^{-Ds}\, F_{(s)} \qquad (7\text{-}54)$$

Thus time delay or dead time in the time domain is equivalent to multiplication by e^{-Ds} in the Laplace domain.

If the input into the dead-time element is $x_{in(t)}$ and the output of the dead-time element is $x_{out(t)}$ then x_{in} and x_{out} are related by

$$x_{out(t)} = x_{in(t-D)}$$

And in the Laplace domain,

$$X_{out(s)} = e^{-Ds}\, X_{in(s)} \qquad (7\text{-}55)$$

Thus the transfer function between output and input variables for a pure dead-time process is e^{-Ds}.

7-5   EXAMPLES

We are ready to apply all these Laplace-transformation techniques to some typical chemical engineering processes.

EXAMPLE 7-3 Consider the isothermal CSTR of Example 6-6. The equation describing the system in terms of perturbation variables is

$$\frac{dC_A}{dt} + \left(\frac{1}{\tau} + k\right)C_{A(t)} = \frac{1}{\tau}C_{A0(t)} \qquad (7\text{-}56)$$

where k and τ are constants. The initial condition is $C_{A(0)} = 0$. We will not specify what $C_{A0(t)}$ is for the moment but will just leave it as an arbitrary function of time. Laplace-transforming each term in Eq. (7-56) gives

$$sC_{A(s)} - C_{A(t=0)} + \left(\frac{1}{\tau} + k\right)C_{A(s)} = \frac{1}{\tau}C_{A0(s)} \qquad (7\text{-}57)$$

The second term drops out because of the initial condition. Grouping like terms in $C_{A(s)}$ gives

$$\left(s + \frac{1}{\tau} + k\right)C_{A(s)} = \frac{1}{\tau}C_{A0(s)}$$

Thus the output-input relationship for the system, the system transfer function $G_{(s)}$, is

$$G_{(s)} \equiv \frac{C_{A(s)}}{C_{A0(s)}} = \frac{1/\tau}{s + k + 1/\tau} \qquad (7\text{-}58)$$

The denominator of the transfer function is exactly the same as the polynomial in s that was called the characteristic equation in Chap. 6. The roots of the denominator of the transfer function are called the *poles* of the transfer function. These are the values of s at which $G_{(s)}$ goes to infinity. The transfer function of Eq. (7-58) has one pole with a value of $-(k + 1/\tau)$. The poles of the transfer function are equal to the roots of the characteristic equation.

Rearranging Eq. (7-58) into the standard form of Eq. (6-34) gives

$$G_{(s)} = \frac{\left(\dfrac{1}{1 + k\tau}\right)}{\left(\dfrac{1}{k + \dfrac{1}{\tau}}\right)S + 1} = \frac{K_p}{\tau_p s + 1} \qquad (7\text{-}59)$$

where K_p is the process steady-state gain and τ_p is the process time constant. The pole of the transfer function is the reciprocal of the time constant.

This particular type of transfer function is called a *first-order lag*. It tells us how the input C_{A0} affects the output C_A, both dynamically and at steady state. The form of the transfer function (one pole) and the numerical values of the parameters (steady-state gain and time constant) give a complete picture of the system in a very compact and usable form. The transfer function is a property of the system only and is applicable for any input. We can determine the dynamics and the steady-state characteristics of the system without having to pick any specific forcing function.

If the same input as used in Example 6-6 is imposed on the system, we should be able to use Laplace transforms to find the response of C_A to a step change of magnitude $\bar{C}_{A0}$.

$$C_{A0(t)} = \bar{C}_{A0} u_{(t)} \qquad (7\text{-}60)$$

We will Laplace-transform $C_{A0(t)}$, substitute into the system transfer function, solve for $C_{A(s)}$, and invert back into the time domain to find $C_{A(t)}$.

$$\mathscr{L}[C_{A0(t)}] = C_{A0(s)} = \bar{C}_{A0}\frac{1}{s} \qquad (7\text{-}61)$$

$$
\begin{aligned}
C_{A(s)} &= G_{(s)} C_{A0(s)} \\
&= \frac{K_p}{\tau_p s + 1}\frac{\bar{C}_{A0}}{s} = \frac{K_p \bar{C}_{A0}}{s(\tau_p s + 1)} \qquad (7\text{-}62)
\end{aligned}
$$

Using partial fractions expansion to invert (see Example 7-1) gives

$$C_{A(t)} = K_p \bar{C}_{A0}(1 - e^{-t/\tau_p})$$

This is exactly the solution obtained in Example 6-6 [Eq. (6-31)]. ////

EXAMPLE 7-4 The ODE of Example 6-8 with an arbitrary forcing function $Q_{(t)}$ is

$$\frac{d^2x}{dt^2} + 5\frac{dx}{dt} + 6x = Q_{(t)} \qquad (7\text{-}63)$$

with the initial conditions

$$x_{(0)} = \left(\frac{dx}{dt}\right)_{(0)} = 0 \qquad (7\text{-}64)$$

Laplace-transforming gives

$$s^2 X_{(s)} + 5sX_{(s)} + 6X_{(s)} = Q_{(s)}$$

$$(s^2 + 5s + 6)X_{(s)} = Q_{(s)}$$

The process transfer function $G_{(s)}$ is

$$\frac{X_{(s)}}{Q_{(s)}} = G_{(s)} = \frac{1}{s^2 + 5s + 6} = \frac{1}{(s+2)(s+3)} \qquad (7\text{-}65)$$

Notice that the denominator of the transfer function is again the same polynomial in s as appeared in the characteristic equation of the system [Eq. (6-53)]. The poles of the transfer function are located at $s = -2$ and $s = -3$.

If $Q_{(t)}$ is a ramp input as in Example 6-13,

$$\mathcal{L}[Q_{(t)}] = \mathcal{L}[t] = \frac{1}{s^2} \qquad (7\text{-}66)$$

$$X_{(s)} = G_{(s)}Q_{(s)} = \left(\frac{1}{s^2 + 5s + 6}\right)\left(\frac{1}{s^2}\right)$$

$$= \frac{1}{s^2(s+2)(s+3)} \qquad (7\text{-}67)$$

Partial fractions expansion gives

$$X_{(s)} = \frac{A}{s^2} + \frac{B}{s} + \frac{C}{s+2} + \frac{D}{s+3}$$

$$A = \lim_{s \to 0}\left[s^2 X_{(s)}\right] = \lim_{s \to 0}\left[\frac{1}{(s+2)(s+3)}\right] = \frac{1}{6}$$

$$B = \lim_{s \to 0}\left[\frac{d}{ds}(s^2 X_{(s)})\right] = \lim_{s \to 0}\left[\frac{d}{ds}\left(\frac{1}{s^2 + 5s + 6}\right)\right]$$

$$= \lim_{s \to 0}\left[\frac{-(2s+5)}{(s^2 + 5s + 6)^2}\right] = -\frac{5}{36}$$

$$C = \lim_{s \to -2}[(s+2)X_{(s)}] = \lim_{s \to -2}\left[\frac{1}{s^2(s+3)}\right] = \frac{1}{4}$$

$$D = \lim_{s \to -3}[(s+3)X_{(s)}] = \lim_{s \to -3}\left[\frac{1}{s^2(s+2)}\right] = -\frac{1}{9}$$

Therefore

$$X_{(s)} = \frac{\frac{1}{6}}{s^2} - \frac{\frac{5}{36}}{s} + \frac{\frac{1}{4}}{s+2} - \frac{\frac{1}{9}}{s+3} \qquad (7\text{-}68)$$

Inverting into the time domain gives the same solution as Eq. (6-87).

$$X_{(t)} = \frac{1}{6}t - \frac{5}{36} + \frac{1}{4}e^{-2t} - \frac{1}{9}e^{-3t}$$

$$(7\text{-}69) \qquad ////$$

EXAMPLE 7-5   The isothermal three CSTR system is described by the three linear ODE's

$$\frac{dC_{A1}}{dt} + \left(k_1 + \frac{1}{\tau_1}\right)C_{A1} = \frac{1}{\tau_1}C_{A0}$$

$$\frac{dC_{A2}}{dt} + \left(k_2 + \frac{1}{\tau_2}\right)C_{A2} = \frac{1}{\tau_2}C_{A1}$$

$$\frac{dC_{A3}}{dt} + \left(k_3 + \frac{1}{\tau_3}\right)C_{A3} = \frac{1}{\tau_3}C_{A2} \qquad (7\text{-}70)$$

The variables can be either total or perturbation variables since the equations are linear (all k's and τ's are constant). Let us use perturbation variables, and therefore the initial conditions for all variables are zero.

$$C_{A1(0)} = C_{A2(0)} = C_{A3(0)} = 0 \qquad (7\text{-}71)$$

Laplace-transforming gives

$$\left(s + k_1 + \frac{1}{\tau_1}\right)C_{A1(s)} = \frac{1}{\tau_1} C_{A0(s)}$$

$$\left(s + k_2 + \frac{1}{\tau_2}\right)C_{A2(s)} = \frac{1}{\tau_2} C_{A1(s)}$$

$$\left(s + k_3 + \frac{1}{\tau_3}\right)C_{A3(s)} = \frac{1}{\tau_3} C_{A2(s)} \qquad (7\text{-}72)$$

These can be rearranged to put them in terms of transfer functions for each tank.

$$G_{1(s)} \equiv \frac{C_{A1(s)}}{C_{A0(s)}} = \frac{1/\tau_1}{s + k_1 + 1/\tau_1}$$

$$G_{2(s)} \equiv \frac{C_{A2(s)}}{C_{A1(s)}} = \frac{1/\tau_2}{s + k_2 + 1/\tau_2} \qquad (7\text{-}73)$$

$$G_{3(s)} \equiv \frac{C_{A3(s)}}{C_{A2(s)}} = \frac{1/\tau_3}{s + k_3 + 1/\tau_3}$$

If we are interested in the total system and want only the effect of the input C_{A0} on the output C_{A3}, the three equations can be combined to eliminate C_{A1} and C_{A2}.

$$C_{A3(s)} = G_3 C_{A2(s)}$$
$$= G_3(G_2 C_{A1(s)})$$
$$= G_3 G_2(G_1 C_{A0(s)}) = (G_{1(s)}G_{2(s)}G_{3(s)})C_{A0(s)} \qquad (7\text{-}74)$$

The overall transfer function $G_{(s)}$ is

$$G_{(s)} \equiv \frac{C_{A3(s)}}{C_{A0(s)}} = G_{1(s)}G_{2(s)}G_{3(s)} \qquad (7\text{-}75)$$

The above demonstrates one very important and useful property of transfer functions. The total effect of a number of transfer functions connected in series is just the product of all the individual transfer functions. Figure 7-2 shows this in block-diagram form. The overall transfer function is a third-order lag with three poles.

$$G_{(s)} = \frac{1/\tau_1 \tau_2 \tau_3}{(s + k_1 + 1/\tau_1)(s + k_2 + 1/\tau_2)(s + k_3 + 1/\tau_3)} \qquad (7\text{-}76)$$

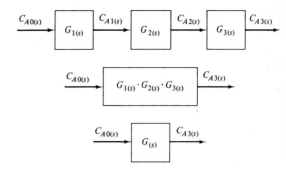

FIGURE 7-2
Transfer functions in series.

Further rearrangement puts the above in the standard form with time constants τ_{pi} and a steady-state gain K_p.

$$G_{(s)} = \frac{\dfrac{1}{1 + k_1\tau_1} \dfrac{1}{1 + k_2\tau_2} \dfrac{1}{1 + k_3\tau_3}}{\left(\dfrac{\tau_1}{1 + k_1\tau_1} s + 1\right)\left(\dfrac{\tau_2}{1 + k_2\tau_2} s + 1\right)\left(\dfrac{\tau_3}{1 + k_3\tau_3} s + 1\right)}$$

$$= \frac{K_p}{(\tau_{p1}s + 1)(\tau_{p2}s + 1)(\tau_{p3}s + 1)} \tag{7-77}$$

Let us assume a unit step change in the feed concentration C_{A0} and solve for the response of C_{A3}. We will take the case where all the τ_{pi} are the same, giving a repeated root of order 3 (a third-order pole at $s = -1/\tau_p$).

$$C_{A0(t)} = u_{(t)}$$

$$C_{A0(s)} = \frac{1}{s}$$

$$C_{A3(s)} = G_{(s)}C_{A0(s)} = \frac{K_p}{(\tau_p s + 1)^3} \frac{1}{s}$$

$$= \frac{K_p/\tau_p{}^3}{s(s + 1/\tau_p)^3} \tag{7-78}$$

Applying partial fractions expansion,

$$C_{A3(s)} = \frac{A}{s} + \frac{B}{(s + 1/\tau_p)^3} + \frac{C}{(s + 1/\tau_p)^2} + \frac{D}{s + 1/\tau_p} \tag{7-79}$$

$$A = \lim_{s \to 0} \left[\frac{K_p/\tau_p^3}{(s + 1/\tau_p)^3} \right] = K_p$$

$$B = \lim_{s \to -1/\tau_p} \left[\frac{K_p/\tau_p^3}{s} \right] = -\frac{K_p}{\tau_p^2}$$

$$C = \lim_{s \to -1/\tau_p} \left[\frac{d}{ds} \left(\frac{K_p/\tau_p^3}{s} \right) \right] = \lim_{s \to -1/\tau_p} \left[-\frac{K_p/\tau_p^3}{s^2} \right] = -\frac{K_p}{\tau_p}$$

$$D = \lim_{s \to -1/\tau_p} \left[\frac{1}{2!} \frac{d^2}{ds^2} \left(\frac{K_p/\tau_p^3}{s} \right) \right] = \lim_{s \to -1/\tau_p} \left(\frac{1}{2} \frac{2K_p/\tau_p^3}{s^3} \right) = -K_p$$

Inverting Eq. (7-79), with the use of Eq. (7-18), yields

$$C_{A3(t)} = K_p \left[1 - \frac{1}{2} \left(\frac{t}{\tau_p} \right)^2 e^{-t/\tau_p} - \frac{t}{\tau_p} e^{-t/\tau_p} - e^{-t/\tau_p} \right] \tag{7-80}$$

EXAMPLE 7-6 The nonisothermal CSTR modeled in Sec. 3-5 can be linearized (see Problem 6-12) to give two linear ODE's in terms of perturbation variables.

$$\frac{dC_A}{dt} = a_{11}C_A + a_{12}T + a_{13}C_{A0} + a_{15}F$$

$$\frac{dT}{dt} = a_{21}C_A + a_{22}T + a_{24}T_0 + a_{25}F + a_{26}T_J \tag{7-81}$$

where

$$a_{11} = -\frac{\bar{F}}{V} - \bar{k} \qquad a_{21} = \frac{-\lambda\bar{k}}{\rho C_p}$$

$$a_{12} = \frac{-\bar{C}_A E\bar{k}}{R\bar{T}^2} \qquad a_{22} = \frac{-\lambda\bar{k}E}{\rho C_p R\bar{T}^2} - \frac{\bar{F}}{V} - \frac{UA}{V\rho C_p}$$

$$a_{13} = \frac{\bar{F}}{V} \qquad a_{24} = \frac{\bar{F}}{V}$$

$$a_{15} = \frac{\bar{C}_{A0} - \bar{C}_A}{V} \qquad a_{25} = \frac{\bar{T}_0 - \bar{T}}{V}$$

$$a_{26} = \frac{UA}{V\rho C_p} \tag{7-82}$$

The variables C_{A0}, T_0, F, and T_J are all considered inputs. The output variables are C_A and T. Therefore eight different transfer functions are required to completely describe the system. This multivariable aspect is the usual situation in most chemical engineering systems.

$$C_{A(s)} = G_{11(s)}C_{A0(s)} + G_{12(s)}T_{0(s)} + G_{13(s)}F_{(s)} + G_{14(s)}T_{J(s)}$$

$$T_{(s)} = G_{21(s)}C_{A0(s)} + G_{22(s)}T_{0(s)} + G_{23(s)}F_{(s)} + G_{24(s)}T_{J(s)} \qquad (7\text{-}83)$$

The G_{ij}'s are, in general, functions of s and are the transfer functions relating inputs and outputs. Since the system is linear the output is the sum of the effects of each individual input. This is called the principle of *superposition*.

To find these transfer functions, Eqs. (7-81) are Laplace-transformed and solved simultaneously.

$$sC_A = a_{11}C_A + a_{12}T + a_{13}C_{A0} + a_{15}F$$

$$sT = a_{21}C_A + a_{22}T + a_{24}T_0 + a_{25}F + a_{26}T_J$$

$$(s - a_{11})C_A = a_{12}T + a_{13}C_{A0} + a_{15}F$$

$$(s - a_{22})T = a_{21}C_A + a_{24}T_0 + a_{25}F + a_{26}T_J$$

Combining,

$$(s - a_{11})C_A = a_{12}\frac{a_{21}C_A + a_{24}T_0 + a_{25}F + a_{26}T_J}{s - a_{22}} + a_{13}C_{A0} + a_{15}F$$

$$\left(s - a_{11} - \frac{a_{12}a_{21}}{s - a_{22}}\right)C_A = \left(\frac{a_{12}a_{24}}{s - a_{22}}\right)T_0 + \left(\frac{a_{12}a_{25}}{s - a_{22}} + a_{15}\right)F$$

$$+ \left(\frac{a_{12}a_{26}}{s - a_{22}}\right)T_J + a_{13}C_{A0}$$

Finally,

$$C_{A(s)} = \left[\frac{a_{13}(s - a_{22})}{s^2 - (a_{11} + a_{22})s + a_{11}a_{22} - a_{12}a_{21}}\right]C_{A0(s)}$$

$$+ \left[\frac{a_{12}a_{24}}{s^2 - (a_{11} + a_{22})s + a_{11}a_{22} - a_{12}a_{21}}\right]T_{0(s)}$$

$$+ \left[\frac{a_{12}a_{25} + a_{15}(s - a_{22})}{s^2 - (a_{11} + a_{22})s + a_{11}a_{22} - a_{12}a_{21}}\right]F_{(s)}$$

$$+ \left[\frac{a_{12}a_{26}}{s^2 - (a_{11} + a_{22})s + a_{12}a_{22} - a_{12}a_{21}}\right]T_{J(s)} \qquad (7\text{-}84)$$

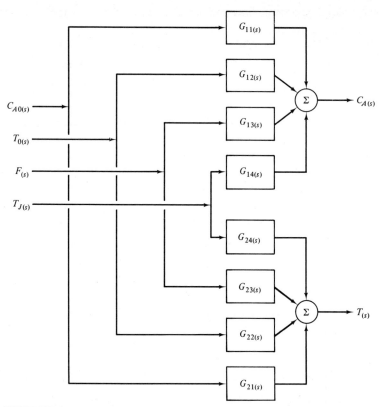

FIGURE 7-3
Block diagram of a multivariable linearized nonisothermal CSTR system.

$$T_{(s)} = \left[\frac{a_{13} a_{21}}{s^2 - (a_{11} + a_{22})s + a_{11}a_{22} - a_{12}a_{21}} \right] C_{A0(s)}$$

$$+ \left[\frac{a_{24}(s - a_{11})}{s^2 - (a_{11} + a_{22})s + a_{11}a_{22} - a_{12}a_{21}} \right] T_{0(s)}$$

$$+ \left[\frac{a_{15}a_{21} + a_{25}(s - a_{11})}{s^2 - (a_{11} + a_{22})s + a_{11}a_{22} - a_{12}a_{21}} \right] F_{(s)}$$

$$+ \left[\frac{a_{26}(s - a_{11})}{s^2 - (a_{11} + a_{22})s + a_{11}a_{22} - a_{12}a_{21}} \right] T_{J(s)} \qquad (7\text{-}85)$$

The system is shown in block-diagram form in Fig. 7-3.

Notice that the G's are ratios of polynomials in s. The $s - a_{11}$ and $s - a_{22}$ terms in the numerators are called first-order *leads*. Notice also that the denominators of all the G's are exactly the same. ////

7-6 PROPERTIES OF TRANSFER FUNCTIONS

An Nth-order system A is described by the linear ODE

$$a_N \frac{d^N x}{dt^N} + a_{N-1} \frac{d^{N-1} x}{dt^{N-1}} + \cdots + a_1 \frac{dx}{dt} + a_0 x = b_M \frac{d^M Q}{dt^M} + b_{M-1} \frac{d^{M-1} Q}{dt^{M-1}} + \cdots$$

$$+ b_1 \frac{dQ}{dt} + b_0 Q \qquad (7\text{-}86)$$

where a_i and b_i = constant coefficients

$\qquad\qquad x$ = output

$\qquad\qquad Q$ = input or forcing function

For this equation to describe a real physical system the order of the right-hand side, M, cannot be greater than the order of the left-hand side, N. This criterion for physical realizability is

$$N \geq M \qquad (7\text{-}87)$$

This requirement can be proved intuitively from the following reasoning. Take a case where $N = 0$ and $M = 1$.

$$a_0 x = b_1 \frac{dQ}{dt} + b_0 Q \qquad (7\text{-}88)$$

This equation says that we have a process whose output x depends on the value of the input and the value of the derivative of the input. Therefore the process must be able to differentiate, perfectly, the input signal. But it is impossible for any real system to differentiate perfectly. This would require that a step change in the input produce an infinite spike in the output. This is physically impossible.

This example can be generalized to any case where $M > N$ to show that differentiation would be required. Therefore N must always be greater than or equal to M.

Laplace-transforming Eq. (7-88) gives

$$\frac{X_{(s)}}{Q_{(s)}} = \frac{b_1}{a_0} s + \frac{b_0}{a_0}$$

This is a first-order lead. It is physically unrealizable; i.e., a real device cannot be built that has exactly this transfer function.

Consider the case where $M = N = 1$.

$$a_1 \frac{dx}{dt} + a_0 x = b_1 \frac{dQ}{dt} + b_0 Q \qquad (7\text{-}89)$$

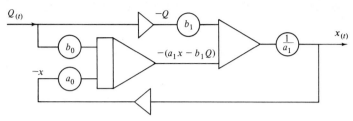

FIGURE 7-4
Analog circuit of lead-lag.

It appears that a derivative of the input is again required. But Eq. (7-89) can be rearranged, grouping the derivative terms together:

$$\frac{d}{dt}(a_1 x - b_1 Q) = b_0 Q - a_0 x \qquad (7\text{-}90)$$

The right-hand side of this equation contains functions of time but no derivatives. If we feed it into an integrator (see Fig. 7-4 for an analog circuit), the output of the integrator will be $a_1 x - b_1 Q$. The output x is then obtained by adding $b_1 Q$ and dividing by a_1. Differentiation is not required and this transfer function is physically realizable.

Remember, nature always integrates. It never differentiates! Laplace-transforming Eq. (7-89) gives

$$\frac{X_{(s)}}{Q_{(s)}} = \frac{b_1 s + b_0}{a_1 s + a_0}$$

This is called a *lead-lag element* and contains a first-order lag and a first-order lead.

Returning now to Eq. (7-86), let us Laplace-transform and solve for the ratio of output $X_{(s)}$ to input $Q_{(s)}$, the system transfer function $G_{(s)}$.

$$G_{(s)} = \frac{X_{(s)}}{Q_{(s)}} = \frac{b_M s^M + b_{M-1} s^{M-1} + \cdots + b_1 s + b_0}{a_N s^N + a_{N-1} s^{N-1} + \cdots + a_1 s + a_0} \qquad (7\text{-}91)$$

The denominator is a polynomial in s that is the same as the characteristic equation of the system. Remember the characteristic equation is obtained from the homogeneous ODE, that is, considering the right-hand side of Eq. (7-86) equal to zero.

The roots of the denominator are called the *poles* of the transfer function. The roots of the numerator are called the *zeros* of the transfer function. Factoring both numerator and denominator yields

$$G_{(s)} = \left(\frac{b_M}{a_N}\right) \frac{(s - z_1)(s - z_2) \cdots (s - z_M)}{(s - p_1)(s - p_2) \cdots (s - p_N)} \qquad (7\text{-}92)$$

where z_i = zeros of transfer function

   p_i = poles of transfer function

As noted in Chap. 6, the roots of the characteristic equation, the poles of the transfer function, must be real or must occur as complex conjugate pairs. In addition, the real parts of all the poles must be negative for the system to be stable; i.e., the poles must all lie in the left-half of the s plane.

The location of the zeros will certainly affect the dynamic response of the system, but their location has *no* effect on the *stability* of the system.

One final point should be made about transfer functions. The steady-state gain K_p for all the transfer functions derived in the examples was obtained by expressing the transfer function in terms of time constants instead of in terms of poles and zeros. For the general system of Eq. (7-91) this would be

$$G_{(s)} = \frac{K_p(\tau_{z1}s + 1)(\tau_{z2}s + 1)\cdots(\tau_{zM}s + 1)}{(\tau_{p1}s + 1)(\tau_{p2}s + 1)\cdots(\tau_{pN}s + 1)} \qquad (7\text{-}93)$$

The steady-state gain is the ratio of output steady-state perturbation over the input steady-state perturbation.

$$K_p = \left(\frac{x_{out}^p}{x_{in}^p}\right)_{(t\to\infty)} = \frac{\bar{x}_{out}^p}{\bar{x}_{in}^p} \qquad (7\text{-}94)$$

In terms of total variables,

$$K_p = \left(\frac{x_{out} - \bar{x}_{out}}{x_{in} - \bar{x}_{in}}\right)_{(t\to\infty)} = \frac{\overline{\Delta x}_{out}}{\overline{\Delta x}_{in}}$$

Thus, for a step change in the input variable of $\overline{\Delta x}_{in}$, the steady-state gain is simply found by dividing the steady state change in the output variable $\overline{\Delta x}_{out}$ by $\overline{\Delta x}_{in}$. See Fig. 7-5.

Instead of rearranging the transfer function to put it into the time-constant form, it is sometimes more convenient to find the steady-state gain by an alternative method that does not require factoring of polynomials. This consists of merely letting $s = 0$ in the transfer function.

$$K_p = \lim_{s\to 0} G_{(s)} \qquad (7\text{-}95)$$

By definition, steady-state corresponds to the condition that all time derivatives are equal to zero. Since the variable s replaces d/dt in the Laplace domain, letting s go to zero is equivalent to the steady state.

This can be proved more rigorously by using the *final-value theorem* of Laplace transforms:

$$\lim_{t\to\infty} [f_{(t)}] = \lim_{s\to 0} [sF_{(s)}] \qquad (7\text{-}96)$$

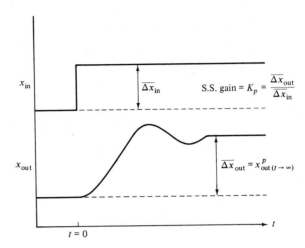

FIGURE 7-5
Steady-state gain.

Consider an arbitrary transfer function

$$G_{(s)} = \frac{X_{(s)}}{Q_{(s)}}$$

If a unit step disturbance is used,

$$Q_{(s)} = \frac{1}{s}$$

This means that the output is

$$X_{(s)} = G_{(s)}\frac{1}{s}$$

The final steady-state value of the output will be equal to the steady-state gain since the magnitude of the input was 1.

$$K_p = \lim_{t \to \infty} [x_{(t)}] = \lim_{s \to 0} [sX_{(s)}] = \lim_{s \to 0} \left(sG_{(s)}\frac{1}{s}\right) = \lim_{s \to 0} G_{(s)}$$

For example, the steady-state gain for the transfer function given in Eq. (7-91) is

$$K_p = \lim_{s \to 0} \left[\frac{b_M s^M + b_{M-1}s^{M-1} + \cdots + b_1 s + b_0}{a_N s^N + a_{N-1}s^{N-1} + \cdots + a_1 s + a_0}\right] = \frac{b_0}{a_0} \qquad (7\text{-}97)$$

It is obvious that this must be the right value of gain since at steady state Eq. (7-86) reduces to

$$a_0 \bar{x} = b_0 \bar{Q} \qquad (7\text{-}98)$$

Table 7-1   COMMON TRANSFER
                  FUNCTIONS

Terminology	G(s)
Gain	K
Derivative	s
Integrator	$\dfrac{1}{s}$
First-order lag	$\dfrac{1}{\tau s + 1}$
First-order lead	$\tau s + 1$
Second-order lag	
$\quad$ Underdamped $\zeta < 1$	$\dfrac{1}{\tau^2 s^2 + 2\tau\zeta s + 1}$
$\quad$ Critically damped $\zeta = 1$	$\dfrac{1}{(\tau s + 1)^2}$
$\quad$ Overdamped	$\dfrac{1}{(\tau_{p1} s + 1)(\tau_{p2} s + 1)}$
Dead time	e^{-Ds}
Lead-lag	$\dfrac{\tau_{z1} s + 1}{\tau_{p1} s + 1}$

PROBLEMS

7-1 Prove that the Laplace transformation of the following functions are:

(a) $\mathcal{L}\left[\dfrac{d^2 f}{dt^2}\right] = s^2 F_{(s)} - s f_{(0)} - \left(\dfrac{df}{dt}\right)_{(t=0)}$

(b) $\mathcal{L}[\cos \omega t] = \dfrac{s}{s^2 + \omega^2}$

(c) $\mathcal{L}[e^{-at} \sin \omega t] = \dfrac{\omega}{(s + a)^2 + \omega^2}$

7-2 Find the Laplace transformation of a rectangular pulse of height H_p and duration T_p.

7-3 An isothermal perfectly mixed batch reactor has consecutive first-order reactions: $A \xrightarrow{k_1} B \xrightarrow{k_2} C$. The initial material charged to the vessel contains only A at a concentration C_{A0}. Use Laplace transform techniques to solve for the changes in C_A and C_B with time during the batch cycle for (a) $k_1 > k_2$; (b) $k_1 = k_2$.

7-4 Two isothermal CSTR's are connected by a long pipe that acts like a pure dead time of D minutes at the steady-state flow rates. Assume constant throughputs and holdups and a first-order irreversible reaction $A \xrightarrow{k} B$ in each tank. Derive the transfer function relating the feed concentration to the first tank C_{A0} and the concentration of A in the stream leaving the second tank C_{A2}. Use inversion to find $C_{A2(t)}$ for a unit step disturbance in C_{A0}.

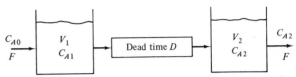

7-5 A general second-order system is described by the ODE

$$\tau_p^2 \frac{d^2x}{dt^2} + 2\tau_p \zeta \frac{dx}{dt} + x = K_p Q_{(t)}$$

If $\zeta > 1$, show that the system transfer function has two first-order lags with time constants τ_{p1} and τ_{p2}. Express these time constants in terms of τ_p and ζ.

7-6 Use Laplace transform techniques to solve Example 6-7 where a ramp disturbance drives a first-order system.

7-7 Find the transfer function of an underdamped second-order system:

$$\tau_p^2 \frac{d^2x}{dt^2} + 2\tau_p \zeta \frac{dx}{dt} + x = K_p Q_{(t)}$$

What are the poles of the transfer function? Solve for the response of $x_{(t)}$ to (a) a unit step disturbance; (b) an impulse disturbance.

7-8 Solve Prob. 6-6 using Laplace transforms. Note that this is a steady-state problem and that radial position r is the independent variable. You must therefore Laplace-transform with respect to r, not time t.

7-9 The imperfect mixing in a chemical reactor can be modeled by splitting the total volume into two perfectly mixed sections with circulation between them. Feed enters and leaves one section. The other section acts like a "side capacity" element.

Assume holdups and flow rates are constant. The reaction is an irreversible, first-order consumption of reactant A. The system is isothermal. Solve for the transfer function relating C_{A0} and C_A. What are the zeros and poles of the transfer function? What is the steady-state gain?

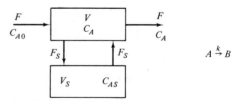

7-10 One way to determine the rate of change of a process variable is to measure the differential pressure $\Delta P \equiv P_{\text{out}} - P_{\text{in}}$ over a device called a *derivative unit* that has a transfer

function

$$\frac{P_{\text{out}(s)}}{P_{\text{in}(s)}} = \frac{\tau s + 1}{(\tau/6)s + 1}$$

(a) Derive the transfer function between ΔP and P_{in}.

(b) Show that the ΔP signal will be equal to the rate of rise of P_{in}, after an initial transient period, when P_{in} is a ramp function.

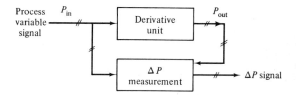

7-11   A convenient way to measure the density of a liquid is to pump it slowly through a vertical pipe and measure the differential pressure between the top and the bottom of the pipe. This differential head is directly related to the density of the liquid in the pipe if frictional pressure losses are negligible.

   Suppose the density can change with time. What is the transfer function relating a perturbation in density to the differential-pressure measurement? Assume the fluid moves up the vertical column in plug flow.

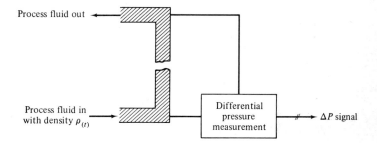

7-12   A thick-walled kettle of mass M_M, temperature T_M, and specific heat C_M is filled with a perfectly mixed process liquid of mass M, temperature T, and specific heat C. A heating fluid at temperature T_J is circulated in a jacket around the kettle wall. The heat transfer coefficient between the process fluid and the metal wall is U, and between the metal outside wall and the heating fluid is U_M. Inside and outside heat transfer areas are approximately the same (A ft^2). Neglecting any radial temperature gradients through the metal wall, show that the transfer function between T and T_J is two first-order lags.

$$G_{(s)} = \frac{K_p}{(\tau_{p1}s + 1)(\tau_{p2}s + 1)}$$

The value of the steady-state gain K_p is unity. Is this reasonable?

7-13 An ideal three-mode PID (proportional, integral, and derivative) feedback controller is described by the equation

$$M_{(t)} = \bar{M} + K_c \left[E_{(t)} + \frac{1}{\tau_I} \int E_{(t)} \, dt + \tau_D \frac{dE}{dt} \right]$$

Derive the transfer function between $M_{(s)}$ and $E_{(s)}$. Is this transfer function physically realizable?

7-14 Show that the linearized nonisothermal CSTR of Example 7-6 can be stable only if

$$\frac{UA}{V\rho C_p} > \frac{-\lambda \bar{k} \bar{C}_A E}{\rho C_p R \bar{T}^2} - 2 \frac{F}{V} - \bar{k}$$

7-15 Develop an analog computer circuit whose output x is given by the following ODE when forced by the input $Q_{(t)}$:

$$a_2 \frac{d^2x}{dt^2} + a_1 \frac{dx}{dt} + a_0 x = b_2 \frac{d^2Q}{dt^2} + b_1 \frac{dQ}{dt} + b_0 Q$$

7-16 A dead-time element is basically a distributed system. We have suggested in Part 2 that one approximate way to get the dynamics of distributed systems is to lump them into a number of perfectly mixed sections. Prove that a series of N mixed tanks is equivalent to a pure dead time as N goes to infinity. HINT: Keep the total volume of the system constant as more and more lumps are used.

7-17 A feedback controller is added to the three-CSTR system of Example 7-5. Now C_{A0} is changed by the feedback controller to keep C_{A3} at its set point, which is the steady-state value of C_{A3}. The error signal is therefore just $-C_{A3}$ (the perturbation in C_{A3}). Find the transfer function of this closed-loop system between the disturbance C_{AD} and C_{A3}. List the values of poles, zeros, and steady-state gain when the feedback controller is:

(a) Proportional: $C_{A0} = C_{AD} + K_c(-C_{A3})$

(b) Proportional-integral: $C_{A0} = C_{AD} + K_c \left[-C_{A3} + \frac{1}{\tau_I} \int (-C_{A3}) \, dt \right]$

Note the above equations are in terms of perturbation variables.

8

FREQUENCY-DOMAIN DYNAMICS

In Chap. 6 we showed that the dynamics of systems could be studied in the time domain by selecting a specific disturbance and solving the ODE describing the system. To find the effects of other disturbances, other values of parameters, or a different system structure (if the process or control components are modified), the equations must be resolved.

In Chap. 7 we found that the Laplace domain offered significant advantages in representing system dynamics and in solving ODE's. However, manipulation of the algebraic equations became more and more difficult as the system became more complex. If the system is Nth order, an Nth-order polynomial in s must be factored into its N roots. For N greater than 2, we usually abandon analytical methods and turn to numerical root-solving techniques (to be discussed in Chap. 11).

In this chapter we will study a third alternative way to look at the dynamics of systems: *frequency-response analysis*. We will find that higher-order, complex systems are very easily handled in the frequency domain. Basically this is because the manipulation of transfer functions becomes a problem of combining (addition, multiplication, etc.) complex numbers numerically.

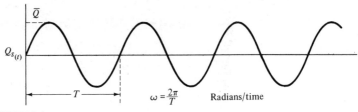

FIGURE 8-1
Sine-wave input.

As in the Laplace domain, a basic restriction of frequency-domain techniques is that they can be applied only to linear systems or systems that have been linearized around some steady-state operating level.

8-1   DEFINITION

The *frequency response* of a process is defined as the steady-state behavior of the system when forced by a sinusoidal input.

Suppose the input $Q_{(t)}$ is a sine wave $Q_{s(t)}$ of amplitude $\bar{Q}$ and frequency ω as shown in Fig. 8-1.

$$Q_{s(t)} = \bar{Q} \sin \omega t \qquad (8\text{-}1)$$

The period of one complete cycle is T units of time, and frequency is given in radians per unit time:

$$\omega = \frac{2\pi}{T} \qquad (8\text{-}2)$$

In degrees per unit time,

$$\omega = \frac{360}{T} \qquad (8\text{-}3)$$

In cycles per unit time,[1]

$$\omega = \frac{1}{T} \qquad (8\text{-}4)$$

In a linear system, if the input is a sine wave with frequency ω, the output will also be a sine wave with the same frequency. The output will, however, have a different

---

[1] A cycle per second (cps) is sometimes called a hertz (Hz).

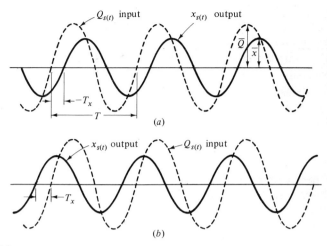

FIGURE 8-2
Sinusoidal input-output. (*a*) Output lags; (*b*) output leads.

amplitude and will lag (fall behind) or lead (rise ahead of) the input. Figure 8-2*a* shows the output $x_{s(t)}$ lagging the input $Q_{s(t)}$ by T_x units of time. Figure 8-2*b* shows the output leading the input by T_x. The *phase angle* θ is defined as the angular difference between the input and the output. In equation form,

$$x_{s(t)} = \bar{x} \sin(\omega t + \theta) \qquad (8\text{-}5)$$

where $x_{s(t)}$ = output with sine-wave input of frequency ω
 $\bar{x}$ = maximum amplitude of output x_s
 θ = phase angle

If the output lags the input, θ is negative. If the output leads the input, θ is positive.

$$\theta = \frac{T_x}{T} 2\pi \qquad \text{radians}$$

$$= \frac{T_x}{T} 360 \qquad \text{degrees} \qquad (8\text{-}6)$$

The magnitude ratio M is defined as the ratio of the maximum amplitude of the output over the maximum amplitude of the input:

$$M = \frac{\bar{x}}{\bar{Q}} \qquad (8\text{-}7)$$

For a given process, both the phase angle θ and the magnitude ratio M will change if frequency ω is changed. We must find out how θ and M vary as ω goes from zero to infinity. Then we know the system's frequency response.

Different processes have different M and θ dependence on ω. By merely looking at curves of M and θ we can tell the kind of system (order, damping, etc.) and what its parameter values are (time constants, steady-state gain, damping coefficient, etc.).

There are a number of ways to obtain the frequency response of a process. Experimental methods, discussed in the next chapter, are used when a mathematical model of the system is not available. If equations can be developed that adequately describe the system, the frequency response can be obtained directly from the system transfer function.

8-2   BASIC THEOREM

As we will show below, the frequency response of a system can be found by simply substituting $i\omega$ for s in the system transfer function. Making the substitution $s = i\omega$ gives a complex number $G_{(i\omega)}$ that has the following:

 1 A magnitude $|G_{(i\omega)}|$ that is the same as the magnitude ratio M that would be obtained by forcing the system with a sine wave of frequency ω
 2 A phase angle or *argument*, arg $G_{(i\omega)}$, that is equal to the phase angle θ that would be obtained when forcing the system with a sine wave of frequency ω

$$|G_{(i\omega)}| = M_{(\omega)} \qquad (8\text{-}8)$$

$$\arg G_{(i\omega)} = \theta_{(\omega)} \qquad (8\text{-}9)$$

$G_{(i\omega)}$ is a complex number, so it can be represented in terms of a real part and an imaginary part:

$$G_{(i\omega)} = \operatorname{Re} G_{(i\omega)} + i \operatorname{Im} G_{(i\omega)} \qquad (8\text{-}10)$$

or, in polar form,

$$G_{(i\omega)} = |G_{(i\omega)}| e^{i \, \arg G_{(i\omega)}} \qquad (8\text{-}11)$$

where

$$|G_{(i\omega)}| = \text{absolute value of } G_{(i\omega)}$$

$$= \sqrt{(\operatorname{Re} G)^2 + (\operatorname{Im} G)^2} \qquad (8\text{-}12)$$

$$\arg G_{(i\omega)} = \arctan\left(\frac{\operatorname{Im} G}{\operatorname{Re} G}\right) \qquad (8\text{-}13)$$

This very remarkable result [Eqs. (8-8) and (8-9)] permits us to go from the Laplace domain to the frequency domain with ease.

$$\text{Laplace domain} \quad \xrightarrow{s=i\omega} \quad \text{frequency domain}$$
$$G_{(s)} \qquad\qquad\qquad G_{(i\omega)}$$

Before we prove that this simple substitution is valid, let us illustrate its application in a specific example.

EXAMPLE 8-1   Suppose we want to find the frequency response of a first-order process with the transfer function

$$G_{(s)} = \frac{K_p}{\tau_p s + 1}$$

Substituting $s = i\omega$ gives

$$G_{(i\omega)} = \frac{K_p}{1 + i\omega\tau_p} \qquad (8\text{-}14)$$

Multiplying numerator and denominator by the complex conjugate of the denominator gives

$$G_{(i\omega)} = \frac{K_p}{1 + i\omega\tau_p} \frac{1 - i\omega\tau_p}{1 - i\omega\tau_p} = \frac{K_p(1 - i\omega\tau_p)}{1 + \omega^2\tau_p^{\,2}}$$

$$= \frac{K_p}{1 + \omega^2\tau_p^{\,2}} + i\,\frac{-K_p\omega\tau_p}{1 + \omega^2\tau_p^{\,2}} \qquad (8\text{-}15)$$

Therefore

$$\text{Re } G = \frac{K_p}{1 + \omega^2\tau_p^{\,2}}$$

$$\text{Im } G = \frac{-K_p\,\omega\tau_p}{1 + \omega^2\tau_p^{\,2}} \qquad (8\text{-}16)$$

Therefore

$$M = |G_{(i\omega)}| = \sqrt{\left(\frac{K_p}{1 + \omega^2\tau_p^{\,2}}\right)^2 + \left(\frac{-K_p\omega\tau_p}{1 + \omega^2\tau_p^{\,2}}\right)^2} = \frac{K_p}{\sqrt{1 + \omega^2\tau_p^{\,2}}} \qquad (8\text{-}17)$$

$$\theta = \arg G_{(i\omega)} = \arctan\left[\frac{-K_p\,\omega\tau_p/(1 + \omega^2\tau_p^{\,2})}{K_p/(1 + \omega^2\tau_p^{\,2})}\right] = \arctan\left(-\omega\tau_p\right) \qquad (8\text{-}18)$$

Notice that both M and θ vary with frequency ω.   ////

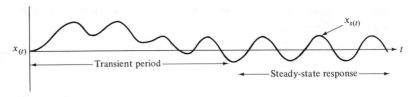

FIGURE 8-3
Response of a system to a sine-wave input.

Now let us prove that this simple substitution $s = i\omega$ really works. Let $G_{(s)}$ be the transfer function of any arbitrary Nth-order system. The only restriction we will place on the system is that it be stable. If the system is initially at rest and we start forcing it with a sine wave $Q_{s(t)}$, the output $x_{(t)}$ will go through some transient period as shown in Fig. 8-3 and then settle down to a steady sinusoidal oscillation. In the Laplace domain, the output is by definition

$$X_{(s)} = G_{(s)} Q_{(s)} \qquad (8\text{-}19)$$

For a sine-wave input

$$Q_{(t)} = \bar{Q} \sin \omega t$$

Laplace-transforming,

$$Q_{(s)} = \bar{Q} \frac{\omega}{s^2 + \omega^2} \qquad (8\text{-}20)$$

Therefore the output with this sine-wave input is

$$X_{(s)} = G_{(s)} Q_{(s)} = G_{(s)} \frac{\bar{Q}\omega}{s^2 + \omega^2}$$

$G_{(s)}$ is a ratio of polynomials in s that can be factored into poles and zeros.

$$G_{(s)} = \frac{Z_{(s)}}{P_{(s)}} = \frac{(s - z_1)(z - z_2) \cdots (s - z_M)}{(s - p_1)(s - p_2) \cdots (s - p_N)} \qquad (8\text{-}21)$$

Then $X_{(s)}$ becomes

$$X_{(s)} = \frac{(s - z_1)(s - z_2) \cdots (s - z_M)}{(s - p_1)(s - p_2) \cdots (s - p_N)} \frac{\bar{Q}\omega}{s^2 + \omega^2}$$

$$= \frac{\bar{Q}\omega Z_{(s)}}{(s + i\omega)(s - i\omega)(s - p_1) \cdots (s - p_N)}$$

Expanding in partial fractions expansion gives

$$X_{(s)} = \frac{A}{s + i\omega} + \frac{B}{s - i\omega} + \frac{C}{s - p_1} + \cdots + \frac{W}{s - p_N} \qquad (8\text{-}22)$$

where

$$A = \lim_{s \to -i\omega} [(s + i\omega)X_{(s)}] = \lim_{s \to -i\omega} \left[\frac{\omega \bar{Q} G_{(s)}}{s - i\omega} \right]$$

$$= -\frac{\bar{Q}}{2i} G_{(-i\omega)}$$

$$B = \lim_{s \to i\omega} [(s - i\omega)X_{(s)}] = \lim_{s \to i\omega} \left[\frac{\omega \bar{Q} G_{(s)}}{s + i\omega} \right]$$

$$= \frac{\bar{Q}}{2i} G_{(i\omega)}$$

$$C = \lim_{s \to p_1} [(s - p_1)X_{(s)}]$$

Substituting into Eq. (8-22) and inverting to the time domain,

$$x_{(t)} = \left(\frac{-\bar{Q}}{2i} G_{(-i\omega)} \right) e^{-i\omega t} + \left(\frac{\bar{Q}}{2i} G_{(i\omega)} \right) e^{i\omega t} + \sum_{j=1}^{N} c_j e^{p_j t} \qquad (8\text{-}23)$$

Now we are interested only in the steady-state response after the initial transients have died out. As time goes to infinity, all the exponential terms in the summation shown in Eq. (8-23) decay to zero. The system is stable so all the poles p_j must be negative. The steady-state output with a sine-wave input, which we have called $x_{s(t)}$, is

$$x_{s(t)} = \frac{\bar{Q}}{2i} (G_{(i\omega)} e^{i\omega t} - G_{(-i\omega)} e^{-i\omega t}) \qquad (8\text{-}24)$$

The $G_{(i\omega)}$ and $G_{(-i\omega)}$ terms are complex numbers and can be put into polar form:

$$G_{(i\omega)} = |G_{(i\omega)}| e^{i \text{ arg } G_{(i\omega)}}$$

$$G_{(-i\omega)} = |G_{(-i\omega)}| e^{i \text{ arg } G_{(-i\omega)}}$$

$$= |G_{(i\omega)}| e^{-i \text{ arg } G_{(i\omega)}} \qquad (8\text{-}25)$$

Equation (8-24) becomes

$$x_{s(t)} = \bar{Q} |G_{(i\omega)}| \frac{e^{i(\omega t + \text{arg } G)} - e^{-i(\omega t + \text{arg } G)}}{2i}$$

Therefore

$$\frac{x_{s(t)}}{\bar{Q}} = |G_{(i\omega)}| \sin (\omega t + \text{arg } G_{(i\omega)}) \qquad (8\text{-}26)$$

Therefore we have proved what we set out to prove: (1) the magnitude ratio M is the absolute value of $G_{(s)}$ with s set equal to $i\omega$ and (2) the phase angle is the argument of $G_{(s)}$ with s set equal to $i\omega$.

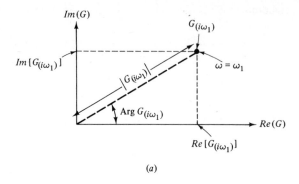

(a)

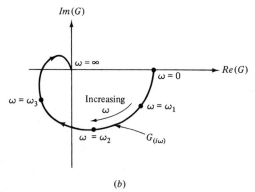

(b)

FIGURE 8-4
Nyquist plots in the G plane. (a) Single point $G_{(i\omega_1)}$; (b) complete curve $G_{(i\omega)}$.

8-3 REPRESENTATION

There are three different kinds of plots that are commonly used to show how magnitude ratio M and phase angle θ vary with frequency ω. They are called *Nyquist*, *Bode* (pronounced "Bow-dee"), and *Nichols* plots. After defining what each of them is, we will show what some common transfer functions look like in the three different plots.

8-3.1 Nyquist Plots

A Nyquist plot (also called a *polar plot* or a *G-plane plot*) is generated by plotting the complex number $G_{(i\omega)}$ in a two-dimensional diagram whose ordinate is the imaginary part of $G_{(i\omega)}$ and whose abscissa is the real part of $G_{(i\omega)}$. A specific value of frequency ω_1 defines a point in this plane. As shown in Fig. 8-4a, either rectangular (real versus imaginary) or polar (absolute magnitude versus phase angle) can be used to locate the point.

As frequency is varied continuously from zero to infinity a line is formed in the G plane as shown in Fig. 8-4b. Frequency is thus a parameter along this curve. The shape and location of this curve are characteristics of the system.

Let us show what the Nyquist plots of some simple transfer functions look like.

First-order lag

$$G_{(s)} = \frac{K_p}{\tau_p s + 1}$$

We developed $G_{(i\omega)}$ for this transfer function in Example 8-1 [Eqs. (8-17) and (8-18)]:

$$M = \frac{K_p}{\sqrt{1 + \omega^2 \tau_p{}^2}}$$

$$\theta = \arctan(-\omega\tau_p)$$

When frequency is zero, M is equal to K_p and θ is equal to zero. When frequency is equal to the reciprocal of the time constant,

$$\omega = \frac{1}{\tau_p}$$

$$M = \frac{K_p}{\sqrt{1 + (1/\tau_p)^2 \tau_p{}^2}} = \frac{K_p}{\sqrt{2}}$$

$$\theta = \arctan\left(-\frac{1}{\tau_p}\tau_p\right) = -45° = -\frac{\pi}{4} \text{ radians}$$

As frequency goes to infinity, M goes to zero and θ goes to $-90°$ or $-\pi/2$ radians. These points are shown in Fig. 8-5. The complete Nyquist plot is a semicircle.

The effect of changing the gain K_p is also shown in Fig. 8-5. The magnitude of each point is changed but the phase angle is not affected.

First-order lead

$$G_{(s)} = \tau_z s + 1$$

$$G_{(i\omega)} = 1 + i\omega\tau_z$$

$$\theta = \arctan \omega\tau_z$$

$$M = \sqrt{1 + \omega^2 \tau_z{}^2} \qquad (8\text{-}27)$$

When $\omega = 0$, $\theta = 0$ and $M = 1$. As ω goes to infinity, M becomes infinite and θ goes to $+90°$ or $+\pi/2$ radians. The Nyquist plot is shown in Fig. 8-6.

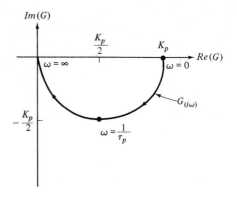

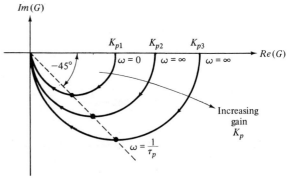

FIGURE 8-5
Nyquist plot of first-order lag.

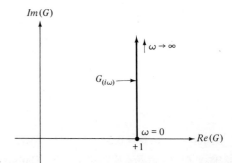

FIGURE 8-6
Nyquist plot for first-order lead.

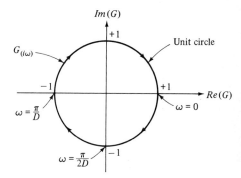

FIGURE 8-7
Nyquist plot for dead time.

Dead time

$$G_{(s)} = e^{-Ds} \Rightarrow G_{(i\omega)} = e^{-i\omega D}$$

$$M = 1$$

$$\theta = -\omega D \qquad (8\text{-}28)$$

Equations (8-28) say that dead time changes the phase angle θ but has no effect on the magnitude ratio M. M is unity at all frequencies. When $\omega = 0$, $\theta = 0$. As ω goes to infinity, θ goes to minus infinity. The Nyquist plot is shown in Fig. 8-7. The curve moves around the unit circle an infinite number of times as ω goes to infinity.

Dead time and first-order lag   Combining these two transfer functions gives

$$G_{(s)} = \frac{K_p e^{-Ds}}{\tau_p s + 1}$$

$$G_{(i\omega)} = \frac{K_p e^{-i\omega D}}{1 + i\omega\tau_p} = \left(\frac{K_p}{\sqrt{1 + \omega^2\tau_p^2}}\, e^{i\,\arctan\,(-\omega\tau_p)} \right) e^{-i\omega D}$$

$$= \frac{K_p}{\sqrt{1 + \omega^2\tau_p^2}}\, e^{i\,[\arctan\,(-\omega\tau_p) - D\omega]}$$

$$M = \frac{K_p}{\sqrt{1 + \omega^2\tau_p^2}}$$

$$\theta = \arctan\,(-\omega\tau_p) - D\omega \qquad (8\text{-}29)$$

The magnitude ratio M is exactly the same as the first-order lag alone. Phase angle is decreased by the dead-time contribution. Figure 8-8 shows the Nyquist plot. It is a spiral that wraps around the origin as it shrinks in magnitude.

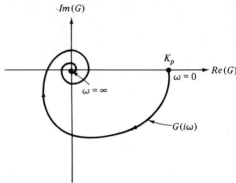

FIGURE 8-8
Nyquist plot for dead time with first-order lag.

Integrator   The transfer function of a pure integrator is

$$G_{(s)} = \frac{1}{s}$$

Going into the frequency domain by substituting $s = i\omega$ gives

$$G_{(i\omega)} = \frac{1}{i\omega} = -\frac{1}{\omega}i$$

$G_{(i\omega)}$ is a pure imaginary number (its real part is zero), lying on the imaginary axis. It starts at minus infinity when ω is zero and goes to the origin as $\omega \to \infty$. The Nyquist plot is sketched in Fig. 8-9.

$$M = \frac{1}{\omega}$$

$$\theta = \arctan \frac{-1/\omega}{0} = -90° = -\frac{\pi}{2} \text{ radians} \qquad (8\text{-}30)$$

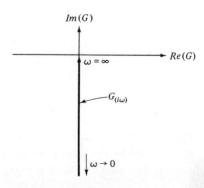

FIGURE 8-9
Nyquist plot for an integrator.

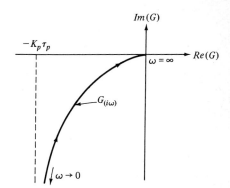

FIGURE 8-10
Nyquist plot of an integrator and first-
order lag.

Integrator and first-order lag   Combining these two transfer functions gives

$$G_{(s)} = \frac{K_p}{s(\tau_p s + 1)}$$

$$G_{(i\omega)} = \frac{K_p}{-\tau_p \omega^2 + i\omega} = \frac{-K_p \tau_p \omega - K_p i}{\omega(\tau_p^2 \omega^2 + 1)}$$

$$M = \frac{K_p}{\omega\sqrt{1 + \tau_p^2 \omega^2}}$$

$$\theta = \arctan\left(\frac{-1}{-\tau_p \omega}\right) \qquad (8\text{-}31)$$

The Nyquist curve is shown in Fig. 8-10.

Second-order underdamped system

$$G_{(s)} = \frac{K_p}{\tau_p^2 s^2 + 2\zeta\tau_p s + 1}$$

$$G_{(i\omega)} = \frac{K_p}{(1 - \tau_p^2 \omega^2) + i(2\zeta\tau_p \omega)} = \frac{K_p(1 - \tau_p^2 \omega^2) - iK_p(2\zeta\tau_p \omega)}{(1 - \tau_p^2 \omega^2)^2 + 4\zeta^2\tau_p^2 \omega^2}$$

$$M = \frac{K_p}{\sqrt{(1 - \tau_p^2 \omega^2)^2 + 4\zeta^2\tau_p^2 \omega^2}}$$

$$\theta = \arctan\left(\frac{-2\zeta\tau_p \omega}{1 - \tau_p^2 \omega^2}\right) \qquad (8\text{-}32)$$

When $\omega = 0$

$$M = K_p \qquad \text{and} \qquad \theta = 0$$

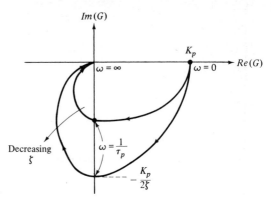

FIGURE 8-11
Nyquist plot of a second-order system.

When $\omega = 1/\tau_p$,

$$M = \frac{K_p}{2\zeta} \quad \text{and} \quad \theta = -\frac{\pi}{2}$$

as $\omega \to \infty$, $M \to 0$ and $\theta \to -\pi$. The Nyquist plot is sketched in Fig. 8-11.

The results of the examples above show that adding lags or poles to the transfer function moves the Nyquist plot clockwise around the origin in the G plane. Adding leads or zeros moves it counterclockwise. We will return to this generalization in Chap. 11 when we start designing controllers that shift these curves in the desired way.

8-3.2 Bode Plots

The Nyquist plot discussed in the previous section presents all the frequency information in a compact, one-curve form. Bode plots require that two curves be plotted instead of one. This increase is well worth the trouble because complex transfer functions can be handled much more easily. The two curves show how magnitude ratio and phase angle vary with frequency.

Phase angle is usually plotted against frequency, using semilog graph paper as illustrated in Fig. 8-12. The magnitude ratio is sometimes plotted against frequency, using log-log graph paper. But usually the magnitude ratio is converted to a *log modulus* defined by the equation[1]

$$L \equiv \log \text{modulus} \equiv 20 \log |M| \quad (8\text{-}33)$$

Then semilog graph paper is used to plot log modulus L versus frequency, as shown in Fig. 8-12.

[1] Logarithm to the base 10.

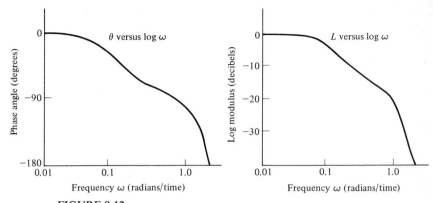

FIGURE 8-12
Bode plots of phase angle and log modulus versus the logarithm of frequency.

The units of log modulus are decibels (db), a term originally used in communications engineering to indicate the ratio of two values of power. Figure 8-13 is convenient to use to convert back and forth from magnitude ratio to decibels.

The log modulus plotted in Bode plots is often the "normalized" magnitude ratio. The magnitude ratio is divided by the absolute value of the steady-state gain of the transfer function. It is convenient to normalize because it makes most of the plots start at 0 db.

$$L = 20 \log \frac{|M|}{|\text{steady-state gain}|} \qquad (8\text{-}34)$$

Since the steady-state gain is $\lim_{s \to 0} [G_{(s)}]$ from Eq. (7-95), it is also given by

$$\text{Steady-state gain} = \lim_{\omega \to 0} G_{(i\omega)} = G_{(0)} \qquad (8\text{-}35)$$

Thus the normalized log modulus is

$$L = 20 \log \frac{|G_{(i\omega)}|}{|G_{(0)}|} \qquad (8\text{-}36)$$

Now let us look at the Bode plots of some common transfer functions.

Gain   If $G_{(s)}$ is just a constant K_p, $M = K_p$ and $\theta = 0$. Neither M or θ varies with frequency. The log modulus is

$$L = 20 \log |K_p| \qquad (8\text{-}37)$$

Both the phase-angle and log modulus curves are horizontal lines. Increasing K_p moves the L curve up; decreasing K_p moves it down. If K_p is greater than unity, L is positive. If K_p is less than 1, L is negative. The Bode plots are shown in Fig. 8-14.

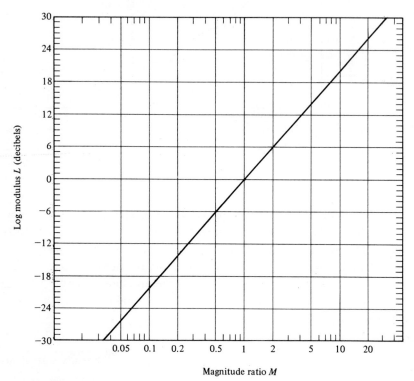

FIGURE 8-13
Conversion between magnitude ratio and log modulus.

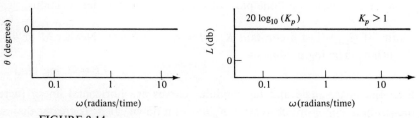

FIGURE 8-14
Bode plots of gain.

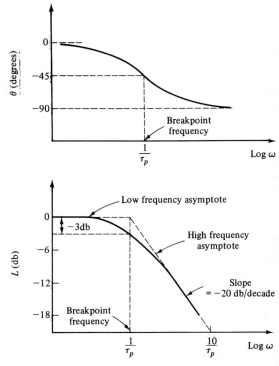

FIGURE 8-15
Bode plots for first-order lag.

First-order lag   From Eq. (8-17),

$$M = \frac{K_p}{\sqrt{1 + \omega^2 \tau_p^2}}$$

We will normalize by dividing out the steady-state gain K_p.

$$L = 20 \log \frac{1}{\sqrt{1 + \omega^2 \tau_p^2}} \qquad (8\text{-}38)$$

From Eq. (8-18),

$$\theta = \arctan\left(-\omega\tau_p\right)$$

The Bode plots are shown in Fig. 8-15. One of the most convenient features of Bode plots is that the L curves can be easily sketched by considering the low- and high-frequency asymptotes. As ω goes to zero, the normalized L curve goes to zero. As

ω becomes very large, Eq. (8-38) becomes

$$L_{\omega \to \infty} = 20 \log \frac{1}{\sqrt{\omega^2 \tau_p^2}} = -20 \log \omega \tau_p$$

$$= -20(\log \omega) - (20 \log \tau_p) \qquad (8\text{-}39)$$

This is the equation of a straight line of L versus $\log \omega$. It has a slope of -20. L will decrease 20 db as $\log \omega$ increases by 1 or as ω increases by a factor of 10. A factor of 10 is called a *decade*; a factor of 2 is called an *octave*. Therefore the slope of the high-frequency asymptote is -20 db/decade or -6 db/octave.

The high-frequency asymptote intersects the $L = 0$ line at $\omega = 1/\tau_p$. This is called the *breakpoint frequency*. The log modulus curve is "flat" (horizontal) out to this point in frequency and then begins to drop off.

Thus the L curve can be easily sketched by drawing a line with slope of -20 db/decade from the breakpoint frequency, which is the reciprocal of the time constant. Notice also that the phase angle is equal to $-45°$ at the breakpoint frequency.

First-order lead

$$G_{(i\omega)} = 1 + i\omega\tau_z$$

$$L = 20 \log \sqrt{1 + \omega^2 \tau_z^2} \qquad (8\text{-}40)$$

$$\theta = \arctan \omega\tau_z$$

These curves are shown in Fig. 8-16. The high-frequency asymptote has a slope of $+20$ db/decade. The breakpoint frequency is $1/\tau_z$. The phase angle goes from zero to $+90°$ and is equal to $+45°$ at $\omega = 1/\tau_z$.

Dead time

$$G_{(i\omega)} = e^{-iD\omega}$$

$$L = 20 \log 1 = 0 \qquad (8\text{-}41)$$

$$\theta = -\omega D$$

As shown in Fig. 8-17, the dead-time transfer function has a flat L curve for all frequencies, but the phase angle drops off to minus infinity.

nth power of s

$$G_{(s)} = s^n \qquad n = \pm 1, \pm 2, \ldots$$

$$G_{(i\omega)} = \omega^n i^n$$

$$L = 20 \log \omega^n = 20n \log \omega \qquad (8\text{-}42)$$

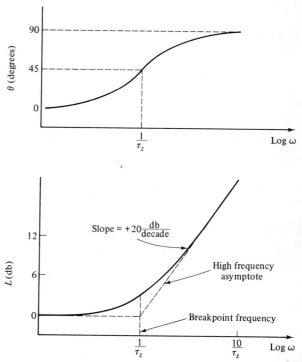

FIGURE 8-16
Bode plots for first-order lead.

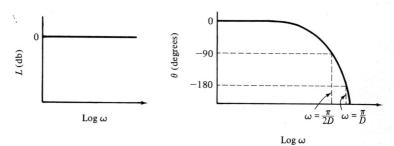

FIGURE 8-17
Bode plots for dead time.

The L curve is a straight line with a slope of $20n$.

$$\theta = \arctan \frac{\text{Im }(G)}{\text{Re }(G)}$$

If n is odd, $G_{(i\omega)}$ is a pure imaginary number and θ is the arctan of infinity. If n is even, $G_{(i\omega)}$ is a real number and θ is the arctan of zero. Therefore θ changes by $90°$ or $\pi/2$ radians for each successive integer value of n.

$$\theta = n\left(\frac{\pi}{2}\right) \text{ radians} \qquad (8\text{-}43)$$

1 $n = 1$: This is the transfer function of an ideal derivative:

$$G_{(i\omega)} = i\omega$$

$$L = 20 \log \omega$$

$$\theta = \arctan \frac{\omega}{0} = +\frac{\pi}{2} \text{ radians} = 90° \qquad (8\text{-}44)$$

2 $n = -1$: This is the transfer function of an integrator.

$$G_{(i\omega)} = \frac{1}{i\omega} = \left(-\frac{1}{\omega}\right)i$$

$$L = -20 \log \omega$$

$$\theta = \arctan \left(\frac{-1/\omega}{0}\right) = -\frac{\pi}{2} \text{ radians} \qquad (8\text{-}45)$$

3 $n = -2$: Two integrators in series give

$$G_{(i\omega)} = -\left(\frac{1}{\omega^2}\right)$$

$$L = -40 \log \omega$$

$$\theta = \arctan \left(\frac{0}{-1/\omega^2}\right) = -\pi \text{ radians} \qquad (8\text{-}46)$$

The $G_{(i\omega)}$'s above are sketched in Fig. 8-18.

Second-order underdamped lag Eqs. (8-32) give

$$L = 20 \log \frac{1}{\sqrt{(1 - \tau_p^2\omega^2)^2 + 4\zeta^2\tau_p^2\omega^2}}$$

$$\theta = \arctan \left(\frac{-2\zeta\tau_p\omega}{1 - \tau_p^2\omega^2}\right) \qquad (8\text{-}47)$$

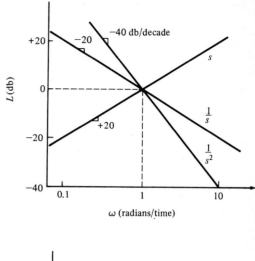

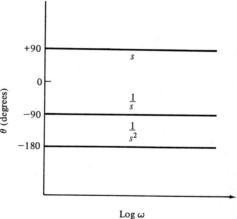

FIGURE 8-18
Bode plots for s^n.

Figure 8-19 shows the Bode plots for several values of damping coefficients ζ. The breakpoint frequency is the reciprocal of the time constant. The high-frequency asymptote has a slope of -40 db/decade.

$$L_{\omega \to \infty} = 20 \log \frac{1}{\tau_p^2 \omega^2} = -40 \log \omega \tau_p$$

General transfer functions in series   The reason Bode plots are used so much is that they make it easy to combine transfer functions. A complex transfer function can be broken down into its simple elements, leads, lags, and dead time; each of these is plotted in Bode diagrams; and finally the total complex transfer function is obtained by adding the log modulus and phase-angle curves.

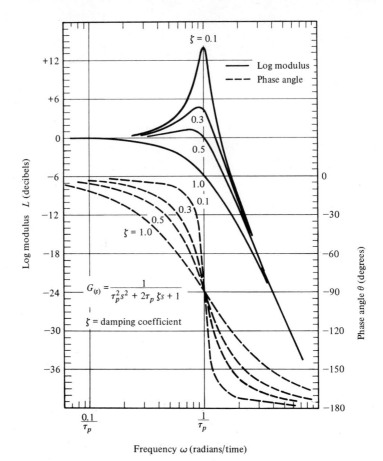

FIGURE 8-19
Second-order-system Bode plots.

Consider a general transfer function $G_{(s)}$ that can be broken up into two simple transfer functions $G_{1(s)}$ and $G_{2(s)}$.

$$G_{(s)} = G_{1(s)}\,G_{2(s)}$$

In the frequency domain,

$$G_{(i\omega)} = G_{1(i\omega)}\,G_{2(i\omega)} \qquad (8\text{-}48)$$

Each of the G's is a complex number and can be expressed in polar form:

$$G_{1(i\omega)} = |G_{1(i\omega)}|\,e^{i\,\text{arg}\,G_{1(i\omega)}}$$

$$G_{2(i\omega)} = |G_{2(i\omega)}|\,e^{i\,\text{arg}\,G_{2(i\omega)}}$$

$$G_{(i\omega)} = |G_{(i\omega)}|\,e^{i\,\text{arg}\,G_{(i\omega)}}$$

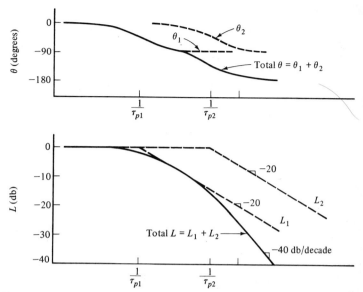

FIGURE 8-20
Bode plots for two lags.

Combining

$$G_{(i\omega)} = (|G_{1(i\omega)}|e^{i \text{ arg } G_1})(|G_{2(i\omega)}|e^{i \text{ arg } G_2})$$

$$|G_{(i\omega)}|e^{i \text{ arg } G_{(i\omega)}} = |G_{1(i\omega)}||G_{2(i\omega)}|e^{i (\text{arg } G_{1(i\omega)} + \text{ arg } G_{2(i\omega)})} \qquad (8\text{-}49)$$

Taking the logarithm of both sides gives

$$\ln |G| + i \text{ arg } G = \ln |G_1| + \ln |G_2| + i(\text{arg } G_1 + \text{arg } G_2)$$

$$\ln |G| = \ln |G_1| + \ln |G_2|$$

$$\text{arg } G = \text{arg } G_1 + \text{arg } G_2 \qquad (8\text{-}50)$$

Therefore log modulus curves and phase-angle curves of the individual components are simply added at each value of frequency to get the total L and θ curves for the transfer function.

EXAMPLE 8-2   Consider the transfer function $G_{(s)}$:

$$G_{(s)} = \frac{1}{(\tau_{p1}s + 1)(\tau_{p2}s + 1)}$$

Bode plots of $1/(\tau_{p1}s + 1)$ and $1/(\tau_{p2}s + 1)$ are sketched in Fig. 8-20 and added to give $G_{(i\omega)}$.   ////

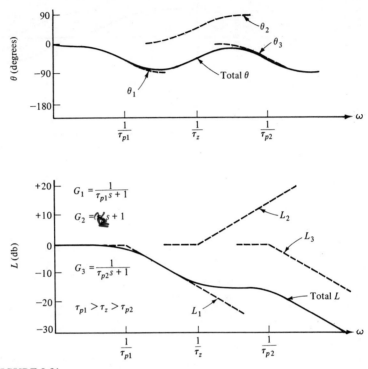

FIGURE 8-21
Bode plots for two lags and one lead.

EXAMPLE 8-3 Bode plots for the transfer function

$$G_{(s)} = \frac{\tau_z s + 1}{(\tau_{p1} s + 1)(\tau_{p2} s + 1)}$$

are sketched in Fig. 8-21.   ////

EXAMPLE 8-4 Figure 8-22 gives Bode plots for a transfer function containing a first-order lag and dead time. Several different values of dead time D are shown. Only the phase-angle curve is changed as D changes. The L curve is the same for all values of D.

$$G_{(s)} = \frac{e^{-Ds}}{s + 1}$$ ////

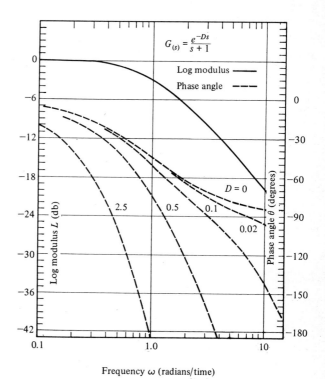

FIGURE 8-22
Bode plots for lag and dead time.

Up to this point we have stressed graphical methods for quickly sketching Bode plots. Since the combining of simple transfer functions is just numerical manipulation of complex numbers, a digital computer that can do complex arithmetic (FORTRAN IV) is easily programmed to generate any of the desired forms of the complex numbers: real and imaginary parts, magnitude ratio, log modulus, and phase angle.

Figure 8-23 gives a program that calculates the frequency response of several simple systems. Figure 8-24 shows the printed output, and Bode plots are shown in Fig. 8-25.

The variables must be declared COMPLEX at the beginning of the program. Table 8-1 lists some of the common complex-number operations.

8-3.3   Nichols Plots

A Nichols plot is a single curve of log modulus versus phase angle with frequency as the parameter along the curve. Figure 8-26 gives Nichols plots of some simple transfer functions.

```
C     DIGITAL PROGRAM TO CALCULATE FREQUENCY RESPONSE
      DIMENSION G(4),DB(4),DEG(4)
      COMPLEX G
      PRINT 1
    1 FORMAT(1H1,*FREQ  REG1  IMG1  REG2  IMG2  REG3  IMG3  REG4  IMG4
     1 DBG1  DEGG1 DBG2  DEGG2 DBG3  DEGG3 DBG4  DEGG4*)
C     W = FREQUENCY IN RADIANS PER TIME
      W=.01
      DW=10.**(.1)
      DO 100 I=1,40
C     G(1) IS A FIRST-ORDER LAG WITH TP = 1
      G(1)=1./CMPLX(1.,W)
C     G(2) IS TWO FIRST-ORDER LAGS WITH TP1 = TP2 = 1
      G(2) = G(1)*G(1)
C     G(3) IS TWO FIRST-ORDER LAGS WITH TP1 = 1 AND TP2 = 10
      G(3)=G(1)*(1./CMPLX(1.,W*10.))
C     G(4) IS A SECOND-ORDER UNDERDAMPED LAG WITH TP = 1 AND ZETA = 0.3
      G(4)=1./CMPLX(1.-W**2,2.*W*0.3)
      DO 10 J=1,4
      DB(J)=20.*ALOG10(CABS(G(J)))
      DEG(J)=ATAN(AIMAG(G(J))/REAL(G(J)))*180./3.1416
      IF(REAL(G(J)).LT.0.) DEG(J)=DEG(J)-180.
   10 CONTINUE
      PRINT 5,W,G,(DB(J),DEG(J),J=1,4)
    5 FORMAT(1X,F6.2,4(2F6.3),8F6.1)
  100 W=W*DW
      STOP
      END
```

FIGURE 8-23
Digital program for calculating frequency responses.

FREQ	REG1	IMG1	REG2	IMG2	REG3	IMG3	REG4	IMG4	DBG1	DEGG1	DBG2	DEGG2	DBG3	DEGG3	DBG4	DEGG4
.01	1.000	-.010	1.000	-.020	.989	-.109	1.000	-.006	-.0	-.6	-.0	-1.1	-.0	-6.3	.0	-.3
.01	1.000	-.013	1.000	-.025	.983	-.136	1.000	-.008	-.0	-.7	-.0	-1.4	-.1	-7.9	.0	-.4
.02	1.000	-.016	.999	-.032	.973	-.170	1.000	-.010	-.0	-.9	-.0	-1.8	-.1	-9.9	.0	-.5
.02	1.000	-.020	.999	-.040	.958	-.211	1.000	-.012	-.0	-1.1	-.0	-2.3	-.2	-12.4	.0	-.7
.03	.999	-.025	.998	-.050	.934	-.260	1.000	-.015	-.0	-1.4	-.0	-2.9	-.3	-15.5	.0	-.9
.03	.999	-.032	.997	-.063	.899	-.315	1.001	-.019	-.0	-1.8	-.0	-3.6	-.4	-19.4	.0	-1.1
.04	.998	-.040	.995	-.079	.848	-.377	1.001	-.024	-.0	-2.3	-.0	-4.6	-.6	-24.0	.0	-1.4
.05	.997	-.050	.992	-.100	.777	-.440	1.002	-.030	-.0	-2.9	-.0	-5.7	-1.0	-29.5	.0	-1.7
.06	.996	-.063	.988	-.125	.684	-.494	1.003	-.038	-.0	-3.6	-.0	-7.2	-1.5	-35.9	.0	-2.2
.08	.994	-.079	.981	-.157	.571	-.532	1.004	-.048	-.0	-4.5	-.1	-9.1	-2.2	-43.0	.0	-2.7
.10	.990	-.099	.970	-.196	.446	-.545	1.006	-.061	-.0	-5.7	-.1	-11.4	-3.1	-50.7	.1	-3.5
.13	.984	-.124	.954	-.244	.320	-.527	1.010	-.078	-.1	-7.2	-.1	-14.4	-4.2	-58.7	.1	-4.4
.15	.975	-.155	.928	-.302	.208	-.484	1.016	-.099	-.1	-9.0	-.2	-18.0	-5.6	-66.8	.2	-5.6
.20	.962	-.192	.836	-.369	.116	-.424	1.026	-.128	-.2	-11.3	-.3	-22.6	-7.1	-74.7	.3	-7.1
.25	.941	-.236	.829	-.445	.047	-.356	1.040	-.167	-.3	-14.1	-.5	-28.2	-8.9	-82.4	.5	-9.1
.32	.909	-.287	.744	-.523	-.000	-.287	1.064	-.224	-.4	-17.5	-.8	-35.1	-10.8	-90.0	.7	-11.9
.40	.863	-.344	.527	-.595	-.030	-.224	1.100	-.312	-.6	-21.7	-1.3	-43.4	-12.9	-97.6	1.2	-15.8
.50	.795	-.401	.478	-.640	-.046	-.169	1.150	-.462	-1.0	-26.6	-1.9	-53.2	-15.1	-105.3	1.9	-21.9
.63	.715	-.451	.309	-.646	-.052	-.122	1.190	-.749	-1.5	-32.3	-2.9	-64.5	-17.6	-113.2	3.0	-32.2
.79	.613	-.487	.139	-.597	-.051	-.084	1.016	-1.312	-2.1	-38.5	-4.2	-76.9	-20.2	-121.3	4.4	-52.2
1.00	.500	-.500	.000	-.500	-.045	-.054	.000	-1.567	-3.0	-45.0	-6.0	-90.0	-23.1	-129.3	4.4	-90.0
1.26	.387	-.487	-.068	-.377	-.036	-.034	-.641	-.828	-4.1	-51.5	-8.2	-103.1	-26.2	-137.0	.4	-127.8
1.58	.285	-.451	-.123	-.257	-.027	-.020	-.474	-.298	-5.5	-57.7	-10.9	-115.5	-29.5	-144.1	-5.0	-147.8
2.00	.201	-.401	-.123	-.161	-.020	-.011	-.289	-.116	-7.0	-63.4	-13.0	-126.8	-33.0	-150.5	-10.1	-158.1
2.51	.137	-.344	-.099	-.094	-.013	-.005	-.174	-.049	-8.6	-68.3	-17.3	-136.6	-36.6	-156.0	-14.8	-164.2
3.15	.091	-.287	-.074	-.052	-.009	-.003	-.105	-.022	-10.4	-72.5	-20.8	-144.9	-40.4	-160.6	-19.3	-168.1
3.98	.059	-.236	-.052	-.028	-.006	-.002	-.066	-.011	-12.3	-75.9	-24.5	-151.8	-44.3	-164.5	-23.5	-170.9
5.01	.038	-.192	-.035	-.015	-.004	-.001	-.041	-.005	-14.2	-78.7	-28.3	-157.4	-48.2	-167.6	-27.7	-172.9
6.31	.025	-.155	-.023	-.008	-.002	-.000	-.026	-.002	-16.1	-81.0	-32.2	-162.0	-52.1	-170.1	-31.8	-174.4
7.94	.016	-.124	-.015	-.004	-.002	-.000	-.016	-.001	-18.1	-82.8	-36.1	-165.6	-56.1	-172.1	-35.9	-175.6
10.00	.010	-.099	-.010	-.002	-.001	-.000	-.010	-.001	-20.0	-84.3	-40.1	-168.6	-60.0	-173.7	-39.9	-176.5
12.59	.006	-.079	-.006	-.001	-.001	-.000	-.006	-.000	-22.0	-85.5	-44.1	-170.9	-64.0	-175.0	-44.0	-177.3
15.85	.004	-.063	-.004	-.001	-.000	-.000	-.004	-.000	-24.0	-86.4	-48.0	-172.8	-68.0	-176.0	-48.0	-177.8
19.95	.003	-.050	-.002	-.000	-.000	-.000	-.003	-.000	-26.0	-87.1	-52.0	-174.3	-72.0	-176.8	-52.0	-178.3
25.12	.002	-.040	-.002	-.000	-.000	-.000	-.002	-.000	-28.0	-87.7	-56.0	-175.4	-76.0	-177.5	-56.0	-178.6
31.62	.001	-.032	-.001	-.000	-.000	-.000	-.001	-.000	-30.0	-88.2	-60.0	-176.4	-80.0	-178.0	-60.0	-178.9
39.81	.001	-.025	-.001	-.000	-.000	-.000	-.001	-.000	-32.0	-88.6	-64.0	-177.1	-84.0	-178.4	-64.0	-179.1
50.12	.000	-.020	-.000	-.000	-.000	-.000	-.000	-.000	-34.0	-88.9	-68.0	-177.7	-88.0	-178.7	-68.0	-179.3
63.10	.000	-.016	-.000	-.000	-.000	-.000	-.000	-.000	-36.0	-89.1	-72.0	-178.2	-92.0	-179.0	-72.0	-179.5
79.43	.000	-.013	-.000	-.000	-.000	-.000	-.000	-.000	-38.0	-89.3	-76.0	-178.6	-96.0	-179.2	-76.0	-179.6

FIGURE 8-24
Printed output from program of Fig. 8-23.

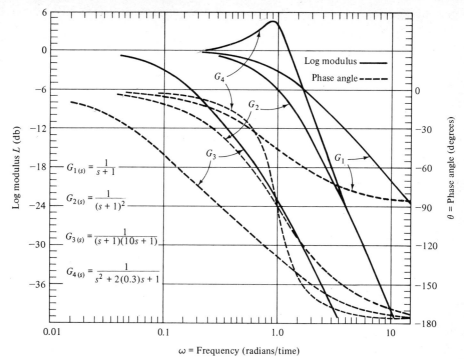

FIGURE 8-25
Bode plots of several systems.

Table 8-1   FORTRAN IV COMPLEX-VARIABLE OPERATIONS

FORTRAN Statement	Explanation
COMPLEX G_1, G_2, G_3	Variables G_1, G_2, and G_3 are declared complex numbers.
$G_1 =$ CMPLX(A,B)	The real part of G_1 is set equal to the real number A, and the imaginary part of G_1 is set equal to the real number B.
$G_3 = G_1*G_2$	G_1 and G_2 are complex-multiplied.[a]
$G_3 = G_1/G_2$	G_1 is complex-divided by G_2.[b]
$X =$ REAL(G_1)	X is set equal to the real part of G_1.
$Y =$ AIMAG(G_1)	Y is set equal to the imaginary part of G_1.
$X =$ CABS(G_1)	X is set equal to the absolute value of the complex number G_1.[c]
$G_3 = G_1 + G_2$	G_1 and G_2 are complex-added.[d]
$G_3 = G_1 - G_2$	G_2 is complex-subtracted from G_1.[e]
$G_1 =$ CEXP(G_2)	The real part of G_1 is set equal to $e^{\text{Re } G_2}$ cos (Im G_2) and the imaginary part of G_1 is set equal to $e^{\text{Re } G_2}$ sin (Im G_2).

[a] If $G_1 = \alpha_1 + i\omega_1$
$\quad G_2 = \alpha_2 + i\omega_2$
$\quad G_1*G_2 = (\alpha_1\alpha_2 - \omega_1\omega_2) + i(\alpha_1\omega_2 + \alpha_2\omega_1)$

[b] $G_1/G_2 = \dfrac{\alpha_1\alpha_2 + \omega_1\omega_2}{\alpha_2{}^2 + \omega_2{}^2} + i\,\dfrac{\alpha_2\omega_1 - \alpha_1\omega_2}{\alpha_2{}^2 + \omega_2{}^2}$

[c] $X = \sqrt{(\text{Re } G_1)^2 + (\text{Im } G_1)^2} = \sqrt{\alpha_1{}^2 + \omega_1{}^2}$
[d] $G_1 + G_2 = (\alpha_1 + \alpha_2) + i(\omega_1 + \omega_2)$
[e] $G_1 - G_2 = (\alpha_1 - \alpha_2) + i(\omega_1 - \omega_2)$

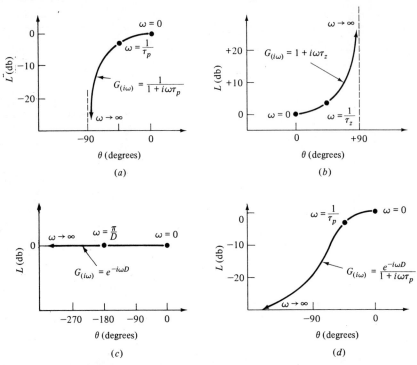

FIGURE 8-26
Nichols plots. (a) First-order lag; (b) first-order lead; (c) dead time; (d) dead time and lag.

8-4   FREQUENCY-DOMAIN SOLUTION TECHNIQUES

In the preceding sections of this chapter we assumed that the system transfer function $G_{(s)}$ was known. Then the simple substitution $s = i\omega$ into $G_{(s)}$ gave the frequency response of the system.

However, it is sometimes difficult to find $G_{(s)}$ by solving all the algebraic equations in s that result when the linearized ODE's describing the system are Laplace-transformed. For example, the equations of the simple second-order nonisothermal CSTR of Example 7-6 got a little complicated when we tried to solve analytically for the eight transfer functions as explicit functions of s. As the systems get more and more complex and higher order, analytical solution for the system transfer functions becomes practically impossible.

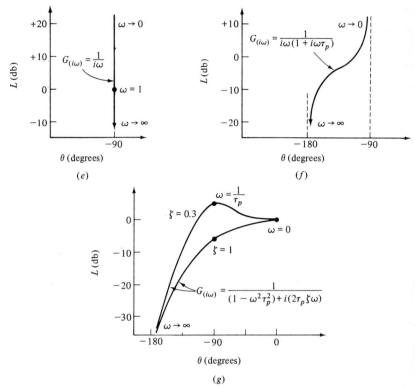

FIGURE 8-26 (*Continued*)
(*e*) integrator; (*f*) integrator and lag; (*g*) second-order underdamped lag.

These large systems of equations can be solved fairly easily by going into the frequency domain. The procedure is:

1 The linear ODE's are Laplace-transformed.
2 Then $i\omega$ is immediately substituted for s.
3 A specific numerical value of frequency ω is chosen.
4 The resulting algebraic equations, which are now in terms of complex variables, are solved numerically to obtain the desired transfer-function relationships. These $G_{(i\omega)}$'s will be complex numbers that are points on Nyquist, Bode, or Nichols plots corresponding to the specific frequency chosen.
5 Another numerical value of ω is specified and step *4* is repeated. Picking a number of frequencies over the range of interest for the process gives the complete frequency-response curves.

We will show how to use these frequency-domain solution techniques for large systems of ODE's. They can also be applied to partial differential equations[1] but we will not discuss that subject here.

Let us illustrate the procedure with two examples.

EXAMPLE 8-5   Consider the nonisothermal CSTR of Example 7-6. The linearized ODE's of the system are

$$\frac{dC_A}{dt} = a_{11}C_A + a_{12}T + a_{13}C_{A0} + a_{15}F$$

$$\frac{dT}{dt} = a_{21}C_A + a_{22}T + a_{24}T_0 + a_{25}F + a_{26}T_J \qquad (8\text{-}51)$$

where the a_{ij}'s are all constants. Laplace-transforming and substituting $s = i\omega$ give

$$(i\omega - a_{11})C_{A(i\omega)} = a_{12}T_{(i\omega)} + a_{13}C_{A0(i\omega)} + a_{15}F_{(i\omega)}$$

$$(i\omega - a_{22})T_{(i\omega)} = a_{21}C_{A(i\omega)} + a_{24}T_{0(i\omega)} + a_{25}F_{(i\omega)} + a_{26}T_{J(i\omega)} \qquad (8\text{-}52)$$

All the variables are now complex numbers with real and imaginary parts.

$$C_{A(i\omega)} = \operatorname{Re} C_A + i \operatorname{Im} C_A \equiv C_A{}^R + iC_A{}^I$$

$$T_{(i\omega)} = \operatorname{Re} T + i \operatorname{Im} T \equiv T^R + iT^I$$

$$C_{A0(i\omega)} = \operatorname{Re} C_{A0} + i \operatorname{Im} C_{A0} \equiv C_{A0}{}^R + iC_{A0}{}^I$$

$$F_{(i\omega)} = \operatorname{Re} F + i \operatorname{Im} F \equiv F^R + iF^I$$

$$T_{0(i\omega)} = \operatorname{Re} T_0 + i \operatorname{Im} T_0 \equiv T_0{}^R + iT_0{}^I$$

$$T_{J(i\omega)} = \operatorname{Re} T_J + i \operatorname{Im} T_J \equiv T_J{}^R + iT_J{}^I \qquad (8\text{-}53)$$

Picking a specific value of frequency ω gives two algebraic complex-variable equations that must be rearranged to get the output variables $C_{A(i\omega)}$ and $T_{(i\omega)}$ in terms of the input variables $C_{A0(i\omega)}$, $T_{0(i\omega)}$, $F_{(i\omega)}$, and $T_{J(i\omega)}$.

$$C_{A(i\omega)} = G_{11(i\omega)}C_{A0(i\omega)} + G_{12(i\omega)}T_{0(i\omega)} + G_{13(i\omega)}F_{(i\omega)} + G_{14(i\omega)}T_{J(i\omega)}$$

$$T_{(i\omega)} = G_{21(i\omega)}C_{A0(i\omega)} + G_{22(i\omega)}T_{0(i\omega)} + G_{23(i\omega)}F_{(i\omega)} + G_{24(i\omega)}T_{J(i\omega)} \qquad (8\text{-}54)$$

The solution of Eqs. (8-52) is made easier if we take one input variable at a time. First let us set C_{A0} equal to 1 and all other input variables equal to zero.

$$C_{A0} = C_{A0}{}^R + iC_{A0}{}^I = 1 + 0i$$

$$T_0 = F = T_J = 0 + 0i \qquad (8\text{-}55)$$

---

[1] J. D. Tinkler and D. E. Lamb, *Chem. Eng. Prog. Symp. Ser.*, no. 55, vol. 61, p. 155, 1965.

Now Eqs. (8-52) become

$$(i\omega - a_{11})C_{A(i\omega)} = a_{12}T_{(i\omega)} + a_{13}$$

$$(i\omega - a_{22})T_{(i\omega)} = a_{21}C_{A(i\omega)} \qquad (8\text{-}56)$$

These two equations can then be solved for C_A and T. Since there are only two equations in this simple example, they can be solved analytically to give C_A and T in terms of any value of frequency.

$$C_{A(i\omega)} = \frac{a_{13}(i\omega - a_{22})}{(i\omega - a_{22})(i\omega - a_{11}) - a_{21}a_{12}}$$

$$T_{(i\omega)} = \frac{a_{21}a_{13}}{(i\omega - a_{22})(i\omega - a_{11}) - a_{21}a_{12}} \qquad (8\text{-}57)$$

However, in a more complex case with many equations where analytical solution would be difficult, the equations can be solved numerically. All the a_{ij}'s and ω are just numbers. Standard simultaneous equation-solving packages available in most digital-computer libraries can be used. Keep in mind, however, that these are complex-variable simultaneous equations.

The numerical values of the complex variables $C_{A(i\omega)}$ and $T_{(i\omega)}$ are equal to the transfer functions $G_{11(i\omega)}$ and $G_{21(i\omega)}$ in Eqs. (8-54) because we set C_{A0} equal to 1 originally.

$$(C_{A(i\omega)})_{C_{A0}=1} = (C_A^R + iC_A^I)_{C_{A0}=1} = G_{11(i\omega)}$$

$$(T_{(i\omega)})_{C_{A0}=1} = (T^R + iT^I)_{C_{A0}=1} = G_{21(i\omega)} \qquad (8\text{-}58)$$

Now T_0 is set equal to 1, with all other input variables zero, and the equations solved again for new values of $C_{A(i\omega)}$ and $T_{(i\omega)}$. These are the transfer functions G_{12} and G_{22}.

$$(C_{A(i\omega)})_{T_0=1} = G_{12(i\omega)}$$

$$(T_{(i\omega)})_{T_0=1} = G_{22(i\omega)} \qquad (8\text{-}59)$$

Repeating the same process with $F = 1$ gives G_{13} and G_{23} and with $T_J = 1$ gives G_{14} and G_{24}. Then a new value of frequency is selected and the complete process is repeated. ////

EXAMPLE 8-6 Let us consider a much more complex system where the advantages of frequency-domain solution will be more apparent. Rippin and Lamb[1] showed how a frequency domain "stepping" technique could be used to find the frequency response of a distillation column. The column has many trays and therefore the system is of very high order.

---

[1] D. W. T. Rippin and D. E. Lamb, paper presented at the American Institute of Chemical Engineers meeting, Washington, D.C., 1960.

The linearized equations for the binary distillation column are (see Sec. 3-10):

Reboiler (assuming holdup M_B is constant):

$$\frac{dx_B}{dt} = a_{B1}L_1 - a_{B2}V + a_{B3}x_1 - a_{B4}x_B$$

$$0 = L_1 - V - B \tag{8-60}$$

Tray 1:

$$\frac{dx_1}{dt} = a_{11}L_2 - a_{12}V + a_{13}x_2 - a_{14}x_1 + a_{15}x_B$$

$$\frac{dL_1}{dt} = \frac{1}{\beta}(L_2 - L_1) \tag{8-61}$$

Tray n:

$$\frac{dx_n}{dt} = a_{n1}L_{n+1} - a_{n2}V + a_{n3}x_{n+1} - a_{n4}x_n + a_{n5}x_{n-1} + a_{n6}x_F + a_{n7}F$$

$$\frac{dL_n}{dt} = \frac{1}{\beta}(L_{n+1} - L_n + F) \tag{8-62}$$

Top tray $(n = N_T)$:

$$\frac{dx_{NT}}{dt} = a_{NT,1}R - a_{NT,2}V + a_{NT,3}x_D - a_{NT,4}x_{NT} + a_{NT,5}x_{NT-1}$$

$$\frac{dL_{NT}}{dt} = \frac{1}{\beta}(R - L_{NT}) \tag{8-63}$$

Condenser–reflux drum $(M_D$ *is assumed constant; total condenser):*

$$\frac{dx_D}{dt} = a_{D1}x_{NT} - a_{D2}x_D$$

$$0 = V - R - D \tag{8-64}$$

The a_{ij} and β are all constants made up of the steady-state holdups, flows, and compositions. Table 8-2 gives their values. The variables in Eqs. (8-60) to (8-64) are all perturbation variables. β is the hydraulic constant, the linearized relationship between a perturbation in liquid holdup on a tray, M_n, and the perturbation in the liquid flow rate L_n leaving the tray.

$$M_n = \beta L_n \tag{8-65}$$

K_n is the linearized relationship between perturbations in vapor composition y_n and liquid composition x_n. It is just the slope of the equilibrium line.

$$y_n = K_n x_n \tag{8-66}$$

As the name implies,[1] the stepping technique involves stepwise calculation from the base of the column to the top. All the equations are Laplace-transformed,

[1] J. P. Shunta and W. L. Luyben, *Ind. Eng. Chem., Fundamentals*, vol. 8, p. 838, 1969.

Table 8-2   BINARY DISTILLATION
COLUMN CONSTANT COEFFICIENTS

$$a_{B1} = \frac{\bar{x}_1 - \bar{x}_B}{\bar{M}_B} \qquad\qquad a_{n4} = \frac{\bar{L}_n + \bar{V}K_n}{\bar{M}_n}$$

$$a_{B2} = \frac{\bar{y}_B - \bar{x}_B}{\bar{M}_B} \qquad\qquad a_{n5} = \frac{\bar{V}K_{n-1}}{\bar{M}_n}$$

$$a_{B3} = \frac{\bar{L}_1}{\bar{M}_B} \qquad\qquad a_{n6} = \frac{\bar{F}}{\bar{M}_n}$$

$$a_{B4} = \frac{\bar{B} + \bar{V}K_B}{\bar{M}_B} \qquad\qquad a_{n7} = \frac{\bar{x}_F - \bar{x}_n}{\bar{M}_n}$$

$$a_{11} = \frac{\bar{x}_2 - \bar{x}_1}{\bar{M}_1} \qquad\qquad a_{NT,1} = \frac{\bar{x}_D - \bar{x}_{NT}}{\bar{M}_{NT}}$$

$$a_{12} = \frac{\bar{y}_1 - \bar{y}_B}{\bar{M}_1} \qquad\qquad a_{NT,2} = \frac{\bar{y}_{NT} - \bar{y}_{NT-1}}{\bar{M}_{NT}}$$

$$a_{13} = \frac{\bar{L}_2}{\bar{M}_1} \qquad\qquad a_{NT,3} = \frac{\bar{R}}{\bar{M}_{NT}}$$

$$a_{14} = \frac{\bar{L}_1 + \bar{V}K_1}{\bar{M}_1} \qquad\qquad a_{NT,4} = \frac{\bar{L}_{NT} + \bar{V}K_{NT}}{\bar{M}_{NT}}$$

$$a_{15} = \frac{\bar{V}K_B}{\bar{M}_1} \qquad\qquad a_{NT,5} = \frac{\bar{V}K_{NT-1}}{\bar{M}_{NT}}$$

$$a_{n1} = \frac{\bar{x}_{n+1} - \bar{x}_n}{\bar{M}_n} \qquad\qquad a_{D1} = \frac{\bar{V}K_{NT}}{\bar{M}_D}$$

$$a_{n2} = \frac{\bar{y}_n - \bar{y}_{n-1}}{\bar{M}_n} \qquad\qquad a_{D2} = \frac{\bar{V}}{\bar{M}_D}$$

$$a_{n3} = \frac{\bar{L}_{n+1}}{\bar{M}_n}$$

s is set equal to $i\omega$, and a value of frequency is specified. One of the variables at the base or at the feed tray (x_F, F, V, B, or x_B) is set equal to $1 + 0i$ and the remaining set equal to zero. For example, let us set $x_B = 1 + 0i$.

Starting with the reboiler equations, the composition x_1 and liquid flow rate L_1 can be calculated.

$$L_1 = V_B + B = 0$$

$$x_1 = [(i\omega + a_{B4})x_B - a_{B1}L_1 + a_{B2}V]\frac{1}{a_{B3}} = \frac{i\omega + a_{B4}}{a_{B3}} \qquad (8\text{-}67)$$

These variables x_1 and L_1 are complex numbers.

Then the equations for tray 1 can be used to calculate x_2 and L_2. This procedure is continued up the column, tray by tray. The top-tray equations give complex values for x_D and R, which are stored as the complex numbers g_{11} and g_{21}.

$$x_D \equiv g_{11}{}^R + ig_{11}{}^I \equiv g_{11}$$

$$R \equiv g_{21}{}^R + ig_{21}{}^I \equiv g_{21} \qquad (8\text{-}68)$$

The first condenser equation [Eqs. (8-64)] gives a second value of x_D, which is stored as g_{31}. These g's are just intermediate numbers that will be used shortly to calculate the desired transfer functions.

$$x_D \equiv g_{31}{}^R + ig_{31}{}^I \equiv g_{31}$$

Then V is set equal to $1 + 0i$, and x_B, B, x_F, and F are set equal to zero. Stepping up the column again gives three new g's. Then the procedure is repeated with $B = 1$, then with $x_F = 1$, and finally with $F = 1$.

These calculations would be very tedious to do by hand, but they can be done easily on a digital computer because they are all numerical calculations.

The resulting g's from the five cycles up the column form three equations:

$$x_D = g_{11}x_B + g_{12}V + g_{13}B + g_{14}x_F + g_{15}F$$

$$R = g_{21}x_B + g_{22}V + g_{23}B + g_{24}x_F + g_{25}F$$

$$x_D = g_{31}x_B + g_{32}V + g_{33}B + g_{34}x_F + g_{35}F \qquad (8\text{-}69)$$

These three equations can then be rearranged to get the output variables x_D and x_B in terms of just the input variables x_F, F, R, and V.

$$x_D = P_{11(i\omega)}x_F + P_{12(i\omega)}F + P_{13(i\omega)}R + P_{14(i\omega)}V$$

$$x_B = P_{21(i\omega)}x_F + P_{22(i\omega)}F + P_{23(i\omega)}R + P_{24(i\omega)}V \qquad (8\text{-}70)$$

The P_{ij}'s are points on Bode, Nyquist, or Nichols plots of the distillation-column transfer functions.

A new value of frequency is specified and the calculations repeated. Figure 8-27 gives a digital program that performs all these calculations. The initial part of

```
C     FREQUENCY DOMAIN STEPPING PROGRAM
      COMPLEX P,XP1,XP2,Z1,ZL,G,FF,XP,XLP
      DIMENSION X(20),KEQ(20),Y(20),A(20,7)
      DIMENSION G(3,5),P(2,4),FF(2,2),DEGF(2,2),SSKP(2,4),SSKF(2,2)
      DIMENSION DBP(2,4),DBF(2,2),DEGP(2,4)
      REAL KEQ,MB,MS,MP,MD,KB,LS,LR
      EQUIL(XX)=ALPHA*XX/(1.+(ALPHA-1.)*XX)
      SLOPE(XX)=ALPHA/((1.+(ALPHA-1.)*XX)**2)
1000  READ 2,NT,NS,ALPHA,XB,XD,XF,V,WMIN,WMAX
   2  FORMAT(2I5,7F10.5)
      IF(NT.LE.0) CALL EXIT
      READ 3,MB,MS,MP,MD,BETA,F
   3  FORMAT(8F10.5)
C.....................
C   STEADYSTATE PROGRAM
C.....................
      DV=V/10.
      YB=EQUIL(XB)
      LOOP=0
      FLAGP=1.
      FLAGM=1.
      B=(XD-XF)*F/(XD-XB)
      D=F-B
C     CONVERGE ON CORRECT VALUE OF V TO GIVE XB AND XD
 100  LS=V+B
      LOOP=LOOP+1
      IF(LOOP.GT.50 ) GO TO 10
C     STRIPPING TRAYS
      X(1)=(V*YB+B*XB)/ LS
      Y(1)=EQUIL(X(1))
      X(2)=X(1)+(Y(1)-YB)*V / LS
      Y(2)=EQUIL(X(2))
      DO 20 K=3,NS
      X(K)=X(K-1)+(Y(K-1)-Y(K-2))*V / LS
      Y(K)=EQUIL(X(K))
  20  CONTINUE
C     FEED TRAY
      LR=LS-F
      R=LR
      X(NS+1)=(LS *X(NS)+V*Y(NS)-V*Y(NS-1)-F*XF)/ LR
      IF(X(NS+1).GT.XD) GO TO 35
      Y(NS+1)=EQUIL(X(NS+1))
      IF(X(NS +1).LE.X(NS )) GO TO 31
C     RECTIFYING TRAYS
      NSP1=NS+1
      NSP2=NS+2
      DO 40 K=NSP2,NT
      X(K)=X(K-1)+(Y(K-1)-Y(K-2))*V / LR
      Y(K)=EQUIL(X(K))
  40  IF(X(K).GT.XD) GO TO 35
      IF(ABS(XD-Y(NT)).LT..00001) GO TO 50
      IF(XD-Y(NT))35,31,31
  11  FORMAT(1X,4HLOOP)
  10  PRINT 11
      STOP
  31  IF(FLAGP)32,32,33
  32  DV=DV/2.
  33  V=V+DV
      FLAGM=-1.
      GO TO 100
  35  IF(FLAGM)36,36,37
  36  DV=DV/2.
  37  V=V-DV
      FLAGP=-1.
      GO TO 100
  50  PRINT 51
```

FIGURE 8-27
Stepping-technique digital computer program and results.

```
      PRINT 150
150 FORMAT(35X,*MOLES/MIN. MOLES/MIN.      MOLES/MIN.*)
 51 FORMAT(1H1,9X,*NT      NS      ALPHA      B        D
   1XF      F*)
      PRINT 52,NT,NS,ALPHA,B,D,XF,F
 52 FORMAT(7X,I2,8X,I2,9X,8F10.5)
      PRINT 53
 53 FORMAT(7X,*  XB      XD      V        R      BETA*)
      PRINT 151
151 FORMAT(23X,*MOLES/MIN.  MOLES/MIN.     MIN.*)
      PRINT 54,XB,XD,V,R,BETA
 54 FORMAT(1X,8F10.5)
      K=0
      KB=SLOPE(XB)
      PRINT 152
152 FORMAT(4X,*   N        X        Y        K*)
      PRINT 55,K,XB,YB,KB
 55 FORMAT(3X,I2,5X,7F10.5)
      DO 56 K=1,NT
      KEQ(K)=SLOPE(X(K))
 56 PRINT 55,K,X(K),Y(K),KEQ(K)
C ...................
C   COEFFICIENTS                       .
C ...................
      K=0
      AB1=(X(1)-XB)/MB
      AB2=(Y1-XB)/MB
      AB3=LS/MB
      AB4=(B+V*KB)/MB
      PRINT 60
 60 FORMAT(4X,14N,9X,2HA1,8X,2HA2,8X,2HA3,9X,2HA4,8X,2HA5,8X,2HA6,9X,
   1 2HA7)
      PRINT 55,K,AB1,AB2,AB3,AB4
      A(1,1)=(X(2)-X(1))/MS
      A(1,2)=(Y(1)-YB)/MS
      A(1,3)=LS/MS
      A(1,4)=(LS+V*KEQ(1))/MS
      A(1,5)=V*KB/MS
      A(1,6)=0.
      A(1,7)=0.
      K=1
      PRINT 55,K,A(1,1),A(1,2),A(1,3),A(1,4),A(1,5),A(1,6),A(1,7)
      DO 70 K=2,NS
      A(K,1)=(X(K+1)-X(K))/MS
      A(K,2)=(Y(K)-Y(K-1))/MS
      A(K,3)=LS/MS
      A(K,4)=(LS+V*KEQ(K))/MS
      A(K,5)=V*KEQ(K-1)/MS
      A(K,6)=0.
      A(K,7)=0.
      IF(K.GE.NS) A(K,3)=LR/MS
      IF(K.GE.NS ) A(K,7)=(XF-X(NS ))/MS
      IF(K.GE.NS ) A(K,6)=F/MS
 70 PRINT 55,K,A(K,1),A(K,2),A(K,3),A(K,4),A(K,5),A(K,6),A(K,7)
      DO 80 K=NS+1,NT
      A(K,1)=(Y(K+1)-X(K))/MR
      A(K,2)=(Y(K)-Y(K-1))/MR
      A(K,3)=LR/MR
      A(K,4)=(LR+V*KEQ(K))/MR
      A(K,5)=V*KEQ(K-1)/MR
      A(K,6)=0.
      A(K,7)=0.
      IF(K.GE.NT) A(NT,1)=(XD-X(NT))/MR
 80 PRINT 55,K,A(K,1),A(K,2),A(K,3),A(K,4),A(K,5),A(K,6),A(K,7)
      AD1=V*KEQ(NT)/MD
```

```
      A02=V/40
      PRINT 31,A01,A02
   81 FORMAT(10X,5F10.5)
C.......................
C   STEPPING UP COLUMN
C.......................
      WN=10.
      DW=10.**(1./WN)
      W=0.
  200 IF(W.GT.WMAX) GO TO 1000
      DO 300 K=1,5
      XBP=0.
      VP=0.
      BP=0.
      XFP=0.
      FP=0.
      GO TO (201,202,203,204,205),K
  201 XBP=1.
      GO TO 210
  202 VP=1.
      GO TO 210
  203 BP=1.
      GO TO 210
  204 XFP=1.
      GO TO 210
  205 FP =1.
  210 XLP=CMPLX((BP+VP),0.)
      Z1=CMPLX(AB4,W)
      XP1=(Z1*XBP-AB1*XLP+AB2*VP)/AB3
      XP2=CMPLX(XBP,0.)
      ZL=CMPLX(1.,W*BETA)
C   STRIPPING TRAYS
      NSM1=NS-1
      DO 220 J=1,NSM1
      XLP=XLP*ZL
      Z1=CMPLX(A(J,4),W)
      XP=(Z1*XP1-A(J,1)*XLP-A(J,5)*XP2+A(J,2)*VP)/A(J,3)
      XP2=XP1
      XP1=XP
  220 CONTINUE
C   FEED TRAY
      XLP=ZL*XLP-FP
      Z1=CMPLX(A(NS ,4),W)
      XP=(Z1*XP1-A(NS ,1)*XLP-A(NS ,5)*XP2-A(NS ,6)*XFP-A(NS ,7)*F P
     1  +A(NS ,2)*VP)/A(NS ,3)
      XP2=XP1
      XP1=XP
C   RECTIFYING TRAYS
      DO 240 J=NSP1,NT
      XLP=XLP*ZL
      Z1=CMPLX(A(J,4),W)
      XP=(Z1*XP1-A(J,1)*XLP-A(J,5)*XP2+A(J,2)*VP)/A(J,3)
      XP2=XP1
  240 XP1=XP
      Z1=CMPLX(A02,W)
      XP=XP2*A01/Z1
      G(1,K)=XP1
      G(2,K)=XLP
      G(3,K)=XP
  300 CONTINUE
      P(2,1)=(G(1,4)-G(3,4))/(G(3,1)-G(1,1))
      P(2,2)=(G(1,5)-G(3,5)+(G(3,3)-G(1,3))*G(2,5)/G(2,3))/(G(3,1)-G(1,1
     1 ))
      P(2,3)=(G(1,3)-G(3,3))/((G(3,1)-G(1,1))*G(2,3))
      P(2,4)=(G(1,2)-G(3,2)+G(2,2)*(G(3,3)-G(1,3))/G(2,3))/(G(3,1)-
```

FIGURE 8-27

Stepping-technique digital computer program and results. (*Continued*)

```
    1 G(1,1))
      P(1,1)=G(1,1)*P(2,1)+G(1,4)
      P(1,7)=G(1,3)/G(2,3) + G(1,1)*P(2,3)
      P(1,2)=G(1,1)*P(2,2)+G(1,5)-G(1,3)*G(2,5)/G(2,3)
      P(1,4)=G(1,1)*P(2,4)+G(1,2)-G(1,3)*G(2,2)/G(2,3)
C ....................................
C   CALCULATE FEEDFORWARD CONTROLLLERS
C ....................................
      FF(2,2)=(G(1,3)*G(3,5)-G(1,5)*G(3,3))/(G(1,2)*G(3,3)-G(1,3)*G(3,2)
     1 )
      FF(2,1)=(G(1,3)*G(3,4)-G(1,4)*G(3,3))/(G(1,2)*G(3,3)-G(1,3)*G(3,2)
     1 )
      FF(1,1)=-(G(1,4)*G(2,3)+FF(2,1)*(G(1,2)*G(2,3)-G(1,3)*G(2,2)))/
     1 G(1,3)
      FF(1,2)=-(G(1,5)*G(2,3)-G(1,3)*G(2,5)+FF(2,2)*(G(1,2)*G(2,3)-
     1 G(1,3)*G(2,2)))/G(1,3)
      IF(W.GT.0.) GO TO 305
      DO 306 L=1,2
      DO 307 M=1,4
307   SSKP(L,M)=REAL(P(L,M))
      DO 308 M=1,2
308   SSKF(L,M)=REAL(FF(L,M))
306   CONTINUE
      PRINT 320
320   FORMAT(1H1,5X,* W    XD/XF   XD/F   XD/R   XD/V   XB/XF   XB/F
     1   XB/R   XB/V   R/XF   R/F   V/XF   V/F*)
      PRINT 150
150   FORMAT(30X,*STEADYSTATE  GAINS*)
      PRINT 313,W,((SSKP(L,M),M=1,4),L=1,2),((SSKF(L,M),M=1,2),L=1,2)
313   FORMAT(1X,F9.3,13F8.4)
310   FORMAT(1X,F9.3,13F8.2)
      PRINT 161
161   FORMAT(1X,*RADIANS/MIN.                   DECIBELS    *)
      PRINT 162
162   FORMAT(27X,*    DEGREES*)
      W=WMIN
      GO TO 200
305   DO 315 L=1,2
      DO 315 M=1,4
      DBP(L,M)=20.*ALOG10(CABS(P(L,M)/SSKP(L,M)))
      DEGP(L,M)=ATAN(AIMAG(P(L,M))/REAL(P(L,M)))*180./3.1416
316   IF((REAL( P(L,M))/SSKP(L,M)).LT.0.)DEGP(L,M)=DEGP(L,M)-180.
      DO 317 M=1,2
      DBF(L,M)=20.*ALOG10(CABS(FF(L,M)/SSKF(L,M)))
      DEGF(L,M)=ATAN(AIMAG(FF(L,M))/REAL(FF(L,M)))*180./3.1416
317   IF((REAL(FF(L,M))/SSKF(L,M)).LT.0.)DEGF(L,M)=DEGF(L,M)-180.
315   CONTINUE
      PRINT 310,W,((DBP(L,M),M=1,4),L=1,2),((DBF(L,M),M=1,2),L=1,2)
      PRINT 311,((DEGP(L,M),M=1,4),L=1,2),((DEGF(L,M),M=1,2),L=1,2)
311   FORMAT(10X,13F8.2)
      W=W*DW
      GO TO 200
      END
```

```
        NT          NS        ALPHA      B          D          XF        F
                                        MOLES/MIN. MOLES/MIN.           MOLES/MIN.
        20          10       2.00000  50.00000   50.00000    .50000 100.00000
        XB          XD        V          R        BETA
                                        MOLES/MIN. MOLES/MIN.  MIN.
      .02000      .99000  178.00369 128.00869    .10000
        N           X         Y          K
        0         .02000    .03922   1.92274
        1         .02500    .06754   1.85701
        2         .05719    .10819   1.78947
        3         .08835    .16320   1.68691
        4         .13130    .23291   1.56131
        5         .18622    .31397   1.42135
        6         .24950    .39937   1.28102
        7         .31617    .48044   1.15452
        8         .37347    .55017   1.05100
        9         .43391    .60521    .97272
       10         .47683    .64530    .91694
       11         .51526    .68009    .87108
       12         .56295    .72037    .81873
       13         .61835    .76463    .75307
       14         .68051    .80383    .70819
       15         .74344    .85284    .65799
       16         .80317    .89085    .61511
       17         .85602    .92243    .58058
       18         .89934    .94733    .55405
       19         .93457    .96513    .53439
       20         .96078    .98000    .52020
        N         A1        A2        A3        A4         A5         A6         A7
        0         .30015    .00019   2.23009   3.92193
        1         .00222    .00284  22.40087  56.03535  34.21928   0.00000    0.00000
        2         .00317    .00406  22.80087  54.65494  33.27448   0.00000    0.00000
        3         .00429    .00550  22.80087  52.82930  31.85407   0.00000    0.00000
        4         .00544    .00697  22.80087  50.59357  30.02843   0.00000    0.00000
        5         .00633    .00811  22.80087  48.10215  27.79270   0.00000    0.00000
        6         .00667    .00854  22.80087  45.60406  25.30128   0.00000    0.00000
        7         .00633    .00811  22.80087  43.35241  22.80320   0.00000    0.00000
        8         .00544    .00697  22.80087  41.50960  20.55154   0.00000    0.00000
        9         .00470    .00550  22.80087  40.11606  18.70874   0.00000    0.00000
       10         .00394    .00406  12.80087  39.12312  17.31519  10.00000     .00231
       11         .00477    .00343  12.80087  28.30686  16.32225   0.00000    0.00000
       12         .00560    .00403  12.40087  27.37502  15.50599   0.00000     .00000
       13         .00615    .00443  12.80087  26.38410  14.57415   0.00000    0.00000
       14         .00629    .00453  12.80087  25.40719  13.58323   0.00000    0.00000
       15         .00597    .00430  12.80087  24.51358  12.60632   0.00000    0.00000
       16         .00528    .00380  12.80087  23.75040  11.71271   0.00000    0.00000
       17         .00439    .00316  12.80087  23.13574  10.94953   0.00000    0.00000
       18         .00346    .00249  12.80087  22.65349  10.33497   0.00000    0.00000
       19         .00262    .00188  12.80087  22.31349   9.86262   0.00000    0.00000
       20         .00192    .00138  12.80087  22.06089   9.51262   0.00000    0.00000
                  .92500   1.78009.
        W       XD/XF     XD/F      XD/B      XD/V     XB/XF     XB/F      XB/B      XB/V       B/XF       B/F      V/XF      V/F
                                             STEADYSTATE GAINS
     0.000      .3226     .0038     .0092    -.0088   1.0774     .0058     .0100    -.0104 -18.0542    1.2801   35.1125    1.7801
RADIANS/MIN.
                                             DECIBELS
                                             DEGREES
      .010       -.07      -.07      -.07      -.07      -.07      -.07      -.07      -.07       .00      -.00       .00      -.00
                 -3.60     -3.50     -9.35     -8.19     -7.60     -6.77     -8.00     -7.10     -2.76     -1.02       .14     -1.22
      .013       -.11      -.11      -.11      -.11      -.11      -.10      -.11      -.11       .00      -.00       .00      -.00
                -10.80    -11.93    -10.49    -10.28     -9.53     -8.49    -10.05     -8.91     -3.48     -1.29       .18     -1.53
      .016       -.18      -.18      -.18      -.18      -.17      -.16      -.17      -.17       .00      -.00       .01      -.00
                -13.54    -14.96    -13.15    -12.89    -11.95    -10.64    -12.59    -11.16     -4.38     -1.62       .22     -1.93
      .020       -.28      -.28      -.28      -.28      -.26      -.27      -.27      -.27       .01      -.01       .01      -.01
                -16.94    -18.73    -15.44    -16.11    -14.93    -13.28    -15.75    -13.95     -5.51     -2.04       .28     -2.43
      .025       -.43      -.44      -.44      -.42      -.44      -.42      -.42      -.40       .01      -.01       .01      -.01
                -21.12    -23.37    -20.49    -20.08    -18.59    -16.52    -19.62    -17.35     -6.93     -2.56       .35     -3.05
      .032       -.67      -.67      -.67      -.65      -.61      -.61      -.64      -.64       .02      -.02       .02      -.02
                -26.19    -29.02    -25.39    -24.88    -23.01    -20.41    -24.30    -21.45     -8.72     -3.23       .43     -3.84
      .040      -1.01     -1.03     -1.02      -.98      -.93      -.98      -.93      -.98       .02      -.03       .04      -.03
                -32.24    -35.80    -31.23    -30.58    -28.24    -24.98    -29.87    -26.28    -10.97     -4.06       .53     -4.83
      .050      -1.52     -1.54     -1.53     -1.47     -1.38     -1.46     -1.46     -1.46       .04      -.04       .06      -.04
                -39.28    -43.77    -38.02    -37.20    -34.26    -30.19    -36.31    -31.79    -13.78     -5.10       .65     -6.08
      .063      -2.21     -2.25     -2.24     -2.22     -2.14     -2.01     -2.13     -2.12       .06      -.06       .09      -.07
                -47.25    -52.89    -45.65    -44.53    -40.95    -35.88    -43.54    -37.85    -17.30     -6.41       .79     -7.63
      .079      -3.14     -3.20     -3.19     -3.16     -3.02     -2.82     -3.00     -2.99       .09      -.10       .14      -.11
                -55.93    -63.06    -53.95    -52.67    -48.08    -41.81    -51.34    -44.19    -21.69     -8.04       .92     -9.58
      .100      -4.71     -4.41     -4.38     -4.34     -4.13     -3.81     -4.10     -4.08       .14      -.16       .22     -.17
                -65.23    -74.13    -62.64    -61.05    -55.37    -47.68    -59.49    -50.49    -27.12    -10.07      1.01    -12.01
      .126      -5.72     -5.88     -5.84     -5.77     -5.44     -4.96     -5.39     -5.37       .22      -.25       .34      -.27
                -74.80    -85.96    -71.50    -69.52    -62.54    -53.25    -67.75    -56.44    -33.78    -12.57      1.02    -15.01
      .158      -7.36     -7.60     -7.54     -7.43     -6.92     -6.22     -6.85     -6.82       .34      -.39       .50      -.42
                -84.59    -94.55    -80.32    -77.90    -69.45    -58.42    -76.05    -61.83    -41.84    -15.62       .80    -18.70
      .200      -9.20     -9.58     -9.47     -9.31     -8.54     -7.53     -8.42     -8.38       .50      -.60       .73      -.69
                -94.61   -112.02    -89.02    -86.09    -75.07    -63.31    -84.46    -66.61    -51.41    -19.28       .19    -23.15
      .251     -11.23    -11.82    -11.64    -11.39    -10.24     -8.84    -10.08    -10.01       .71      -.91      1.03      -.98
```

FIGURE 8-27

Stepping-technique digital computer program and results. (*Continued*)

-104.98	-126.57	-97.55	-94.09	-92.56	-68.25	-93.26	-70.86	-62.49	-23.57	-1.12	-28.43
.316 -13.45	-14.35	-14.05	-13.67	-12.02	-10.16	-11.78	-11.70	.99	-1.35	1.37	-1.47
-115.82	-142.44	-105.79	-101.86	-93.17	-73.67	-102.88	-74.79	-74.86	-28.41	-3.45	-34.52
.399 -15.86	-17.21	-15.70	-16.17	-13.87	-11.49	-13.52	-13.42	1.30	-1.95	1.74	-2.15
-127.47	-159.84	-113.51	-109.32	-96.25	-80.04	-113.87	-78.63	-88.13	-33.63	-7.18	-41.29
.501 -18.43	-20.47	-19.59	-18.89	-15.80	-12.87	-15.31	-15.19	1.64	-2.73	2.07	-3.05
-139.96	-178.85	-120.34	-115.28	-104.10	-87.70	-126.86	-82.59	-101.77	-38.95	-12.59	-48.52
.671 -21.33	-24.17	-22.64	-21.80	-17.95	-14.35	-17.18	-17.04	1.97	-3.68	2.29	-4.19
-153.53	-199.50	-125.93	-122.51	-112.99	-96.90	-142.50	-86.79	-115.07	-43.97	-19.89	-55.87
.794 -24.43	-28.39	-25.76	-24.89	-20.06	-15.95	-19.16	-18.99	2.29	-4.75	2.35	-5.57
-168.41	-221.71	-130.25	-127.75	-123.11	-107.84	-161.51	-91.21	-127.63	-48.36	-29.20	-62.98
1.000 -27.82	-33.16	-28.86	-28.10	-22.47	-17.72	-21.31	-21.07	2.59	-5.85	2.15	-7.16
-184.77	-245.40	-133.92	-131.81	-134.57	-120.77	-184.73	-95.78	-139.06	-51.82	-40.68	-69.38
1.259 -31.54	-38.54	-31.98	-31.36	-25.12	-19.67	-23.70	-23.29	2.91	-6.85	1.59	-8.94
-202.78	89.52	-137.83	-134.60	-147.47	-136.04	-213.17	-100.37	-149.15	-54.25	-54.40	-74.36
1.585 -35.64	-44.62	-35.31	-34.59	-28.05	-21.84	-26.42	-25.65	3.34	-7.55	.49	-10.73
-222.54	63.25	-142.06	-136.72	-161.84	-154.12	-248.04	-104.81	-157.66	-55.76	-70.24	-76.55
1.995 -40.14	-51.48	-38.96	-37.74	-31.30	-24.31	-29.62	-28.15	4.11	-7.62	-1.46	-11.99
-244.17	36.29	-145.11	-137.45	-177.72	-175.61	69.23	-108.93	-164.35	-56.92	-87.37	-74.28
2.512 -45.08	-59.22	-42.69	-40.79	-34.90	-27.17	-33.56	-30.78	5.09	-6.41	-4.91	-11.44
-267.82	9.90	-144.90	-138.67	-195.10	-201.16	17.06	-112.57	-170.05	-59.76	-102.31	-69.51
3.162 -50.50	-67.75	-45.98	-43.81	-38.88	-30.59	-38.56	-33.50	10.22	-2.52	-10.12	-7.37
66.26	-13.40	-142.75	-140.42	-214.00	-231.44	-46.11	-115.59	-183.22	-74.05	-80.52	-77.20
3.981 -55.47	-75.37	-48.97	-46.89	-43.25	-34.79	-45.15	-36.30	13.91	.60	-1.43	-3.90
37.83	-32.01	-142.55	-142.72	-234.50	-266.89	-121.49	-117.94	-253.88	-150.53	-101.08	-151.09
5.012 -63.04	-84.39	-52.15	-50.05	-48.05	-40.07	-53.97	-39.14	7.61	-6.76	-6.51	-11.20
5.64	-51.60	-143.61	-145.29	-256.76	52.53	-209.39	-119.63	66.62	-200.34	-146.83	-199.55
6.310 -70.71	-92.55	-55.45	-53.31	-53.30	-46.78	-65.83	-42.00	5.27	-11.00	-10.33	-15.47
-27.49	-78.35	-143.79	-147.87	79.00	7.80	51.60	-120.70	46.33	-234.05	-161.73	-230.75
7.943 -73.35	-101.62	-59.66	-56.64	-59.04	-55.26	-81.60	-44.86	3.24	-16.07	-12.58	-20.41
-64.70	-109.97	-143.32	-150.33	52.54	-38.67	-54.53	-121.23	11.01	76.94	-185.21	83.39
10.000 87.29	-111.55	-61.78	-60.01	-65.35	-55.65	-102.05	-47.71	-.39	-23.94	-16.04	-28.00
-105.05	-143.87	-142.88	-152.69	23.61	-82.68	-160.30	-121.27	-27.31	29.15	-215.20	38.49

FIGURE 8-27
Stepping-technique digital computer program and results. (*Concluded*)

the program solves for all the steady-state compositions and flow rates, given feed composition and feed flow rate and the desired bottoms and distillate compositions, by converging on the correct value of vapor boilup V. Next the coefficients for the linearized equations are calculated. Then the stepping technique is used to calculate the intermediate g's and the final P_{ij} process transfer functions in the frequency domain.

The numerical case given is for a 20-tray column with 10 trays in the stripping section. A constant relative volatility of 2 is used. The column steady-state profile is given in Fig. 8-27, together with the values of coefficients and the transfer functions in terms of log modulus (decibels) and phase angle (degrees) at frequencies from 0 to 1 radian/minute. The values at zero frequency are the steady-state gains of the transfer functions. The last four transfer functions shown relating R and V to x_F and F are feedforward controllers to which we will return in Part 5 of this book.   ////

PROBLEMS

8-1 Sketch Nyquist, Bode, and Nichols plots for the following transfer functions:

(a) $G_{(s)} = \dfrac{1}{(s+1)^3}$

(b) $G_{(s)} = \dfrac{1}{(s+1)(10s+1)(100s+1)}$

(c) $\quad G_{(s)} = \dfrac{1}{s^2(s+1)}$

(d) $\quad G_{(s)} = \dfrac{\tau s + 1}{(\tau/6)s + 1}$

(e) $\quad G_{(s)} = \dfrac{s}{2s + 1}$

(f) $\quad G_{(s)} = \dfrac{1}{(10s + 1)(s^2 + s + 1)}$

8-2 Draw the Bode plots for the transfer functions:
  (a) $G_{(s)} = 0.5$
  (b) $G_{(s)} = 5.0$

8-3 Sketch Nyquist, Bode, and Nichols plots for the proportional-integral feedback controller $B_{(s)}$:

$$B_{(s)} = K_c\left(1 + \dfrac{1}{\tau_I s}\right)$$

8-4 Sketch Nyquist, Bode, and Nichols plots for a system with the transfer function

$$G_{(s)} = \dfrac{-3s + 1}{(s+1)(5s+1)}$$

8-5 Draw the Bode plots of the transfer function

$$G_{(s)} = \dfrac{7.5(s + 0.2)}{s(s+1)^3}$$

8-6 Write a digital computer program that gives the real and imaginary parts, log modulus, and phase angle for the transfer functions:

  (a) $G_{(s)} = B_{(s)}\dfrac{P_{11}P_{22} - P_{12}P_{21}}{P_{22}}$

  where
$$B_{(s)} = 8\left(1 + \dfrac{1}{400s}\right)$$

$$P_{11(s)} = \dfrac{1}{(1 + 167s)(1 + s)(1 + 0.1s)^4}$$

$$P_{12(s)} = \dfrac{0.85}{(1 + 83s)(1 + s)^2}$$

$$P_{21(s)} = \dfrac{0.85}{(1 + 167s)(1 + 0.5s)^3(1 + s)}$$

$$P_{22(s)} = \dfrac{1}{(1 + 167s)(1 + s)^2}$$

(b) $\quad G_{(s)} = \dfrac{e^{-0.1s}}{s + 1 + e^{-0.1s}}$

8-7 Draw Bode, Nyquist, and Nichols plots for the transfer functions:

(a) $\quad A_{L(s)} = \dfrac{G_{(s)}}{1 + B_{(s)}G_{(s)}}$

(b) $\quad A_{S(s)} = \dfrac{B_{(s)}G_{(s)}}{1 + B_{(s)}G_{(s)}}$

where
$$B_{(s)} = K_c\left(1 + \dfrac{1}{\tau_I s}\right) \qquad K_c = 6$$
$$\tau_I = 6$$
$$G_{(s)} = \dfrac{1}{\tau s + 1} \qquad \tau = 10$$

8-8 Draw the Bode plot of

$$G_{(s)} = \dfrac{1 - e^{-Ds}}{s}$$

8-9 A process is forced by a sinusoidal input $Q_{s(t)}$. The output is a sine wave $x_{s(t)}$. If these two signals are connected to an $x - y$ recorder, we get a Lissajous plot. Time is the parameter along the curve, which repeats itself with each cycle. The shape of the curve will change if the frequency is changed and will be different for different kinds of processes.

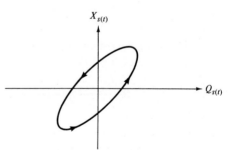

(a) How can the magnitude ratio M and phase angle θ be found from this curve?

(b) Sketch Lissajous curves for the following systems:

(i) $\quad G_{(s)} = K_p$

(ii) $\quad G_{(s)} = \dfrac{1}{s} \qquad$ at $\omega = 1$ radian/time

(iii) $\quad G_{(s)} = \dfrac{1}{\tau_p s + 1} \qquad$ at $\omega = \dfrac{1}{\tau_p}$ radians/time

8-10 Sketch the Bode plots for the transfer function of $(C_A/C_{A0})_{(s)}$ derived in Prob. 7-9.

9

PROCESS IDENTIFICATION

9-1 PURPOSE

The dynamic relationships discussed thus far in this book were determined from mathematical models of the process. Mathematical equations, based on fundamental physical and chemical laws, were developed to describe the time-dependent behavior of the system. We assumed that the values of all parameters, such as holdups, reaction rates, heat transfer coefficients, etc., were known. Thus the dynamic behavior was predicted on essentially a theoretical basis.

For a process that is already in operation, there is an alternative approach that is essentially empirical. The dynamic behavior can be found from experimental tests.

The experimental approach is sometimes used when the process is thought to be too complex to model from first principles. It is also used to find the values of some parameters that are unknown. Many of the parameters can be calculated from steady-state plant data, but some parameters must be found from dynamic tests (e.g., holdups in nonreactive systems).

A third and very important use of dynamic experiments is to confirm the predictions of a theoretical mathematical model. As we indicated in Part 1, the verification of the model is a very desirable step in its development and application.

Experimental identification of process dynamics has been an active area of research in recent years by many workers in many areas of engineering. The literature is extensive, and entire books are devoted to this subject.[1]

A number of techniques have been proposed. We will discuss only the more conventional, proved methods that are currently used widely in the chemical and petroleum industries: sine-wave testing, step testing, and pulse testing.

9-2 DIRECT METHODS

9-2.1 Time-domain Fitting of Step Test Data

The most direct way of obtaining an empirical dynamic model of a process is to find the parameters (dead time, time constant, damping coefficient, etc.) that fit the experimentally obtained step response. We put in a step disturbance $Q_{(t)}$ and record the output variable $x_{(t)}$ as a function of time, as illustrated in Fig. 9-1.

We look at the shape of the curve $x_{(t)}$ and find an approximate transfer function $G_{(s)}$ that would give the same type of step response. $G_{(s)}$ will be a ratio of polynomials in s with a steady-state gain K_p and perhaps some dead time D.

$$G_{(s)} = K_p \frac{Z_{(s)} e^{-Ds}}{P_{(s)}} = K_p \frac{(\tau_{z1}s + 1)(\tau_{z2}s + 1)\cdots(\tau_{zM}s + 1)e^{-Ds}}{(\tau_{p1}s + 1)(\tau_{p2}s + 1)\cdots(\tau_{pN}s + 1)} \qquad (9\text{-}1)$$

The steady-state gain K_p is easily obtained from the ratio of the final steady-state change in output $\overline{\Delta x}$ over the size of the step input $\overline{\Delta Q}$. The dead time D is also easily found from the output curve as the time when the output begins to respond. The system damping coefficient ζ can be found from the degree of overshoot or the rate of decay of any oscillation. If there is no oscillation the poles of the transfer function must all be real. The shape and rate of change of $x_{(t)}$ can be used to estimate the poles and zeros of $G_{(s)}$.

This method is simple and is easy to use. However it is difficult to distinguish between second- or third- and higher-order systems. It is also difficult to detect widely differing time constants with any precision.

9-2.2 Direct Sine-wave Testing

The next level of dynamic testing is direct sine-wave testing. The input of the plant, which is usually a control-valve position or a controller set point, is varied sinusoidally. This can be accomplished in a number of ways, but mechanical, electronic, or pneumatic sine-wave generators that are commercially available are usually employed.

---

[1] A. P. Sage and J. L. Melsa, "System Identification," Academic, 1971.
 C. W. Helstrom, "Statistical Theory of Signal Detection," 2d ed., Pergamon, 1968.
 D. M. Himmelblau, "Process Analysis by Statistical Methods," Wiley, 1970.

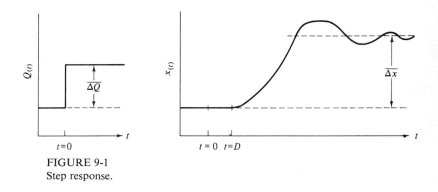

FIGURE 9-1
Step response.

After waiting for all transients to die out and for a steady oscillation in the output to be established, the amplitude ratio and phase angle are found by recording input and output data. See Fig. 8-2. The data points are then plotted on Bode, Nyquist, or Nichols plots. The frequency of the input signal is changed and a new amplitude ratio and phase angle are determined. Thus the complete frequency-response curves are found experimentally by varying frequency over the range of interest.

Once the $G_{(i\omega)}$ curves have been found, they can be used directly to examine the dynamics and stability of the system or to design controllers in the frequency domain (see Chap. 12). Or an approximate transfer function can be fitted to the experimental $G_{(i\omega)}$ curves. The zero-frequency asymptote gives the steady-state gain. The time constants (poles and zeros) can be found from the breakpoint frequencies on the log modulus Bode plot. The damping can be found from the resonant peaks.

Once the log modulus curve has been adequately fitted by an approximate transfer function $G_{(i\omega)}^A$, the phase angle of $G_{(i\omega)}^A$ is compared with the experimental phase-angle curve. The difference is usually the contribution of dead time. The procedure is illustrated in Fig. 9-2.

Direct sine-wave testing is an extremely useful way of obtain precise dynamic data. Damping, time constants, and the order of the system can all be quite accurately found.

The main disadvantage of direct sine-wave testing is that it can be very time-consuming when applied to large-scale process equipment and plants. Many chemical engineering processes have time constants that can be many minutes or even hours. The steady-state oscillation must be established at each value of frequency. It can take days to generate the complete frequency-response curves of a slow process.

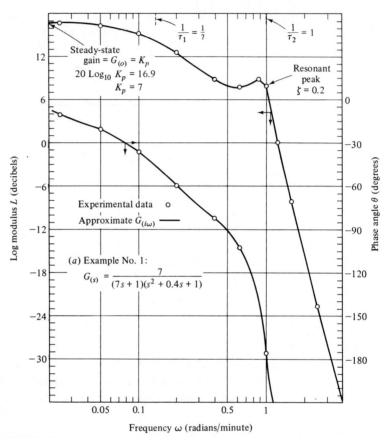

FIGURE 9-2a
Fitting approximate transfer function to experimental frequency-response data.

9-3 PULSE TESTING

Pulse testing retains many of the advantages of direct sine-wave testing in that it yields reasonably accurate frequency-response curves. Pulse tests can be performed in only a fraction of the time that direct sine-wave tests would require.

An input pulse $Q_{(t)}$ of fairly arbitrary shape is put into the process. The response of the output is recorded as shown in Fig. 9-3. Note that both the input and the output return to their original steady-state values. If $x_{(t)}$ and $Q_{(t)}$ are perturbations from steady state, they start and end at zero. The situation where the output does not return to zero is discussed in Sec. 9-3.4 below.

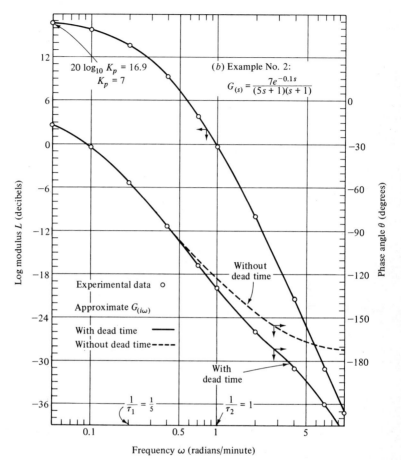

FIGURE 9-2*b*

The input and output functions are then Fourier-transformed and divided to give the system transfer function in the frequency domain $G_{(i\omega)}$. The details of this procedure are discussed in the following sections.

In theory only one pulse input is required to generate the entire frequency-response curve. In practice several pulses are usually needed to establish the required size and duration of the input pulse. Some tips on the practical aspects of pulse testing are discussed in Sec. 9-3.3. The history and status of pulse testing were summarized by Hougen.[1]

[1] Joel O. Hougen, Experiences and Experiments with Process Dynamics, *Chem. Eng. Prog., Monogr. Ser*, vol. 60, no. 4, 1964.
W. C. Clements and K. B. Schnelle, *Ind. Eng. Chem., Process Design Dev.*, vol. 2, p. 94, 1963.

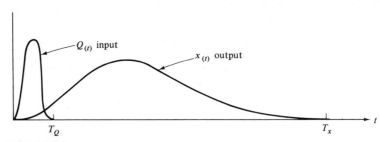

FIGURE 9-3
Pulse test input and output curves.

9-3.1   Calculation of $G_{(i\omega)}$ from Pulse Test Data

Consider a process with an input $Q_{(t)}$ and an output $x_{(t)}$. By definition, the transfer function of the process is

$$G_{(s)} = \frac{X_{(s)}}{Q_{(s)}} \qquad (9\text{-}2)$$

Using the definition of Laplace transformation,

$$G_{(s)} = \frac{\displaystyle\int_0^\infty x_{(t)}\, e^{-st}\, dt}{\displaystyle\int_0^\infty Q_{(t)}\, e^{-st}\, dt} \qquad (9\text{-}3)$$

We now go into the frequency domain by substituting $s = i\omega$.

$$G_{(i\omega)} = \frac{\displaystyle\int_0^\infty x_{(t)}\, e^{-i\omega t}\, dt}{\displaystyle\int_0^\infty Q_{(t)}\, e^{-i\omega t}\, dt} \qquad (9\text{-}4)$$

The numerator is the Fourier transformation of the time function $x_{(t)}$. The denominator is the Fourier transformation of the time function $Q_{(t)}$. Therefore the frequency response of the system $G_{(i\omega)}$ can be calculated from the experimental pulse test data $x_{(t)}$ and $Q_{(t)}$ as shown in Fig. 9-3.

$$G_{(i\omega)} = \frac{\displaystyle\int_0^\infty x_{(t)} \cos{(\omega t)}\, dt - i\int_0^\infty x_{(t)} \sin{(\omega t)}\, dt}{\displaystyle\int_0^\infty Q_{(t)} \cos{(\omega t)}\, dt - i\int_0^\infty Q_{(t)} \sin{(\omega t)}\, dt} \qquad (9\text{-}5)$$

$$= \frac{A - iB}{C - iD} = \frac{(AC + BD) + i(AD - BC)}{C^2 + D^2} \qquad (9\text{-}6)$$

$$= \operatorname{Re} G_{(i\omega)} + i \operatorname{Im} G_{(i\omega)} \qquad (9\text{-}7)$$

where

$$A = \int_0^{T_x} x_{(t)} \cos (\omega t)\, dt$$

$$B = \int_0^{T_x} x_{(t)} \sin (\omega t)\, dt$$

$$C = \int_0^{T_Q} Q_{(t)} \cos (\omega t)\, dt$$

$$D = \int_0^{T_Q} Q_{(t)} \sin (\omega t)\, dt \qquad (9\text{-}8)$$

The problem reduces to being able to evaluate the integrals A, B, C, and D given in Eqs. (9-8) for known functions $x_{(t)}$ and $Q_{(t)}$. The integrations are with respect to time between the definite limits of zero and the times that the experimental time functions go to zero, T_x for $x_{(t)}$ and T_Q for $Q_{(t)}$.

A specific numerical value of frequency ω is picked. The integrations are performed on either an analog or a digital computer, giving one point on the frequency-response curves. Then frequency is changed and the integrations repeated, using the same experimental time functions $x_{(t)}$ and $Q_{(t)}$ but a new value of frequency ω. Repeating for frequencies over the range of interest gives the complete $G_{(i\omega)}$. The $x_{(t)}$ and $Q_{(t)}$ data are used over and over again.

The integrations shown in Eqs. (9-8) are usually performed on a digital computer because of the ease of handling the input data. The problem of numerical integration again rears its ugly head. The problem is made particularly difficult by the oscillatory behavior of the sine and cosine terms at high values of frequency.

9-3.2   Digital Evaluation of Fourier Transformations

The experimental data from a pulse test are usually two continuous curves of x and Q recorded as functions of time. A reasonable number of points are selected from these curves and fed into the digital computer. We will discuss later what a reasonable number is.

Let the value of $x_{(t)}$ at the kth increment in time be x_k as shown in Fig. 9-4. We feed into the computer values of x at specified points in time:

$$(x_1, t_1),\ (x_2, t_2),\ \ldots,\ (x_k, t_k),\ \ldots,\ (x_N, t_N)$$

Notice that $t_N = T_x$ and $x_N = 0$. These data points need *not* be selected at equally spaced intervals Δt_k. The total number of intervals is N.

From Eq. (9-4), we wish to evaluate the Fourier integral transform (FIT) of $x_{(t)}$.

$$\text{FIT} \equiv \int_0^{T_x} x_{(t)} e^{-i\omega t}\, dt \qquad (9\text{-}9)$$

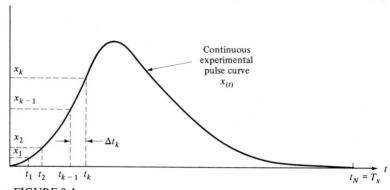

FIGURE 9-4
Discrete data points picked from an experimental pulse curve.

We can break up the total interval (0 to T_x) into a number of unequal subintervals of length Δt_k. Then the FIT can be written, with no loss of rigor, as a sum of integrals:

$$\text{FIT} = \sum_{k=1}^{N} \left(\int_{t_{k-1}}^{t_k} x_{(t)} e^{-i\omega t} \, dt \right) \qquad (9\text{-}10)$$

Over each interval t_{k-1} to t_k the true time function $x_{(t)}$ is now approximated by some polynomial approximating function $\phi_{k(t)}$. A number of types can be used, but the simplest is a first-order approximation. This corresponds to using a straight line between the data points.

$$x_{(t)} \simeq \phi_{k(t)} \qquad \text{for } t_{k-1} < t < t_k$$

$$\phi_{k(t)} = \alpha_{0k} + \alpha_{1k}(t - t_{k-1}) \qquad (9\text{-}11)$$

The constant α_{1k} is the slope of the line over the kth interval.

$$\alpha_{1k} = \frac{x_k - x_{k-1}}{\Delta t_k} \qquad (9\text{-}12)$$

where

$$\Delta t_k = t_k - t_{k-1} \qquad (9\text{-}13)$$

The constant α_{0k} is the value of ϕ_k at the beginning of the interval.

$$\alpha_{0k} = x_{k-1} \qquad (9\text{-}14)$$

The constants α_{0k} and α_{1k} change with each interval. Equation (9-10) can thus be approximated by

$$\text{FIT} \simeq \sum_{k=1}^{N} \left[\int_{t_{k-1}}^{t_k} [\alpha_{0k} + \alpha_{1k}(t - t_{k-1})] e^{-i\omega t} \, dt \right] \qquad (9\text{-}15)$$

$$\text{FIT} \equiv \sum_{k=1}^{N} \dot{I}_k \qquad (9\text{-}16)$$

Each of the I_k integrals above can be evaluated analytically.

$$I_k = \int_{t_{k-1}}^{t_k} [\alpha_{0k} + \alpha_{1k}(t - t_{k-1})]e^{-i\omega t}\, dt$$

$$= \frac{-\alpha_{0k}}{i\omega} e^{-i\omega t}\Big]_{t_{k-1}}^{t_k} + \alpha_{1k}\int_{t_{k-1}}^{t_k} (t - t_{k-1})e^{-i\omega t}\, dt$$

Integrating the integral by parts gives

$$u = t - t_{k-1} \qquad dv = e^{-i\omega t}\, dt$$

$$du = dt \qquad v = -\frac{e^{-i\omega t}}{i\omega}$$

$$I_k = \frac{\alpha_{0k}}{i\omega}\left(e^{-i\omega t_{k-1}} - e^{-i\omega t_k}\right) - \left[\alpha_{1k}(t - t_{k-1})\frac{e^{-i\omega t}}{i\omega}\right]_{t_{k-1}}^{t_k} + \frac{\alpha_{1k}}{i\omega}\int_{t_{k-1}}^{t_k} e^{-i\omega t}\, dt$$

$$= \frac{\alpha_{0k}}{i\omega}\left(e^{-i\omega t_{k-1}} - e^{-i\omega t_k}\right) - \frac{\alpha_{1k}}{i\omega}(t_k - t_{k-1})e^{-i\omega t_k} + \frac{\alpha_{1k}}{\omega^2}\left(e^{-i\omega t_k} - e^{-i\omega t_{k-1}}\right) \qquad (9\text{-}17)$$

Substituting for α_{0k} and α_{1k} from Eqs. (9-12) and (9-14) gives

$$I_k = \frac{x_{k-1}}{i\omega}\left(e^{-i\omega t_{k-1}} - e^{-i\omega t_k}\right) - \frac{x_k - x_{k-1}}{\Delta t_k}\frac{\Delta t_k}{i\omega}e^{-i\omega t_k}$$

$$+ \frac{x_k - x_{k-1}}{\Delta t_k}\frac{1}{\omega^2}\left(e^{-i\omega t_k} - e^{-i\omega t_{k-1}}\right)$$

$$= \left(x_{k-1}e^{-i\omega t_{k-1}} - x_{k-1}e^{-i\omega t_k} - x_k e^{-i\omega t_k} + x_{k-1}e^{-i\omega t_k}\right)\frac{1}{i\omega}$$

$$+ \frac{x_k - x_{k-1}}{\omega^2\,\Delta t_k}\left(e^{-i\omega t_k} - e^{-i\omega t_{k-1}}\right)$$

$$= x_k\left(\frac{-e^{-i\omega t_k}}{i\omega} + \frac{e^{-i\omega t_k} - e^{-i\omega t_{k-1}}}{\omega^2\,\Delta t_k}\right)$$

$$+ x_{k-1}\left(\frac{e^{-i\omega t_{k-1}}}{i\omega} - \frac{e^{-i\omega t_k} - e^{-i\omega t_{k-1}}}{\omega^2\,\Delta t_k}\right)$$

$$I_k = e^{-i\omega t_{k-1}}\left[x_k\left(\frac{e^{-i\omega\Delta t_k} - 1}{\omega^2\,\Delta t_k} - \frac{e^{-i\omega\Delta t_k}}{i\omega}\right) - x_{k-1}\left(\frac{e^{-i\omega\Delta t_k} - 1}{\omega^2\,\Delta t_k} - \frac{1}{i\omega}\right)\right] \qquad (9\text{-}18)$$

Finally, the Fourier transformation of $x_{(t)}$ becomes

$$\int_0^\infty x_{(t)}e^{-i\omega t}\, dt \simeq \sum_{k=1}^N e^{-i\omega t_{k-1}}\left[x_k\left(\frac{e^{-i\omega\Delta t_k} - 1}{\omega^2\,\Delta t_k} - \frac{e^{-i\omega\Delta t_k}}{i\omega}\right)\right.$$

$$\left. - x_{k-1}\left(\frac{e^{-i\omega\Delta t_k} - 1}{\omega^2\,\Delta t_k} - \frac{1}{i\omega}\right)\right] \qquad (9\text{-}19)$$

Equation (9-19) looks a little complicated but it is easily programmed on a digital computer. Figure 9-5 gives a digital computer program that reads input and output data cards, calculates the Fourier transformations of the input and of the output, divides the two to get the transfer function $G_{(i\omega)}$, and prints out log modulus and phase angle at different values of frequency.

Notice that the computed values of log modulus and phase angle begin to oscillate at the higher values of frequency. This is due to numerical-integration problems and to the limited "frequency content" of the input forcing function (i.e., the Fourier transformation of the input becomes smaller and smaller as frequency increases). We will discuss this problem further in the next section. The computed results are meaningless at these high frequencies and should be ignored.

The steady-state gain of the transfer function is $G_{(0i)}$ or just the ratio of the areas under the input and output curves.

$$K_p = G_{(0i)} = \frac{\int_0^{T_x} x_{(t)}\, dt}{\int_0^{T_Q} Q_{(t)}\, dt} \qquad (9\text{-}20)$$

If the input pulse is a rectangular pulse of height h and duration D, its Fourier transformation is simply

$$\int_0^\infty Q_{(t)} e^{-i\omega t}\, dt = h \int_0^D e^{-i\omega t}\, dt = -\frac{h}{i\omega} e^{-i\omega t}\Big]_0^D$$

$$= \frac{h}{i\omega}(1 - e^{-i\omega D}) \qquad (9\text{-}21)$$

This, of course, involves no approximation whatsoever. This special case is included in the program in Fig. 9-5. The general formula of Eq. (9-19) will give exact Fourier transformations of any functions that have straight-line segments. Therefore triangles, trapezoids, etc., are handled with no approximation at all.

When reading the literature on pulse testing you should exercise some caution when using the equations presented since some assume equally spaced data points. There is also considerable confusion about the number of data points required to give a meaningful $G_{(i\omega)}$ out to a desired frequency. Messa et al.[1] have pointed out that the criterion for picking the number of data points should be that enough points are used to make the approximating function match the real function $x_{(t)}$ over all intervals. For example, Eq. (9-21) gives the Fourier transformation of a rectangular pulse out to *any* frequency and only one data point is required.

[1] C. J. Messa, W. L. Luyben, and G. W. Poehlein, *Ind. Eng. Chem., Fundamentals*, vol. 8, p. 745, 1969.

```
C       PULSE TEST PROGRAM
        DIMENSION QIN(200),TIN(200),XOUT(200),TOUT(200)
        COMPLEX GNUM,GDENOM,G1,G2,G3,G4,G5,G
C    READ INPUT AND OUTPUT DATA
  200 READ 1,NIN,NOUT,WO,WMAX,WNUM
    1 FORMAT(2I5,7F10.5)
      IF(NIN.EQ.0) STOP
      DO 5 I=1,NIN,4
      IP3=I+3
    5 READ 6,(QIN(K),TIN(K),K=I,IP3)
      PRINT 11
   11 FORMAT(1H1,*      TIN      QIN*)
      DO 12 I=1,NIN
   12 PRINT 9,TIN(I),QIN(I)
    6 FORMAT (8F10.5)
      DO 10 I=1,NOUT,4
      IP3=I+3
   10 READ 6,(XOUT(K),TOUT(K),K=I,IP3)
      PRINT 7
    7 FORMAT(1H0,*      TOUT     XOUT*)
      DO 8 I=1,NOUT
    8 PRINT 9,TOUT(I),XOUT(I)
    9 FORMAT(1X,10F10.5)
      DW=10.**(1./WNUM)
      W=0.
  100 IF(W.GT.WMAX) GO TO 200
      IF(NIN.GT.1) GO TO 30
C    CALCULATE FIT FOR RECTANGULAR PULSE INPUT
      IF(W.EQ.0.) GO TO 25
      G1=CMPLX(0.,W)
      G2=CMPLX(0.,-W*TIN(1))
      GDENOM=QIN(1)*(1.-CEXP(G2))/G1
      GO TO 50
C    FOR ZERO FREQUENCY
   25 GDENOM= CMPLX(QIN(1)*TIN(1),0.)
      GO TO 50
C    CALCULATE FIT FOR ARBITRARY INPUT
   30 IF(W.EQ.0.) GO TO 40
      G1=CMPLX(0.,W)
      G2=CMPLX(0.,-W*TIN(1))
      GDENOM=QIN(1)*((CEXP(G2)-1.)/(TIN(1)*W**2)-CEXP(G2)/G1)
      DO 35 N=2,NIN
      DELTA=TIN(N)-TIN(N-1)
      G2=CMPLX(0.,-W*DELTA)
      G3=CMPLX(0.,-W*TIN(N-1))
      G4=CEXP(G2)
      G5=(G4-1.)/(DELTA*W**2)
      GDENOM=GDENOM+CEXP(G3)*(QIN(N)*(G5-G4/G1)-QIN(N-1)*(G5-1./G1))
   35 CONTINUE
      GO TO 50
   40 AREA=QIN(1)*TIN(1)/2.
      DO 41 N=2,NIN
      DELTA=TIN(N)-TIN(N-1)
   41 AREA=AREA+(QIN(N)+QIN(N-1))*DELTA/2.
      GDENOM=CMPLX(AREA,0.)
C    CALCULATE FIT FOR ARBITRARY OUTPUT
   50 IF(W.EQ.0.) GO TO 60
      G2=CMPLX(0.,-W*TOUT(1))
      GNUM=XOUT(1)*((CEXP(G2)-1.)/(TOUT(1)*W**2)-CEXP(G2)/G1)
      DO 55 N=2,NOUT
      DELTA=TOUT(N)-TOUT(N-1)
      G2=CMPLX(0.,-W*DELTA)
      G3=CMPLX(0.,-W*TOUT(N-1))
      G4=CEXP(G2)
      G5=(G4-1.)/(DELTA*W**2)
```

FIGURE 9-5
Pulse test program.

```
      GNUM=GNUM+CEXP(G3)*(XOUT(N)*(G5-G4/G1)-XOUT(N-1)*(G5-1./G1))
55    CONTINUE
      GO TO 70
60    AREA =XOUT(1)*TOUT(1)/2.
      DO 61 N=2,NOUT
      DELTA=TOUT(N)-TOUT(N-1)
61    AREA=AREA+(XOUT(N)+XOUT(N-1))*DELTA/2.
      GNUM=CMPLX(AREA,0.)
C     CALCULATE TRANSFER FUNCTION
70    G=GNUM/GDENOM
      IF(W.EQ.0.) GO TO 90
      DB=20.*ALOG10(CABS(G)/ABS(GAIN))
      DEG=ATAN(AIMAG(G)/REAL(G))*180./3.1416
      IF((REAL(G)/GAIN).LT.0.) DEG=DEG-180.
      PRINT 75,W,G,DB,DEG
75    FORMAT(1X,F10.3,2F10.5,2F10.2)
      W=W*DW
      GO TO 100
90    GAIN=REAL(G)
      PRINT 91,GAIN
91    FORMAT(1H1,*STEADYSTATE GAIN = *,F10.3)
      PRINT 92
92    FORMAT(1X,*FREQUENCY    REAL    IMAGINARY  LOG MODULUS   ANGLE*)
      PRINT 93
93    FORMAT(1X,*(RADIANS/TIME)                          (DB)     (DEGREES)*)
      W=WO
      GO TO 100
      END
```

TTN	QIN
2.00000	2.00000
TOUT	XOUT
.50000	8.00000
1.00000	14.00000
1.50000	18.00000
2.00000	20.00000
2.50000	15.00000
3.00000	10.00000
4.00000	8.00000
6.00000	4.00000
8.00000	1.00000
10.00000	0.00000

STEADYSTATE GAIN =   16.750

FREQUENCY (RADIANS/TIME)	REAL	IMAGINARY	LOG MODULUS (DB)	ANGLE (DEGREES)
.100	15.15247	-3.25677	-.14	-11.40
.112	16.00175	-3.62760	-.18	-12.77
.126	15.81429	-4.03305	-.23	-14.31
.141	15.58187	-4.47322	-.28	-16.02
.158	15.29488	-4.94672	-.36	-17.92
.178	14.94228	-5.44999	-.45	-20.04
.200	14.51186	-5.97647	-.57	-22.38
.224	13.99071	-6.51557	-.71	-24.97
.251	13.36624	-7.05156	-.89	-27.81
.282	12.62782	-7.56243	-1.12	-30.92
.316	11.76338	-8.01915	-1.41	-34.27
.355	10.79302	-8.38571	-1.77	-37.85
.398	9.71363	-8.52092	-2.21	-41.59
.447	8.56384	-8.68293	-2.76	-45.40
.501	7.39782	-8.53761	-3.42	-49.09
.562	6.29103	-8.17122	-4.21	-52.41
.631	5.33182	-7.60556	-5.12	-54.97
.708	4.60094	-6.91001	-6.10	-56.34
.794	4.13916	-6.19975	-7.03	-56.27
.891	3.91400	-5.60731	-7.78	-55.08
1.000	3.81150	-5.22483	-8.27	-53.89
1.122	3.68336	-5.04455	-8.57	-53.86

1.259	3.44283	-4.95995	-8.86	-55.23
1.413	3.12173	-4.86728	-9.24	-57.32
1.585	2.78309	-4.76792	-9.64	-59.73
1.778	2.39771	-4.68236	-10.06	-62.88
1.995	1.97872	-4.53856	-10.59	-66.44
2.239	1.61549	-4.45273	-10.97	-70.06
2.512	.88747	-4.43343	-11.28	-78.80
2.818	-.09755	-3.62007	-13.30	-91.54
3.162	.37495	-2.53381	-16.31	-81.58
3.548	.51496	-3.06161	-14.64	-80.45
3.981	-.31710	-2.58472	-16.17	-96.99
4.467	-.37517	-1.89572	-18.76	-101.19
5.012	-.19475	-1.25642	-22.39	-98.81
5.623	.50922	-.86184	-24.47	-59.42
6.310	-23.95515	-.00363	3.11	-179.99
7.079	-.26390	-.69572	-27.05	-110.77
7.943	.20392	-.38951	-24.38	-78.02
8.913	-.10366	-1.27009	-22.37	-94.67
10.000	-.17421	-1.13570	-23.27	-98.72

FIGURE 9-5
Pulse test program.   (*Concluded*)

9-3.3   Practical Tips on Pulse Testing

Theoretically, the best possible input pulse would be an impulse or a Dirac delta function $\delta_{(t)}$. The Fourier transformation of $\delta_{(t)}$ is equal to unity at all frequencies.

$$\int_0^\infty \delta_{(t)}\, e^{-i\omega t}\, dt = (e^{-i\omega t})_{t=0} = 1 \qquad (9\text{-}22)$$

Therefore $G_{(i\omega)}$ would be simply the Fourier transformation of the output function. No division by a small number would be required.

Practically, however, we can never have an infinitely high pulse with zero width. In general, we need to keep the width of the pulse fairly small to keep its "frequency content" from becoming too small at higher frequencies. For example, Eq. (9-21) gives the Fourier transform of a rectangular pulse of width D.

$$\text{FIT} = \frac{h}{i\omega}(1 - e^{-i\omega D}) = \frac{h}{i\omega}(1 - \cos \omega D + i \sin \omega D)$$

$$= h\,\frac{\sin \omega D}{\omega} - i\,\frac{h}{\omega}(1 - \cos \omega D) \qquad (9\text{-}23)$$

When frequency ω is equal to $2\pi/D$, the FIT goes to zero and the calculation of the transfer function is meaningless. Therefore the smaller D can be made, the higher is the frequency to which $G_{(i\omega)}$ can be found.

A good rule of thumb is to keep the width of the pulse less than about half the smallest time constant of interest. If the dynamics of the process are completely unknown, it takes a few trials to establish a reasonable pulse width.

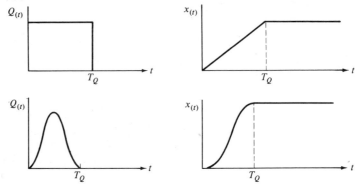

FIGURE 9-6
Pulse test of an integrator.

If the width of the pulse is too small, for a given pulse height, the system is disturbed very little, and it becomes difficult to separate the real output signal from noise and experimental error. The height of the pulse can be increased to jolt the system more, but there is a limit here too.

We want to obtain an experimental linear dynamic model of the system in the form of $G_{(i\omega)}$. It must be a linear model since the notion of a transfer function applies only to a linear system. The process is usually nonlinear, and we are obtaining a model that is linearized around the steady-state operating level. If the height of the pulse is too high we may drive the process out of the linear range. Therefore pulses of various heights should be tried. It is also a good idea to make both positive and negative pulses (increasing and decreasing) in the input. The computed $G_{(i\omega)}$'s should be identical if the region of linearity is not exceeded.

9-3.4 Processes with Integration

The input disturbance for a pulse test begins and ends at the same value. In terms of perturbation variables, the input $Q_{(t)}$ is initially zero and is returned to zero after some time T_Q.

The perturbation in the output variable $x_{(t)}$ will usually also return to zero. Once in a while, however, a process will give an output curve that will not return to zero. This occurs if the process contains a pure integration element. For example, suppose the process is a tank, with the output variable the liquid level in the tank and the input variable the flow rate into the tank. Assume the flow rate out of the tank is constant. If the feed flow is pulsed, the liquid level will rise by the total incremental amount of material added during the pulse. The liquid level will stay at this new higher level, as shown in Fig. 9-6.

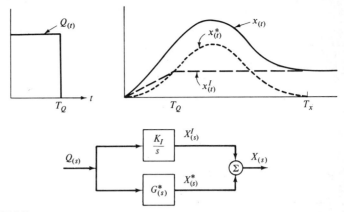

FIGURE 9-7
Separation of the output signal into contributions from the integrator and G^* transfer function.

If the output signal does not return to zero, the integrals A and B of Eqs. (9-8) become infinitely large. This situation can be handled by separating out the effect of the integration. We assume the total output signal is the sum of the output of an integrator plus another transfer function $G^*_{(s)}$.

First the gain of the integrator is found from the final steady-state offset of $x_{(t)}$ from zero, $\overline{\Delta x}$, and the integral of the input pulse.

$$K_I = \frac{\overline{\Delta x}}{\int_0^{T_Q} Q_{(t)}\, dt} \qquad (9\text{-}24)$$

The integrator contributes to the total output signal only when the input signal is not equal to zero. Therefore, integrating the input signal times the integrator gain K_I and subtracting this function from the original output function at each instant in time gives a function $x^*_{(t)}$ that does return to zero at some time T_x, as shown in Fig. 9-7.

$$x^*_{(t)} = x_{(t)} - K_I \int_0^t Q_{(t)}\, dt \qquad (9\text{-}25)$$

The $G^*_{(i\omega)}$ transfer function is found by using $x^*_{(t)}$ and the input $Q_{(t)}$ in the integrals of Eqs. (9-8). Then the total system transfer function is

$$G_{(s)} = \frac{X_{(s)}}{Q_{(s)}} = \frac{K_I}{s} + G^*_{(s)} \qquad (9\text{-}26)$$

$$G_{(i\omega)} = \frac{K_I}{i\omega} + G^*_{(i\omega)} \qquad (9\text{-}27)$$

$$= \operatorname{Re} G^* + i\left(\operatorname{Im} G^* - \frac{K_I}{\omega}\right) \qquad (9\text{-}28)$$

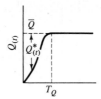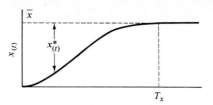

FIGURE 9-8
Step test data.

9-4 STEP TESTING

A plant operator makes changes from time to time in various input variables such as feed rate, steam flow, and reflux rate from one operating level to a new level. These changes can be either instantaneous or gradual, as sketched in Fig. 9-8. These step-response data are often easily obtained by merely recording the variables of interest for a few hours or days of plant operation.

These data can also be converted into frequency-response curves,[1] basically by differentiating both curves in the frequency domain. The process transfer function $G_{(s)}$ is

$$G_{(s)} = \frac{X_{(s)}}{Q_{(s)}}$$

We multiply both numerator and denominator by s, which is equivalent to differentiation in the time domain.

$$G_{(s)} = \frac{sX_{(s)}}{sQ_{(s)}} = \frac{\int_0^\infty (dx/dt)e^{-st}\,dt}{\int_0^\infty (dQ/dt)e^{-st}\,dt} \tag{9-29}$$

Going into the frequency domain,

$$G_{(i\omega)} = \frac{\int_0^\infty (dx/dt)e^{-i\omega t}\,dt}{\int_0^\infty (dQ/dt)e^{-i\omega t}\,dt} \tag{9-30}$$

Two new variables are defined as the departure of the input and output variables from their *final* steady-state values.

$$Q_{(t)}^* = \bar{Q} - Q_{(t)}$$
$$x_{(t)}^* = \bar{x} - x_{(t)} \tag{9-31}$$

[1] R. S. Schechter and E. H. Wissler, *Ind. Eng. Chem.*, vol. 51, p. 945, 1959.
J. K. Nyquist, R. N. Schindler, and R. E. Gilbert, *Chem. Eng. Prog. Symp. Ser.*, vol. 59, no. 46, p. 98, 1963.

Both Q^* and x^* go to zero after some finite time. Their derivatives are

$$\frac{dQ^*}{dt} = -\frac{dQ}{dt}$$

$$\frac{dx^*}{dt} = -\frac{dx}{dt} \qquad (9\text{-}32)$$

Then Eq. (9-30) becomes

$$G_{(i\omega)} = \frac{-\int_0^\infty (dx^*/dt)e^{-i\omega t}\, dt}{-\int_0^\infty (dQ^*/dt)e^{-i\omega t}\, dt} \qquad (9\text{-}33)$$

Integrating the numerator by parts gives

$$u = e^{-i\omega t} \qquad\qquad dv = \frac{dx^*}{dt}\, dt$$

$$du = -i\omega e^{-i\omega t}\, dt \qquad v = x^*$$

$$\int_0^\infty \left(\frac{dx^*}{dt}\right) e^{-i\omega t}\, dt = x^* e^{-i\omega t}\Big]_0^\infty + i\omega \int_0^\infty x^*_{(t)} e^{-i\omega t}\, dt$$

$$= -x^*_{(0)} + i\omega \int_0^\infty x^*_{(t)} e^{-i\omega t} dt$$

$$= -\bar{x} + i\omega \int_0^\infty x^*_{(t)} e^{-i\omega t}\, dt \qquad (9\text{-}34)$$

The denominator can be handled in exactly the same way. Equation (9-33) becomes

$$G_{(i\omega)} = \frac{\bar{x} - i\omega \int_0^\infty x^*_{(t)} e^{-i\omega t}\, dt}{\bar{Q} - i\omega \int_0^\infty Q^*_{(t)} e^{-i\omega t}\, dt} \qquad (9\text{-}35)$$

The integrals can be evaluated in the same way as for pulse tests [Eq. (9-19)].

9-5   OTHER PROCESS IDENTIFICATION METHODS

We have presented in this chapter only simple, deterministic dynamic testing methods. A host of more sophisticated and more powerful techniques have been proposed. These methods use statistics to help offset the problems of noisy signals. Himmelblau[1] delves into this area in detail.

[1] D. M. Himmelblau, "Process Analysis by Statistical Methods," Wiley, 1970.

The methods discussed here are usually applied "off line." That is, the process is disturbed, data are recorded, and then calculations are performed to find an empirical $G_{(s)}$ or $G_{(i\omega)}$. This information can be subsequently used for whatever purpose desired: evaluation of parameters, verification of a mathematical model, designing controllers, etc.

There has been considerable research in recent years directed at doing this identification "on line," i.e., continuously generating a dynamic model of the process. Thus any change in the process with time is detected (e.g., catalyst reactivity decay, fouling of heat transfer area, changes in ambient temperatures, etc.). This information is then used to retune controllers to achieve some desired performance. A number of applications of this "adaptive control" have been reported in the aerospace field.

With on-line process control computers, such schemes are now feasible in chemical processes. The principal stumbling block for their widespread application has been the lack of sufficient economic incentives. It is the rare chemical plant that changes so rapidly that on-line methods are justified.

9-6   RELATIONSHIPS AMONG TIME, LAPLACE, AND FREQUENCY DOMAINS

At this point it might be useful to pull together some of the concepts that you have waded through in the last four chapters. We now know how to look at and think about dynamics in the time, Laplace, or frequency domains. For example, a third-order, underdamped system would have the time-domain step responses sketched in Fig. 9-9 for two different values of the real root. In the Laplace domain, the system is represented by a transfer function $G_{(s)}$ or by plotting the poles of the transfer function (the roots of the system's characteristic equation) in the s plane, as shown in Fig. 9-9. In the frequency domain, the system could be represented by a Bode plot of $G_{(i\omega)}$.

Do we know how to convert from one domain to another? These conversions are summarized below.

9-6.1   Laplace to Frequency Domain

Substitute $s = i\omega$ in the system transfer function.

9-6.2   Frequency to Laplace Domain

To go the other direction, the Bode plots can be approximated, as discussed in Sec. 9-2.2.

Time domain: $(\tau_1\tau_2^2)\dfrac{d^3x}{dt^3} + (\tau_2^2 + 2\tau_1\tau_2\zeta)\dfrac{d^2x}{dt^2} + (\tau_1 + 2\tau_2\zeta)\dfrac{dx}{dt} + x = K_pQ_{(t)}$

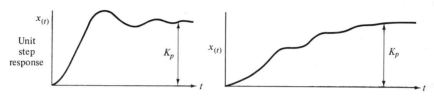

Laplace domain: $G_{(s)} = \dfrac{K_p}{(\tau_1 s + 1)(\tau_2^2 s^2 + 2\tau_2\zeta s + 1)}$

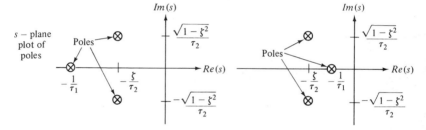

s – plane
plot of
poles

Frequency domain: $G(i\omega)$

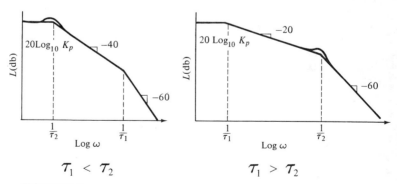

$$\mathcal{T}_1 < \mathcal{T}_2 \qquad\qquad \mathcal{T}_1 > \mathcal{T}_2$$

FIGURE 9-9
Third-order process in the time, Laplace, and frequency domains.

9-6.3   Time to Laplace Domain

Laplace transformation converts time functions into Laplace transforms and converts ordinary differential equations into transfer functions $G_{(s)}$.

9-6.4   Laplace to Time Domain

Inversion of the Laplace transform gives the time function. If we have the transfer function $G_{(s)}$, the unit step response is $\mathscr{L}^{-1}[G_{(s)}/s]$. The impulse response is $\mathscr{L}^{-1}[G_{(s)}]$.

9-6.5   Time to Frequency Domain

The ordinary differential equations could be solved in the time domain with a sinusoidal forcing function, but it is easier to go into the Laplace domain first and then substitute $s = i\omega$.

9-6.6   Frequency to Time Domain

We could go through the Laplace domain by approximating $G_{(i\omega)}$ and then inverting. However, there is a direct conversion.[1]

Suppose we want to find the impulse response of a stable system (defined as $g_{(t)}$), given the system's frequency response $G_{(i\omega)}$. Since the Laplace transformation of the impulse input is unity,

$$g_{(t)} = \mathscr{L}^{-1}[G_{(s)}] \qquad (9\text{-}36)$$

Using the inversion formula of Eq. (7-23) gives

$$g_{(t)} = \frac{1}{2\pi i} \int_{a-i\infty}^{a+i\infty} e^{st} G_{(s)}\, ds \qquad (9\text{-}37)$$

If we pick the path of this contour integration along the imaginary axis in the s plane $s = i\omega$.

$$g_{(t)} = \frac{1}{2\pi i} \int_{-i\infty}^{i\infty} G_{(i\omega)} e^{i\omega t}\, d(i\omega) \qquad (9\text{-}38)$$

$$g_{(t)} = \frac{1}{2\pi} \int_{-\infty}^{\infty} (\operatorname{Re} G + i \operatorname{Im} G)(\cos \omega t + i \sin \omega t)\, d\omega$$

$$= \frac{1}{2\pi} \int_{-\infty}^{\infty} [\operatorname{Re}(G) \cos \omega t - \operatorname{Im}(G) \sin \omega t]\, d\omega$$

$$+ \frac{i}{2\pi} \int_{-\infty}^{\infty} [\operatorname{Re}(G) \sin \omega t + \operatorname{Im}(G) \cos \omega t]\, d\omega \qquad (9\text{-}39)$$

[1] V. V. Solodovnikov, "Introduction to Statistical Dynamics of Automatic Control," Dover, 1960.

Now

$$\text{Re } G = |G| \cos (\arg G)$$

is an even function.[1]

$$\text{Im } G = |G| \sin (\arg G)$$

is an odd function.[2] Therefore

$$\text{Re } (G) \cos \omega t \quad \text{and} \quad \text{Im } (G) \sin \omega t \quad \text{are even.}$$

$$\text{Re } (G) \sin \omega t \quad \text{and} \quad \text{Im } (G) \cos \omega t \quad \text{are odd.}$$

Integrating an even function from $-\infty$ to $+\infty$ is the same as integrating it from 0 to $+\infty$ and multiplying the result by 2.

$$\int_{-\infty}^{\infty} (even \ function) \ dt = 2 \int_{0}^{\infty} (even \ function) \ dt \qquad (9\text{-}40)$$

Integrating an odd function from $-\infty$ to $+\infty$ gives zero.

$$\int_{-\infty}^{\infty} (odd \ function) \ dt = 0 \qquad (9\text{-}41)$$

Therefore Eq. (9-39) reduces to

$$g_{(t)} = \frac{1}{\pi} \int_{0}^{\infty} [\text{Re } (G) \cos \omega t - \text{Im } (G) \sin \omega t] \ d\omega \qquad (9\text{-}42)$$

Now $g_{(t)}$ must, by definition, be equal to zero for time less than zero. For this to be true, the integrand must equal zero for negative values of t.

$$\text{Re } (G) \cos (-\omega t) - \text{Im } (G) \sin (-\omega t) = 0$$

$$\text{Re } (G) \cos \omega t + \text{Im } (G) \sin \omega t = 0$$

$$\text{Re } (G) \cos \omega t = - \text{Im } (G) \sin \omega t \qquad (9\text{-}43)$$

Equation (9-42) can be written in two ways:

$$g_{(t)} = \frac{2}{\pi} \int_{0}^{\infty} \text{Re } (G_{(i\omega)}) \cos \omega t \ d\omega$$

$$g_{(t)} = -\frac{2}{\pi} \int_{0}^{\infty} \text{Im } (G_{(i\omega)}) \sin \omega t \ d\omega \qquad (9\text{-}44)$$

Therefore the time-domain impulse response can be calculated from the frequency domain $G_{(i\omega)}$ by evaluating either of these integrals.

---

[1] An even function satisfies $f_{(x)} = f_{(-x)}$.
[2] An odd function satisfies $f_{(x)} = -f_{(-x)}$.

PROBLEMS

9-1 Write a digital computer program that will calculate $G_{(i\omega)}$ from step test data.

9-2 Identify experimentally on an analog computer the time constant, gain, and $G_{(i\omega)}$ for the three-CSTR system simulated in Example 4-1 by:

(a) Direct sine-wave testing (NOTE: The sinusoidal input signal can be generated on the analog by simulating a second-order system with a damping coefficient ζ set equal to zero.)

(b) Step testing, using the program developed in Prob. 9-1.

$$G_{(s)} = \left(\frac{C_{A3}}{C_{A0}}\right)_{(s)}$$

9-3 Repeat Prob. 9-2 using pulse testing. Use pulses of $C_{A0(t)}$ with various heights and durations and shapes as given below. Compare the computed $G_{(i\omega)}$'s.

(a) Rectangular pulses:

Height	Duration (min)
1	0.4
1	0.8
1	1.6
1	3.2
−1	0.4
2	0.4

(b) Triangular pulses:

Height	Duration (min)
1	0.4
2	0.8
5	0.1

9-4 Write a digital computer program that will calculate $G_{(i\omega)}$ from pulse test data when the process contains an integrator.

9-5 The frequency-response data given below were obtained from direct sine-wave tests of a chemical plant. Fit an approximate transfer function $G_{(s)}$ to these data.

Frequency, radians/minute	Real part	Imaginary part	Log modulus, db	Phase angle, degrees
0.01	6.964	−0.522	16.88	−4.2
0.02	6.859	−1.028	16.82	−8.5
0.04	6.467	−1.942	16.59	−16.7
0.08	5.254	−3.202	15.78	−31.3
0.10	4.568	−3.554	15.25	−37.9
0.20	2.096	−3.673	12.52	−60.2
0.40	0.324	−2.741	8.82	−83.2
0.63	−0.557	−2.234	7.49	−103
0.80	−1.462	−2.083	8.11	−125
1.00	−2.472	−0.104	7.87	−177
1.41	−0.282	0.547	−4.21	−243
2.00	−0.021	0.160	−15.81	−262
4.00	0.004	0.016	−35.5	−285
8.00	0.001	0.001	−53.9	−312

9-6 Use the approximate transfer function found in Prob. 9-5 to calculate analytically by inverse Laplace transformation the impulse response of the system, $g_{(t)}$. Compare this with the $g_{(t)}$ calculated directly from the experimental frequency-response data, using Eq. (9-44).

PART FOUR

Feedback Control

In Part 3 we studied several ways to look at dynamics. Given a system, we learned techniques for analyzing its dynamic behavior in the time, Laplace, and frequency domains. Usually we studied an open-loop process with no controllers; but if a controller was included, its form and parameters were given. Thus up to this point we have developed tools for systems *analysis*.

Now we are ready to turn to the more challenging problem of systems *synthesis* or *compensation*. Given a process, we want to design a control system that will give some desired dynamic performance for the closed-loop system (the process plus the control system). For example, the controller's job may be to hold a process variable (such as temperature) within a certain range ($\pm 10°F$) of its set-point value despite load disturbances (± 50 percent throughput changes).

Historically, feedback control devices, which we will consider here in Part 4, were used almost exclusively to achieve system compensation. Feedforward control, which offers significant advantages in many chemical engineering processes, will be discussed in Part 5.

We will explore the dynamics of closed-loop systems in the same three domains that we used in analyzing the dynamics of open-loop systems: time, Laplace, and frequency.

10

TIME-DOMAIN SYNTHESIS

In this chapter we will study control equipment, controller performance and tuning, and general control-systems design concepts. First we will look at some of the control hardware that is currently used in process control systems: transmitters, valves, controllers, etc. Then we will discuss the performance of conventional controllers and present empirical tuning techniques. Finally we will talk about some of the important design concepts for specifying a control system for a process.

10-1 CONTROL INSTRUMENTATION

Some familiarity with control hardware is required before we can discuss selection and tuning. We are not concerned with the details of how the various mechanical, pneumatic, hydraulic, and electronic gadgets are constructed. We need to know only how they basically work and what they are supposed to do. Pictures and diagrams of some typical hardware are given in the Appendix.

As we preliminarily discussed in Chap. 1, the basic feedback control loop consists of a sensor to detect the process variable; a transmitter to convert the sensor signal into an equivalent air pressure or electrical signal; a controller that compares

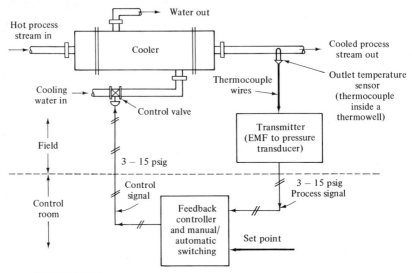

FIGURE 10-1
Feedback control loop (pneumatic instrumentation).

this process signal with a set point and produces an appropriate control signal; and a final control element that changes the manipulative variable. Usually the final control element is an air-operated control valve that opens and closes to change the flow rate of the manipulative stream. See Fig. 10-1.

The sensor, transmitter, and control valve are physically located on the process equipment ("in the field"). The controller is usually located on a panel in a control room that is some distance from the process equipment.

Most control equipment used in chemical and petroleum plants is either pneumatic or electronic. Pneumatic devices contain mechanical linkages, bellows, diaphragms, etc. They are driven or powered by an instrument air stream that is supplied at about 20 to 25 psig. They usually accept pneumatic 3 to 15 psig air-pressure input signals and produce output air-pressure signals over the same 3 to 15 psig range. Pneumatic control elements are widely used because they are reliable, inexpensive, and explosion-proof. The last factor can be extremely important in many plants.

Electronic control devices are basically special-purpose electronic analog computers which are usually made of solid-state printed-circuit elements. They are powered by conventional 117 volts ac or 24 volts dc. The form of their input and output signals varies from one manufacturer to the next. They can be an ac voltage, a dc voltage, or a dc current signal. Electronic devices are more expensive than their pneumatic counterparts, sometimes by a factor of 2. Their use is justified when the control room

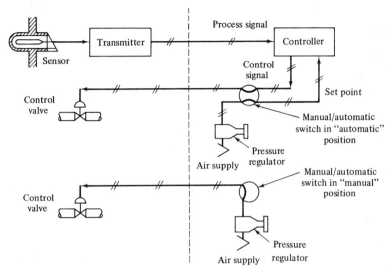

FIGURE 10-2
Manual-automatic switching (pneumatic system).

is located a long distance from the process and when rapid transmission of signals between the plant and the control room is required.

In a pneumatic system the plastic or metal tubing that connects the transmitter to the controller and the controller to the valve represents a dynamic lag in the control loop. When long lengths of tubing are used, these transmission lags can become significant and degrade control performance in fast loops (e.g., flow control loops and some pressure control loops).[1]

Pneumatic systems will be used in this book for illustrative purposes because they are easier for chemical engineers to understand and work with and because pneumatics are still widely used in the process industries. All the concepts of analysis and design are equally applicable to electronic systems.

Also located in the control room is the manual-automatic switching hardware. During start-up or under abnormal conditions, the plant operator may want to be able to set the position of the control valve himself instead of having the controller position it. A switch is usually provided on the control panel as sketched in Fig. 10-2. In the "manual" position the operator can stroke the valve by changing a knob (a pressure regulator in a pneumatic system or a potentiometer in an electronic system). In the "automatic" position the controller output signal goes to the valve. The knob on the control panel now regulates the set point to the controller. Detailed information on these devices is available in the manufacturers' brochures.

[1] P. S. Buckley and W. L. Luyben, *Instrum. Technol.*, vol. 17, p. 61, 1969.

10-1.1 Sensors

Instruments for on-line measurement of many properties have been developed. The most important variables are flow rate, temperature, pressure, and level. Devices for measuring other properties, such as pH, density, viscosity, infrared and ultraviolet absorption, refractive index, etc., are also available. Direct measurement of chemical composition by means of on-line gas chromatographs has increased rapidly in recent years. Their use would be even more widespread if they were more reliable as regards continuity of operation and were not so expensive ($10,000 to 20,000 for a complete installed system). Chromatographs pose interesting control problems because of their intermittent operation (a composition signal is generated only every few minutes). We will study the analysis of these discontinuous, sampled-data systems in Part 6.

We will discuss briefly some of the common sensing elements. For details of their operation, construction, relative merits, and costs, consult the handbooks.[1]

Flow Orifice plates are by far the most common type of flow-rate sensor. The pressure drop across the orifice varies with the square of the flow in turbulent flow, so measuring the differential pressure gives a signal that can be related to flow rate. Normally orifice plates are designed to give pressure drops in the range of 20 to 200 in. of water. Venturi tubes and turbine meters are also used. They are more expensive but give more accurate flow measurement.

When a flow sensor is installed for accurate accounting measurements of the absolute flow rate, many precautions must be taken, such as providing a long section of straight pipe before the orifice plate. For control purposes, however, one may not need to know the absolute value of flow but only the changes in flow rate. Therefore pressure drops over pieces of equipment, around elbows, or over sections of pipe can often be used to get a rough indication of flow rate.

Temperature Thermocouples are the most commonly used temperature sensing devices. The two dissimilar wires produce a millivolt emf that varies with the "hot-junction" temperature. Iron-constantan thermocouples are commonly used over the 0 to 1300°F temperature range.

Filled-bulb sensors are also widely used. A fixed amount of an inert gas or liquid is enclosed in a constant-volume system. Changes in process temperature cause the

[1] D. M. Considine, "Process Instruments and Controls Handbook," McGraw-Hill, 1957.

E. M. Grabbe, S. Ramo, and D. E. Wooldridge, "Handbook of Automation, Computation and Control," Wiley, 1961.

D. P. Eckman, "Automatic Process Control," Wiley, 1958.

B. G. Liptak, "Instrument Engineers Handbook," vol. 2, Process Control, Chilton, 1970.

pressure exerted by the fluid to change. Resistance thermometers are used where very accurate temperature or differential-temperature measurement is required. They use the principle that the electrical resistance of a wire changes with temperature.

The dynamic response of most sensors is usually much faster than the dynamics of the process itself. Temperature sensors are a notable and sometimes troublesome exception. The time constant of a thermocouple and a heavy thermowell can be of the order of 30 sec and can significantly affect control performance. Shielded or bare thermocouples can sometimes be used directly in the process to cut this measurement lag to a few seconds or less.

Pressure and differential pressure Bourdon tubes, bellows, and diaphragms are used to sense pressure and differential pressure. For example, in a mechanical system the process pressure force is balanced by the movement of a spring. The spring position can be related to process pressure.

Level Liquid levels are detected in a variety of ways. The three most common are

1 Following the position of a float that is lighter than the fluid (as in a bathroom toilet).
2 Measuring the apparent weight of a heavy cylinder as it is buoyed up more or less by the liquid (these are called *displacement meters*).
3 Measuring the difference in static pressure between two fixed elevations, one in the vapor above the liquid and the other under the liquid surface. As sketched in Fig. 10-3, the differential pressure between the two level taps is directly related to the liquid level in the vessel.

In the last scheme the process liquid and vapor are normally piped up directly to the differential-pressure measuring device (ΔP transmitter). Some care has to be taken to account for or to prevent condensation of vapor in the connecting lines. Because of plugging or corrosion problems, it is sometimes necessary to keep the process fluid out of the ΔP transmitter. This is accomplished by mechanical diaphragm seals or purges (introducing a small amount of liquid or gas into the connecting lines which flows back into the process).

If it is difficult to provide a level tap in the base of a vessel (for mechanical design reasons, for example) a bubble tube can be suspended from the top of the vessel down under the liquid surface, as shown in Fig. 10-3. A small gas purge through the tube gives a pressure on the high-pressure side of the ΔP transmitter that is the same as the static pressure at the base of the bubble tube.

For very hard-to-handle process fluids nuclear radiation gauges are used to detect interfaces and levels.

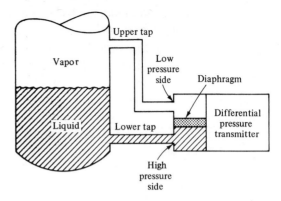

Conventional

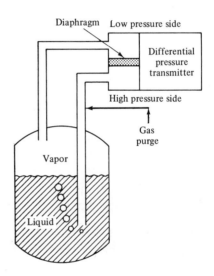

FIGURE 10-3
Differential-pressure level measurement.

Bubble Tube

10-1.2 Transmitters

The transmitter is the interface between the process and its control system. The job of the transmitter is to convert the sensor signal (millivolts, mechanical movement, pressure differential, etc.) into a control signal (3 to 15 psig air-pressure signal, 1 to 5 or 10 to 50 milliampere electrical signal, etc.).

Consider the pneumatic pressure transmitter shown in Fig. 10-4a. Let us assume that this particular transmitter is set up so that its output pressure signal varies from

3 to 15 psig as the process pressure in the vessel varies from 0 to 500 psig. The range of the pressure transmitter is 500 psi.

The dynamic response of most transmitters is usually much faster than the process and the control valves. Consequently we can normally consider the transmitter as a simple "gain" (an element with a transfer function that is just a constant) in the control loop. The gain of the pressure transmitter is

$$\frac{15 \text{ psig} - 3 \text{ psig}}{500 \text{ psig} - 0 \text{ psig}} = \frac{12 \text{ psi}}{500 \text{ psi}} \qquad (10\text{-}1)$$

Thus transmitters convert from process variables into equivalent control signals.

Figure 10-4*b* shows a temperature transmitter which accepts thermocouple input signals and is set up so that its pneumatic output goes from 3 to 15 psig as the process temperature varies from 50 to 250°F. The range of the transmitter is 50 to 250°F, its span is 200°F, and its "zero" is 50°F. If its dynamics are fast, it acts like a gain.

$$\frac{15 \text{ psig} - 3 \text{ psig}}{250°F - 50°F} = \frac{12 \text{ psi}}{200F°} \qquad (10\text{-}2)$$

As noted in Section 10-1.1, the dynamics of the thermowell-thermocouple sensor are often not negligible and should be included in the dynamic analysis.

Figure 10-4*c* shows a ΔP transmitter used with an orifice plate as a flow transmitter. The pressure drop over the orifice plate (the sensor) is converted into a pneumatic control signal. Suppose the orifice plate is sized to give a pressure drop of 100 in. of water at a process flow rate of 200 gpm. The ΔP transmitter converts inches H_2O into psig, and its gain is 12 psi/100 in. H_2O. However, we really want flow rate, not orifice-plate pressure drop. Since ΔP is proportional to the square of the flow rate, there is a nonlinear relationship between flow rate F and the transmitter output signal.

$$P_T = 3 + 12\left(\frac{F}{200}\right)^2 \qquad (10\text{-}3)$$

where $P_T = \Delta P$ transmitter output signal, psig

$\quad\quad F$ = process flow rate, gpm

Dropping flow by a factor of 2 cuts the ΔP signal by a factor of 4. For system analysis we usually linearize Eq. (10-3) to give

$$P_T = \frac{24\bar{F}}{F_{max}^2} F \qquad (10\text{-}4)$$

where P_T and F = perturbations from steady state

$\quad\quad \bar{F}$ = steady-state flow rate, gpm

$\quad\quad F_{max}$ = maximum full-scale flow rate = 200 gpm in this example

312

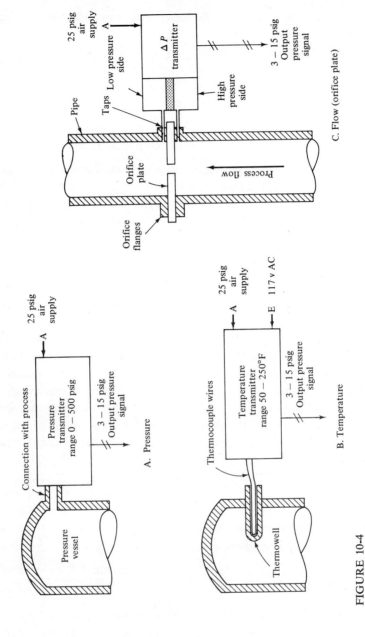

FIGURE 10-4

Typical transmitters. (a) Pressure; (b) temperature; (c) flow (orifice plate).

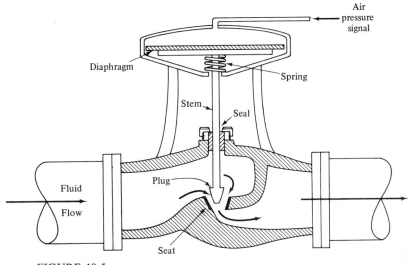

FIGURE 10-5
Typical air-operated control valve.

10-1.3 Control Valves

The interface with the process at the other end of the control loop is made by the final control element. In a vast majority of systems the final control element is an automatic control valve which throttles the flow of a manipulative variable. Most control valves consist of a plug on the end of a stem that opens or closes an orifice opening as the stem is raised or lowered. As sketched in Fig. 10-5, the stem is attached to a diaphragm that is driven by changing air pressure above the diaphragm. The force of the air pressure is opposed by a spring.

The valve shown in Fig. 10-5 is closed when the stem is down and open when the stem is up. Since air pressure pushes the valve down, this valve is an "air-to-close" (A-C) valve. If the instrument air supply were lost in an emergency, this valve would fail open since the spring would push the valve open. The valve can be made "air-to-open" (A-O) by reversing the action of the plug to close off the opening in the up position or by reversing the locations of the spring and air pressure (put the air pressure under the diaphragm).

The flow rate through a control valve depends on the size of the control valve, the pressure drop over the valve, the stem position, and the fluid properties. The design equation for liquids (nonflashing) is

$$F = C_V f_{(x)} \sqrt{\frac{\Delta P}{\text{sp.gr.}}} \qquad (10\text{-}5)$$

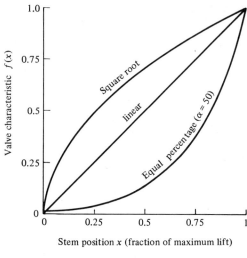

FIGURE 10-6
Control-valve characteristics.

3 psig ◄——— air-to-open valve ———► 15 psig
15 psig ◄——— air-to-close valve ———► 3 psig

where F = flow rate, gpm

C_V = valve size coefficient

x = valve stem position (fraction of wide open)

$f_{(x)}$ = valve flow characteristic curve (defined below)

sp.gr. = specific gravity of liquid (relative to water)

ΔP = pressure drop over valve, psi

By changing the shape of the plug and seat, valves can be made with a number of flow characteristics $f_{(x)}$. Three commonly used characteristics are *linear trim, equal-percentage trim* (= %),[1] and *square-root trim* ($\sqrt{}$) as shown in Fig. 10-6.

If constant pressure drop over the valve is assumed, a half-open square-root valve gives about 70 percent of maximum flow, a linear valve gives 50 percent, and an = % valve gives only 15 percent. The equations for these valves are:

Linear:

$$f(x) = x \qquad (10\text{-}6)$$

Square root:

$$f(x) = \sqrt{x} \qquad (10\text{-}7)$$

Equal percentage:

$$f(x) = \alpha^{x-1} \qquad (10\text{-}8)$$

---

[1] The term "equal percentage" comes from the slope of the curve df/dx being a constant fraction of $f(x)$.

where α is a constant (20 to 50) that depends on the valve design. A value of 50 is used in the $= \%$ curve in Fig. 10-6.

The basic reason for using different control-valve trims is to keep the stability of the control loop fairly constant over a wide range of flows.[1] Linear-trim valves are used, for example, when the pressure drop over the control valve is fairly constant and a linear relationship exists between the controlled variable and the flow rate of the manipulative variable. Consider the flow of steam from a constant pressure supply through a control valve into the shell side of a heat exchanger. A process liquid stream flows through the tube side and is heated by the steam. There is a linear relationship between the process outlet temperature and steam flow (with constant process flow and inlet temperature) since every pound of steam provides a certain amount of heat.

Equal-percentage valves are often used when the pressure drop available over the control valve is not constant. This occurs when there are other pieces of equipment in the system that act as fixed resistances. For example, consider the system sketched in Fig. 10-7. Liquid is pumped from a constant-pressure vessel by a pump whose discharge pressure is essentially constant at P_1. The stream flows through a heat exchanger and control valve into another vessel which is held at a lower constant pressure P_2. The total available driving force is $P_1 - P_2$. As flow rate is increased, the pressure drop over the heat exchanger[2] ΔP_H increases. Therefore the pressure drop over the control valve ΔP_V must decrease. That means that the control valve has to open more than it would if its pressure drop were constant.

At low flow rates, most of the pressure drop $(P_1 - P_2)$ will be taken over the control valve since the pressure drop over the heat exchanger drops off as the square of the flow rate. In this situation the $= \%$ trim tends to give a more linear relationship between flow and control-valve position than does linear trim. The actual relationship depends, of course, on the values of ΔP_H and ΔP_V at design flow rate, as sketched in the curves in Fig. 10-7.

From a control standpoint, the bigger ΔP_V, the better the control of the flow will be. The control system will be able to handle large disturbances and upsets. From a heat exchanger and pump design standpoint, the ΔP_V through the control valve should be kept as small as possible. Thus an engineering compromise must be made between controllability and power requirements. A good rule of thumb is to design the system so that the control valve in its half-open position ($f_{(x)} = 0.5$) takes about 25 percent of the total system pressure drop at design flow rate. Therefore if the pressure drop over the heat exchanger ΔP_H is 30 psi, the control valve and pump should be sized to give at least a 10-psi pressure drop at the design flow rate. Assume the

---

[1] P. S. Buckley, Selection of Optimum Final Control Elements, in G. H. Robinson (ed.), "Instrumentation in the Chemical and Petroleum Industries," p. 107, Plenum, 1964.
[2] Piping pressure drop is included in ΔP_H.

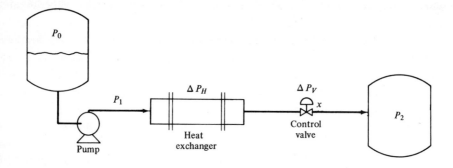

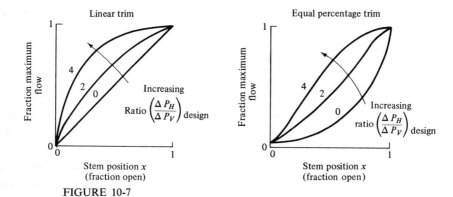

FIGURE 10-7
Control-valve performance in a system ("installed characteristics").

design rate is 200 gpm and liquid specific gravity is 1. Then Eq. (10-5) gives the required valve size coefficient as

$$C_V = \frac{200}{0.5\sqrt{10}} = 127$$

This corresponds to approximately a 4-in. control valve.[1]

The above example points up another problem that must be considered when designing a control system: control-valve rangeability. Most control valves can work effectively between $f_{(x)}$ values of 0.05 to 0.95. At low flows and corresponding high pressure drops over the control valve, it may be almost on its seat, and poor flow

---

[1] Charts and tables of C_V values for various types and sizes of control valves are given in the handbooks referenced earlier and in valve manufacturer's data books. Equations for sizing control valves in flashing service, with gases, and with sonic flow are also given in these sources.

regulation can result. For example, suppose the flow rate in the example above is reduced to 25 percent of design, 50 gpm. The pressure drop through the heat exchanger will drop to $30/(4)^2 = 1.87$ psi. If the discharge pressure P_1 of the pump stays constant (actually it will go up if the pump is a centrifugal pump and we back up the pump curve, making the control-valve ΔP even higher), the pressure drop over the control valve must be 38.1 psi, giving a required $f_{(x)}$ of

$$f_{(x)} = \frac{50}{127\sqrt{38.1}} = 0.06$$

The valve is almost completely closed, and flow oscillations can occur as the valve alternately seats and cracks open.

In conventional valves the air-pressure signal to the diaphragm comes directly from the output of a controller. Valve positioners are often used to improve control, particularly for large valves and with dirty or gooky fluids which can make the valve stick. These devices are little feedback controllers that sense the position of the stem, compare it with the desired position as given by the signal from the controller, and adjust the air pressure on the diaphragm to drive the stem to its correct position. Valve positioners are also used to make valves open and close over various ranges (split-range valves as discussed in Example 5-8).

Control valves are usually fairly fast compared with the process. With large valves (greater than 4-in.) it may take 20 to 40 sec for the valve to move full stroke. Air boosters on the valve air inlet and valve positioners can improve valve dynamics if they become significant.

We have discussed at some length some of the basic fundamentals of control-valve performance and design. This subject is of great practical importance, and the applied literature in this area is extensive.[1]

10-1.4   Controllers

Now we get to the real heart of the control system. The job of the controller is to compare the process signal from the transmitter with the set-point signal and to send out an appropriate signal to the control valve.

There are three basic types of controllers that are conventionally used for continuous feedback control. The details of construction and principles of operation vary from manufacturer to manufacturer and from pneumatic to electronic devices, but their basic functions are essentially the same.

[1] "ISA Handbook of Control Valves," J. W. Hutchison, Ed., Instrument Society of America, 1971.
C. S. Beard, "Final Control Elements," Chilton, 1969.

Proportional action   A proportional-only feedback controller changes the output signal in direct proportion to the error signal.

$$m_{(t)} = \overline{m} + K_c(c^{set} - c) \qquad \text{(10-9)}$$

where $m_{(t)}$ = controller output pressure that goes (normally) to control valve, psig
$\quad\quad \overline{m}$ = bias value of controller or its output pressure when error is zero, psig
$\quad\quad K_c$ = controller gain, psi/psi
$\quad\quad c$ = process signal from transmitter, psig
$\quad\quad c^{set}$ = set-point signal, psig

We will use the notation m and c, implying manipulative and controlled variables. Remember that the controller "sees" a transmitted process signal (in psig in a pneumatic system) so the c variable is really the transmitted equivalent of the real process variable being controlled. Likewise the $m_{(t)}$ is really just the controller output signal to a control valve. The valve then changes the pressure signal into stem position and eventually into flow rate of the real manipulative variable.

The larger the controller gain K_c, the more the controller output will change for a given error. For example, if the gain is 1, a 1-psi error will change the controller output 1 psi from its biased value $\overline{m}$. If the gain is 10, a 1-psi error will change the controller output 10 psi.

Almost all commercial controllers are calibrated in terms of *proportional band* (PB) instead of gain.

$$PB = \frac{100}{K_c} \qquad \text{(10-10)}$$

The higher or "wider" the proportional band, the lower is the gain and vice versa. The term "proportional band" refers to the range over which the error must change to drive the controller output over its full range. Thus a wide PB is a low gain, and a narrow PB is a high gain. Figure 10-8a sketches the action of a proportional controller for given error signals $e_{(t)} = c^{set} - c$.

The gain can be made either positive or negative by setting a switch or direction plate on the controller. A positive gain corresponds to having the controller output increase when the process signal decreases (a reverse-acting controller). For a negative gain the controller output decreases as the process signal decreases (direct-acting controller). The correct sign for the gain depends on the action of the transmitter (which is usually direct), the action of the valve (air-to-open or air-to-close), and the effect of the manipulative variable on the controlled variable.

For example, suppose we are controlling the process outlet temperature of a heat exchanger by throttling steam through an air-to-open valve. The temperature transmitter is direct-acting (when the process temperature goes up, the transmitter output goes up). We want the steam flow to decrease when the temperature goes

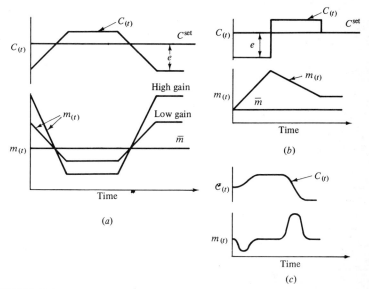

FIGURE 10-8
Action of a feedback controller. (a) Proportional; (b) integral; (c) ideal derivative.

up, and therefore the controller output should go down when temperature goes up. Therefore the controller should be reverse-acting.

If we were cooling instead of heating, we would want the coolant flow to increase when the temperature increased. But the controller action may still be reverse if the control valve is now an air-to-close valve, which it normally would be so that it would fail open to ensure maximum cooling.

One of the most important items to be checked in setting up a feedback control loop on a plant is that the action of the controller is correct.

The transfer function of a proportional controller $B_{(s)}$ is

$$B_{(s)} = \left(\frac{M}{E}\right)_{(s)} = K_c \qquad (10\text{-}11)$$

Integral action (reset)   Proportional action moves the control valve in direct proportion to the magnitude of the error. Integral action moves the control valve based on the time integral of the error, as sketched in Fig. 10-8b.

$$m_{(t)} = \overline{m} + \frac{1}{\tau_I} \int e_{(t)} \, dt \qquad (10\text{-}12)$$

where τ_I is the integral or reset time (minutes).

If there is no error the controller output does not move. As the error goes positive or negative, the integral of the error drives the controller output either up or down, depending on the action of the controller (reverse or direct).

Most controllers are calibrated in *minutes/repeat*, a term that comes from the test of putting into the controller a fixed 1-psi error signal and seeing how long the integral action takes to ramp up the controller output 1 psi (repeating the same action that a proportional controller would make with a PB of 100). However, some caution should be exercised in tuning controllers, because some manufacturers calibrate their instruments in repeats/minute, the reciprocal of the convention we will use here.

The basic purpose of integral action is to drive the process back to its set point when it has been disturbed. This is called zero *steady-state error* or zero *offset*. We will show later that integral or reset action is usually dynamically *undesirable*. It tends to make the control loop more oscillatory and moves it toward instability. But it is usually required to eliminate steady-state error. Thus another one of those ubiquitous engineering compromises must be made between dynamic response and steady-state response.

The transfer function for a pure integral controller is

$$B_{(s)} = \left(\frac{M}{E}\right)_{(s)} = \frac{1}{\tau_I} \frac{1}{s} \qquad (10\text{-}13)$$

Ideal derivative action   The purpose of derivative action (also called *rate action* or *preact*) is to anticipate where the process is heading by looking at the time rate of change of the error, its derivative.

$$m_{(t)} = \bar{m} + \tau_D \frac{de}{dt} \qquad (10\text{-}14)$$

where τ_D is the derivative time (minutes).

In theory, derivative action should always improve dynamic response, and it does in many loops. In others, however, the noise problems make the use of derivative action undesirable. The transfer function for an ideal derivative controller is

$$B_{(s)} = \left(\frac{M}{E}\right)_{(s)} = \tau_D s \qquad (10\text{-}15)$$

As we discussed in Chap. 6, it is physically impossible to make a gadget that can take a perfect derivative. Therefore the ideal derivative action cannot be realized. Derivative units (lead-lag units) are used to get approximate derivative action. In the Laplace domain their transfer function is

$$\left(\frac{M}{E}\right)_{(s)} = \frac{\tau_D s + 1}{\alpha \tau_D s + 1} \qquad (10\text{-}16)$$

where α for commercial controllers is in the range $\frac{1}{6}$ to $\frac{1}{20}$. Converting to the time domain gives

$$\alpha \tau_D \frac{dm}{dt} + m = \tau_D \frac{de}{dt} + e$$

$$m = e + \tau_D \frac{d}{dt}(e - \alpha m) \qquad (10\text{-}17)$$

Commercial controllers The three actions described above are used individually or combined in three basic commercial controllers:

1 Proportional (P): with just proportional action.
2 Proportional-integral (PI): with proportional plus integral action:

$$m = \bar{m} + K_c\left(e + \frac{1}{\tau_I}\int e\, dt\right) \qquad (10\text{-}18)$$

The transfer function of a PI controller is

$$B_{(s)} = \left(\frac{M}{E}\right)_{(s)} = K_c\left(1 + \frac{1}{\tau_I}\frac{1}{s}\right) = K_c\frac{\tau_I s + 1}{\tau_I s} \qquad (10\text{-}19)$$

3 Proportional-integral-derivative (PID): All three actions or "modes" are included. The ideal, but physically unrealizable, PID controller is

$$m = \bar{m} + K_c\left(e + \frac{1}{\tau_I}\int e\, dt + \tau_D \frac{de}{dt}\right) \qquad (10\text{-}20)$$

Actual commercial PID controllers have transfer functions that are the product of a PI controller and a lead-lag.

$$B_{(s)} = K_c\left(\frac{\tau_I s + 1}{\tau_I s}\right)\left(\frac{\tau_D s + 1}{\alpha \tau_D s + 1}\right) \qquad (10\text{-}21)$$

10-1.5 Computing Relays and Other Useful Gadgets

A host of special devices that perform a variety of computations with control signals are on the market. Signals can be added, multiplied by constants, multiplied together, divided, etc. The little pneumatic and electronic boxes that perform these functions are just like modular components in an analog computer. They are piped or wired together to construct control systems that are somewhat more complex than a simple single feedback loop. Some of the most useful are listed below. We will describe a few of their uses later in this chapter (Sec. 10-5) and in the feedforward control systems of Part 5.

In the list below the output of the box is O; inputs are A, B, and C; and K is a gain. Pneumatic devices are assumed but the same functions can be achieved electronically (at considerably higher cost). Inputs and outputs are all in psig with a "live" zero at 3 psig and a 12-psi span.

1   *Addition*: $O = A + B - 3$

2   *Subtraction*: $O = A - B + 3$

3   *Combinations*: $O = A + B - C$

4   *Multiplication by Gain* (K may be fixed or variable): $O = K(A - B) + C$

5   *Multiplication*: $O = (A - 3)(B - 3) + 3$

6   *Division*: $O = 3 + (A - 3)/(B - 3)$

7   *Square-root Extraction*: $O = 3 + \sqrt{A - 3}$

8   *High selector* (HS): O is equal to the input A or B that has the *higher* pressure.

9   *Low selector* (LS): O is equal to the input A or B that has the *lower* pressure.

10 *High limiter*: O follows the input A up to some set maximum pressure and then holds at this limit as long as A is greater than the limit.

11 *Low limiter*: O tracks the input A down to some set minimum pressure and then holds at this limit as long as A is lower than the limit.

12 *Derivative units*: lead-lag elements like Eq. (10-16).

10-1.6 Digital Process-control Computers

Digital computers are being used in increasing numbers to monitor and control chemical engineering processes. Their ability to look at many variables and do complex calculations make them a powerful control tool.

They are, however, inherently "sampled-data" in operation because they look at any individual control loop only periodically. Between the sampling times the control signal is held constant. Consequently for most processes digital control is not as good as continuous analog control. We will discuss these sampled-data systems in Part 6.

The hardware aspects of digital process-control computers are beyond the scope of this book. Since the field is so new, the equipment and even the basic strategies are still in a state of flux and vary considerably from manufacturer to manufacturer.

Let us merely sketch the main components of a digital loop. The continuous (analog) process signal from the transmitter is changed into a digital signal by an A/D (analog-to-digital) converter, which is usually multiplexed with a number of inputs. The computer uses the digital signal and a control equation (algorithm) that has been programmed into it to determine an appropriate control signal. This digital signal is converted to an analog signal by a multiplexed D/A (digital-to-analog) converter. The analog signal is picked up by a "hold" device at each sampling instant.

The hold sends this fixed signal to a control valve or to the set point of an analog controller until the next sampling time.

We will learn how to analyze the performance of digital loops and design sampled-data controllers in Part 6.

10-2   PERFORMANCE OF CONVENTIONAL FEEDBACK CONTROLLERS

10-2.1   Specifications for Closed-loop Response

There are a number of criteria by which the desired performance of a closed-loop system can be specified in the time domain. For example, we could specify that the closed-loop system be critically damped so that there is no overshoot or oscillation. We must then select the type of controller and set (tune) its constants (gain, integral, and derivative times) so that it will give, when coupled with the process, the desired closed-loop response. Naturally the control specifications must be physically attainable. We cannot violate any constraints on the manipulative variable (the control valve can only go wide open or shut), and we cannot require a physically unrealizable control element.

There are a number of time-domain specifications. A few of the most frequently used dynamic specifications are listed below (see also Prob. 6-11). The traditional test input signal is a step change in set point.

1   *Overshoot*: the amount of swing past the set point
2   *Rise time* (*speed of response*): the time it takes the process to come up to the new set point
3   *Decay ratio*: the ratio of maximum amplitudes of successive oscillations
4   *Settling time*: the time it takes the amplitude of the oscillations to decay to some fraction (0.05) of the change in set point
5   *Integral of the squared error* (*ISE*) $= \int_0^\infty e_{(t)}^2 \, dt$

The steady-state error is another time-domain specification. It is not a dynamic specification, but it is an important performance criterion. In many loops (but not all) a steady-state error of zero is desired; i.e., the value of the controlled variable should eventually level out at the set point.

10-2.2   Load Performance

The job of most control loops in a process is one of regulation, i.e., holding the controlled variable at its set point in the face of load disturbances. Let us look at the effects of load changes with several types of controllers.

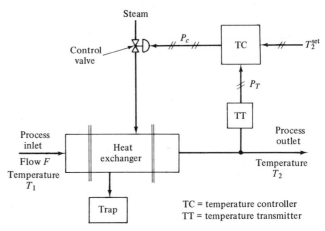

FIGURE 10-9
Heat-exchanger temperature control.

We will use a simple heat-exchanger process (Fig. 10-9) with process outlet temperature T_2 controlled by manipulation of steam flow to the shell side. The process flow rate F and inlet temperature T_1 are load disturbances. T_2^{set} is the temperature-controller set point.

On-off controller   The on-off controller is a proportional controller with a very high gain. As the error signal changes sign the control valve is either wide open or shut ("bang-bang" control). This type of control is only occasionally used in process plants because of the resulting cyclical response, surging flows, and wear on the control valve.

In our heat-exchanger example the controlled variable T_2 cycles as shown in Fig. 10-10a. A load disturbance in inlet temperature (a step decrease in T_1) occurs at time t_1. Both the period and the average value of the controlled variable T_2 are changed by the load.

This system is really unstable in the classic linear sense. The nonlinear bounds or constraints on the manipulative variable (control-valve position) keep it in a "limit cycle."

Proportional controller   The output of a proportional controller changes only if the error signal changes. Since a load change requires a new control-valve position, the controller must end up with a new error signal. This means that a proportional controller usually gives a steady-state error, "offset" or "droop."

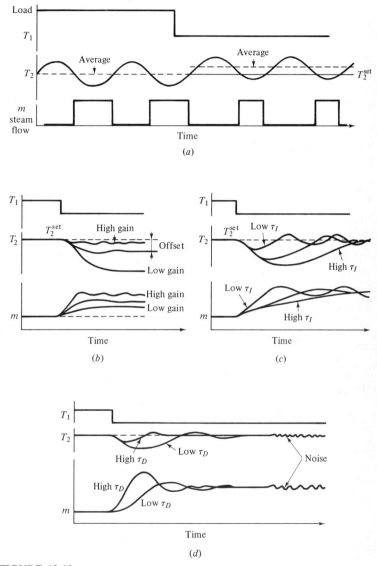

FIGURE 10-10
Controller load performance. (*a*) On-off controller; (*b*) proportional (P);
(*c*) proportional-integral (PI); (*d*) proportional-integral-derivative (PID).

As shown in Fig. 10-10*b* for our heat-exchanger example, a decrease in process inlet temperature T_1 requires more steam. Therefore the error must increase to open the steam valve more. The magnitude of the offset depends on the size of the load change and the controller gain. The bigger the gain, the smaller is the offset. If the gain is increased too much, however, the process becomes underdamped and eventually unstable.

We should point out that steady-state errors are not always undesirable. On many level control loops the absolute level is unimportant as long as the tank does not run dry or overflow. Thus a proportional controller is the best type to use in this service.

Proportional-integral (PI) controller   Probably 75 percent of the feedback controllers on a typical plant are PI. The integral action eliminates the steady-state error in T_2 (Fig. 10-10*c*). The smaller the integral time constant τ_I, the faster the error is reduced. But the system becomes more underdamped as τ_I is reduced. If it is made too small, the loop becomes unstable.

Proportional-integral-derivative (PID) controller   PID controllers are used in loops where the derivative action can help to compensate for a lag somewhere in the loop. A very common application is in temperature control loops where the adverse effect of the lag of the thermocouple and thermowell can be partially reduced by the derivative action. The controller senses the rate of movement away from the set point and starts moving the control valve earlier than with only P or PI action (Fig. 10-10*d*).

The principal problem with derivative action is that it amplifies any noise in the process signal, producing fluctuations in control-valve position. Therefore derivative action is used only on signals that are reasonably free of noise (e.g., temperature loops and gas pressure loops). It is never used on flow loops and very seldom on level loops.

Cascade control   Cascade control loops are frequently used in plants. A cascade loop has two feedback controllers with the output signal of the "master" controller going to the set point of the "slave" controller. The output of the slave controller goes to the control valve, as shown in Fig. 10-11.

The primary purpose of cascade control is to eliminate the effects of minor disturbances. For example, consider the distillation-column–reboiler system shown in Fig. 10-11*a*. Suppose the steam supply pressure drops. The pressure drop over the control valve will be less, so the steam flow rate will decrease. With the single-loop temperature controller, no correction will be made until the lower steam rate reduces the vapor boilup and the lower vapor rate begins to drop the temperature on tray 5. Thus the whole column is disturbed by a supply-steam pressure change.

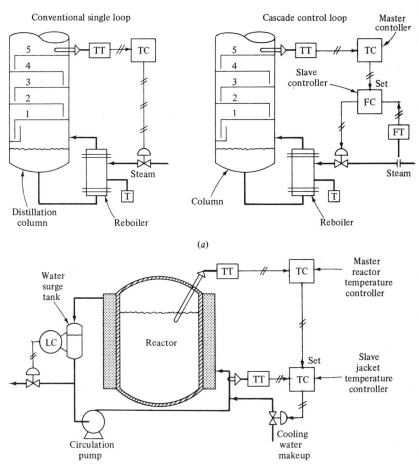

FIGURE 10-11
Conventional versus cascade control. (*a*) Distillation-column–reboiler temperature control; (*b*) CSTR temperature control.

With the cascade control system, the steam-flow controller will immediately see the drop in steam flow and will open the steam valve to return the steam flow to its set point. Thus the reboiler and the column are never affected by the supply steam-pressure disturbance.

Figure 10-11*b* shows another common system where cascade control is used. The reactor temperature control is isolated by the cascade system from disturbances in cooling-water temperature and supply pressure.

10-3   CONTROLLER TUNING

There are a variety of feedback controller tuning methods. Probably 90 percent of all loops are tuned experimentally by an instrument mechanic, and 75 percent of the time he can guess approximately what the settings will be by drawing on his experience with similar loops. We will discuss a few of the time-domain methods below. In subsequent chapters we will present other techniques for finding controller constants in the Laplace and frequency domains.

10-3.1   Rules of Thumb

The common types of control loops are level, flow, temperature, and pressure. The type of controller and the settings used for any one type of system are usually pretty much the same from one application to another. For example, most flow control loops use PI controllers with a wide proportional band and fast integral action.

Some generalizations or rules of thumb are given below. They are not to be taken as gospel. They merely indicate common practice.

Flow loops   PI controllers are used almost exclusively. A wide proportional-band setting (PB = 150) or low gain is used to reduce the effect of the noisy flow signal (orifice differential pressure is very noisy because of the flow turbulence). A low value of integral or reset time ($\tau_I = 0.1$ minute/repeat) is used to get fast, snappy set-point tracking.

Level loops   Most liquid levels represent material inventory used as surge capacity. In these cases it is unimportant where the level is, as long as it is between some maximum and minimum levels. Therefore proportional controllers are often used on level loops to give averaging level control.

For example, suppose the level is held by a control valve regulating the flow of liquid out of the vessel. The proportional band would be set up so that the valve is shut when the level has dropped to the minimum desired value and is wide open when the level has climbed to its maximum level. If the maximum and minimum levels are

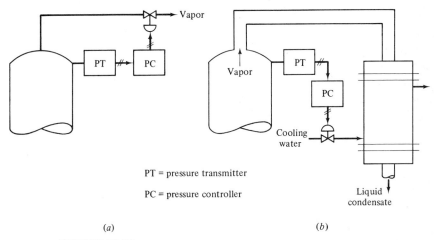

PT = pressure transmitter

PC = pressure controller

(a)   (b)

FIGURE 10-12
Pressure control. (a) Fast pressure loop; (b) slow pressure loop.

the full range of the level transmitter, a proportional band of 100 (gain of 1) would be used. The set point would be set at 50 percent level (9-psig signal) and the controller would be "zeroed" at 9 psig. By "zeroing" we mean adjusting the "zero" screw on the controller to change the bias signal to give the desired output signal when the error is zero. Thus the controller output would go from 3 to 15 psig as the level transmitter output went from 3 to 15 psig. If the valve is air-to-open, the controller will have the valve shut when the level is low and wide open when the level is high.

If we wanted to keep the level between 30 and 80 percent of the full range of the level transmitter, we would set the proportional band at 50 (gain 2) and zero the controller at 9 psig with the level and set point at 55 percent.

Pressure loops   Pressure loops vary from very tight, fast loops (almost like flow control) to slow averaging loops (almost like level control). An example of a fast pressure loop is the case of a valve throttling the flow of vapor from a vessel, as shown in Fig. 10-12a. The valve has a direct handle on pressure, and tight control can be achieved. An example of a slower pressure loop is shown in Fig. 10-12b. Pressure is held by throttling the water flow to a condenser. The water flow changes the ΔT driving force for condensation in the condenser. Therefore the heat transfer dynamics and the lag of the water flowing through the shell side of the condenser are introduced into the pressure control loop.

Temperature loops Temperature control loops are usually slow because of the sensor lags and the process heat transfer lags. PID controllers are often used. Proportional band settings are usually moderate (50 to 100), depending on transmitter spans, control-valve sizes, etc. The reset time is of the same order as the process time constant; i.e., the faster the process the smaller τ_I can be set. Derivative time is set something like one-fourth the process time constant, depending on the amount of noise.

10-3.2 On-line Trial and Error

To tune a controller on line, a good instrument mechanic follows a procedure something like the following:

1 Take all the integral and derivative action out of the controller, i.e., set τ_I at maximum minutes/repeat and τ_D at minimum minutes.
2 Set the PB at a high value, perhaps 200.
3 Put the controller on automatic.
4 Make a small set-point or load change and observe the response of the controlled variable. The gain is low so the response will be sluggish.
5 Reduce the PB by a factor of 2 (double the gain) and make another small set-point or load change.
6 Keep reducing the PB, repeating step 5, until the loop becomes very underdamped and oscillatory. The gain at which this occurs is called the *ultimate gain*.
7 Back off on the PB to twice this ultimate value.
8 Now start bringing in integral action by reducing τ_I by factors of 2, making small disturbances at each change to see the effect.
9 Find the value of τ_I which makes the loop very underdamped and set τ_I at twice this value.
10 Start bringing in derivative action by increasing τ_D until the noise in the process signal begins to be seen on the controller output. On some controllers only the process signal comes through the derivative unit, not the set-point signal. Therefore load changes should be made to see the effects of the derivative action.
11 Set τ_D at half this maximum value.
12 Reduce the PB again by steps of 10 percent until the desired specification on overshoot or decay ratio is satisfied.

It should be noted that there are some loops where these procedures do *not* work. Systems that exhibit "conditional stability" are the classic example. These processes are unstable at high values of feedback controller gain *and* at low values of feedback gain, but they are stable over some intermediate range of gains. We will discuss some of these in Chaps. 11 and 12.

10-3.3 Ziegler-Nichols Method

The Ziegler-Nichols (Z-N) controller settings[1] are pseudo-standards in the control field. They are easy to find and to use and give reasonable performance on most loops. A number of other methods[2] have been proposed but they have shown little or no improvement over Z-N. The Z-N settings are used as bench marks against which the performance of other control systems and settings are compared in many studies.

Despite their wide use, the Z-N settings should be considered only as reasonable first guesses of settings. There are many loops for which the Z-N settings are *not* very good, and a few tests on the plant can improve control significantly.

The Z-N method consists of first finding the ultimate gain K_u, the value of gain at which the loop is at the limit of stability with a proportional-only feedback controller. The period of the resulting oscillation P_u is observed (minutes per cycle). The Z-N settings are then calculated from K_u and P_u by the formulas given in Table 10-1 for the three types of controllers. Notice that a lower gain is used when integration is included in the controllers (PI) and that the addition of derivative permits a higher gain and faster reset.

The isothermal three-CSTR system of Examples 4-1 and 7-5 has, as we will show in the next chapter, an ultimate gain of 64 and an ultimate period of 3.63 min. The Ziegler-Nichols settings for this system are given in Table 10-2.

Table 10-1   ZIEGLER-NICHOLS SETTINGS

	P	PI	PID
K_c	$K_u/2$	$K_u/2.2$	$K_u/1.7$
τ_I (minutes)	...	$P_u/1.2$	$P_u/2$
τ_D (minutes)	...	...	$P_u/8$

Table 10-2   ZIEGLER-NICHOLS SETTINGS FOR 3-CSTR SYSTEM

	P	PI	PID
K_c	32	29.1	37.6
τ_I (minutes)	...	3.03	1.82
τ_D (minutes)	...	...	0.453

[1] J. G. Ziegler and N. B. Nichols, *Trans. ASME.*, vol. 64, p. 759, 1942.
[2] G. H. Cohen and G. A. Coon, *Trans. ASME*, vol. 75, p. 827, 1953.
  P. W. Murrill, "Automatic Control of Processes," International Textbook, 1967.

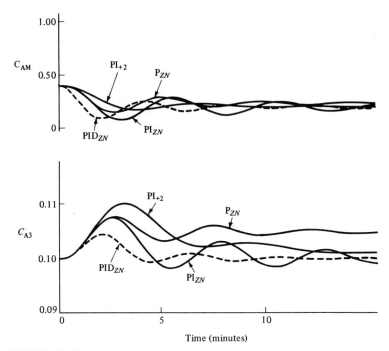

FIGURE 10-13
Three-CSTR example with Ziegler-Nichols settings.

The response of the system to a step load disturbance in C_{AD} is shown in Fig. 10-13 with P, PI, and PID controllers and the Z-N settings. The curve marked "PI$_{+2}$" will be explained in Chap. 12.

10-4 CONTROL-SYSTEMS DESIGN CONCEPTS

One of the basic objectives of this book is to show how to apply the knowledge of how processes vary with time in order to come up with a controllable process and a workable control system.

A consideration of dynamics should be factored into the design of a plant at an early stage, preferably during pilot-plant design and operation. It is often easy and inexpensive in the early stages of a project to design a piece of process equipment so that it is easy to control. If the plant is designed with little or no consideration of control, it may take an elaborate control system to try to make the most of a poor situation.

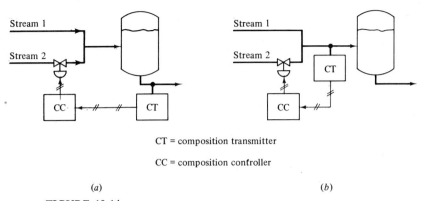

CT = composition transmitter

CC = composition controller

(a)   (b)

FIGURE 10-14
Blending systems. (a) With tank inside loop; (b) with tank outside loop.

For example, it is important to have large enough holdups in surge vessels, reflux drums, column bases, etc., to provide effective damping of disturbances (a much-used rule of thumb is 5 to 10 min). A sufficient excess of heat transfer area must be available in reboilers, condensers, cooling jackets, etc., to be able to handle the dynamic changes and upsets during operation. Measurements and sensors should be located so that they can be used for effective control.

Some general guidelines and recommendations are listed below, together with a few examples of their application. The books by Buckley[1] and Shinskey[2] are highly recommended for more detailed coverage of this important topic. There are also many articles in the applied literature.[3]

1 Use feedforward control to compensate for large, frequent disturbances. We will discuss the reasons for using feedforward control in Part 5.
2 Avoid lags and dead times in feedback loops. Feedback control is improved by keeping the lags and dead times in the loop as small as possible. This means sensors should be located close to where the manipulative variable enters the process.

EXAMPLE 10-1 Consider the two blending systems shown in Fig. 10-14. The flow rate or composition of stream 1 is the disturbance. The flow rate of stream 2 is the manipulative variable. In scheme *A* the sensor is located after the tank

[1] P. S. Buckley, "Techniques of Process Control," Wiley, 1964.
[2] F. G. Shinskey, "Process-control Systems," McGraw-Hill, 1967.
[3] J. O. Hougen and N. F. Brockmeier, *Instrum. Technol.*, August, 1969, p. 45; October, 1969, p. 81.

and therefore the dynamic lag of the tank is included in the feedback control loop. In scheme *B* the sensor is located at the inlet of the tank. The process lag is now very small since the tank is not inside the loop. Control performance of scheme *B*, in terms of speed of response, integral of the squared error, etc., would be better than the performance of scheme *A*. In addition, the tank now acts as a filter to average out any fluctuations in composition.   ////

EXAMPLE 10-2   The location of the best temperature-control tray in a distillation column is a popular subject in the distillation literature. Ideally the best location for controlling distillate composition x_D with reflux flow would be at the top of the column. This is desirable dynamically because it keeps the measurement lags as small as possible. It is also desirable from a steady-state standpoint because it keeps the distillate composition x_D constant at steady state in a constant-pressure binary system. Holding a temperature on a tray farther down in the column does not guarantee that x_D will be constant.

In applications, however, the temperature profile is sometimes quite flat (very little temperature change per tray) near the top if the overhead product is of reasonable purity. The sensitivity of the temperature sensor may become limiting. Also the effects of small pressure changes can swamp the effects of composition changes on temperature. Therefore an intermediate tray is selected down the column where the temperature profile begins to break. This control tray should be kept as close to the top of the column as possible. See Fig. 10-15a. Pressure compensation should be used if column pressure varies significantly (see Sec. 10-5.1).

If the bottoms composition is to be controlled by vapor boilup the control tray should be located as close to the base of the column as possible. Pressure compensation is even more important near the base because the pressure changes with vapor and liquid loading as well as with absolute pressure changes.   ////

3   Use "averaging level" control (proportional-only controllers) to maintain inventories in surge columns. (See "Level loops" in Sec. 10-3.1.) A consistent material-balance control strategy for the whole plant should be developed so that the individual pieces of equipment are tied together in a logical, controllable manner.
4   Eliminate minor disturbances by using cascade control systems where possible. (See "Cascade control" in Sec. 10-2.2.)
5   Avoid control-loop interaction where possible or use interaction compensation. Up to this point we have discussed tuning only single control loops.

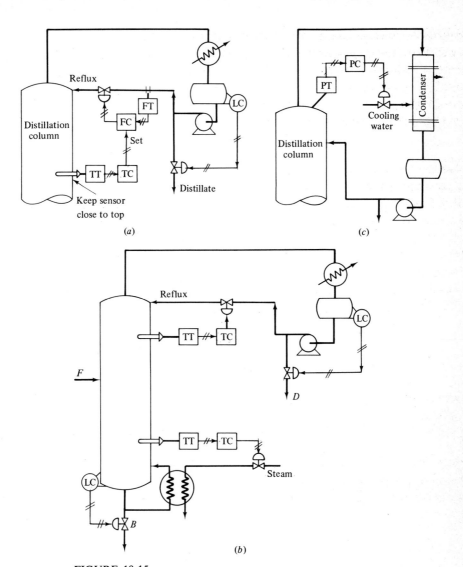

FIGURE 10-15
(*a*) Temperature-control-tray location; (*b*) interaction;
(*c*) pressure control.

Most chemical engineering systems are multivariable and inherently interacting; i.e., one control loop affects other control loops.

A classic example of an interacting system is a distillation column in which two temperatures are being controlled. As shown in Fig. 10-15b, the upper temperature changes reflux flow and the lower temperature changes vapor boilup. Interaction occurs because both manipulative variables affect both controlled variables.

A common way to avoid interaction is to tune one loop very tight and the other loop loose. The performance of the slow loop is thus sacrificed. Other techniques involve designing controllers so that they are stable despite the interaction or using interaction compensators or decouplers to remove the interaction. We will discuss the design of interacting systems and decouplers in Chaps. 11 and 12.

6 Be sure to check for dynamic problems at start-up and during low throughput operation. We alluded to the "turndown" or rangeability problems of control valves in Sec. 10-1.3. The performance of process equipment can often change drastically with throughput (changing steady-state gains and time constants). Stable low-flow operation may require controller retuning, installation of dual control valves (one big and one little), etc.

Rangeability problems can also be caused by seasonal variations in cooling-water temperature. Consider the distillation-column pressure control system shown in Fig. 10-15c. During the summer, cooling-water temperatures may be as high as 90°F and require a large water flow rate and a big control valve. During the winter, the cooling-water temperatures may drop to 50°F, requiring much less water. The big control valve may be almost on its seat, and poor pressure control may result. The water outlet temperature may get quite high under these low-flow conditions, presenting corrosion problems. In fact, if the process side temperature is above 212°F the water can boil.

Ambient effects are even worse with air-fin coolers.

7 Avoid saturation of a manipulative variable. A good example of saturation is the level control of a reflux drum in a high-reflux-ratio distillation column. Suppose the reflux ratio R/D is 20, as shown in Fig. 10-16. Scheme A uses distillate flow rate D to control the drum level. If vapor boilup dropped only 5 percent, the distillate flow would go to zero. Any bigger drop in vapor boilup would cause the drum to run dry. Scheme B is preferable for this high-reflux-ratio case.

8 Avoid "nesting" control loops. Control loops are nested if the operation of the external loop depends on the operation of the internal loop. Figure 10-17 illustrates a nested system. A vapor sidestream is drawn off a column to

Scheme A

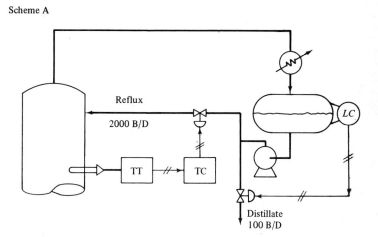

Scheme B

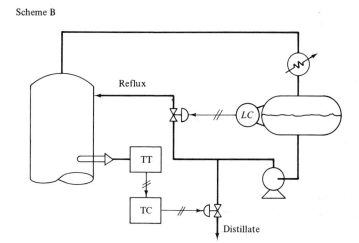

FIGURE 10-16
High-reflux-ratio column.

hold the column base level, and a temperature in the column is held by heat input to the reboiler. The base liquid level "sees" only the liquid entering and the vapor boiled off, and therefore it is really not affected by the amount of vapor sidestream withdrawn. Thus the base level cannot be held by the vapor sidestream unless the temperature control loop is in operation. Then the change in net vapor sent up the column will affect the temperature, and vapor boilup will be changed. If the temperature loop is on "manual,"

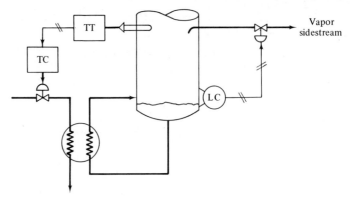

FIGURE 10-17
Nested control loops.

the level loop cannot work. Notice that if the sidestream were being removed as a liquid, the control system would not be nested.

Sometimes, of course, nested loops cannot be avoided. Notice that the recommended scheme *B* in Fig. 10-16 is just such a nested system.

10-5 NONCONVENTIONAL CONTROL

Most feedback control loops use standard, linear P, PI, and PID controllers with one measurement and one control valve. A number of nonconventional control schemes have been proposed over the years. Interest in this area has been accelerated recently by the availability of process-control computers in which all kinds of complex control equations can be easily tested (according to the salesmen[1]).

We will discuss a few of these below and try to point out their principal features and advantages. Hardware implementation will be illustrated with pneumatic devices, but the basic strategies can be used in electronic and digital computer systems.

10-5.1 Computed Variables

One of the most logical and earliest extensions of conventional control was the idea of controlling the variable that was of real interest by computing its value from other measurements.

---

[1] Loflin's first law of instrumentation is "Never believe everything the instrument salesman tells you." His second law is "Never try to solve a problem you can't define." The latter is a modern version of the old Moslem saying "If you don't know where you're going, any road will get you there!"

For example, suppose we want to control the mass flow rate of a gas. Controlling the pressure drop over the orifice plate gives us only an approximate mass flow rate because gas density varies with temperature and pressure in the line. By measuring temperature, pressure, and orifice-plate pressure drop and feeding these signals into a mass-flow-rate computer, the mass flow rate can be controlled as shown in Fig. 10-18a.

Another example is sketched in Fig. 10-18b. A hot oil stream is used to reboil a distillation column. Controlling the flow rate of the hot oil does not guarantee a fixed heat input because the inlet oil temperature can vary. The heat input Q can be computed from the flow rate and the inlet and outlet temperatures, and this Q can then be controlled.

As a final example, consider the problem mentioned in Sec. 10-4 of both pressure and composition affecting the temperature in a distillation column. We really want to measure and control composition. In a binary system, composition depends only on pressure and temperature:

$$x = f_{(T, P)}$$

Thus changes in composition depend on changes in temperature and pressure.

$$\Delta x = \left(\frac{\partial x}{\partial P}\right)_T \Delta P + \left(\frac{\partial x}{\partial T}\right)_P \Delta T \qquad (10\text{-}22)$$

where x = mole fraction of more volatile component in the liquid.

The partial derivatives are usually assumed to be constants that are evaluated at the steady-state operating level from the vapor-liquid equilibrium data. Thus pressure and temperature on a tray can be measured, as shown in Fig. 10-18c, and a composition signal or a pressure-compensated temperature signal generated and controlled.

$$\Delta T^{PC} = K_1 \Delta P - K_2 \Delta T \qquad (10\text{-}23)$$

where T^{PC} = pressure-compensated temperature signal
K_1 = constant = $(\partial x/\partial P)_T$
K_2 = constant = $-(\partial x/\partial T)_P$

10-5.2   Nonlinear Controllers

Since many of our chemical engineering processes are nonlinear, it would seem intuitively to be advantageous to use nonlinear controllers in some systems. For example, we could use a variable gain controller in which the gain K_c varies with the magnitude of the error.

$$K_c = K_c{}^0(1 + b|e|) \qquad (10\text{-}24)$$

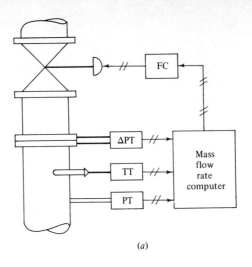

(a)

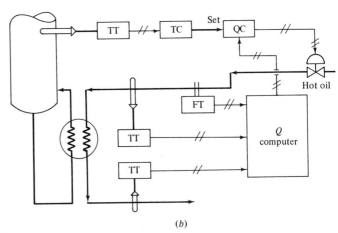

(b)

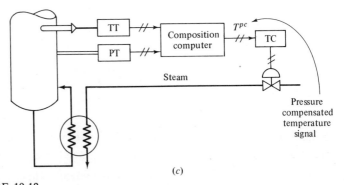

(c)

FIGURE 10-18
Computed-variable control. (a) Mass flow rate; (b) heat input; (c) composition
(pressure-compensated temperature).

where $K_c{}^0$ = controller gain with zero error
  $|e|$ = absolute magnitude of error
    b = adjustable coefficient

This would permit us to use a low value of gain $K_c{}^0$ so that the system is stable near the set point over a broad range of operating levels with changing process gains. When the process is disturbed away from the set point, the gain will be large. The system may even be closed-loop unstable at this point. But the instability is in the direction of driving the loop rapidly back toward the stable set-point region.

Another advantage of this kind of nonlinear controller is that the low gain at the set point reduces the effects of noise.

The parameter b can be different for positive or negative errors if the nonlinearity of the process is different for increasing or decreasing changes. Both b and $K_c{}^0$ can also be made functions of the set point itself or of some other variable, such as throughput rate, in an adaptive manner.

There are any number of ways to build nonlinearity into a controller.[1] Very few have actually been evaluated. The basic notion of any of these techniques is to modify the controller action and settings in some way to compensate for nonlinearity in the process.

10-5.3   Anti-reset Windup

When a conventional PI or PID controller sees an error signal for a long period of time, it integrates the error until it saturates. This is called *reset windup*. Physically, the air pressure in the bellows or tank that contributes the integral action in a pneumatic controller will increase until it equals the air supply pressure (assuming the controller action drives its output pressure up).

A sustained error signal can occur for a number of reasons but one common situation is in a discontinuous or batch process. When the unit is down for recharging between batches the process variable is not at the set point. If the controller is left on "automatic" it will "wind up." When the process is started up again, a large overshoot usually occurs because the integral action does not start to back off on the pressure in the reset tank until the error has changed signs, i.e., not until the controlled process-variable signal has crossed the set point.

The control lercan be switched into "manual" to prevent reset windup but this requires operator attention. Special "anti-reset windup" or "batch" controllers are sold that automatically stop the integration when the controller reaches the limit of its range.

[1] W. B. Field, *ISA J.*, vol. 6, January, 1959, p. 42.
  F. G. Shinskey, *op. cit.*
  L. M. Zoss, A. G. Witte, and J. E. Marsch, *Instrum. Technol.*, February, 1969, p. 54.

Reset windup can also occur when a control valve is driven by more than one controller. We will discuss some of these below.

10-5.4   Selective Control Loops

There are situations where the control loop should be aware of more than just one controlled variable. This is particularly true in highly automated plants where the operator cannot be expected to make logical decisions about what to do under abnormal conditions.

For example, suppose the base level of a distillation column is normally held by bottoms product withdrawal. A temperature in the stripping section is held by steam to the reboiler. See Fig. 10-19a. At start-up or shutdown or during upsets, the situation can arise where the base level continues to drop even with bottoms flow at zero (vapor boilup is greater than the liquid rate from tray 1). If no corrective action is taken, the reboiler may boil dry.

If an operator saw this problem developing, he would switch the temperature loop into "manual" and cut back on the steam flow. The control system in Fig. 10.19a will perform this "override" control[1] automatically. The low selector (LS) sends to the steam valve the lower of two signals. If the steam valve is air-to-open, the valve will be pinched back by either high temperature (through the reverse-acting controller) or by low base level.

The proportional level controller is set up so that the bottoms valve is closed when the level transmitter output is 5 psig. As the level transmitter output goes from 5 to 3 psig, the output of the fixed-gain relay (with a gain of 6) goes from 15 to 3 psig. Therefore the base level will override the temperature loop and pinch back on the steam valve.

When the temperature control is "overridden," it will see an error signal and will wind up unless prevented. Most pneumatic feedback controllers achieve integration action by feeding their output pressure back through a resistor into the reset tank (Fig. 10-19b). The output pressure is

$$P_o = P_s - P_p + P_I \qquad (10\text{-}25)$$

where P_o = controller output pressure
P_s = set-point pressure signal
P_p = process-variable pressure signal
P_I = pressure in reset tank

[1] P. S. Buckley, *Instrum. Technol.*, August, 1968, p. 51.

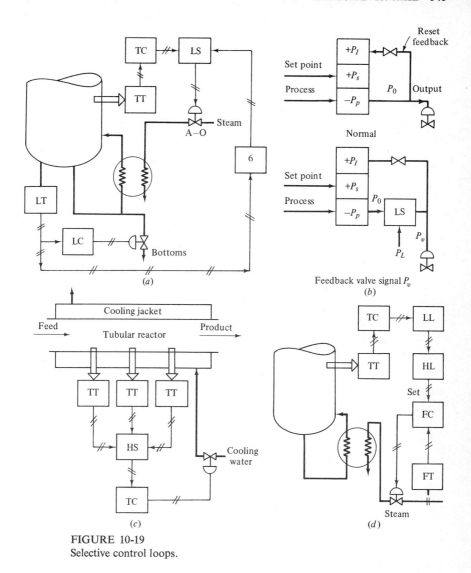

FIGURE 10-19
Selective control loops.

Now the resistance and volume in the reset tank give a first-order relationship between P_o and P_I:

$$\frac{P_{I(s)}}{P_{o(s)}} = \frac{1}{\tau_I s + 1} \qquad (10\text{-}26)$$

Combining Eqs. (10-25) and (10-26) gives

$$\frac{P_{o(s)}}{P_{s(s)} - P_{p(s)}} = \frac{\tau_I s + 1}{\tau_I s} \qquad (10\text{-}27)$$

Reset windup can be prevented by using the output of the low selector as the feedback signal. This gives the temperature controller a reset feedback signal that is not its own output when it is overridden and it will not wind up.

$$P_{o(s)} = P_{s(s)} - P_{p(s)} + \frac{1}{\tau_I s + 1} P_L \qquad (10\text{-}28)$$

where P_L is the pressure signal from the level loop.

Another example of a selective control loop is shown in Fig. 10-19c. The highest temperature along the length of a tubular reactor is selected and controlled.

High and low limiting of variables is a common form of selective control. In the example shown in Fig. 10-19d, heat input is limited at both high and low levels. The high level might correspond to the maximum vapor velocity before flooding will occur. The minimum might correspond to the lowest vapor rate that will keep the trays from weeping.

10-5.5 Ratio Control

Ratio control systems are used very frequently. The flow rate of the "wild" or uncontrolled stream is measured and the flow of the manipulated stream is changed to keep the two streams at a constant ratio with each other. Common examples are (1) holding a constant reflux ratio on a distillation column, (2) keeping stoichiometric amounts of two reactants being fed into a reactor, (3) purging off a fixed percentage of the feed stream to a unit, etc.

Ratio control is achieved by two basic schemes, shown in Fig. 10-20. In scheme A the two flow rates are measured and their ratio is computed (by the divider). This computed ratio signal is fed into a conventional PI controller as the process signal. The set point of the controller is the desired ratio. The output of the controller goes to a valve on the manipulative stream that changes its flow rate in the correct direction to hold the ratio of the two flows constant. This scheme is used when it is necessary to know at all times what the actual ratio is. The computed ratio signal can be used for alarm, override, or interlock[1] purposes.

In scheme B the wild flow is measured and the flow signal is multiplied by a constant, which is the desired ratio. The output of the multiplier is the set point of a remote-set flow controller on the manipulative variable.

If orifice plates are used as flow sensors, the signal from the differential-pressure transmitter is really the square of the flow rate. Some instrument engineers prefer to put in square-root extractors and convert everything to linear flow signals. If both flow signals are squared or linear, the ratio schemes in Fig. 10-20 both work.

---

[1] Interlocks are pressure, mechanical, or electrical switches that automatically open or close valves or switches to shut down equipment if they are actuated by variables exceeding safe operating ranges.

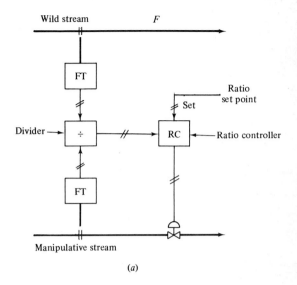

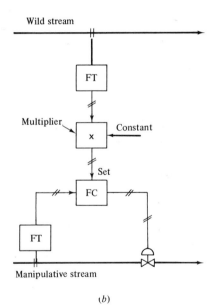

FIGURE 10-20
Ratio control. (*a*) Ratio compute;
(*b*) flow set.

PROBLEMS

10-1 (*a*) Calculate the gain of an orifice plate and differential-pressure transmitter for flow rates from 10 percent to 90 percent of full scale.

(*b*) Calculate the gain of linear, equal-percentage, and square-root valves over the same range, assuming constant pressure drop over the valve.

(*c*) Calculate the total loop gain of the valve and sensor-transmitter system over this range.

10-2 The temperature of a CSTR is controlled by a pneumatic feedback control system containing (1) a 100 to 200°F temperature transmitter, (2) a PI controller with integral time set at 3 minutes/repeat and proportional band at 25, and (3) a control valve with linear trim, air-to-close action, and a $C_V = 4$ through which cooling water flows. The pressure drop across the valve is a constant 25 psi. If the steady-state controller output pressure is 9 psig, how much cooling water is going through the valve? If a sudden disturbance increases reactor temperature by 5°F, what will be the immediate effect on the controller output pressure and the water flow rate?

10-3 Simulate the three-CSTR system on an analog computer with an on-off feedback controller. Assume the manipulative variable C_{AM} is limited to ± 1 mole of A/ft³ around the steady-state value. Find the period of oscillation and the average value of C_{A3} for values of the load variable C_{AD} of 0.6 and 1.

10-4 The heat exchanger shown in Fig. 10-9 was found to have the following transfer functions[1]:

Control valve:

$$\frac{x}{P_c} = \frac{0.047 \text{ in./psi}}{0.083s + 1}$$

$$\frac{F_s}{x} = 112 \text{ lb/min-in.}$$

Process:

$$\frac{T_2}{F_s} = \frac{2°\text{F/lb-min}}{(0.017s + 1)(0.432s + 1)}$$

Temperature transmitter:

$$\frac{P_T}{T_2} = \frac{0.12 \text{ psi/°F}}{0.024s + 1}$$

(*a*) Simulate the system on either an analog or a digital computer and show that the ultimate gain K_u is 12 and the ultimate period P_u is 0.36 min.

(*b*) Simulate P, PI, and PID controllers with Ziegler-Nichols settings and evaluate their performance for set-point changes of 1°F in T_2^{set}.

---

[1] Based on a problem given by H. S. Wilson and L. M. Zoss, *ISA J.*, vol. 9, no. 12, p. 59, 1962.

10-5   (*a*)   Simulate on a digital computer the process with a transfer function

$$G_{(s)} = \frac{e^{-2s}}{s+1}$$

(*b*)   Find the ultimate gain and period.
(*c*)   Test the Z-N settings for P, PI, and PID controllers.

10-6   Repeat Prob. 10-5 for a process with a transfer function

$$G_{(s)} = \frac{4}{(10s+1)(s^2+0.4s+1)}$$

10-7   Process designers sometimes like to use dephlegmators or partial condensers mounted directly in the top of the distillation column when the overhead product is taken off as a vapor. They are particularly popular for a corrosive or hard-to-handle process since they eliminate a separate condenser shell, a reflux drum, and reflux pump and simplify the instrumentation. Comment on the relative controllability of the two process systems sketched below.

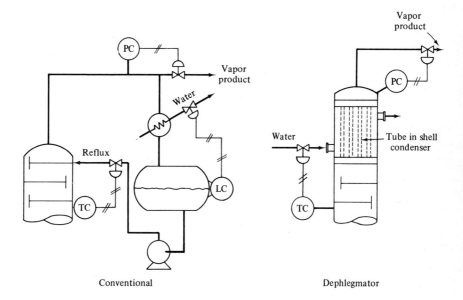

Conventional   Dephlegmator

10-8   Two ways to control the outlet temperature of a heat-exchanger cooler are sketched below. Comment on the relative merits of these two systems from the standpoints of both control and heat-exchanger design.

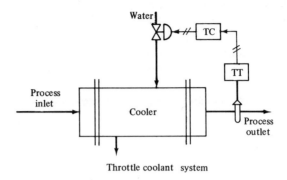

Throttle coolant system

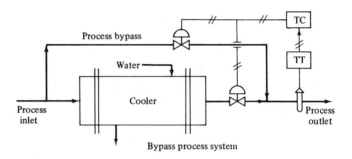

Bypass process system

10-9 Specify the following items for the bypass cooler system of Prob. 10-8:
   (a) The action of the valves (direct or reverse; kind of trim; range).
   (b) The action and type of controller.

10-10 Assume that the bypass cooling system of Prob. 10-8 is designed so that the total process flow of 50,000 lb$_m$/hr (heat capacity 0.5 Btu/lb$_m$-°F) is split under normal conditions, 25 percent going around the bypass and 75 percent going through the cooler. Process inlet and outlet temperatures under these conditions are 250 and 130°F. Inlet and outlet water temperatures are 80 and 120°F. Process side pressure drop through the exchanger is 10 psi. The control valves are designed to be half open at design rates with a 5-psi drop over the valve in series with the cooler. The upstream and downstream pressures are constant. Liquid density is constant at 62.3 lb$_m$/ft^3.
   (a) To what will the process outlet temperature rise if the process flow rate through the cooler is made as high as possible?
   (b) What will the valve positions be if the total process flow is reduced to 25 percent of design and the process outlet temperature is held at 130°F?

10-11 Why does a house feel colder on a cold winter day than on a mild day with the same thermostat setting?

10-12 The process sketched below has a transfer function

$$G_{(s)} = \frac{0.01e^{-10s}(°F/lb\text{-}hr)}{(15)^2 s^2 + 2(15)(0.4)s + 1}$$

The temperature transmitter gain is 12 psi/100°F. The valve gain is 50,000 lb_m/hr-psi.
(*a*) Simulate this process on a digital computer.
(*b*) Find the Z-N settings for a PI controller and test their effectiveness.
(*c*) Test a pure integral controller on this system and compare with the Z-N PI of part (*b*).

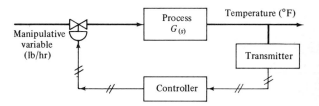

10-13 Compare quantitatively by digital simulation the dynamic performance of the three coolers sketched below with countercurrent flow, cocurrent flow, and circulating water systems. Assume the tube and shell sides can be represented by four perfectly mixed lumps. Process design conditions are:
  Flow rate 50,000 lb_m/hr
  Inlet temperature 250°F
  Outlet temperature 130°F
  Heat capacity 0.5 Btu/lb_m-°F
Cooling-water design conditions are:
Countercurrent
  Inlet temperature 80°F
  Outlet temperature 130°F
Cocurrent
  Inlet temperature 80°F
  Outlet temperature 125°F
Circulating system
  Inlet to cooler 120°F
  Outlet of cooler 125°F
  Makeup to system 80°F
Neglect the tube and shell metal. Tune PI controllers for each system. Find the outlet temperature deviations for a 25 percent step increase in process flow rate.

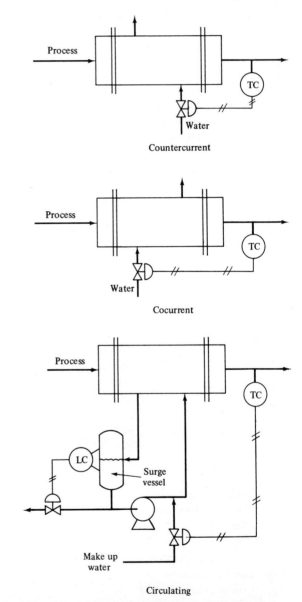

Countercurrent

Cocurrent

Circulating

10-14   Discuss qualitatively the effectiveness of two alternative pressure control loops on a distillation column. Cooling water to the condenser is throttled in both schemes, but the first senses pressure at the top of the column whereas the second system senses pressure at the base of the column.

10-15 The suction pressure of an air compressor is controlled by manipulating an air stream from an off-site process. An override system is to be used in conjunction with the basic loop to prevent overpressuring or underpressuring the compressor suction during upsets. The system is pneumatic. Valve actions are indicated on the sketch below.

The pressure transmitter span is 0 to 20 psig. The pressure controller set point is 10 psig. If the pressure gets above 15 psig the vent valve is to start opening and is to be wide open at 20 psig. If the pressure drops below 5 psig the recycle valve is to start opening and is to be wide open at 0 psig.

Specify the range and action of the override control elements required to achieve this control strategy.

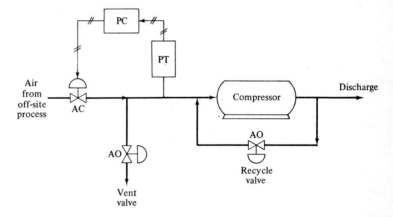

10-16 A liquid (sp. gr. = 1) is to be pumped through a heat exchanger and a control valve at a design rate of 200 gpm. The exchanger pressure drop is 30 psi at design throughput.

Make plots of flow rate versus valve stem position X for linear and equal-percentage ($\alpha = 50$) control valves. Both valves are set at $f_{(x)} = 0.5$ at design rate. The total pressure drop over the entire system is constant. The pressure drop over the control valve at design rate is:

(*a*)   5 psi
(*b*)   10 psi
(*c*)   30 psi
(*d*)   60 psi
(*e*)   120 psi

11

LAPLACE-DOMAIN SYNTHESIS

In Chap. 7 we made some statements to the effect that the Laplace domain offers significant computational and notational advantages. In this chapter we will prove these claims by demonstrating the ease with which feedback controllers can be designed in the Laplace domain. Laplace-domain techniques involve finding the transfer function for the process, specifying the desired performance of the closed-loop system of process plus controller, and finding the feedback controller transfer function that is required to do the job.

11-1 STABILITY

The most important dynamic aspect of any system is its stability. We learned in Chap. 6 that stability was dictated by the location of the roots of the characteristic equation of the system. In Chap. 7 we learned that the roots of the denominator of the system transfer function, its poles, are exactly same as the roots of the characteristic equation. Thus, for the system to be stable, the roots of the denominator of the system transfer function must lie in the left-half of the s plane (LHP).

This stability requirement applies to any system, open-loop or closed-loop. The open-loop stability of a given process depends upon the location of the poles of its *open-loop* transfer function. The closed-loop stability of the same process and a feedback controller depends upon the location of the poles of its *closed-loop* transfer function. These closed-loop poles will naturally be different from the open-loop poles.

However, there is a definite relationship between the open-loop and the closed-loop transfer functions. Let us develop this very important and useful relationship.

11-1.1 Relationship between Open-loop and Closed-loop Transfer Functions

Consider the general open-loop system sketched in Fig. 11-1a. The load input variable $L_{(s)}$ enters through the system transfer function $G_{L(s)}$. The manipulative input variable $M_{(s)}$ enters through the system transfer function $G_{M(s)}$. The system output $X_{(s)}$ is the sum of the effects of the manipulative variable and the load variable. Remember we are working with linear systems in the Laplace domain.

The open-loop stability of this system depends upon the roots of the denominators of the two open-loop transfer functions $G_{L(s)}$ and $G_{M(s)}$. The denominators are often identical (Example 7-6).

$$G_{M(s)} = \frac{Z_{M(s)}}{P_{M(s)}} \qquad G_{L(s)} = \frac{Z_{L(s)}}{P_{L(s)}} \qquad (11\text{-}1)$$

Thus the open-loop stability of the system depends on the roots of the polynomials $P_{M(s)}$ and $P_{L(s)}$. If all the roots lie in the LHP the system is open-loop stable. If any of the roots lies in the RHP the system is open-loop unstable.

Now let us put a feedback controller into the system, as shown in Fig. 11-1b. The output of the process $X_{(s)}$ is sensed and compared with a set point $X^{\text{set}}_{(s)}$. The error $E_{(s)} = X^{\text{set}}_{(s)} - X_{(s)}$ is fed into a feedback controller with a transfer function $B_{(s)}$. The output of the feedback controller is the manipulative variable $M_{(s)}$. All variables are in the Laplace domain.

In the system shown in Fig. 11-1b, all the gains and dynamics of the sensors, transmitters, and control valves are lumped into the $G_{M(s)}$ transfer function. A more detailed breakdown of a typical loop is shown in Fig. 11-1c. We will use the simpler version in all our subsequent work, but keep in mind the need to include sensor, transmitter, and control-valve transfer functions. These will normally be just gain elements since their dynamics are usually much faster than the process.

Looking at the block diagram in Fig. 11-1b, we can see that the output $X_{(s)}$ in the closed-loop system is given by

$$X_{(s)} = G_{L(s)} L_{(s)} + G_{M(s)} M_{(s)} \qquad (11\text{-}2)$$

But $M_{(s)}$ is related to $X_{(s)}$:

$$M_{(s)} = B_{(s)}(X^{\text{set}}_{(s)} - X_{(s)}) \qquad (11\text{-}3)$$

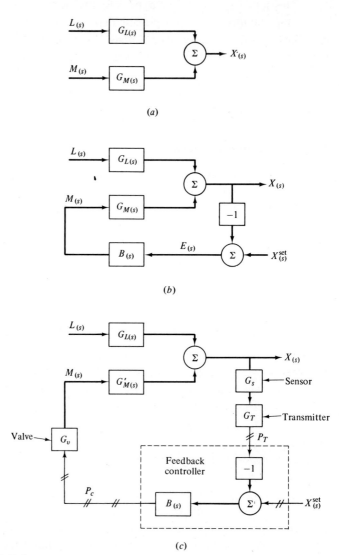

FIGURE 11-1
Open-loop and closed-loop transfer functions. (a) Open loop; (b) closed loop;
(c) detailed closed loop.

Combining Eqs. (11-2) and (11-3) gives

$$X_{(s)} = G_{L(s)} L_{(s)} + G_{M(s)} B_{(s)} (X_{(s)}^{\text{set}} - X_{(s)})$$

$$X_{(s)} + G_{M(s)} B_{(s)} X_{(s)} = G_{L(s)} L_{(s)} + G_{M(s)} B_{(s)} X_{(s)}^{\text{set}}$$

$$X_{(s)} = \frac{G_{L(s)}}{1 + B_{(s)} G_{M(s)}} L_{(s)} + \frac{B_{(s)} G_{M(s)}}{1 + B_{(s)} G_{M(s)}} X_{(s)}^{\text{set}} \qquad (11\text{-}4)$$

Thus the closed-loop transfer function between the output $X_{(s)}$ and the load $L_{(s)}$ is

$$\frac{X_{(s)}}{L_{(s)}} = \frac{G_{L(s)}}{1 + B_{(s)} G_{M(s)}} \qquad (11\text{-}5)$$

And the closed-loop transfer function between the output $X_{(s)}$ and the set point $X_{(s)}^{\text{set}}$ is

$$\frac{X_{(s)}}{X_{(s)}^{\text{set}}} = \frac{B_{(s)} G_{M(s)}}{1 + B_{(s)} G_{M(s)}} \qquad (11\text{-}6)$$

The denominators of these two closed-loop transfer functions are identical. The roots of the polynomial $1 + B_{(s)} G_{M(s)}$ will dictate the stability of the closed-loop system.

Thus the closed-loop characteristic equation of the system is

$$1 + B_{(s)} G_{M(s)} = 0 \qquad (11\text{-}7)$$

If any of the roots of $1 + B_{(s)} G_{M(s)}$ lies in the right-half of the s plane the system is *closed-loop* unstable.

Remember that the open-loop characteristic equation is

$$P_{M(s)} = 0 \qquad \text{or} \qquad P_{L(s)} = 0 \qquad (11\text{-}8)$$

If any of the roots of $P_{M(s)}$ or $P_{L(s)}$ lies in the right-half of the s plane the system is *open-loop* unstable.

Thus the criteria for open-loop and closed-loop stability are different. Most systems are open-loop stable but can be either closed-loop stable or unstable, depending on the values of the controller parameters. We will show that any physical process can be made closed-loop unstable by making the gain high enough.

We will also show that systems that are open-loop unstable can usually be made closed-loop stable by the correct choice of the type of controller and its settings.

11-1.2 Routh Stability Criterion

The Routh stability criterion is a technique for finding out if there are any roots of a characteristic equation in the right-half of the s plane. It can be applied to either open-loop or closed-loop systems by merely using the appropriate characteristic equation. The method is given below without proof.[1]

[1] E. J. Routh, "Dynamics of a System of Rigid Bodies," 3d ed., Macmillan, London, 1877.

Assume the characteristic equation of interest is an Nth-order polynomial:

$$a_N s^N + a_{N-1} s^{N-1} + \cdots + a_1 s + a_0 = 0 \qquad (11\text{-}9)$$

The Routh array is formed as given below:

$$\begin{bmatrix} a_N & a_{N-2} & a_{N-4} & \cdots & a_0 \\ a_{N-1} & a_{N-3} & a_{N-5} & & \\ A_1 & A_2 & A_3 & & \\ B_1 & B_2 & B_3 & & \\ C_1 & C_2 & & & \\ \hdotsfor{5} \end{bmatrix} \qquad (11\text{-}10)$$

where the A, B, ... are calculated from the equations

$$A_1 = \frac{a_{N-1} a_{N-2} - a_N a_{N-3}}{a_{N-1}}$$

$$A_2 = \frac{a_{N-1} a_{N-4} - a_N a_{N-5}}{a_{N-1}}$$

$$\cdots \cdots \cdots \cdots \cdots \cdots$$

$$B_1 = \frac{A_1 a_{N-3} - a_{N-1} A_2}{A_1}$$

$$\cdots \cdots \cdots \cdots \cdots \cdots \qquad (11\text{-}11)$$

Then the first column of the array of Eq. (11-10) is examined. The number of sign changes of this first column is equal to the number of roots of the characteristic equation that are in the RHP.

$$\textit{First column} = \begin{bmatrix} a_N \\ a_{N-1} \\ A_1 \\ B_1 \\ C_1 \\ \vdots \end{bmatrix} \qquad (11\text{-}12)$$

Thus for the system to be stable there must be *no* sign changes in the first column of the Routh array.

Let us illustrate the application of the Routh stability criterion in some specific examples.

EXAMPLE 11-1   Assume the characteristic equation of a system is

$$s^5 + 2s^4 + s^3 + 3s^2 + 4s + 5 = 0 \qquad (11\text{-}13)$$

The Routh array is

$$
\begin{bmatrix}
1 & 1 & 4 \\
2 & 3 & 5 \\
\left(\dfrac{2-3}{2} = -\dfrac{1}{2}\right) & \left(\dfrac{8-5}{2} = \dfrac{3}{2}\right) & 0 \\
\left(\dfrac{-\frac{3}{2}-3}{-\frac{1}{2}} = 9\right) & \left(\dfrac{-\frac{5}{2}-0}{-\frac{1}{2}} = 5\right) & \\
\left(\dfrac{\frac{27}{2}+\frac{5}{2}}{9} = \dfrac{32}{18}\right) & 0 & \\
5 & & \\
0 & &
\end{bmatrix}
\qquad (11\text{-}14)
$$

Examining the first column, we see that there are two sign changes. There must be two roots in the RHP. The system is unstable. ////

EXAMPLE 11-2 Consider our old friend the three-CSTR process with a process transfer function

$$
G_{M(s)} = \frac{\frac{1}{8}}{(s+1)^3} = \left(\frac{C_{A3}}{C_{A0}}\right)_{(s)} \qquad (11\text{-}15)
$$

We want to look at the stability of the closed-loop system with a proportional controller.

$$
B_{(s)} = K_c
$$

First, however, let us check the open-loop stability of this system. The open-loop characteristic equation is

$$
s^3 + 3s^2 + 3s + 1 = 0 \qquad (11\text{-}16)
$$

The Routh array becomes

$$
\begin{bmatrix}
1 & 3 \\
3 & 1 \\
\left(\dfrac{9-1}{3} = \dfrac{8}{3}\right) & 0 \\
1 &
\end{bmatrix}
\qquad (11\text{-}17)
$$

There are no sign changes in the first column, so the system is open-loop stable. This finding should be no great shock since, from our simulations, we know the open-loop system is stable.

Now let us check for closed-loop stability. The system is sketched in Fig. 11-2a. The closed-loop characteristic equation is

$$1 + B_{(s)} G_{M(s)} = 0$$

$$1 + K_c \frac{\frac{1}{8}}{(s+1)^3} = 0$$

$$s^3 + 3s^2 + 3s + \left(1 + \frac{K_c}{8}\right) = 0 \qquad (11\text{-}18)$$

The Routh array is

$$\begin{bmatrix} 1 & 3 \\[2mm] 3 & 1 + \dfrac{K_c}{8} \\[4mm] \dfrac{9 - (1 + K_c/8)}{3} & 0 \\[4mm] 1 + \dfrac{K_c}{8} & \end{bmatrix} \qquad (11\text{-}19)$$

Looking at the first column we can see that there will be a sign change if the third term is negative.

$$\frac{8 - K_c/8}{3} < 0 \quad \Rightarrow \quad -8 + \frac{K_c}{8} > 0 \quad \Rightarrow \quad K_c > 64 \qquad (11\text{-}20)$$

Therefore the system is closed-loop stable for feedback controller gains less than 64 but closed-loop unstable for gains greater than 64. This maximum stable value of K_c is what we defined in Chap. 10 as the ultimate gain K_u. ////

The Routh stability criterion is quite useful, but it has definite limitations. It cannot handle systems with dead time. It tells if the system is stable or unstable but it gives no information about how stable or unstable the system is. That is, if the test

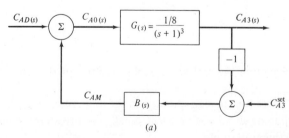

(a)

FIGURE 11-2a
Three-CSTR system.

tells us that the system is stable, we do not know how close to instability it is. Another limitation of the Routh method is the need to express the characteristic equation explicitly as a polynomial in s. This can become involved and fairly difficult in higher-order systems.

11-1.3   Direct Substitution for Stability Limit

The direct-substitution method is a simple but useful method for finding the values of parameters in the characteristic equation that put the system just at the limit of stability.

We know the system is stable if all the roots of the characteristic equation are in the LHP and unstable if any is in the RHP. Therefore the imaginary axis represents the limit of stability. On the imaginary axis s is equal to some pure imaginary number.

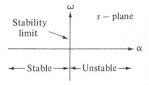

The technique consists of substituting $i\omega$ for s in the characteristic equation and solving for the values of ω and other parameters (e.g., controller gain) that satisfy the resulting equations. The method is best understood by looking at the example below.

EXAMPLE 11-3   Consider again the three-CSTR system. We have already developed its closed-loop characteristic equation with a proportional controller [Eq. (11-18)].

$$s^3 + 3s^2 + 3s + 1 + \frac{K_c}{8} = 0$$

Substituting $s = i\omega$ gives

$$-i\omega^3 - 3\omega^2 + 3i\omega + 1 + \frac{K_c}{8} = 0$$

$$\left(1 + \frac{K_c}{8} - 3\omega^2\right) + i(3\omega - \omega^3) = 0 + i0 \qquad (11\text{-}21)$$

Equating the real and imaginary parts of the left- and right-hand sides of the above equation gives two equations:

$$1 + \frac{K_c}{8} - 3\omega^2 = 0$$

$$3\omega - \omega^3 = 0 \qquad (11\text{-}22)$$

Therefore,

$$\omega^2 = 3 \quad \Rightarrow \quad \omega = \pm\sqrt{3} \qquad (11\text{-}23)$$

$$\frac{K_c}{8} = 3\omega^2 - 1$$

$$= 3(3) - 1 \quad \Rightarrow \quad K_c = 64 \qquad (11\text{-}24)$$

The value of the gain at the limit of stability is 64. This is the same value that the Routh stability criterion gave us. It is K_u. The ω at this limit is the value of the imaginary part of s when the roots lie right on the imaginary axis. Since the real part of s is zero, the system will show a sustained oscillation with this frequency ω_u, called the *ultimate frequency*, in radians per unit time. The period of the oscillation is exactly the same as the ultimate period P_u that we defined in Chap. 10 in the Ziegler-Nichols tuning method.

$$P_u = \frac{2\pi}{\omega_u} \qquad (11\text{-}25) \qquad ////$$

Notice that this direct-substitution method is similar to the conversion from the Laplace to the frequency domain. The two operations are completely different. There we substituted $s = i\omega$ into the system transfer function. Here we make the same substitution but it is made in the characteristic equation.

11-2 PERFORMANCE SPECIFICATIONS

In order to design feedback controllers, we must have some way to evaluate their effect on the performance of the closed-loop system, both dynamically and at steady state.

11-2.1 Steady-state Performance

The usual steady-state performance specification is zero steady-state error. We will show below that this steady-state performance depends on both the system (process and controller) and the type of disturbance. This is different from the question of stability of the system which, as we have previously shown, is only a function of the system (roots of the characteristic equation) and does not depend on the input.

The error signal in the Laplace domain, $E_{(s)}$, is defined as the difference between the set point $X_{(s)}^{\text{set}}$ and the process output $X_{(s)}$.

$$E_{(s)} = X_{(s)}^{\text{set}} - X_{(s)} \qquad (11\text{-}26)$$

Substituting for $X_{(s)}$ from Eq. (11-6) gives

$$E_{(s)} = X_{(s)}^{\text{set}} - \frac{B_{(s)} G_{M(s)}}{1 + B_{(s)} G_{M(s)}} X_{(s)}^{\text{set}}$$

$$\frac{E_{(s)}}{X_{(s)}^{\text{set}}} = \frac{1}{1 + B_{(s)} G_{M(s)}} \qquad (11\text{-}27)$$

To find the steady-state value of the error, we will use the final-value theorem (Chap. 7).

$$\bar{e} \equiv \lim_{t \to \infty} e_{(t)} = \lim_{s \to 0} (s E_{(s)}) \qquad (11\text{-}28)$$

Now let us look at two types of set-point inputs: a step and a ramp.

Unit step input

$$X_{(s)}^{\text{set}} = \frac{1}{s}$$

$$\bar{e} = \lim_{s \to 0} \left(s \frac{1}{1 + B_{(s)} G_{M(s)}} \frac{1}{s} \right) = \lim_{s \to 0} \left(\frac{1}{1 + B_{(s)} G_{M(s)}} \right)$$

If the steady-state error is to go to zero, the term $1/(1 + B_{(s)} G_{M(s)})$ must go to zero as s goes to zero. This means that the term $B_{(s)} G_{M(s)}$ must go to infinity as s goes to zero. Thus $B_{(s)} G_{M(s)}$ must contain a $1/s$ term, which is integration. If the process $G_{M(s)}$ does not contain integration, we must put it into the controller $B_{(s)}$. We add reset or integral action to eliminate steady-state error for a step input in set point.

If we use a proportional controller, the steady-state error is

$$\bar{e} = \lim_{s \to 0} \left(\frac{1}{1 + B_{(s)} G_{M(s)}} \right) = \frac{1}{1 + K_c(z_1 z_2 \cdots z_M / p_1 p_2 \cdots p_N)} \qquad (11\text{-}29)$$

where $z_1, z_2, \ldots$ = zeros of $G_{M(s)}$
$p_1, p_2, \ldots$ = poles of $G_{M(s)}$
Thus the steady-state error is reduced by increasing K_c, the controller gain.

Ramp input

$$X_{(s)}^{\text{set}} = \frac{1}{s^2}$$

$$\bar{e} = \lim_{s \to 0} \left(s \frac{1}{1 + B_{(s)} G_{M(s)}} \frac{1}{s^2} \right) = \lim_{s \to 0} \left(\frac{1}{s(1 + B_{(s)} G_{M(s)})} \right)$$

If the steady-state error is to go to zero, the term $1/s(1 + B_{(s)} G_{M(s)})$ must go to zero as s goes to zero. This requires that $B_{(s)} G_{M(s)}$ must contain a $1/s^2$ term. Double integration is needed to drive the steady-state error to zero for a ramp input (to make the output track the changing input).

11-2.2   Dynamic Specifications

The dynamic performance of a system can be deduced by merely observing the location of the roots of the system characteristic equation in the s plane. The time-domain specifications of time constants and damping coefficients for a closed-loop system can be used directly in the Laplace domain.

  1 If all the roots lie in the LHP, the system is stable.
  2 If all the roots lie on the real axis, we know the system is overdamped or critically damped (all real roots).
  3 The farther out on the negative real axis the roots lie, the faster will be the dynamics of the system (the smaller the time constants).
  4 The roots that lie close to the imaginary axis will dominate the dynamic response since the ones farther out will die out quickly.
  5 The farther any complex conjugate roots are from the real axis the more underdamped the system will be.

There is a quantitative relationship between the location of roots in the s plane and the damping coefficient. Assume we have a second-order system or, if it is of higher order, it is dominated by the second-order roots closest to the imaginary axis. As shown in Fig. 11-2b the two roots are s_1 and s_2 and they are, of course, complex

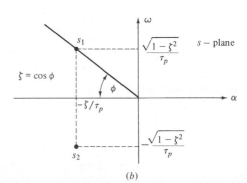

FIGURE 11-2b
Dominant second-order root in the s plane.

(b)

conjugates. From Eq. (6-65) the two roots are

$$s_1 = -\frac{\zeta}{\tau_p} + i\frac{\sqrt{1-\zeta^2}}{\tau_p}$$

$$s_2 = -\frac{\zeta}{\tau_p} - i\frac{\sqrt{1-\zeta^2}}{\tau_p}$$

The hypotenuse of the triangle shown in Fig. 11-2b, the distance from the origin out to the root s_1, is

$$\sqrt{\left(\frac{\sqrt{1-\zeta^2}}{\tau_p}\right)^2 + \left(\frac{\zeta}{\tau_p}\right)^2} = \frac{1}{\tau_p} \qquad (11\text{-}30)$$

The angle ϕ can be defined from the hypotenuse and the adjacent side of the triangle.

$$\cos\phi = \frac{\zeta/\tau_p}{1/\tau_p} = \zeta \qquad (11\text{-}31)$$

Thus the location of a complex root can be converted directly to a damping coefficient and a time constant. The damping coefficient is equal to the cosine of the angle between the negative real axis and a radial line from the origin to the root. The time constant is equal to the reciprocal of the radial distance from the origin to the root.

Notice that lines of constant damping coefficient are radial lines in the s plane. Lines of constant time constant are circles.

11-3   ROOT LOCUS ANALYSIS AND SYNTHESIS TECHNIQUES

11-3.1   Definition

A *root locus* curve is a plot of the roots of the closed-loop characteristic equation of a system as a function of the feedback controller gain. The examples below illustrate the types of curves obtained.

EXAMPLE 11-4   The system and controller transfer functions are given:

$$B_{(s)}G_{M(s)} = \frac{K_c}{(s+1)(5s+1)} \qquad (11\text{-}32)$$

The closed-loop characteristic equation is

$$1 + B_{(s)}G_{M(s)} = 0$$

$$1 + \frac{K_c}{(s+1)(5s+1)} = 0$$

$$5s^2 + 6s + 1 + K_c = 0 \qquad (11\text{-}33)$$

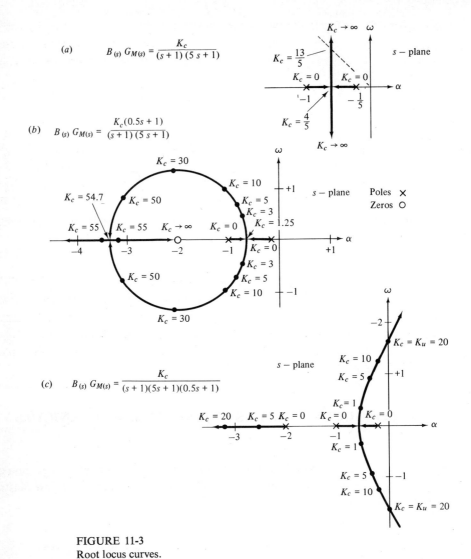

$(a) \quad B_{(s)} G_{M(s)} = \dfrac{K_c}{(s+1)(5s+1)}$

$(b) \quad B_{(s)} G_{M(s)} = \dfrac{K_c(0.5s+1)}{(s+1)(5s+1)}$

$(c) \quad B_{(s)} G_{M(s)} = \dfrac{K_c}{(s+1)(5s+1)(0.5s+1)}$

FIGURE 11-3
Root locus curves.

The quadratic formula gives the roots:

$$ s = -\tfrac{3}{5} \pm \tfrac{1}{5}\sqrt{4 - 5K_c} \qquad (11\text{-}34) $$

The locations of these roots for various values of K_c are shown in Fig. 11-3a.

When K_c is zero the roots are at $-\tfrac{1}{5}$ and -1 (which are the poles of the system open-loop transfer function). For K_c between zero and $\tfrac{4}{5}$, the two roots are real and lie on the negative real axis. The closed-loop system is critically damped at $K_c = \tfrac{4}{5}$ since the roots are equal and any larger value of K_c gives complex conjugate roots.

As K_c goes from $\frac{4}{5}$ to infinity, the real parts of both roots are constant at $-\frac{3}{5}$ and the imaginary parts go to plus and minus infinity. Thus the system becomes increasingly underdamped. However, it never becomes closed-loop unstable since the roots never go over into the RHP.

Suppose we wanted to design this system for a closed-loop damping coefficient of 0.707. Equation (11-31) tells us that

$$\phi = \arccos 0.707 = 45°$$

Therefore we must find the value of gain on the root locus plot where it intersects a 45° line from the origin. At the point of intersection the real and imaginary parts of the roots must be equal. This occurs when $K_c = \frac{13}{5}$. The closed-loop time constant of the system at this value of gain would be $5/3\sqrt{2}$.   ////

EXAMPLE 11-5   Let us change the system transfer function from the above example by adding a lead or a zero.

$$B_{(s)} G_{M(s)} = \frac{K_c(\frac{1}{2}s + 1)}{(s + 1)(5s + 1)} \qquad (11\text{-}35)$$

The closed-loop characteristic equation becomes

$$1 + B_{(s)} G_{M(s)} = 1 + \frac{K_c(\frac{1}{2}s + 1)}{(s + 1)(5s + 1)}$$

$$5s^2 + \left(6 + \frac{K_c}{2}\right)s + K_c + 1 = 0 \qquad (11\text{-}36)$$

The roots are

$$s = -\left(\frac{3}{5} + \frac{K_c}{20}\right) \pm \frac{1}{10}\sqrt{\frac{K_c^2}{4} - 14K_c + 16} \qquad (11\text{-}37)$$

For low values of K_c the term inside the square root will be positive, since the $+16$ will dominate; the roots are real. For very big values of gain, the K_c^2 term will dominate and the roots will again be real. For intermediate values of K_c the term inside the square root will be negative and the roots will be complex.

The range of K_c values that give complex roots can be found from the roots of

$$\frac{K_c^2}{4} - 14K_c + 16 = 0 \qquad (11\text{-}38)$$

$$K_{c1} = 28 - 12\sqrt{5}$$

$$K_{c2} = 28 + 12\sqrt{5} \qquad (11\text{-}39)$$

where K_{c1} = smaller value of K_c where square-root term is zero

K_{c2} = larger value of K_c where square-root term is zero

The root locus curves are shown in Fig. 11-3b.

   Note that the effect of adding a zero or a lead is to pull the root locus toward a more stable region of the s plane. As the gain goes to infinity the two paths of the root locus go to minus infinity and to the zero of the transfer function at $s = -2$. When K_c is zero the roots are at the poles of the open-loop transfer function. The system is closed-loop stable for all values of gain. The fastest responding system would be obtained with $K_c = K_{c2}$, where the two roots are equal and real.   ////

EXAMPLE 11-6   Now let us add a pole or a lag, instead of a zero, to the system of Example 11-4.

$$B_{(s)} G_{M(s)} = \frac{K_c}{(s + 1)(5s + 1)(\frac{1}{2}s + 1)} \quad (11\text{-}40)$$

The closed-loop characteristic equation becomes

$$1 + B_{(s)} G_{M(s)} = 1 + \frac{K_c}{(s + 1)(5s + 1)(\frac{1}{2}s + 1)}$$

$$\tfrac{5}{2}s^3 + 8s^2 + \tfrac{13}{2}s + 1 + K_c = 0 \quad (11\text{-}41)$$

The root locus curves are sketched in Fig. 11-3c. We will discuss how to solve for the roots in the next section.

   The effect of adding a lag or pole is to pull the root locus toward the unstable region. There are three root loci. The two that start at $s = -\frac{1}{5}$ and $s = -1$ become complex conjugates and curve off into the RHP. Therefore this system is closed-loop unstable if K_c is greater than K_u.   ////

   One of the basic limitations of root locus techniques is that dead time cannot be handled conveniently. The *first-order Pade* approximation of dead time is frequently used, but it is often not very accurate.

$$e^{-Ds} \simeq \frac{1 - (D/2)s}{1 + (D/2)s} \quad (11\text{-}42)$$

11-3.2   Construction of Root Locus Curves

Root locus plots are easy to generate for first- and second-order systems since the roots can be found analytically as explicit functions of controller gain. For higher-order systems things become more difficult. A number of graphical techniques have been developed over the years to enable engineers to quickly sketch the curves. We will list some of the most important of these construction rules below.

Graphical

1 The root loci start ($K_c = 0$) at the poles of the system open-loop transfer function $B_{(s)} G_{M(s)}$.

2 The root loci end ($K_c = $ infinity) at the zeros of $B_{(s)} G_{M(s)}$.

3 The number of loci is equal to the order of the system, i.e., the number of poles of $B_{(s)} G_{M(s)}$.

4 The complex parts of the curves always appear as complex conjugates.

5 The angle of the asymptotes of the loci (as $s \to \infty$) is equal to $\pm 180°/(N - M)$, where N is the number of poles of $B_{(s)} G_{M(s)}$ and M is the number of zeros of $B_{(s)} G_{M(s)}$. In Example 11-4, $N - M = 2$ so the asymptotes make a $\pm 90°$ angle with the real axis. In Example 11-5, $N - M = 1$, so the angle is $\pm 180°$. In Example 11-6, $N - M = 3$, and the angle is $\pm 60°$.

Rules 1 to 4 are fairly self-evident. Rule 5 comes from the fact that at a point on the root locus plot the complex number s must satisfy the equation:

$$1 + B_{(s)} G_{M(s)} = 0$$

$$B_{(s)} G_{M(s)} = -1 + i0 \qquad (11\text{-}43)$$

Therefore the argument of $B_{(s)} G_{M(s)}$ on a root locus must always be

$$\arg B_{(s)} G_{M(s)} = \arctan \frac{0}{-1} = \pm \pi \qquad (11\text{-}44)$$

Now $B_{(s)} G_{M(s)}$ is a ratio of polynomials, Mth-order in the numerator and Nth-order in the denominator.

$$B_{(s)} G_{M(s)} = \frac{b_M s^M + b_{M-1} s^{M-1} + \cdots + b_1 s + b_0}{a_N s^N + a_{N-1} s^{N-1} + \cdots + a_1 s + a_0}$$

On the asymptotes, s gets very big, so only the s^N and s^M terms remain significant.

$$\lim_{s \to \infty} B_{(s)} G_{M(s)} = \frac{b_M s^M}{a_N s^N} = \frac{b_M/a_N}{s^{N-M}} \qquad (11\text{-}45)$$

Putting s in polar form ($s = r e^{i\theta}$) gives

$$\lim_{s \to \infty} B_{(s)} G_{M(s)} = \frac{b_M/a_N}{r^{N-M} e^{i\theta(N-M)}}$$

The angle or argument of $B_{(s)} G_{M(s)}$ is

$$\lim_{s \to \infty} (\arg B_{(s)} G_{M(s)}) = -(N - M)\theta$$

Equation (11-44) must still be satisfied on the asymptote, and therefore Q.E.D.

$$(N - M)\theta = \pm \pi$$

The above rules are easy to remember and can be used to get a quick idea of the general shape of the root locus curves. More extensive sets of graphical rules and other construction techniques are given in some texts.[1]

Digital computer numerical solution   With the wide availability of digital computers, root locus plots are easily obtained by using numerical techniques. Special-purpose programs have been written for this purpose.[2] However, the standard polynomial root-solving packages that are available in most computer libraries are readily accessible and easy to use. They are computationally inefficient for generating the root locus curves, but this is not worth worrying about unless you plan to generate a very large number of root locus curves.

The polynomial root-solving program POLRT was used in the examples below. It is from the IBM Scientific Subroutines. A listing of the source program is given in the Appendix. Other root-finding programs are presented in the literature.[3]

POLRT is very fast. It solved for the five roots of a fifth-order polynomial in about 0.05 sec on the CDC 6400 digital computer.

EXAMPLE 11-7   Our three-CSTR system is an interesting one to explore via root locus. With the same process $G_{M(s)}$ as shown in Fig. 11-2a we will use different kinds of feedback controllers and different settings and see how the root loci change.

(a) *Proportional controller:* $\hspace{6cm} B_{(s)} = K_c$

The closed-loop characteristic equation is

$$1 + B_{(s)} G_{M(s)} = 1 + \frac{K_c(\frac{1}{8})}{(s+1)^3} = s^3 + 3s^2 + 3s + 1 + \frac{K_c}{8} = 0 \qquad (11\text{-}46)$$

Figure 11-4a gives the root locus curves that were generated by solving for the three roots numerically on a digital computer at different values of gain K_c.

Notice that the construction rules are satisfied. The root loci start ($K_c = 0$) at the poles of the system open-loop transfer function, $s = -1$. There are three loci. The angle of the asymptotes is $180°/3 = 60°$.

Notice also that the two curves cross over into the RHP when $K_c = 64$ and when s has the values $\pm i\sqrt{3}$. This confirms our findings of Examples 11-3 and 11-2.

[1] John J. D'Azzo and Constantine H. Houpis, "Feedback Control System Analysis and Synthesis," 2d ed., McGraw-Hill, 1966.
[2] R. H. Ash and G. R. Ash, *IEEE Trans., Autom. Control.*, October, 1968, p. 576.
[3] James L. Melsa, "Computer Programs for Computational Assistance in the Study of Linear Control Theory," McGraw-Hill, 1970.

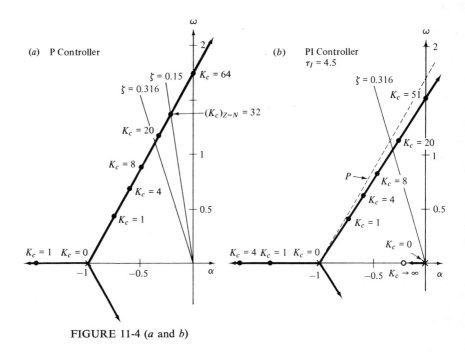

FIGURE 11-4 (*a* and *b*)

A gain of 17 gives a closed-loop system with a damping coefficient of 0.316 and a dominant second-order time constant of 0.85 min. The third root is real and lies far out on the negative real axis at -2.3. Thus the largest first-order time constant is 0.43 min.

The Ziegler-Nichols recommended value of gain for this system ($K_c = 32$) is also shown on the plot. This setting gives a closed-loop system that has a damping coefficient of only 0.15. This is more underdamped than most instrument engineers would normally like to see on a process loop. The Ziegler-Nichols settings are usually found to be more underdamped than desired.

(*b*) *Proportional-integral controller:*
$$B_{(s)} = K_c \frac{\tau_I s + 1}{\tau_I s} = K_c \frac{s + 1/\tau_I}{s}$$

The closed-loop characteristic equation of the system now is

$$1 + B_{(s)} G_{M(s)} = 1 + K_c \frac{s + 1/\tau_I}{s} \frac{\frac{1}{8}}{(s + 1)^3}$$

$$s^4 + 3s^3 + 3s^2 + \left(1 + \frac{K_c}{8}\right)s + \frac{K_c}{8\tau_I} = 0 \qquad (11\text{-}47)$$

Figure 11-4*b* and *c* give the root locus plots for two values of the reset time constant τ_I. With $\tau_I = 4.5$ in Fig. 11-4*b*, the ultimate gain is reduced to 51, and the gain that gives a damping coefficient of 0.316 is 15. There is a first-order root on the real axis near the origin.

With $\tau_I = 3.03$, the recommended Ziegler-Nichols value, the ultimate gain is 44 and the gain that gives a damping coefficient of 0.316 is 13. The Ziegler-Nichols value of gain, $K_c = 29.1$, gives a damping coefficient of 0.09. These results are summarized in Table 11-1.

Table 11-1   ROOT LOCUS RESULTS FOR THREE-CSTR SYSTEM

	τ_D	τ_I	K_u	K_c	τ_2	τ_1
				$\leftarrow$ for $\zeta = 0.316 \rightarrow$		
Proportional	...	...	64	17	0.85	0.43
Proportional-integral	...	3.03	44	13	1.03	3.8
	...	4.5	51	15	0.94	6.3
Proportional-integral-	0.45	1.82	275	17	0.86	1.9
derivative	0.9	1.82	280	30	0.53	1.9
	1.8	1.82	111	22	0.43	2.3

The construction rules are again satisfied. The root loci start at the poles $s = 0$ and $s = -1$. They end at the zero $s = -1/\tau_I$. There are four curves. The angle of the asymptotes is equal to $60°$ since $N = 4$ and $M = 1$.

(c) *Proportional-integral-derivative controller:*

$$B_{(s)} = K_c \frac{\tau_I s + 1}{\tau_I s} \frac{\tau_D s + 1}{(\tau_D/20)s + 1} \qquad (11\text{-}48)$$

The closed-loop characteristic equation is

$$1 + B_{(s)} G_{M(s)} = 1 + K_c \frac{s + 1/\tau_I}{s} \frac{\tau_D s + 1}{(\tau_D/20)s + 1} \frac{\frac{1}{8}}{(s + 1)^3} \qquad (11\text{-}49)$$

$$s^5 + \left(3 + \frac{20}{\tau_D}\right)s^4 + \left(3 + \frac{60}{\tau_D}\right)s^3 + \left(1 + \frac{60}{\tau_D} + \frac{20K_c}{8}\right)s^2$$

$$+ \left[\frac{20}{\tau_D} + \frac{20K_c}{8}\left(\frac{1}{\tau_I} + \frac{1}{\tau_D}\right)\right]s + \frac{20K_c}{8\tau_I\tau_D} = 0 \qquad (11\text{-}50)$$

Figure 11-4d, e, and f give root locus curves for three values of derivative time τ_D with integral time τ_I constant at 1.82. There are now five loci. They start at the poles $s = -1$, $s = 0$, and $s = -20/\tau_D$. They end at the zeros $s = -1/\tau_I$ and $s = -1/\tau_D$. The angle of the asymptotes is $180/(5 - 2) = 60°$.

The addition of the derivative (lead-lag) unit makes the system more stable. It pulls the root locus away from the imaginary axis. The Ziegler-Nichols value of τ_D and gain are shown in Fig. 11-4d. They give a damping coefficient of only 0.175.

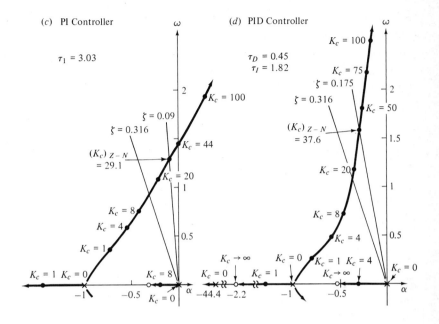

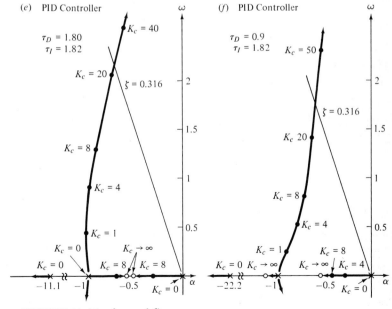

FIGURE 11-4 (c, d, e, and f)
Root locus curves for a three-CSTR system.

Table 11-1 summarizes the effects of increasing τ_D. There is an optimum value of τ_D around 0.9 that gives the highest gain with small second- and first-order time constants when designing for a damping coefficient of 0.316.

Figure 11-5 shows the time-domain performance of these PI and PID controllers. The disturbance is a step load change in C_{AD}.   ////

11-4   OPEN-LOOP UNSTABLE PROCESSES

We remarked earlier in this book that one of the most interesting processes that chemical engineers have to control is the exothermic chemical reactor. This process can be open-loop unstable.

Open-loop instability means that reactor temperature will take off when there is no feedback control of cooling rate. It is easy to visualize qualitatively how this can occur. The reaction rate increases as the temperature climbs and more heat is given off. This heats the reactor to an even higher temperature, at which the reaction rate is still faster and even more heat is generated.

We will explore this phenomenon quantitatively in the s plane. We will discuss

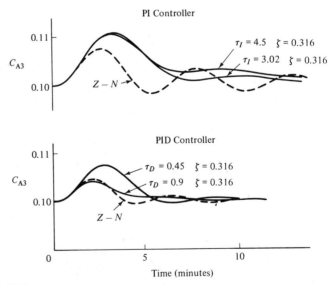

FIGURE 11-5
Load step response of a three-CSTR system with Ziegler-Nichols and $\zeta = 0.316$ controller settings.

linear systems in which instability means that the reactor temperature would theoretically go off to infinity. Actually, in any real system, reactor temperature will not go to infinity because the real system is nonlinear. This nonlinearity makes reactor temperature climb to some high temperature at which it levels out. This is the high-conversion steady state discussed in Sec. 6-4. The concentration of reactant, C_A, becomes so low that the reaction rate is limited.

Nevertheless linear techniques are very useful in looking at stability near some operating level (*local stability*). Mathematically, if a system is open-loop unstable, it must have an open-loop transfer function $G_{M(s)}$ that has at least one pole in the right-half of the s plane. That is, the open-loop characteristic equation of the system has one or more roots in the RHP.

$$G_{M(s)} = \frac{Z_{(s)}}{P_{(s)}} = \frac{Z_{(s)}}{(s - p_1)(s - p_2) \cdots (s - p_N)} \qquad (11\text{-}51)$$

For the system to be open-loop unstable, only one of the roots of the denominator has to lie in the RHP.

As a simple example let us look at the energy equation of the nonisothermal CSTR system of Example 7-6. [Eqs. (7-81)]. We will neglect any changes in C_A for the moment.

$$\frac{dT}{dt} = a_{22}T + a_{24}T_J + \cdots \qquad (11\text{-}52)$$

Laplace transforming gives

$$(s - a_{22}) T_{(s)} = a_{24} T_{J(s)} + \cdots$$

$$T_{(s)} = \frac{a_{24}}{s - a_{22}} T_{J(s)} + \cdots \qquad (11\text{-}53)$$

Thus the stability of the system depends on the location of the coefficient a_{22}. If a_{22} is positive, the system is open-loop unstable. Substituting from Eqs. (7-82) gives

$$a_{22} = \frac{-\lambda \bar{k} E}{\rho C_p R \bar{T}^2} - \frac{\bar{F}}{V} - \frac{UA}{V \rho C_p} \qquad (11\text{-}54)$$

For open-loop stability,

$$a_{22} < 0$$

$$\frac{-\lambda \bar{k} E}{\rho C_p R \bar{T}^2} < \frac{\bar{F}}{V} + \frac{UA}{V \rho C_p} \qquad (11\text{-}55)$$

The left side of Eq. (11-55) represents heat generation. The right side represents heat removal. Thus our simple linear analysis tells us that the heat-removal capacity must be greater than the heat generation if the system is to be stable.

The actual stability requirement for the nonisothermal CSTR system is a little more complex than Eq. (11-55) because the concentration C_A does change (Prob. 11-1).

11-4.1 First-order Open-loop Unstable Process

A first-order open-loop unstable process has a transfer function

$$G_{M(s)} = \frac{K_p}{\tau_p s - 1} \qquad (11\text{-}56)$$

Can we make the system stable by using feedback control? That is, can an open-loop unstable process be made closed-loop stable by appropriate design of the feedback controller? Let us try a proportional controller: $B_{(s)} = K_c$. The system closed-loop characteristic equation is

$$1 + B_{(s)}G_{M(s)} = 1 + K_c \frac{K_p}{\tau_p s - 1}$$

$$\tau_p s - 1 + K_c K_p = 0 \qquad (11\text{-}57)$$

The closed-loop root of the characteristic equation is

$$s = \frac{1 - K_c K_p}{\tau_p} \qquad (11\text{-}58)$$

The root locus plot of the system is shown in Figure 11-6a. There is only one path since the system is first-order. It starts in the RHP at the pole of the open-loop transfer function. The system is thus closed-loop unstable for small values of gain. For feedback controller gains greater than $1/K_p$, the root locus crosses over into the LHP, showing that the system is now closed-loop stable. Thus in this system there is a *minimum* stable gain. Some of the examples up to this point have shown a maximum or ultimate gain beyond which the system was closed-loop unstable. Now we have a system that has a minimum gain K_{min} *below* which the system is closed-loop unstable.

11-4.2 Second-order Open-loop Unstable Process

Consider the second-order process that is open-loop unstable with a transfer function

$$G_{M(s)} = \frac{K_p}{(\tau_{p1}s + 1)(\tau_{p2} s - 1)} \qquad (11\text{-}59)$$

One of the roots of the open-loop characteristic equation lies in the RHP at $s = +1/\tau_{p2}$.

Can we make this system closed-loop stable? A proportional feedback controller gives a closed-loop characteristic equation:

$$1 + B_{(s)}G_{M(s)} = 1 + K_c \frac{K_p}{(\tau_{p1}s + 1)(\tau_{p2} s - 1)}$$

$$\tau_{p1}\tau_{p2} s^2 + (\tau_{p2} - \tau_{p1})s + (K_c K_p - 1) = 0 \qquad (11\text{-}60)$$

The Routh array for this closed-loop system is

$$
\begin{bmatrix}
\tau_{p1}\tau_{p2} & K_c K_p - 1 \\
\tau_{p2} - \tau_{p1} & 0 \\
K_c K_p - 1 & 0 \\
0 &
\end{bmatrix}
\qquad (11\text{-}61)
$$

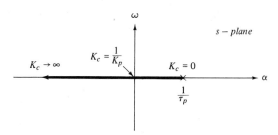

(a)   First-order: $B_{(s)} G_{M(s)} = \dfrac{K_c K_p}{\tau_p s - 1}$

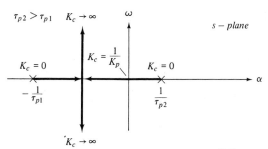

(b)   Second-order: $B_{(s)} G_{M(s)} = \dfrac{K_c K_p}{(\tau_{p1} s + 1)(\tau_{p2} - 1)}$

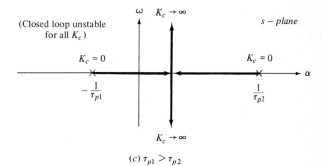

(c) $\tau_{p1} > \tau_{p2}$

FIGURE 11-6 (*a, b,* and *c*)

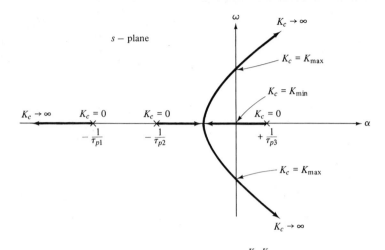

(d) Third $-$ order : $B_{(s)} \, G_{M(s)} = \dfrac{K_c \, K_p}{(\tau_{p1} \, s + 1) \, (\tau_{p2} \, s + 1) \, (\tau_{p3} \, s - 1)}$

FIGURE 11-6d
Root locus curves for open-loop unstable processes (positive poles).

There are two conditions that must be satisfied if there are to be no sign changes in the first column.

$$\tau_{p2} > \tau_{p1}$$

$$K_c > \frac{1}{K_p} \qquad (11\text{-}62)$$

Therefore, if $\tau_{p1} > \tau_{p2}$ a proportional controller cannot make the system closed-loop stable. A PID controller must be used in this situation.[1] The root locus plots for the two cases of $\tau_{p2} > \tau_{p1}$ and $\tau_{p1} > \tau_{p2}$ are sketched in Fig. 11-6b and c.

11-4.3   Third-order Open-loop Unstable Process

Assume we have a third-order process with one open-loop root in the RHP (at $s = +1/\tau_{p3}$) and a proportional controller.

$$G_{M(s)} = \frac{K_p}{(\tau_{p1}s + 1)(\tau_{p2} \, s + 1)(\tau_{p3} \, s - 1)} \qquad (11\text{-}63)$$

[1] W. R. Ellingsen and N. H. Ceaglske, *A.I.Ch.E. J.*, vol. 5, p. 30, 1959.

The root-locus curves depend on the relative values of the roots (Prob. 11-13), but one possible case is sketched in Fig. 11-6d. We now have a case of *conditional stability*. Below K_{min} the system is closed-loop unstable. Above K_{max} the system is again closed-loop unstable. A range of stable values of controller gain exists between these limits.

$$K_{min} < K_c < K_{max} \qquad (11\text{-}64)$$

11-5 PROCESSES WITH INVERSE RESPONSE

Another interesting type of process is one that exhibits *inverse response*. This phenomenon, which occurs in a not insignificant number of real systems,[1] is sketched in Fig. 11-7b. The initial response of the output variable $x_{(t)}$ is in the opposite direction to where it eventually ends up. Thus the process starts out in the wrong direction. You can imagine what this sort of behavior would do to a poor feedback controller in such a loop. We will show quantitatively below how inverse response degrades control-loop performance.

An important example of a physical process that shows inverse response is the base of a distillation column. The response of bottoms composition to a change in vapor boilup can show inverse behavior.[2] In a binary distillation column, we know that an increase in vapor boilup V must drive more low boiling material up the column and therefore decrease the mole fraction in the bottoms product x_B. However, the tray hydraulics can produce some unexpected results. When the vapor rate through a tray is increased, it tends to (1) back up more liquid in the downcomer and (2) reduce the liquid density on the active part of the tray. The former effect reduces the liquid rates through the column while the liquid holdup in the downcomer is building up. The latter effect tends to increase the liquid rates since the liquid holdup must be depleted. You can think of this effect as blowing froth off the trays.

Which of these two opposing effects dominates depends on the tray design and operating level. Sieve and ballast trays are more affected by froth density changes. If the density effect is more important, an increase in vapor boilup produces a transient increase in liquid rates down the column. This increase in liquid rate into the reboiler can produce an initial increase in the amount of low boiler in the bottoms. Consequently x_B starts to increase.

Eventually, of course, the liquid rates will return to normal when the liquid inventory on the trays has dropped to its new steady-state level. Then the effect of the vapor boilup will drive x_B down.

Thus the vapor-liquid hydraulics can produce inverse response in the effect of V on x_B.

[1] K. Iinoya and R. J. Altpeter, *Ind. Eng. Chem.*, vol. 54, p. 39, 1962.
[2] W. L. Luyben, *Inst. Chem. Eng. (London), Symp. Ser.*, no. 32, p. 6: 39, 1969.

Mathematically, inverse response can be represented by a system that has a transfer function with a *positive* zero, a zero in the right-half of the s plane. Consider the system sketched in Fig. 11-7a. There are two parallel first-order lags with gains of opposite sign. The transfer function for the overall system is

$$\frac{X_{(s)}}{Q_{(s)}} = \frac{K_1}{\tau_{p1}s + 1} - \frac{K_2}{\tau_{p2}s + 1}$$

$$= \frac{(K_1\tau_{p2} - K_2\tau_{p1})s - (K_2 - K_1)}{(\tau_{p1}s + 1)(\tau_{p2}s + 1)} \qquad (11\text{-}65)$$

If the K's and τ_p's are such that

$$\frac{\tau_{p2}}{\tau_{p1}} > \frac{K_2}{K_1} > 1 \qquad (11\text{-}66)$$

the system will show inverse response as sketched in Fig. 11-7b. Equation (11-65) can be rewritten

$$\frac{X_{(s)}}{Q_{(s)}} = \frac{-\left(\dfrac{K_1\tau_{p2} - K_2\tau_{p1}}{K_2 - K_1}\right)s + 1}{(\tau_{p1}s + 1)(\tau_{p2}s + 1)} \qquad (11\text{-}67)$$

Thus the system has a positive zero at

$$s = \frac{K_2 - K_1}{K_1\tau_{p2} - K_2\tau_{p1}}$$

Keep in mind that the positive zero does not make the system open-loop unstable. Stability depends on the poles of the transfer function, not on the zeros. Positive zeros in a system do, however, affect closed-loop stability as the example below illustrates.

EXAMPLE 11-8   Let us take the same system used in Example 11-4 and add a positive zero at $s = +\tfrac{1}{3}$.

$$G_{M(s)} = \frac{-3s + 1}{(s + 1)(5s + 1)} \qquad (11\text{-}68)$$

With a proportional feedback controller the closed-loop characteristic equation is

$$1 + B_{(s)}G_{M(s)} = 1 + \frac{K_c(-3s + 1)}{(s + 1)(5s + 1)}$$

$$5s^2 + (6 - 3K_c)s + 1 + K_c = 0 \qquad (11\text{-}69)$$

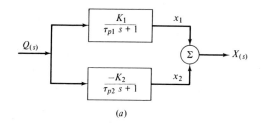

(a)

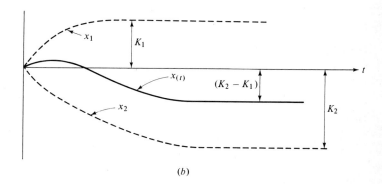

(b)

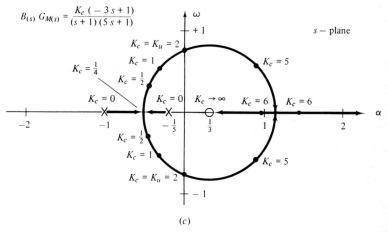

(c)

FIGURE 11-7
Process with inverse response. (a) Block diagram; (b) step response; (c) root locus plot.

The root locus curves are shown in Fig. 11-7c. The loci start at the poles $s = -1$ and $s = -\frac{1}{3}$. Since the loci must end at the zeros of the open-loop transfer function ($s = +\frac{1}{3}$) the curves swing over into the RHP. Therefore the system is closed-loop unstable for gains greater than 2.

Remember that in Example 11-5 adding a lead or a negative zero made the closed-loop system more stable. In this example we have shown that adding a positive zero has just the reverse effect.   ////

11-6   INTERACTING CONTROL SYSTEMS

In Chap. 10 we referred to the tuning problems that can arise when two or more control loops are interacting or coupled. We can now study this problem quantitatively in the Laplace domain.

Let us study the two-variable open-loop system shown in Fig. 11-8a and described by the equations

$$X_1(s) = P_{11(s)}M_{1(s)} + P_{12(s)}M_{2(s)}$$
$$X_{2(s)} = P_{21(s)}M_{1(s)} + P_{22(s)}M_{2(s)} \qquad (11\text{-}70)$$

where X_1 and X_2 = process output variables

M_1 and M_2 = process inputs that are manipulative variables

P_{ij} = open-loop transfer functions

If feedback controllers are connected to the loops (Fig. 11-8b) two more equations are added:

$$M_{1(s)} = B_{1(s)}(X_{1(s)}^{\text{set}} - X_{1(s)})$$
$$M_{2(s)} = B_{2(s)}(X_{2(s)}^{\text{set}} - X_{2(s)}) \qquad (11\text{-}71)$$

After considerable algebraic manipulation, Eqs. (11-70) and (11-71) combine to give the closed-loop relationships between outputs and input set points.

$$X_{1(s)} = K_{11(s)}X_{1(s)}^{\text{set}} + K_{12(s)}X_{2(s)}^{\text{set}}$$
$$X_{2(s)} = K_{21(s)}X_{1(s)}^{\text{set}} + K_{22(s)}X_{2(s)}^{\text{set}} \qquad (11\text{-}72)$$

where

$$K_{11(s)} = \frac{B_1 P_{11} + B_1 B_2 (P_{11}P_{22} - P_{12}P_{21})}{1 + B_1 P_{11} + B_2 P_{22} + B_1 B_2 (P_{11}P_{22} - P_{12}P_{21})}$$

$$K_{12(s)} = \frac{B_2 P_{12}}{1 + B_1 P_{11} + B_2 P_{22} + B_1 B_2 (P_{11}P_{22} - P_{12}P_{21})}$$

$$K_{21(s)} = \frac{B_1 P_{21}}{1 + B_1 P_{11} + B_2 P_{22} + B_1 B_2 (P_{11}P_{22} - P_{12}P_{21})}$$

$$K_{22(s)} = \frac{B_2 P_{22} + B_1 B_2 (P_{11}P_{22} - P_{12}P_{21})}{1 + B_1 P_{11} + B_2 P_{22} + B_1 B_2 (P_{11}P_{22} - P_{12}P_{21})} \qquad (11\text{-}73)$$

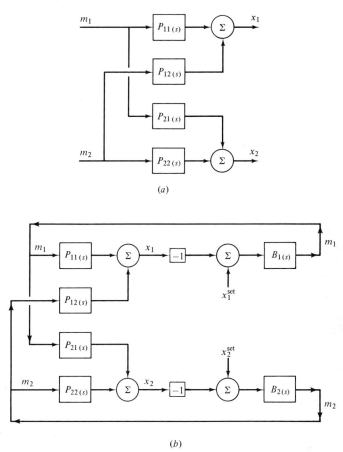

FIGURE 11-8
Interacting system. (a) Open loop; (b) closed loop coupled.

Two important points should be noted. First, changing either set point affects both output variables. Second, the stability of the closed-loop system depends in a complex way on both controllers $B_{1(s)}$ and $B_{2(s)}$, since the closed-loop characteristic equation is

$$1 + B_1 P_{11} + B_2 P_{22} + B_1 B_2 (P_{11} P_{22} - P_{12} P_{21}) = 0 \qquad (11\text{-}74)$$

Both of the above can be eliminated by adding decouplers or interaction compensators that are designed to separate the two loops. There are several ways to decouple systems. The simplest is an intuitive approach. Consider the variable X_1. If it is right on the set point, the $B_{1(s)}$ controller will not change M_1. Now suppose a disturbance in the other loop causes the $B_{2(s)}$ controller to change M_2. This change in M_2 will cause an unwanted change in X_1 if we do nothing about it. If, however, we

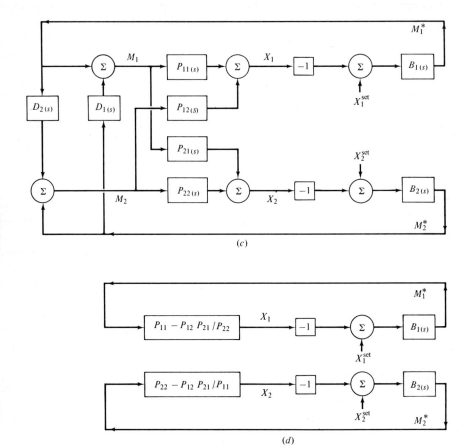

FIGURE 11-8
(c) Closed loop with decouplers; (d) net decoupled system.

change M_1 just enough to overcome the effect of M_2, X_1 will not change. But how much should M_1 be changed? We use the top equation of Eqs. (11-70) to find the change in M_1 required to compensate for a change in M_2 so that X_1 is held constant. Since X_1 is at its set point, the perturbation in X_1 should be zero.

$$X_1 = P_{11(s)}M_1 + P_{12(s)}M_2 = 0 \qquad (11\text{-}75)$$

Solving for the transfer between M_1 and M_2 gives

$$D_{1(s)} = \left(\frac{M_{1(s)}}{M_{2(s)}}\right)_{x_1=0} = \frac{-P_{12(s)}}{P_{11(s)}} \qquad (11\text{-}76)$$

A similar argument for the other loop gives a second transfer function showing how M_2 must be changed when M_1 changes so that X_2 is not disturbed.

$$D_{2(s)} = \left(\frac{M_{2(s)}}{M_{1(s)}}\right)_{x_2=0} = \frac{-P_{21(s)}}{P_{22(s)}} \qquad (11\text{-}77)$$

The decouplers $D_{1(s)}$ and $D_{2(s)}$ are shown inserted in the loop in Fig. 11-8c. They make the closed-loop transfer functions become

$$\frac{X_{1(s)}}{X_{1(s)}^{\text{set}}} = \frac{B_1(P_{11} - P_{12}P_{21}/P_{22})}{1 + B_1(P_{11} - P_{12}P_{21}/P_{22})} \equiv K_{1(s)}^D \qquad (11\text{-}78)$$

$$\frac{X_{2(s)}}{X_{2(s)}^{\text{set}}} = \frac{B_2(P_{22} - P_{12}P_{21}/P_{11})}{1 + B_2(P_{22} - P_{12}P_{21}/P_{11})} \equiv K_{2(s)}^D \qquad (11\text{-}79)$$

Thus the controlled variables are affected by the change in only their set point. And the two loops can be tuned independently since they are affected only by their respective controller. Remember, however, there is no guarantee that the decouplers will be physically realizable. Perfect decoupling is not always possible.

For those familiar with matrix notation, the above equations can be handled more compactly by setting the two equations in each of Eqs. (11-70) and (11-71) to

$$\mathbf{x}_{(s)} = \boldsymbol{P}_{(s)}\mathbf{m}_{(s)} \qquad (11\text{-}80)$$

$$\mathbf{m}_{(s)} = \boldsymbol{B}_{(s)}(\mathbf{x}_{(s)}^{\text{set}} - \mathbf{x}_{(s)}) \qquad (11\text{-}81)$$

where $\mathbf{x}_{(s)}$, $\mathbf{x}_{(s)}^{\text{set}}$ and $\mathbf{m}_{(s)}$ are vectors of variables and $\boldsymbol{P}_{(s)}$ and $\boldsymbol{B}_{(s)}$ are matrices of process and feedback controller transfer functions.

$$\mathbf{x}_{(s)} = \begin{bmatrix} X_1 \\ X_2 \end{bmatrix} \qquad \mathbf{x}_{(s)}^{\text{set}} = \begin{bmatrix} X_1^{\text{set}} \\ X_2^{\text{set}} \end{bmatrix}$$

$$\mathbf{m}_{(s)} = \begin{bmatrix} M_1 \\ M_2 \end{bmatrix} \qquad (11\text{-}82)$$

$$\boldsymbol{P}_{(s)} = \begin{bmatrix} P_{11(s)} & P_{12(s)} \\ P_{21(s)} & P_{22(s)} \end{bmatrix} \qquad \boldsymbol{B}_{(s)} = \begin{bmatrix} B_{1(s)} & 0 \\ 0 & B_{2(s)} \end{bmatrix} \qquad (11\text{-}83)$$

Equations (11-80) and (11-81) can be combined using matrix algebra to give

$$\mathbf{x} = \boldsymbol{P}_{(s)}\mathbf{m} = \boldsymbol{P}\boldsymbol{B}(\mathbf{x}^{\text{set}} - \mathbf{x})$$
$$\boldsymbol{I}\mathbf{x} + \boldsymbol{P}\boldsymbol{B}\mathbf{x} = \boldsymbol{P}\boldsymbol{B}\mathbf{x}^{\text{set}}$$
$$[\boldsymbol{I} + \boldsymbol{P}\boldsymbol{B}]\mathbf{x} = \boldsymbol{P}\boldsymbol{B}\mathbf{x}^{\text{set}}$$
$$\mathbf{x} = [(\boldsymbol{I} + \boldsymbol{P}\boldsymbol{B})^{-1}\boldsymbol{P}\boldsymbol{B}]\,\mathbf{x}^{\text{set}} \qquad (11\text{-}84)$$

where $\boldsymbol{I}$ is the identity matrix:

$$\boldsymbol{I} = \begin{bmatrix} 1 & 0 \\ 0 & 1 \end{bmatrix} \qquad (11\text{-}85)$$

The matrix in the brackets in Eq. (11-84) contains the four closed-loop transfer functions. With no decouplers, the elements are those given in Eqs. (11-73).

$$\mathbf{x} = \mathbf{K}_{(s)}\mathbf{x}^{\text{set}} = \begin{bmatrix} K_{11(s)} & K_{12(s)} \\ K_{21(s)} & K_{22(s)} \end{bmatrix} \mathbf{x}^{\text{set}} \qquad (11\text{-}86)$$

With decouplers, Eq. (11-81) is modified to

$$\mathbf{m}_{(s)} = \mathbf{D}_{(s)}\mathbf{B}_{(s)}(\mathbf{x}^{\text{set}} - \mathbf{x}) \qquad (11\text{-}87)$$

where $\mathbf{D}_{(s)}$ is the matrix of decouplers:

$$\mathbf{D}_{(s)} = \begin{bmatrix} 1 & D_{1(s)} \\ D_{2(s)} & 1 \end{bmatrix} \qquad (11\text{-}88)$$

Equation (11-84) becomes

$$\mathbf{x} = [(\mathbf{I} + \mathbf{PDB})^{-1}\mathbf{PDB}]\,\mathbf{x}^{\text{set}} \qquad (11\text{-}89)$$

Then if the elements of the decoupler matrix are chosen as given in Eqs. (11-76) and (11-77), the equation describing the closed-loop system is

$$\begin{bmatrix} X_1 \\ X_2 \end{bmatrix} = \begin{bmatrix} K_{1(s)}^D & 0 \\ 0 & K_{2(s)}^D \end{bmatrix} \begin{bmatrix} X_1^{\text{set}} \\ X_2^{\text{set}} \end{bmatrix} \qquad (11\text{-}90)$$

where the $K_{1(s)}^D$ and $K_{2(s)}^D$ are defined in Eqs. (11-78) and (11-79).

Thus the decoupled system has a diagonal matrix of closed-loop transfer functions. This shows the noninteracting nature of the final decoupled system.

The design of decouplers for the interacting loops in a distillation column (Sec. 10-4) has been discussed in the literature.[1]

PROBLEMS

11-1 (a) Use the Routh stability criterion to find the open-loop stability requirements for the linearized nonisothermal CSTR system of Example 7-6.

(b) Use the numerical values of the parameters of Example 4-4 to see if the system is open-loop stable.

(c) Add to the system a proportional controller that changes cooling-jacket temperature by the relationship

$$T_J = \bar{T}_J + K_c(T^{\text{set}} - T)$$

What are the closed-loop stability requirements?

[1] W. L. Luyben, *A.I.Ch.E. J.*, vol. 16, p. 198, 1970.

11-2 Find the ultimate gain and period of the closed-loop heat-exchanger system of Prob. 10-4. The controller is proportional and the system open-loop transfer function is

$$G_{M(s)} = \frac{(0.047)(112)(2)(0.12)}{(0.083s + 1)(0.017s + 1)(0.432s + 1)(0.024s + 1)}$$

11-3 Use the Routh stability criterion to find the ultimate gain of the closed-loop three-CSTR system with a PI controller: (*a*) for $\tau_I = 3.03$; (*b*) for $\tau_I = 4.5$.

11-4 Find the ultimate gain and period of a closed-loop system with a proportional controller and an open-loop transfer function:

$$G_{M(s)} = \frac{1}{(s + 1)(5s + 1)(\frac{1}{2}s + 1)}$$

11-5 Find the value of feedback controller gain that gives a closed-loop damping coefficient of $\frac{1}{2}\sqrt{5}$ for the system with a proportional controller and an open-loop transfer function:

$$G_{M(s)} = \frac{s + 4}{s(s + 2)}$$

11-6 The liquid level $h_{(t)}$ in a tank is held by a PI controller that changes the flow rate $F_{(t)}$ out of the tank. The flow rate $F_{0(t)}$ into the tank and the level set point $h_{(t)}^{\text{set}}$ are disturbances. The vertical cylindrical tank is 10 ft² in cross-sectional area. The transfer function of the feedback controller plus the control valve is

$$\frac{F_{(s)}}{h_{(s)}} = K_c\left(1 + \frac{1}{\tau_I s}\right) \qquad \diamond \frac{\text{ft}^3/\text{min}}{\text{ft}}$$

(*a*) Write the equations describing the open-loop system.
(*b*) Write the equations describing the closed-loop system.
(*c*) Derive the open-loop transfer functions of the system:

$$G_{M(s)} = \frac{h_{(s)}}{F_{(s)}} \quad \text{and} \quad G_{L(s)} = \frac{h_{(s)}}{F_{0(s)}}$$

(*d*) Derive the closed-loop transfer functions of the system:

$$\frac{h_{(s)}}{h_{(s)}^{\text{set}}} \quad \text{and} \quad \frac{h_{(s)}}{F_{0(s)}}$$

(*e*) Make a root locus plot of the closed-loop system with a value of integral time $\tau_I = 10$ min.
(*f*) What value of gain K_c gives a closed-loop system with a damping coefficient of 0.707? What is the closed-loop time constant at this gain?
(*g*) What gain gives critical damping? What is the time constant with this gain?

11-7 Make a root locus plot of a system with an open-loop transfer function

$$B_{(s)} G_{M(s)} = \frac{K_c}{(s + 1)(5s + 1)(\frac{1}{2}s + 1)} \frac{\tau_D s + 1}{(\tau_D/20)s + 1}$$

(*a*) for $\tau_D = 2.5$; (*b*) for $\tau_D = 5$; (*c*) for $\tau_D = 7.5$.

11-8 Find the ultimate gain and period of the closed-loop three-CSTR system with a PID controller tuned at $\tau_I = \tau_D = 1$. Make a root locus plot of the system.

11-9 Make a root locus plot of a system with an open-loop transfer function

$$B_{(s)} G_{M(s)} = \frac{K_c e^{-2s}}{s+1}$$

Use the first-order Pade approximation of a dead time. Find the ultimate gain.

11-10 When a system has poles that are widely different in value, it is difficult to plot them all on a root locus plot using conventional rectangular coordinates in the s plane. It is sometimes more convenient to make the root locus plots in the ln s plane. Instead of using the conventional axis Re s and Im s, an ordinate of the arg s and an abscissa of the ln $|s|$ are used, since the logarithm of a complex number is defined:

$$\ln s = \ln |s| + i \arg s$$

(*a*) Show that the region of stability becomes a horizontal band in the ln s plane.

(*b*) Show that lines of constant time constant in the s plane transform into vertical lines in the ln s plane.

(*c*) Show that lines of constant damping coefficient in the s plane transform into horizontal lines in the ln s plane.

(*d*) Make ln s plane root locus plots of systems with the open-loop transfer functions $B_{(s)} G_{M(s)}$:

(i) $\dfrac{\frac{1}{8}K_c}{(s+1)^3}$

(ii) $\dfrac{K_c}{(s+1)(5s+1)(\frac{1}{2}s+1)}$

(iii) $\dfrac{K_c(-3s+1)}{(s+1)(5s+1)}$

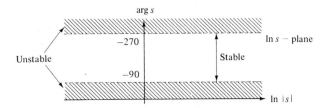

11-11 A two-tank system with recycle is sketched below. Liquid levels are held by proportional controllers: $F_1 = K_1 h_1$ and $F_2 = K_2 h_2$. Flow into the system, F_0, and recycle flow F_R can be varied by the operator.

(*a*) Derive the four closed-loop transfer functions relating the two levels and the two load disturbances:

$$\left(\frac{h_1}{F_0}\right)_{(s)} \quad \left(\frac{h_1}{F_R}\right)_{(s)} \quad \left(\frac{h_2}{F_0}\right)_{(s)} \quad \left(\frac{h_2}{F_R}\right)_{(s)}$$

(b) Does the steady-state level in the second tank vary with the recycle flow rate F_R? Use the final-value theorem of Laplace transforms.

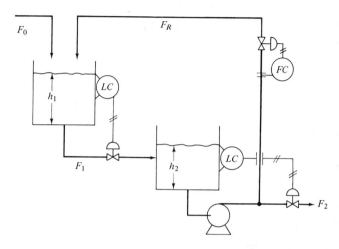

11-12 Make root locus plots of first- and second-order open-loop unstable processes with PI feedback controllers.

11-13 Find the closed-loop stability requirements for a third-order open-loop unstable process with a proportional controller:

$$B_{(s)} G_{M(s)} = \frac{K_c K_p}{(\tau_{p1}s + 1)(\tau_{p2} s + 1)(\tau_{p3} s - 1)}$$

11-14 Find the value of feedback controller gain K_c that gives a closed-loop system with a damping coefficient of 0.707 for a second-order open-loop unstable process with $\tau_{p2} > \tau_{p1}$:

$$B_{(s)} G_{M(s)} = \frac{K_p K_c}{(\tau_{p1} s + 1)(\tau_{p2} s - 1)}$$

11-15 What is the ultimate gain and period of the system with a positive zero:

$$G_{M(s)} = \frac{-3s + 1}{(s + 1)(5s + 1)}$$

(a) With a proportional controller?
(b) With a PI controller for $\tau_I = 2$?

11-16 (a) Sketch the root locus plot of a system with an open-loop transfer function

$$B_{(s)} G_{M(s)} = \frac{K_c}{(s + 1)(s + 5)(s - 0.5)}$$

(b) For what values of gain K_c is the system closed-loop stable?
(c) Make a root locus plot of this system in the ln s plane (see Prob. 11-10).

11-17 The system of Prob. 11-4 is modified by using the cascade control system sketched below.

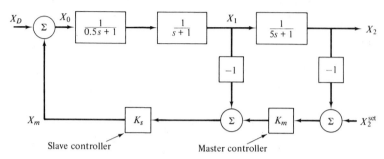

(a) Find the value of the gain K_s in the proportional controller that gives a 0.707 damping coefficient for the closed-loop slave loop.

(b) With this value of K_s, find the maximum closed-loop stable value of the master controller gain K_m. Compare this with the ultimate gain found without cascade control in Prob. 11-4. Also compare ultimate periods.

11-18 Consider the second-order open-loop unstable process Prob. 11-14, but now with $\tau_{p1} > \tau_{p2}$. Can this system be made closed-loop stable by using a PD (proportional-derivative) controller?

$$B_{(s)} = K_c \frac{\tau_D s + 1}{(\tau_D/20)s + 1}$$

Sketch root locus curves for τ_D equal to $2\tau_{p1}$, τ_{p1}, and $\frac{1}{2}\tau_{p1}$.

11-19 Repeat Prob. 11-6 using a proportional feedback controller [parts (b) and (d)]. Will there be a steady-state error in the closed-loop system for a step change in set point h^{set}? For a step change in feed rate F_0?

12

FREQUENCY-DOMAIN SYNTHESIS

The design of feedback controllers in the frequency domain is the subject of this chapter. Frequency-domain synthesis techniques are widely used because they have some significant advantages over time- and Laplace-domain methods.

They are easy to use, even with high-order systems. We will show in Sec. 12-1 that *closed-loop* stability or instability can be deduced from the frequency-response plot of the *open-loop* transfer function of the system (process and controller $B_{(s)}G_{M(s)}$). This means that a Bode plot of $B_{(i\omega)}G_{M(i\omega)}$ is all we need. As you should remember from Chap. 8, the total frequency-response curve of a complex system is easily obtained on a Bode plot by splitting the system into its simple elements, plotting each of these and merely adding log moduli and phase angles together. Therefore the graphical generation of the required $B_{(i\omega)}G_{M(i\omega)}$ curve is relatively easy. Of course all this algebraic manipulation of complex numbers can be even more easily performed on a digital computer.

Another advantage of frequency-domain techniques is that processes with dead time are easily handled. The contribution that dead time makes to the phase angle is simply added on to the Bode-plot curves.

Also, in frequency-domain synthesis, experimentally determined dynamics can be used directly. Suppose we have performed a pulse test on a process (as in Chap. 9) and have computed the frequency-response curves. We can use these curves directly since they represent $G_{M(i\omega)}$. All we have to do is pick a feedback controller $B_{(i\omega)}$ and add its curves (log modulus and phase angle) to the experimental $G_{M(i\omega)}$ Bode plot. Process transfer functions obtained by the frequency-domain solution techniques of Chap. 9 are handled in the same way.

12-1 NYQUIST STABILITY CRITERION

The Nyquist stability criterion is a method for determining the stability of systems in the frequency domain. It is almost always applied to closed-loop systems. A working, but not completely general, statement of the Nyquist stability criterion is:

>   *If a polar plot of the* open-loop *transfer function of the system* $B_{(i\omega)}G_{M(i\omega)}$ *wraps around the* $(-1, 0)$ *point in the* BG_M *plane as frequency* ω *goes from zero to infinity, the system is* closed-loop *unstable.*

The two polar plots sketched in Fig. 12-1a show that system A is closed-loop unstable whereas system B is closed-loop stable.

12-1.1 Proof of Nyquist Stability Criterion

Complex variable $Z - P = N$ **theorem**   The Nyquist stability criterion is derived from a theorem of complex variables that says:

>   *If a complex function* $F_{(s)}$ *has Z zeros and P poles inside a certain area of the s plane, the number N of encirclements that a mapping of a closed contour around the area makes in the F plane around the origin is equal to* $Z - P$.

$$N = Z - P \qquad (12\text{-}1)$$

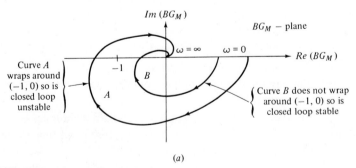

(a)

FIGURE 12-1a
Polar plots showing closed-loop stability or instability.

Consider the hypothetical function $F_{(s)}$ of Eq. (12-2) with two zeros at $s = z_1$ and $s = z_2$ and one pole at $s = p_1$.

$$F_{(s)} = \frac{(s - z_1)(s - z_2)}{s - p_1} \qquad (12\text{-}2)$$

The location of the zeros and the pole is sketched in the s plane in Fig. 12-1b.
The argument of $F_{(s)}$ is

$$\arg F_{(s)} = \arg \frac{(s - z_1)(s - z_2)}{s - p_1}$$

$$\arg F_{(s)} = \arg (s - z_1) + \arg (s - z_2) - \arg (s - p_1) \qquad (12\text{-}3)$$

Remember, the argument of the product of two complex numbers z_1 and z_2 is the sum of the arguments.

$$z_1 z_2 = (r_1 e^{i\theta_1})(r_2 e^{i\theta_2}) = r_1 r_2 e^{i(\theta_1 + \theta_2)}$$

$$\arg z_1 z_2 = \theta_1 + \theta_2$$

And the argument of the quotient of two complex numbers is the difference between the arguments.

$$\frac{z_1}{z_2} = \frac{r_1 e^{i\theta_1}}{r_2 e^{i\theta_2}} = \frac{r_1}{r_2} e^{i(\theta_1 - \theta_2)}$$

$$\arg \frac{z_1}{z_2} = \theta_1 - \theta_2$$

Let us pick an arbitrary point s on the contour and draw a line from the zero z_1 to this point (Fig. 12-1c). The angle between this line and the horizontal, θ_{z1}, is equal to the argument of $(s - z_1)$. Now let the point s move completely around the contour. The arg $(s - z_1)$ or θ_{z1} will increase by 2π radians. Therefore the arg $F_{(s)}$ will increase by 2π radians for each zero inside the contour.

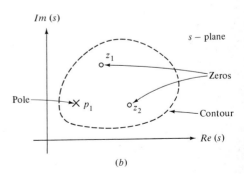

FIGURE 12-1b
s-plane location of zeros and poles.

(b)

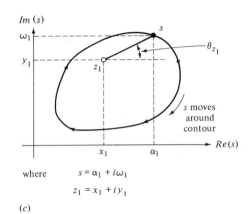

$$\theta_{z1} = \arctan\left(\frac{\omega_1 - y_1}{\alpha_1 - x_1}\right)$$

$$= \arctan\left[\frac{Im(s - z_1)}{Re(s - z_1)}\right]$$

$$= \arg(s - z_1)$$

where $\quad s = \alpha_1 + i\omega_1$

$\quad z_1 = x_1 + iy_1$

(c)

FIGURE 12-1c
Argument of $(s - z_1)$.

A similar development shows that the arg $F_{(s)}$ decreases by 2π for each pole inside the contour because of the negative sign in Eq. (12-3). Two zeros and one pole will mean that the arg $F_{(s)}$ must show a net increase of $+2\pi$. Thus a plot of $F_{(s)}$ in the complex F plane (real part of $F_{(s)}$ versus imaginary part of $F_{(s)}$) must encircle the origin once as s goes completely around the contour.

In this system $Z = 2$ and $P = 1$, and we have found that $N = Z - P = 2 - 1 = 1$. Generalizing to a system with Z zeros and P poles gives the desired theorem [Eq. (12-1)].

If any of the zeros or poles are repeated, of order M, they contribute $2\pi M$ radians. Thus Z is the number of zeros inside the contour with Mth-order zeros counted M times. And P is the number of poles inside the contour with Mth-order poles counted M times.

Application of $Z - P = N$ theorem to stability   To check the stability of a system, we are interested in the roots or zeros of the characteristic equation. If any of them lie in the right-half of the s plane, the system is unstable. For closed-loop stability the characteristic equation is

$$1 + B_{(s)}G_{M(s)} = 0 \qquad (12\text{-}4)$$

The function that we are interested in is

$$F_{(s)} = 1 + B_{(s)}G_{M(s)} \qquad (12\text{-}5)$$

If we pick a contour that goes completely around the entire right-half of the s plane and plot $1 + B_{(s)}G_{M(s)}$, Eq. (12-1) tells us that the number of encirclements of the origin in this $(1 + BG_M)$ plane will be equal to the difference between the zeros and poles of $1 + B_{(s)}G_{M(s)}$ that lie in the RHP. Figure 12-2 shows a case where there are two zeros in the RHP and no poles. There are two encirclements of the origin in the $(1 + BG_M)$ plane.

We are familiar with making polar plots of complex functions like $B_{(i\omega)}G_{M(i\omega)}$ in the BG_M plane. It is therefore easier to use the BG_M plane instead of the $(1 + BG_M)$ plane. The origin in the $(1 + BG_M)$ plane maps into the $(-1,0)$ point in the BG_M plane since the real part of every point is moved to the left one unit.

We then must look at the encirclements of the $(-1,0)$ point in the BG_M plane, instead of the encirclements of the origin in the $(1 + BG_M)$ plane.

After we map the contour into the BG_M plane and count the number N of encirclements of the $(-1,0)$ point, we know the difference between the number of zeros Z and the number of poles P that lie in the RHP. We want to find out if there are any zeros of $1 + B_{(s)}G_{M(s)}$ in the RHP. Therefore we must find the number of poles in the RHP before we can determine the number of zeros.

$$Z = N + P \qquad (12\text{-}6)$$

If the process is open-loop stable, $1 + B_{(s)}G_{M(s)}$ will have no poles in the right-half of the s plane. The poles of $1 + B_{(s)}G_{M(s)}$ are the same as the poles of $B_{(s)}G_{M(s)}$. If the system is open-loop stable there can be no poles of $B_{(s)}G_{M(s)}$ in the RHP. Thus an open-loop stable process means that $P = 0$.

Therefore the number N of encirclements of the $(-1,0)$ point is equal to the number of zeros of $1 + B_{(s)}G_{M(s)}$ in the RHP for an open-loop stable process. Thus any encirclement means closed-loop instability.

If the process is open-loop unstable, $1 + B_{(s)}G_{M(s)}$ will have poles in the RHP. We can find out how many there are by using the Routh stability criterion on the open-loop characteristic equation:

$$P_{(s)}{}^M = 0 \qquad (12\text{-}7)$$

Once the number of poles P is known, the number of zeros can be found from Eq. (12-6).

This mapping of a contour in the s plane into the BG_M plane is illustrated in the examples below.

12-1.2 Examples

EXAMPLE 12-1 Consider our favorite process

$$G_{M(s)} = \frac{\frac{1}{8}}{(s + 1)^3}$$

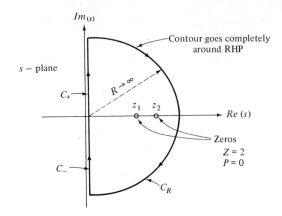

FIGURE 12-2a
s-plane area of interest.

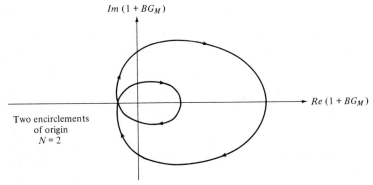

FIGURE 12-2b
$(1 + B_{(s)} G_{M(s)})$ plane.

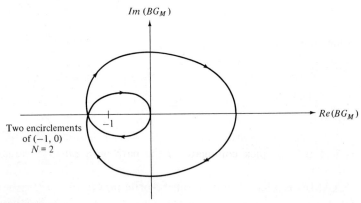

FIGURE 12-2c
$B_{(s)} G_{M(s)}$ plane.

With a proportional feedback controller, the open-loop system transfer function is

$$B_{(s)}G_{M(s)} = \frac{K_c/8}{(s+1)^3} \qquad (12\text{-}8)$$

This system is open-loop stable, so $P = 0$. The contour around the entire RHP is shown in Fig. 12-2a. Let us split it up into three parts: C_+, the path out along the positive imaginary axis from the origin; C_R, the path around the infinitely large semi-circle from $+\infty$ to $-\infty$; and C_-, the path back up the negative imaginary axis to the origin.

(a) C_+ contour: On the C_+ contour the variable s is a pure imaginary number. Thus $s = i\omega$ as ω goes from 0 to $+\infty$. Substituting $i\omega$ for s in the system open-loop transfer function gives

$$B_{(i\omega)}G_{M(i\omega)} = \frac{K_c/8}{(1+i\omega)^3} \qquad (12\text{-}9)$$

We now let ω take on values from 0 to $+\infty$ and plot the real and imaginary parts of $B_{(i\omega)}G_{M(i\omega)}$. This, of course, is just a polar plot of $B_{(s)}G_{M(s)}$ as sketched in Fig. 12-3a. The plot starts ($\omega = 0$) at $K_c/8$ on the positive real axis. It ends at the origin, as ω goes to $+\infty$, with a phase angle of $-270°$.

(b) C_R contour: On the C_R contour,

$$s = Re^{i\theta} \qquad (12\text{-}10)$$

R will go to infinity and θ will take on values from $+\pi/2$ through 0 to $-\pi/2$ radians. Substituting into $B_{(s)}G_{M(s)}$ gives

$$B_{(s)}G_{M(s)} = \frac{K_c/8}{(Re^{i\theta}+1)^3} \qquad (12\text{-}11)$$

As R becomes large, the $+1$ term in the denominator can be neglected.

$$\lim_{R\to\infty} BG_M = \lim_{R\to\infty} \left(\frac{K_c}{8R^3} e^{-3\theta i}\right) \qquad (12\text{-}12)$$

The argument of BG_M goes from $-3\pi/2$ through 0 to $+3\pi/2$ radians as θ goes from $+\pi/2$ to $-\pi/2$. The magnitude of BG_M goes to zero as R goes to infinity. The infinitely large semicircle in the s plane maps into a point (the origin) in the BG_M plane (Fig. 12-3b).

(c) C_- contour: On the C_- contour, $s = i\omega$ as ω goes from $-\infty$ to 0. BG_M on this path is just the complex conjugate of the path with positive values of frequency. See Fig. 12-3c.

The complete contour is shown in Fig. 12-3d. The bigger the value of K_c, the farther out on the positive real axis the BG_M plot starts, and the farther out on the negative real axis is the intersection of the BG_M plot with the axis.

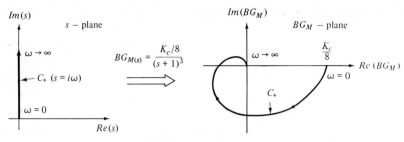

(a)   Contour C_+

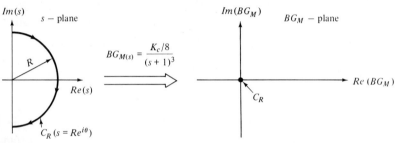

(b)   Contour C_R

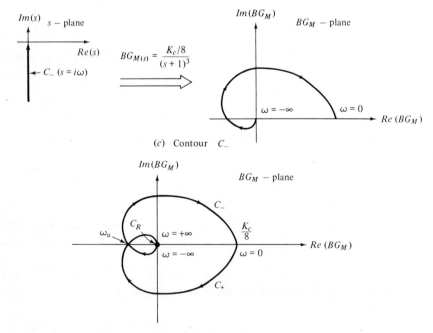

(c)   Contour C_-

(d)   Complete contour

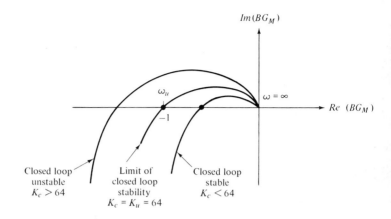

$Im(BG_M)$

ω_u

$\omega = \infty$

-1

$Re\ (BG_M)$

Closed loop
unstable
$K_c > 64$

Limit of
closed loop
stability
$K_c = K_u = 64$

Closed loop
stable
$K_c < 64$

(e) Intersections on negative real axis

FIGURE 12-3
Nyquist plots of three-CSTR system with proportional controller.

If the BG_M plot crosses the negative real axis beyond (to the left of) the critical $(-1,0)$ point, the system is closed-loop unstable. There would then be two encirclements of $(-1,0)$ and therefore $N = 2$. Since we know P is zero, there must be two zeros in the RHP.

If the BG_M plot crosses the negative real axis between the origin and the $(-1,0)$ point, the system is closed-loop stable. Now $N = 0$ and therefore $Z = N = 0$.

There is some critical value of gain K_c at which the BG_M plot goes right through the $(-1,0)$ point. This is the limit of closed-loop stability. See Fig. 12-3e. The value of K_c at the limit should be ultimate gain K_u that we have dealt with in Chaps. 10 and 11. Let us see if it is. At the limit of closed-loop stability,

$$B_{(i\omega)}G_{M(i\omega)} = -1 + 0i \qquad (12\text{-}13)$$

$$\left(\frac{K_c/8}{s^3 + 3s^2 + 3s + 1}\right)_{s = i\omega} = \frac{K_c/8}{(1 - 3\omega^2) + i(3\omega - \omega^3)}$$

$$= \frac{(K_c/8)(1 - 3\omega^2)}{(1 - 3\omega^2)^2 + (3\omega - \omega^3)^2} + i\frac{(K_c/8)(\omega^3 - 3\omega)}{(1 - 3\omega^2)^2 + (3\omega - \omega^3)^2} \qquad (12\text{-}14)$$

Equating the imaginary part of the above to zero gives

$$\frac{(K_c/8)(\omega^3 - 3\omega)}{(1 - 3\omega^2)^2 + (3\omega - \omega^3)^2} = 0$$

$$\Rightarrow \omega = \sqrt{3} = \omega_u \qquad (12\text{-}15)$$

This is the value of frequency at the intersection of the BG_M plot with the negative real axis. Equating the real part of Eq. (12-14) to -1 gives

$$\frac{(K_c/8)(1 - 3\omega^2)}{(1 - 3\omega^2)^2 + (3\omega - \omega^3)^2} = -1$$

$$\frac{(K_c/8)[1 - 3(3)]}{[1 - 3(3)]^2 + (3\sqrt{3} - 3\sqrt{3})^2} = -1$$

$$\frac{-K_c}{64} = -1 \qquad \Rightarrow K_c = 64 = K_u \qquad (12\text{-}16)$$

These are exactly the values of ultimate gain and ultimate frequency that we found in Chap. 11.   ////

EXAMPLE 12-2   The system of Example 11-4 is second order.

$$B_{(s)}G_{M(s)} = \frac{K_c}{(s + 1)(5s + 1)} \qquad (12\text{-}17)$$

It has two poles, both in the LHP: $s = -1$ and $s = -1/5$. Thus the number of poles of BG_M in the RHP is zero: $P = 0$. Let us break up the contour around the entire RHP into the same three parts used in the previous example.
(a) On C_+ contour: $s = i\omega$ as ω goes from 0 to $+\infty$.

$$B_{(s)}G_{M(s)} = \left(\frac{K_c}{5s^2 + 6s + 1}\right)_{s=i\omega} = \frac{K_c}{(1 - 5\omega^2) + i6\omega} \qquad (12\text{-}18)$$

Again, this is just a polar plot of the open-loop system transfer function.
(b) On C_R contour: $s = Re^{i\theta}$ as $R \to \infty$ and θ goes from $\pi/2$ to $-\pi/2$.

$$B_{(s)}G_{M(s)} = \frac{K_c}{(Re^{i\theta} + 1)(5Re^{i\theta} + 1)}$$

$$\lim_{R \to \infty} B_{(s)}G_{M(s)} = \lim_{R \to \infty} \left(\frac{K_c}{5R^2} e^{-2\theta i}\right) = 0 \qquad (12\text{-}19)$$

Thus the infinite semicircle again maps into the origin in the BG_M plane.
(c) On C_- contour: $s = i\omega$ as ω goes from $-\infty$ to 0. The $B_{(i\omega)}G_{M(i\omega)}$ curve for negative values of ω is the reflection over the real axis of the curve for positive values of ω.

The complete Nyquist plot is shown in Fig. 12-4a for several values of gain K_c. Notice that the curves will *never* encircle the $(-1,0)$ point, even as the gain is made infinitely large. Thus this second-order system can never be closed-loop unstable. This is exactly what our root locus curves showed in Chap. 11. As gain is increased,

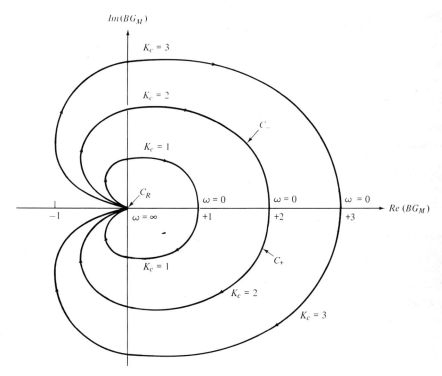

(a)   Second — order system

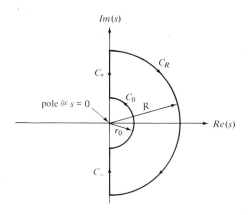

(b)   s — plane contour with integrator in system

FIGURE 12-4
(a) Nyquist plot of second-order system; (b) s-plane contour to avoid pole at origin.

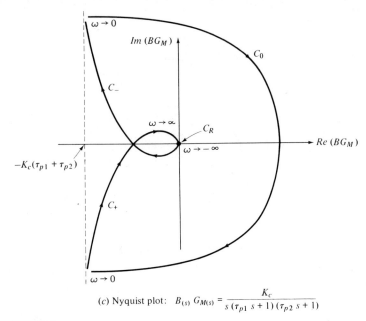

(c) Nyquist plot: $B_{(s)}\, G_{M(s)} = \dfrac{K_c}{s\,(\tau_{p1}\,s + 1)\,(\tau_{p2}\,s + 1)}$

FIGURE 12-4
(c) Nyquist plot of system with integrator.

the BG_M curve gets closer and closer to instability. The closeness to the $(-1,0)$ point is what we will use as a design specification in the frequency domain (Sec. 12-2).

////

EXAMPLE 12-3 If the open-loop transfer function of the system has poles that lie on the imaginary axis, the s-plane contour must be modified slightly to exclude the poles. A system with an integrator is a common example.

$$B_{(s)}G_{M(s)} = \frac{K_c}{s(\tau_{p1}s + 1)(\tau_{p2}s + 1)} \qquad (12\text{-}20)$$

This system has a pole at the origin. We pick a contour in the s plane that goes counterclockwise around the origin, excluding the pole from the area enclosed by the contour. As shown in Fig. 12-4b, the C_o contour is a semicircle of radius r_o; and r_o is made to approach zero.

(a) *On C_+ contour:* $s = i\omega$ as ω goes from r_o to R, with r_o going to 0 and R going to $+\infty$.

$$B_{(i\omega)}G_{M(i\omega)} = \frac{K_c}{i\omega(1 + i\omega\tau_{p1})(1 + i\omega\tau_{p2})}$$

$$= \frac{-K_c\omega(\tau_{p1} + \tau_{p2}) - iK_c(1 - \tau_{p1}\tau_{p2}\,\omega^2)}{\omega^3(\tau_{p1} + \tau_{p2})^2 + \omega(1 - \tau_{p1}\tau_{p2}\,\omega^2)^2} \qquad (12\text{-}21)$$

The polar plot is shown in Fig. 12-4c.

(b) *On C_R contour:* $s = Re^{i\theta}$

$$B_{(s)}G_{M(s)} = \frac{K_c}{Re^{i\theta}(1 + \tau_{p1}Re^{i\theta})(1 + \tau_{p2}Re^{i\theta})}$$

$$\lim_{R\to\infty} B_{(s)}G_{M(s)} = \lim_{R\to\infty} \left(\frac{K_c}{R^3\tau_{p1}\tau_{p2}} e^{-3\theta i} \right) = 0 \qquad (12\text{-}22)$$

The C_R contour maps into the origin in the BG_M plane.

(c) *On C_- contour:* $s = i\omega$ as ω goes from $-R$ to $-r_o$. The BG_M curve is the reflection over the real axis of the BG_M curve for the C_+ contour.

(d) *On C_o contour:* $\hspace{6cm} s = r_o e^{i\theta} \qquad (12\text{-}23)$

as r_o goes to zero and θ goes from $-\pi/2$ through 0 to $+\pi/2$ radians. The system transfer function $B_{(s)}G_{M(s)}$ becomes

$$B_{(s)}G_{M(s)} = \frac{K_c}{r_o e^{i\theta}(1 + \tau_{p1}r_o e^{i\theta})(1 + \tau_{p2}r_o e^{i\theta})} \qquad (12\text{-}24)$$

As r_o gets very small, the $\tau_{p1}r_o e^{i\theta}$ and $\tau_{p2}r_o e^{i\theta}$ terms become negligible compared with unity.

$$\lim_{r_o\to0} B_{(s)}G_{M(s)} = \lim_{r_o\to0} \frac{K_c}{r_o e^{i\theta}} = \lim_{r_o\to0} \left(\frac{K_c}{r_o} e^{-i\theta} \right) \qquad (12\text{-}25)$$

Thus the C_o contour maps into a semicircle in the BG_M plane that has a radius that goes to infinity and a phase angle that goes from $+\pi/2$ through 0 to $-\pi/2$. See Fig. 12-4c.

The Nyquist plot does not encircle the $(-1,0)$ point if the polar plot of $B_{(i\omega)}G_{M(i\omega)}$ crosses the negative real axis inside the unit circle. The system would then be closed-loop stable.

The maximum value of K_c for which the system is still closed-loop stable can be found by setting the real part of $B_{(i\omega)}G_{M(i\omega)}$ equal to -1 and the imaginary part equal to 0. The results are

$$K_u = \frac{\tau_{p1} + \tau_{p2}}{\tau_{p1}\tau_{p2}}$$

$$\omega_u = \frac{1}{\sqrt{\tau_{p1}\tau_{p2}}} \qquad (12\text{-}26)$$

////

As we have seen in the three examples above, the C_+ contour usually is the only one that we need to map into the BG_M plane. Therefore from now on we will make only polar (or Bode or Nichols) plots of $B_{(i\omega)}G_{M(i\omega)}$.

EXAMPLE 12-4   Figure 12-5a shows the polar plot of an interesting system that has conditional stability. The system open-loop transfer function has the form

$$B_{(s)}G_{M(s)} = \frac{K_c(\tau_{z1}s + 1)}{(\tau_{p1}s + 1)(\tau_{p2}s + 1)(\tau_{p3}s + 1)(\tau_{p4}s + 1)} \qquad (12\text{-}27)$$

If the controller gain K_c is such that the $(-1,0)$ point is in the stable region indicated in Fig. 12-5a, the system is closed-loop stable. Let us define three values of controller gain:

$$K_1 = value\ of\ K_c\ when \quad |B_{(i\omega_1)}G_{M(i\omega_1)}| = 1$$

$$K_2 = value\ of\ K_c\ when \quad |B_{(i\omega_2)}G_{M(i\omega_2)}| = 1$$

$$K_3 = value\ of\ K_c\ when \quad |B_{(i\omega_3)}G_{M(i\omega_3)}| = 1 \qquad (12\text{-}28)$$

The system is closed-loop stable for two ranges of feedback controller gain:

$$K_c < K_1$$

$$K_2 < K_c < K_3 \qquad (12\text{-}29)$$

This conditional stability is shown on a root locus plot for this system sketched in Fig. 12-5b.   ////

12-1.3   Representation

In Chap. 8 we presented three different kinds of graphs that were used to represent the frequency response of a system: Nyquist, Bode, and Nichols plots. The Nyquist stability criterion was developed in the previous section for Nyquist or polar plots.

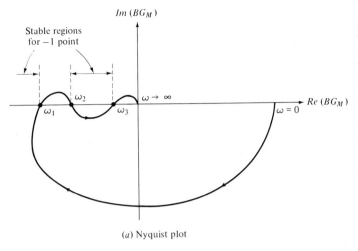

(a) Nyquist plot

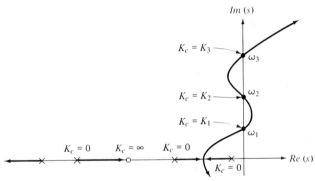

(b) Root locus plot

FIGURE 12-5
System with conditional stability.

The critical point for closed-loop stability was shown to be the $(-1,0)$ point on the Nyquist plot.

Naturally we also can show closed-loop stability or instability on Bode and Nichols plots. The $(-1,0)$ point has a phase angle of $-180°$ and a magnitude of unity or a log modulus of zero decibels. The stability limit on Bode and Nichols plots is, therefore, the $(0 \text{ db}, -180°)$ point. At the limit of closed-loop stability,

$$L = 0 \text{ db}$$

$$\theta = -180° \qquad (12\text{-}30)$$

The system is closed-loop stable if

$$L < 0 \text{ db} \qquad \text{at } \theta = -180°$$
$$\theta > -180° \qquad \text{at } L = 0 \text{ db} \qquad (12\text{-}31)$$

Figure 12-6 illustrates stable and unstable closed-loop systems on the three types of plots.

Keep in mind that we are talking about *closed-loop* stability and that we are studying it by making frequency-response plots of the *open-loop* system transfer function. We are also considering open-loop stable systems most of the time. We will show how to deal with an open-loop unstable process in Sec. 12-4.

12-2 SPECIFICATIONS IN THE FREQUENCY DOMAIN

There are two basic types of specifications that are commonly used in the frequency domain. The first type (*phase margin* and *gain margin*) specifies how near the open-loop system polar plot is to the critical $(-1,0)$ point. The second type (*maximum closed-loop log modulus*) specifies the height of the resonant peak in the log modulus Bode plot of the closed-loop system.

These specifications are easy to use, as we will show with some examples in Sec. 12-4. They can be related qualitatively to time-domain specifications such as time constants and damping coefficients.

12-2.1 Phase Margin

Phase margin (PM) is defined as the angle between the negative real axis and a radial line drawn from the origin to the point where the BG_M polar plot intersects the unit circle. See Fig. 12-7. The definition is more compact in equation form.

$$\text{PM} = 180° + (\text{arg } BG_M)_{|BG_M|=1} \qquad (12\text{-}32)$$

If the BG_M polar plot goes through the $(-1,0)$ point, the phase margin is zero. If the BG_M polar plot crosses the negative real axis to the right of the $(-1,0)$ point, the phase margin will be some positive angle. The bigger the phase margin, the more stable the closed-loop system will be. A negative phase margin means an unstable closed-loop system.

Phase margins of around 45° are often used. Figure 12-7 shows how phase margin is found on Bode and Nichols plots.

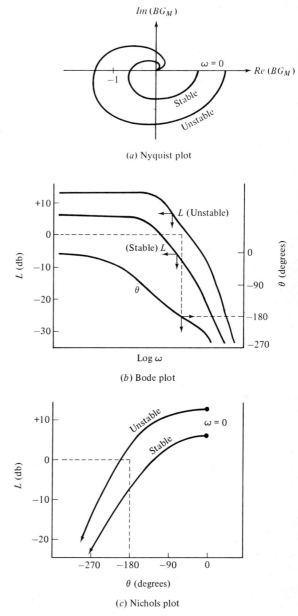

(a) Nyquist plot

(b) Bode plot

(c) Nichols plot

FIGURE 12-6
Stable and unstable closed-loop systems in Nyquist, Bode, and Nichols plots.

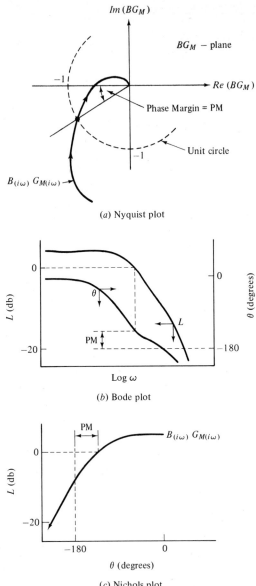

(a) Nyquist plot

(b) Bode plot

(c) Nichols plot

FIGURE 12-7
Phase margin.

12-2.2 Gain Margin

Gain margin (GM) is defined as the reciprocal of the intersection of the BG_M polar plot on the negative real axis.

$$GM = \frac{1}{|BG_M|_{\arg BG_M = -180°}} \qquad (12\text{-}33)$$

Figure 12-8 shows gain margins on Nyquist, Bode and Nichols plots. Gain margins are sometimes reported in decibels.

If the BG_M curve goes through the critical $(-1, 0)$ point, the gain margin is unity (0 db). If the BG_M curve crosses the negative real axis between the origin and -1, the gain margin will be greater than 1. Therefore, the bigger the gain margin, the more stable the closed-loop system will be. Gain margins of around 2 are often used. As we will see in the examples of Sec. 12-4, the actual specification used depends on the kind of system.

A system must be third or higher order (or have dead time) to have a meaningful gain margin. Polar plots for first- and second-order systems do not intersect the negative real axis.

12-2.3 Maximum Closed-loop Log Modulus (LM)

The LM specification is probably the most generally useful frequency-domain specification. This is because it can be meaningfully applied to many types of systems. It refers to the closed-loop servo transfer function:

$$\frac{X_{(s)}}{X_{(s)}^{\text{set}}} = \frac{B_{(s)} G_{M(s)}}{1 + B_{(s)} G_{M(s)}} \qquad (12\text{-}34)$$

The feedback controller is designed to give a specified maximum resonant peak or hump on the *closed-loop* log modulus Bode plot.

All the Nyquist, Bode, and Nichols plots discussed in previous sections have been for *open-loop* system transfer functions $B_{(i\omega)} G_{M(i\omega)}$. Plots can be made of closed-loop transfer functions. The two closed-loop transfer functions that we derived in Chap. 11 show how the output $X_{(s)}$ is affected in a closed-loop system by a set-point input $X_{(s)}^{\text{set}}$ and by a load $L_{(s)}$. Equation (12-34) gives the former and Eq. (12-35) gives the latter.

$$\frac{X_{(s)}}{L_{(s)}} = \frac{G_{L(s)}}{1 + B_{(s)} G_{M(s)}} \qquad (12\text{-}35)$$

Typical log modulus Bode plots of these two closed-loop transfer functions are shown in Fig. 12-9a.

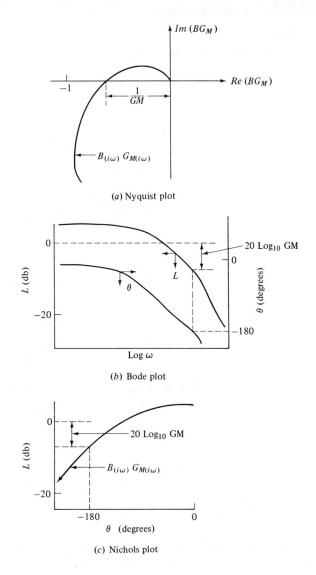

(a) Nyquist plot

(b) Bode plot

(c) Nichols plot

FIGURE 12-8
Gain margin.

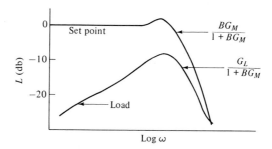

(a) Load and set-point closed-loop transfer functions

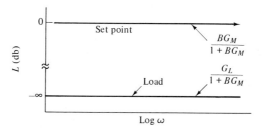

(b) Ideal load and set-point closed-loop transfer functions

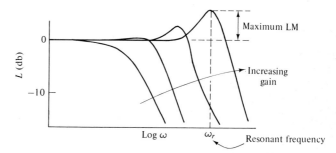

(c) Typical set-point closed-loop transfer functions

FIGURE 12-9
Closed-loop log modulus curves.

If it were possible to achieve perfect or ideal control, the two ideal closed-loop transfer functions would be

$$\left(\frac{X_{(s)}}{X_{(s)}^{\text{set}}}\right)_{\text{ideal}} = 1 \qquad (12\text{-}36)$$

$$\left(\frac{X_{(s)}}{L_{(s)}}\right)_{\text{ideal}} = 0 \qquad (12\text{-}37)$$

Equation (12-36) says we want the output to track the set point perfectly for all frequencies. Equation (12-37) says we want the output to be unaffected by the load disturbance for all frequencies. Log modulus curves for these ideal (but unattainable) closed-loop systems are shown in Fig. 12-9b.

In most systems, the closed-loop servo or set-point log modulus curves (X/X^{set}) move out to higher frequencies as the gain is increased. This is desirable since it means a faster closed-loop system.

But the height of the resonant peak also increases with gain. This means that the closed-loop system becomes more underdamped. To refresh your memory of what a second-order underdamped system frequency response looks like, see Fig. 8-19. The effects of increasing gain are sketched in Fig. 12-9c.

A commonly used closed-loop LM specification is +2 db. The controller parameters are adjusted to give a maximum peak in the closed-loop servo log modulus curve of +2 db. This corresponds to a magnitude ratio of 1.3 and is approximately equivalent to an underdamped system with a damping coefficient of 0.4.

Both the open-loop and the closed-loop frequency-response curves can be easily generated on a digital computer by using the complex variables and functions discussed in Chap. 8. The frequency-response curves for the closed-loop servo (set-point) transfer function can also be found fairly easily graphically by using a Nichols chart. A Nichols chart is a graph that shows what the closed-loop log modulus L_c and phase angle θ_c are for any given open-loop log modulus L_o and phase angle θ_o. See Fig. 12-10a. The graph is a general one and can be used for any system. To prove this, let us choose any arbitrary open-loop $B_{(i\omega)} G_{M(i\omega)}$. In polar form the open-loop complex function is

$$B_{(i\omega)} G_{M(i\omega)} = r_o e^{i\theta_o} \qquad (12\text{-}38)$$

where r_o = magnitude of open-loop complex function at frequency ω
θ_o = argument of open-loop complex function at frequency ω

The closed-loop servo transfer function is then

$$\frac{BG_M}{1 + BG_M} = \frac{r_o e^{i\theta_o}}{1 + r_o e^{i\theta_o}} \qquad (12\text{-}39)$$

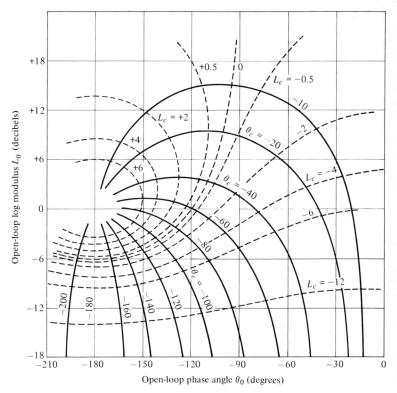

FIGURE 12-10a
Nichols chart.

Putting this into polar form also gives

$$r_c e^{i\theta_c} = \frac{r_o e^{i\theta_o}}{1 + r_o e^{i\theta_o}} \qquad (12\text{-}40)$$

where r_c = magnitude of closed-loop complex function at frequency ω
$\quad\quad\;\theta_c$ = argument of closed-loop complex function at frequency ω

Equation (12-40) can be rearranged to get r_c and θ_c as explicit functions of r_o and θ_o.

$$r_c = \frac{r_o}{\sqrt{1 + 2r_o \cos\theta_o + r_o^2}}$$

$$\theta_c = \arctan\left(\frac{\sin\theta_o}{r_o + \cos\theta_o}\right) \qquad (12\text{-}41)$$

Thus, for any arbitrary system with a given r_o and θ_o, Eqs. (12-41) give the closed-loop r_c and θ_c. The Nichols chart is a plot of these relationships.

To use a Nichols chart, we first construct the open-loop BG_M Bode plots. Then we draw an open-loop Nichols plot of $B_{(i\omega)} G_{M(i\omega)}$. Finally we sketch this open-loop curve of L_o versus θ_o onto a Nichols chart. At each point on this curve (which corresponds to a certain value of frequency), the values of the closed-loop log modulus L_c and phase angle θ_c can be read off. Figure 12-10b is a Nichols chart with two BG_M curves plotted on it. They are from the three-CSTR system with a proportional controller.

$$B_{(s)} G_{M(s)} = \frac{K_c/8}{(s+1)^3} \qquad (12\text{-}42)$$

The two curves have two different values of gain: $K_c = 8$ and $K_c = 20$. The open-loop Bode plots of BG_M and the closed-loop Bode plots of $BG_M/(1 + BG_M)$, with $K_c = 20$, are given in Fig. 12-11.

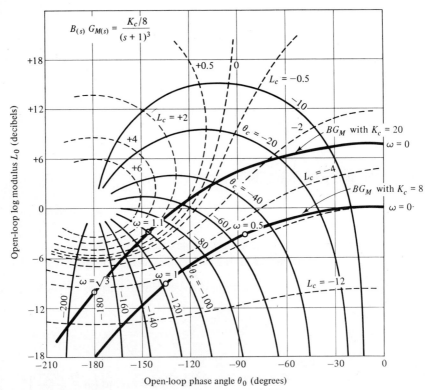

FIGURE 12-10b
Nichols chart with a three-CSTR system open-loop $B_{(i\omega)} G_{M(i\omega)}$ plotted.

The lines of constant closed-loop log modulus L_c are part of a Nichols chart. If we are designing a closed-loop system for an LM specification, we merely have to adjust the controller type and settings so that the open-loop BG_M curve is tangent to the desired L_c line on the Nichols chart. For example, the BG_M curve in Fig. 12-10b with $K_c = 20$ is just tangent to the +2-db L_c line of the Nichols chart. The value of frequency at the point of tangency, 1.1 radians/minute, is the closed-loop resonant frequency ω_r. It and the peak in the log modulus plot are clearly seen in the closed-loop curves in Fig. 12-11.

These lines of constant closed-loop log modulus (or magnitude ratio) and phase angle can also be drawn using polar or Nyquist coordinates.[1]

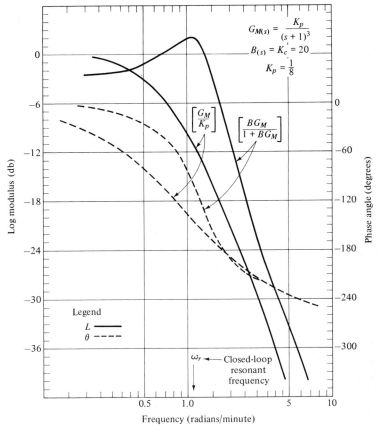

FIGURE 12-11
Open-loop and closed-loop Bode plots for a three-CSTR system.

[1] John J. D'Azzo and Constantine H. Houpis, "Feedback Control System Analysis and Synthesis," 2d ed., p. 365, McGraw-Hill, 1965.

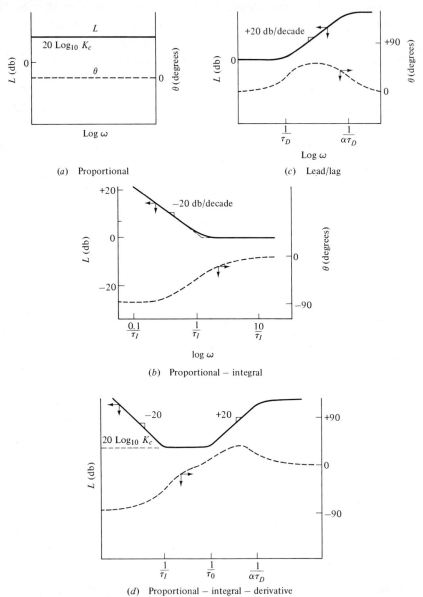

FIGURE 12-12
Bode plots of controllers.

12-3   FREQUENCY RESPONSE OF FEEDBACK CONTROLLERS

Before we give some examples of the design of feedback controllers in the frequency domain, it would be wise to show what the common P, PI, and PID controllers look like in the frequency domain. These will be the $B_{(i\omega)}$'s that we will add to the process $G_{M(i\omega)}$ to get the total open-loop Bode plots of $B_{(i\omega)} G_{M(i\omega)}$.

12-3.1   Proportional Controller (P)

$$B_{(s)} = K_c$$

$$B_{(i\omega)} = K_c \qquad (12\text{-}43)$$

A proportional controller merely multiplies the magnitude of $G_{M(i\omega)}$ at every frequency by a constant K_c. On a Bode plot, this means a proportional controller raises the log modulus curve by $20 \log K_c$ decibels but has no effect on the phase-angle curve. See Fig. 12-12a.

12-3.2   Proportional-Integral Controller (PI)

$$B_{(s)} = K_c \left(1 + \frac{1}{\tau_I} \frac{1}{s} \right)$$

$$B_{(i\omega)} = K_c \frac{\tau_I \omega i + 1}{\tau_I \omega i} \qquad (12\text{-}44)$$

The Bode plot of this combination of an integrator and a first-order lead is shown in Fig. 12-12b. At low frequencies, a PI controller amplifies magnitudes and contributes $-90°$ of phase-angle lag. This loss of phase angle is undesirable from a dynamic standpoint since it moves the BG_M polar plot closer to the $(-1,0)$ point.

12-3.3   Proportional-Integral-Derivative Controller (PID)

$$B_{(s)} = K_c \left(1 + \frac{1}{\tau_I s} \right) \left(\frac{\tau_D s + 1}{\alpha \tau_D s + 1} \right) \qquad (12\text{-}45)$$

The Bode plot for the lead-lag element is sketched in Fig. 12-12c. It contributes positive phase-angle advance over a range of frequencies between $1/\tau_D$ and $1/\alpha\tau_D$.

The lead-lag element can move the BG_M curve away from the $(-1,0)$ point and improve stability. When the derivative setting on a PID controller is tuned, the location of the phase-angle advance is shifted so that it occurs near the critical $(-1,0)$ point.

12-4 EXAMPLES

12-4.1 Three-CSTR System

The process open-loop transfer function is

$$G_{M(s)} = \frac{\frac{1}{8}}{(s+1)^3}$$

Before we design controllers in the frequency domain, it might be interesting to see what the frequency-domain indicators of closed-loop performance turn out to be when the Ziegler-Nichols settings are used on this system. Table 12-1 shows the phase and gain margins and the maximum closed-loop log moduli that the Ziegler-Nichols settings give. Also shown in Table 12-1 are the results when the settings for a damping coefficient of 0.316 are used. See Table 11-1.

The Ziegler-Nichols settings give quite small phase and gain margins and large maximum closed-loop log moduli. The $\zeta = 0.316$ settings are more conservative. Figure 12-13 shows the closed-loop and open-loop Bode plots for the PI controllers with the two different settings.

Now we are ready to find the controller settings required to give various frequency-domain specifications with P, PI, and PID controllers.

Proportional controller

GAIN MARGIN Suppose we want to find the value of feedback controller gain K_c that gives GM = 2. We must find the value of K_c that makes the Nyquist plot of

$$B_{(s)} G_{M(s)} = \frac{K_c/8}{(s+1)^3}$$

Table 12-1 FREQUENCY-DOMAIN INDICATORS THAT RESULT
FROM ZIEGLER-NICHOLS SETTINGS AND 0.316 DAMPING
COEFFICIENT SETTINGS FOR P, PI, AND PID CONTROLLERS

	Ziegler-Nichols			0.316 damping coefficient			
	P	PI	PID	P	PI	PID	PID
K_c	32	29.1	37.6	17	13	30	17
τ_I	...	3.03	1.82	...	3.03	1.82	1.82
τ_D	...	...	0.45	...	...	0.9	0.45
Phase margin PM (degrees)	28	13	22	64	52	38	41
Gain margin GM	2	1.6	7	3.8	3.5	10	15
LM (db)†	6.9	13	8.3	0.5	1.9	3.8	3.2
Resonant frequency ω_r (radians/minute)	1.3	1.3	1.6	1.0	0.8	1.6	1.0

† Maximum closed-loop log modulus.

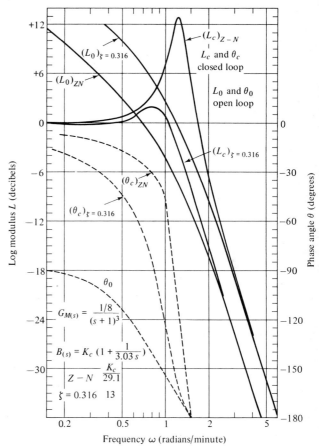

FIGURE 12-13

Bode plots of open-loop BG_M and closed-loop $BG_M/(1 + BG_M)$ for a three-CSTR system and PI controllers.

cross the negative real axis at $(-0.5,0)$. As shown in Fig. 12-14a, the ultimate gain is 64. Thus a gain of 32 will reduce the magnitude of each point by one-half and make the BG_M polar curve pass through the $(-0.5,0)$ point.

Figure 12-15 shows the same result in Bode-plot form. When the phase angle is $-180°$ (at frequency $\omega_u = \sqrt{3}$), the magnitude must be 0.5 or the log modulus must be -6 db. Thus the log modulus curve must be raised $+12$ db (gain 4) above its position when the gain is 8. Therefore the total gain must be 32 for a $GM = 2$. Notice that this is the Ziegler-Nichols setting.

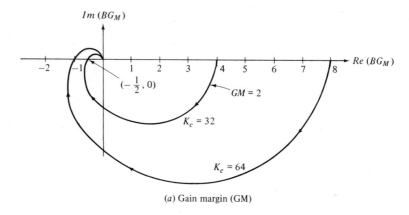

(a) Gain margin (GM)

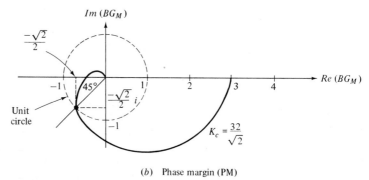

(b)   Phase margin (PM)

FIGURE 12-14
Nyquist plots for a three-CSTR system with proportional controllers.

PHASE MARGIN   To get a 45° phase margin we must find the value of K_c that makes the Nyquist plot pass through the unit circle when the phase angle is $-135°$, as shown in Fig. 12-14b. The real and imaginary parts of BG_M [Eq. (12-14)] must both be equal to $-\frac{1}{2}\sqrt{2}$. Solving the two simultaneous equations gives

$$K_c = \frac{32}{\sqrt{2}} = 22.6$$

$$\omega = 1 \text{ radian/minute}$$

On a Bode plot (Fig. 12-15), the log modulus curve of BG_M must pass through the 0-db point when the phase-angle curve is at $-135°$. This occurs at $\omega = 1$ radian/minute. The log modulus curve for $K_c = 8$ must be raised $+9$ db (gain 2.82). Therefore the gain must be $8(2.82) = 22.6$.

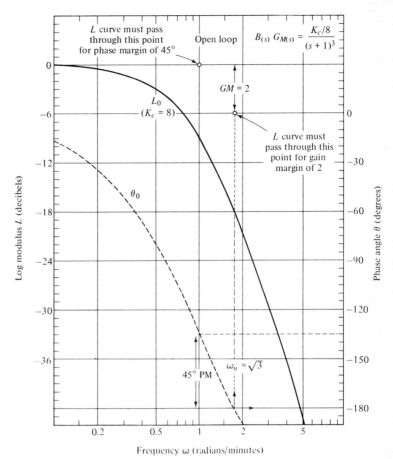

FIGURE 12-15
Bode plots of a three-CSTR system with proportional controller.

Notice that this gain is lower than that needed to give a gain margin of 2. The gain margin with a K_c of 22.6 can be easily found from the Bode plot. When the phase angle is $-180°$, the log modulus is -18 db (for $K_c = 8$). If a gain of 22.6 is used, the log modulus is raised $+9$ db. The log modulus is now -9 db at the $-180°$ frequency, giving a gain margin of 2.82.

MAXIMUM CLOSED-LOOP LOG MODULUS (LM) We have already designed in Sec. 12-2.3 a proportional controller that gave an LM of $+2$ db. Figure 12-10b gives a Nichols chart with the BG_M curve for this system. A gain of 20 makes the open-loop BG_M curve tangent to the $+2$-db L_c curve.

From the three cases above we can conclude that, for this third-order system, the +2-db LM specification is the most conservative, the 45° PM is next, and the 2 GM gives the gain that is closest to instability.

Proportional-integral controllers A PI controller has two adjustable parameters, and therefore we should, theoretically, be able to set two frequency-domain specifications and find the values of τ_I and K_c that satisfy them. We cannot make this choice of specifications completely arbitrary. For example, we cannot achieve a 45° phase margin and a gain margin of 2 with a PI controller in this three-CSTR system. A PI controller cannot reshape the Nyquist plot to make it pass through both the $(-\frac{1}{2}\sqrt{2}, -\frac{1}{2}\sqrt{2})$ point and the $(-0.5, 0)$ point because of the loss of phase angle at low frequencies.

Let us design a PI controller for a +2-db LM specification. For proportional controllers, all we have to do is find the value of K_c that makes the BG_M curve on a Nichols chart tangent to the +2-db L_c line. For a PI controller there are two parameters to find. Design procedures and guides have been developed over the years for finding reasonable values of τ_I. The procedure is outlined below.

1 Plot the open-loop $G_{M(i\omega)}$ on a Bode and then on a Nichols plot (see Figs. 12-11 and 12-10b).
2 Move the G_M curve vertically on the Nichols chart until it is tangent to the +2-db L_c curve. Read off the resonant frequency ω_r. (Figure 12-10b shows $\omega_r = 1.1$.)
3 Set the integral time constant at

$$\frac{1}{\tau_I} = 0.2\omega_r \qquad (12\text{-}46)$$

$1/\tau_I$ is made smaller than ω_r in order to remove most of the integration phase-angle lag from the total phase-angle curve at the frequency where the resonant peak occurs. [For our example $1/\tau_I = 0.2(1.1) = 0.22$; $\tau_I = 4.5$ min.].
4 Plot $B_{(i\omega)} = (1 + i\omega\tau_I)/i\omega\tau_I$ on the Bode plot and add it to $G_{M(i\omega)}$ to get the total BG_M curves (Fig. 12-16).
5 Plot the open-loop $B_{(i\omega)} G_{M(i\omega)}$ curve on a Nichols chart (Fig. 12-17 shows the new BG_M curves for $K_c = 8$ and $K_c = 16$).
6 Move the BG_M curve vertically until it is tangent to the +2-db L_c line on the Nichols chart. The decibels that the plot must be moved give the controller gain (a gain of 16 is required in Fig. 12-17).
7 Find the new resonant frequency (the frequency at the point of tangency). If it has changed appreciably, repeat steps 3 to 6.

The time-domain performance of this PI controller is the +2-db curve shown in Fig. 10-13.

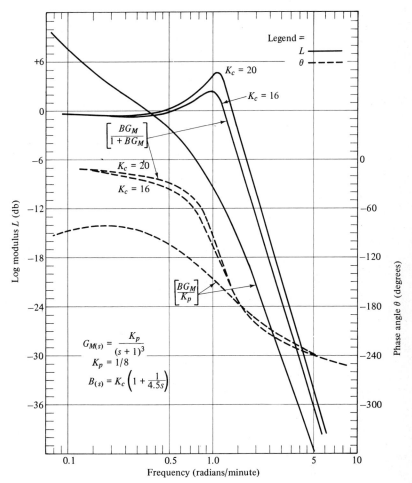

FIGURE 12-16
Open-loop and closed-loop Bode plots with PI controllers.

Proportional-integral-derivative controllers PID controllers provide three adjustable parameters. We should theoretically be able to satisfy three specifications. Design guides have been developed for finding reasonable values for τ_I and τ_D. The procedures are similar to those given above for PI design with the addition of picking τ_D to give its maximum phase-angle advance at the $-180°$ point of the BG_M curves for a PI controller.[1]

[1] For more details see P. S. Buckley, "Techniques of Process Control," p. 76, Wiley, 1963.

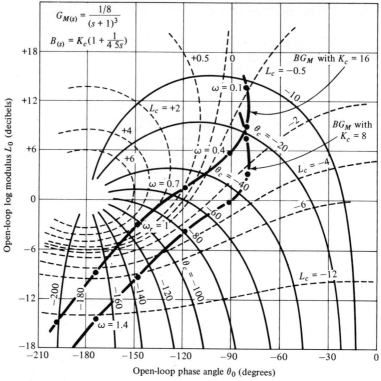

FIGURE 12-17
Nichols chart with PI controllers.

12-4.2 First-order Lag with Dead Time

Consider the open-loop process transfer function

$$G_{M(s)} = \frac{e^{-0.5s}}{s+1} \qquad (12\text{-}47)$$

The Bode plot of $G_{M(i\omega)}$ is given in Fig. 12-18 (and also Fig. 8-22). The ultimate gain is 3.9 (11.6 db), and the ultimate frequency is 3.7 radians/minutes. The Ziegler-Nichols controller settings and the corresponding phase and gain margins and log moduli are shown in Table 12-2. Figure 12-18 shows the closed-loop Bode plots for P and PI controllers with these settings.

Table 12-2 ZIEGLER-NICHOLS SETTINGS AND FREQUENCY-DOMAIN PERFORMANCE FOR FIRST-ORDER LAG WITH DEAD TIME

	P	PI
K_c	1.95	1.77
τ_I (minutes)	...	1.42
Gain margin	2	2
Phase margin (degrees)	72	53
Maximum closed-loop log modulus (db)	2	3.2

The effect of the dead time on the first-order lag is to drop the phase angle below $-180°$. The system can be made closed-loop unstable if the gain is high enough. Since there is always some dead time in any real system, all real processes can be made closed-loop unstable by making the feedback controller gain high enough.

12-4.3 Open-loop Unstable Process

Consider the open-loop unstable process

$$G_{M(s)} = \frac{K_p}{\tau_p s - 1} \qquad (12\text{-}48)$$

We found in Chap. 11 that we could make this system closed-loop stable by using a proportional controller with a gain K_c that was greater than $1/K_p$. Let us see if the Nyquist stability criterion leads us to the same conclusion.

First of all, we know that the open-loop system transfer function $B_{(s)} G_{M(s)}$ has a pole in the right-half of the s plane.

$$B_{(s)} G_{M(s)} = \frac{K_c K_p}{\tau_p s - 1} \qquad (12\text{-}49)$$

It is located at $s = +1/\tau_p$, and therefore $P = 1$.

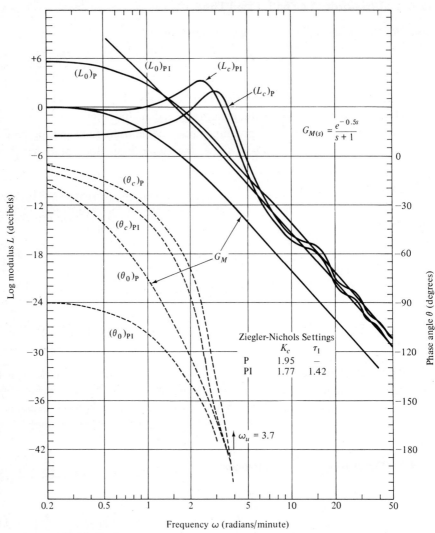

FIGURE 12-18
Open-loop and closed-loop plots for dead time with lag process.

On the C_+ contour up the imaginary axis, $s = i\omega$. We must make a polar plot of $B_{(i\omega)} G_{M(i\omega)}$.

$$B_{(i\omega)} G_{M(i\omega)} = \frac{K_c K_p}{-1 + i\omega\tau_p} = K_c K_p \frac{-1 - i\omega\tau_p}{1 + \omega^2\tau_p^2} \qquad (12\text{-}50)$$

Figure 12-19 shows that the curve starts ($\omega = 0$) at $-K_c K_p$ on the negative real axis. It ends at the origin, coming in with an angle of $-90°$.

The C_R contour maps into the origin. The C_- contour is the reflection of the C_+ over the real axis.

If $K_c > 1/K_p$, the $(-1,0)$ point is encircled. *But* the encirclement is in a counterclockwise direction. You will recall that all the curves considered up to now have encircled the $(-1,0)$ point in a clockwise direction. A clockwise encirclement is a positive N. A counterclockwise encirclement is a negative N.

Therefore $N = -1$ for this example if $K_c > 1/K_p$. The number of zeros of $1 + B_{(s)} G_{M(s)}$ in the RHP is then

$$Z = P + N = 1 + (-1) = 0$$

Thus the closed-loop system is stable if $K_c > 1/K_p$. This was the conclusion of Chap. 11.

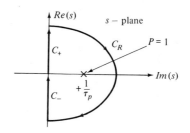

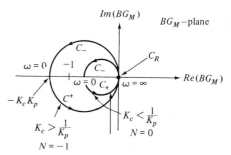

FIGURE 12-19
Nyquist stability criterion applied to an open-loop unstable process.

If $K_c < 1/K_p$ the $(-1,0)$ point is not encircled and $N = 0$. The number of zeros of $1 + B_{(s)} G_{M(s)}$ in the RHP is

$$Z = P + N = 1 + 0 = 1$$

The system is therefore closed-loop unstable if $K_c < 1/K_p$.

PROBLEMS

12-1 (a) Make Bode, Nyquist, and Nichols plots of the system with $K_c = 1$:

$$B_{(s)} G_{M(s)} = \frac{K_c}{(s+1)(5s+1)(\frac{1}{2}s+1)}$$

(b) Find the value of gain K_c that gives a phase margin of 45°. What is the gain margin?
(c) Find the value of gain K_c that gives a gain margin of 2. What is the phase margin?
(d) Find the value of gain K_c that gives a maximum closed-loop log modulus of $+2$ db. What are the gain and phase margins with this value of gain?
(e) Find the Ziegler-Nichols settings for this process and calculate the gain and phase margins and maximum closed-loop log moduli that they give for P, PI, and PID controllers.

12-2 (a) Make Bode, Nyquist, and Nichols plots of the system with $K_c = 1$:

$$B_{(s)} G_{M(s)} = \frac{K_c(\frac{1}{2}s+1)}{(s+1)(5s+1)}$$

(b) Find the value of gain K_c that gives a phase margin of 45°. What is the maximum closed-loop log modulus with this value of gain?
(c) Find the value of gain K_c that gives a maximum closed-loop log modulus of $+2$ db. What is the phase margin with this value of gain?

12-3 (a) Make Bode, Nyquist, and Nichols plots of the system with $K_c = 1$:

$$B_{(s)} G_{M(s)} = \frac{K_c(-3s+1)}{(s+1)(5s+1)}$$

(b) Find the ultimate gain and frequency.
(c) Find the value of K_c that gives a phase margin of 45°.
(d) Find the value of K_c that gives a gain margin of 2.
(e) Find the value of K_c that gives a maximum closed-loop log modulus of $+2$ db.

12-4 Repeat Prob. 12-3 for the system

$$B_{(s)} G_{M(s)} = K_c\left(1 + \frac{1}{2s}\right)\frac{-3s+1}{(s+1)(5s+1)}$$

12-5 How would you use the $Z - P = N$ theorem to develop a test for open-loop stability?

12-6 Suppose the C_0 contour of Example 12-3 had been chosen to go clockwise around the origin and thus included the pole at $s = 0$ inside the area. Sketch the BG_M-plane curves. Are the conclusions about closed-loop stability still the same?

12-7 (*a*) Make Bode plots of $B_{(i\omega)}G_{M(i\omega)}$ for the liquid-level control system of Prob. 11-6 with a **PI** controller. Use values of $K_c = 0.1$ and $K_c = 1$. The integral time constant is $\tau_I = 10$ min.

(*b*) Calculate phase margins with these two values of gain. Are your results unexpected?

(*c*) Add 0.1 min of dead time to the process, and make a plot showing how phase margin varies with gain K_c.

12-8 (*a*) Sketch Bode, Nichols, and Nyquist plots of the closed-loop servo and load transfer functions of the process

$$G_{L(s)} = G_{M(s)} = \frac{1}{10s + 1}$$

$$B_{(s)} = 6\left(1 + \frac{1}{6s}\right)$$

(*b*) Calculate the phase margin and maximum closed-loop log modulus for the system.

12-9 (*a*) Design a proportional controller that gives a phase margin of 45° with the process of Probs. 10-4 and 11-2. What is the gain margin with this value of K_c?

(*b*) Design a proportional controller that gives a gain margin of 2 for this process. What is the phase margin?

(*c*) Design a PI controller for this process that gives a +2-db maximum closed-loop log modulus, using the recommended procedure of Sec. 12-4.

12-10 Using a first-order Pade approximation of dead time, find the ultimate gain and frequency of the system

$$B_{(s)}G_{M(s)} = \frac{K_c e^{-0.5s}}{s + 1}$$

Compare your answers with Sec. 12-4.2.

12-11 (*a*) Draw Bode, Nyquist, and Nichols plots of the system

$$B_{(s)}G_{M(s)} = \frac{K_c}{(s + 1)(s + 5)(s - 0.5)}$$

(*b*) Use the Nyquist stability criterion to find the values of K_c for which the system is closed-loop stable.

12-12 (*a*) Make Nyquist and Bode plots of the open-loop transfer function

$$B_{(s)}G_{M(s)} = \frac{K_c}{s^2(s + 1)}$$

(*b*) Is this system closed-loop stable? Will using a PI controller stabilize it?

(*c*) Will a lead-lag element used as a feedback controller provide enough phase-angle advance to meet a 45° phase-margin specification? Will two lead-lags in series be enough?

(*d*) Use two elements and find the values of τ_D and K_c that give a 45° phase margin. What is the gain margin?

$$B_{(s)} = K_c \left[\frac{\tau_D s + 1}{(\tau_D/20)s + 1} \right]^2$$

12-13 Find the largest value of dead time D that can be tolerated in a process $G_{M(s)} = e^{-Ds}/s$ and still achieve a 45° phase margin with a **PI** feedback controller having a reset time constant $\tau_I = 1$ min. Find the value of gain K_c that gives the 45° of phase margin with the value of dead time found above.

12-14 A distillation column has the following four open-loop transfer functions:

$$\frac{x_D}{R} = \frac{0.0092}{(5s+1)^2} \qquad \frac{x_D}{V} = \frac{-0.0088}{(5s+1)^2}$$

$$\frac{x_B}{R} = \frac{0.01e^{-1.5s}}{12.5s+1} \qquad \frac{x_B}{V} = \frac{-0.0104}{11.1s+1}$$

PI controllers are used at both ends of the column, sensing x_D and manipulating R and sensing x_B and manipulating V. The top-loop settings are $K_c = 1{,}000$ and $\tau_I = 5$. For the base loop they are $K_c = 1{,}000$ and $\tau_I = 1.25$.

(*a*) Find gain and phase margins for both loops individually.

(*b*) Find the gain and phase margins for the interacting system.

PART FIVE

Feedforward Control

All the control systems we have discussed, simulated, and designed thus far in this book have been feedback control devices. A deviation of an output variable from a set point is detected. This error signal is fed into a feedback controller that changes the manipulative variable. The controller makes no use of any information about the source, magnitude, or direction of the disturbance that has caused the output variable to change.

The next chapter discusses feedforward control systems. The basic idea of feedforward control is to sense a disturbance as it enters a process and then to make an appropriate change in the manipulative variable so that the output variable is undisturbed.

Feedforward control systems have gained wide acceptance in chemical engineering systems in the past decade. They have demonstrated their ability to improve control, sometimes quite spectacularly. We will illustrate this improvement in the next chapter by comparing the responses of systems with feedforward control and with conventional feedback control when load disturbances occur.

Feedforward control is probably used more in chemical engineering systems than in any other field of engineering. Our systems are often slow-moving, nonlinear, and multivariable and contain appreciable dead time. All these characteristics make life miserable for feedback controllers. Feedforward controllers can handle all these with relative ease.

13

FEEDFORWARD CONTROL

13-1 FUNDAMENTALS

The basic notion of feedforward control is to detect disturbances as they enter the
process and make adjustments in manipulative variables so that output variables are
held constant. We do not wait until the disturbance has worked its way through the
process and has disturbed everything to produce an error signal. If a disturbance can
be detected as it enters the process, it makes sense to take immediate action in order
to compensate for its effect on the process.

A block diagram of a simple open-loop system is sketched in Fig. 13-1. The
load disturbance $L_{(s)}$ and the manipulative variable $M_{(s)}$ affect the output variable
$X_{(s)}$. A conventional feedback control system is shown in Fig. 13-1b. The error
signal $E_{(s)}$ is fed into a feedback controller $B_{(s)}$ that changes the manipulative variable $M_{(s)}$.

Figure 13-1c shows a feedforward control system. The load disturbance $L_{(s)}$
still enters the process through the $G_{L(s)}$ process transfer function. The load disturbance is also fed into a feedforward control device that has a transfer function $F_{(s)}$.
The feedforward controller detects changes in the load $L_{(s)}$ and makes changes in the
manipulative variable $M_{(s)}$.

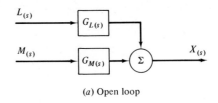

(a) Open loop

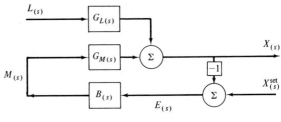

(b) Feedback control

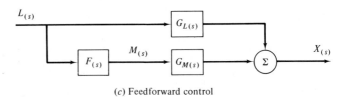

(c) Feedforward control

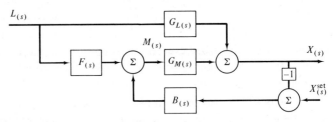

(d) Combined feedforward/feedback control

FIGURE 13-1
Block diagrams.

Thus the transfer function of a feedforward controller is a relationship between a manipulative variable and a disturbance variable (usually a load change).

$$F_{(s)} = \left(\frac{M}{L}\right)_{(s)} = \left(\frac{manipulative\ variable}{disturbance}\right)_{X\ is\ constant} \qquad (13\text{-}1)$$

To design a feedforward controller, that is, to find $F_{(s)}$, we must know both $G_{L(s)}$ and $G_{M(s)}$. The objective of most feedforward controllers is to hold the output variable constant at its steady-state value. Therefore the change or perturbation in $X_{(s)}$ should be zero. The output $X_{(s)}$ is given by the equation

$$X_{(s)} = G_{L(s)}\, L_{(s)} + G_{M(s)}\, M_{(s)} \qquad (13\text{-}2)$$

Setting $X_{(s)}$ equal to zero and solving for the relationship between $M_{(s)}$ and $L_{(s)}$ give the feedforward controller transfer function.

$$\left(\frac{M_{(s)}}{L_{(s)}}\right)_{X=0} \equiv F_{(s)} = \left(\frac{-G_L}{G_M}\right)_{(s)} \qquad (13\text{-}3)$$

EXAMPLE 13-1   Suppose we have a distillation column with the process transfer functions $G_{M(s)}$ and $G_{L(s)}$ relating bottoms composition x_B to steam flow rate F_S and to feed flow rate F_L.

$$\left(\frac{x_B}{F_S}\right)_{(s)} = G_{M(s)} = \frac{K_M}{\tau_M s + 1} \qquad \left(\frac{x_B}{F_L}\right)_{(s)} = G_{L(s)} = \frac{K_L}{\tau_L s + 1} \qquad (13\text{-}4)$$

All these variables are perturbations from steady-state. These transfer functions could have been derived from a mathematical model of the column or found experimentally from, perhaps, pulse tests.

We want to use a feedforward controller $F_{(s)}$ to make adjustments in steam flow to the reboiler, whenever the feed rate to the column changes, so that bottoms composition is held constant. The feedforward-controller design equation [Eq. (13-3)] gives

$$F_{(s)} = \frac{-G_{L(s)}}{G_{M(s)}} = \frac{-K_L/(\tau_L s + 1)}{K_M/(\tau_M s + 1)} = \frac{-K_L}{K_M} \frac{\tau_M s + 1}{\tau_L s + 1} \qquad (13\text{-}5)$$

The feedforward controller contains a steady-state gain and dynamic terms. For this system the dynamic element is a first-order lead-lag.   ////

The advantage of feedforward control over feedback control is that perfect control can, in theory, be achieved. A disturbance will produce no error in the controlled output variable if the feedforward control is perfect. The disadvantages of feedforward control are:

1 The disturbance must be detected. If we cannot measure it, we cannot use feedforward control. This is one reason why feedforward control for throughput changes is commonly used, whereas feedforward control for feed composition disturbances is only occasionally used. The former requires a flow-measurement device, which is almost always available. The latter requires a composition analyzer, which is seldom available.

2 We must know how the disturbance and manipulative variables affect the process. The transfer functions $G_{L(s)}$ and $G_{M(s)}$ must be known, at least approximately. One of the nice features of feedforward control is that even crude, inexact feedforward controllers can be quite effective in reducing the upset caused by a disturbance.

In practice, many feedforward control systems are implemented by using ratio control systems. In Example 13-1, the steam flow would be ratioed to the feed flow. The hardware used in these systems is discussed in Sec. 13-2.

Also, in practice, most feedforward control systems are installed as combined feedforward-feedback systems. The feedforward controller takes care of the large and frequent disturbances. The feedback controller takes care of any errors that come through the process because of inaccuracies in the feedforward controller or other unmeasured disturbances. Figure 13-1d shows the block diagram of a simple linear combined feedforward-feedback system. The manipulative variable is changed by both the feedforward controller and the feedback controller.

The addition of the feedforward controller has no effect on the closed-loop stability of the system for linear systems. The denominators of the closed-loop transfer functions are unchanged.

With feedback control:

$$\frac{X_{(s)}}{L_{(s)}} = \frac{G_{L(s)}}{1 + B_{(s)}G_{M(s)}} \qquad \frac{X_{(s)}}{X_{(s)}^{\text{set}}} = \frac{B_{(s)}G_{M(s)}}{1 + B_{(s)}G_{M(s)}} \qquad (13\text{-}6)$$

With feedforward-feedback control:

$$\frac{X_{(s)}}{L_{(s)}} = \frac{G_{L(s)} + F_{(s)}G_{M(s)}}{1 + B_{(s)}G_{M(s)}} \qquad \frac{X_{(s)}}{X_{(s)}^{\text{set}}} = \frac{B_{(s)}G_{M(s)}}{1 + B_{(s)}G_{M(s)}} \qquad (13\text{-}7)$$

In a nonlinear system the addition of a feedforward controller often permits tighter tuning of the feedback controller because the magnitude of the disturbances that the feedback controller must cope with is reduced.

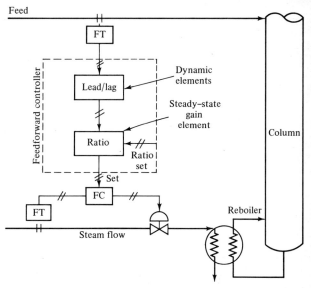

(a) Feedforward control

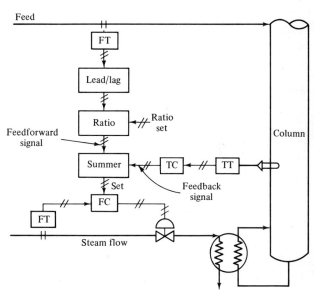

(b) Feedforward/feedback control with additive signals

FIGURE 13-2 (a and b)
Feedforward systems.

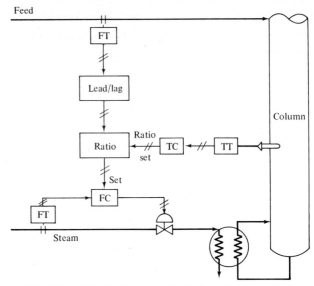

(*c*) Feedforward/feedback control with feedforward gain modified

FIGURE 13-2*c*

13-2   TYPICAL HARDWARE IMPLEMENTATION

Before we discuss the design of feedforward controllers and evaluate their performance, let us present some typical feedforward systems and illustrate the kind of
analog hardware that is frequently used. Implementation with a digital process
control computer follows the same basic strategy.

The distillation column of Example 13-1 is shown in Fig. 13-2*a*. The feedforward
control system consists of a ratio control system between steam flow to the reboiler and
feed-flow rate. The ratio device multiplies the feed-flow signal by an adjustable constant. This constant is set equal to the required feedforward gain [Eq. (13-5)]. If the
flow transmitter outputs are flow-squared signals, the ratio is set equal to the square of
the feedforward gain. The minus sign in Eq. (13-5) is taken care of by the negative
value of K_L. An increase in steam flow decreases x_B.

The dynamics of the feedforward controller are achieved with a lead-lag device on
the feed-flow transmitter output. These lead-lag, lag, and gain devices can be bought
commercially (see Sec. 10-1.5).

Figure 13-2*b* shows a combined feedforward-feedback system where the feedback
signal is added to the feedforward signal in a summing device.

Figure 13-2*c* shows a combined feedforward-feedback system where the feedback signal is used as the "ratio set" signal. In this system the feedback controller
changes the feedforward controller gain. The ratio box is a multiplier.

Figure 13-3 shows a combined feedforward-feedback control system for a distillation column where feed-rate disturbances are detected and both steam flow and reflux flow are changed to hold both overhead and bottoms compositions constant. Two feedforward controllers are required.

13-3 EXAMPLES OF FEEDFORWARD CONTROLLER DESIGN FOR LINEAR SYSTEMS

13-3.1 Three-CSTR System

Let us assume that a composition load disturbance C_{AL} enters the three-CSTR system through a first-order lag with a 5-min time constant, as shown in Fig. 13-4a. This might correspond to a physical system with a feed tank upstream of the three reactors. The composition of the stream entering the feed tank, C_{AL}, is continuously measured with an on-stream analyzer of some kind. The holdup time in the feed tank is 5 min. The block diagram can be rearranged to put it in terms of $G_{L(s)}$ and $G_{M(s)}$ as shown in Fig. 13-4b.

The feedforward control system that we wish to design is to detect the changes in load, C_{AL}, and manipulate C_{AM} to hold product concentration C_{A3} constant. Equation (13-3) gives the feedforward controller $F_{(s)}$:

$$F_{(s)} = \left(\frac{C_{AM}}{C_{AL}}\right)_{(s)} = \frac{-G_{L(s)}}{G_{M(s)}}$$

$$= \frac{-\frac{1}{8}/(s+1)^3(5s+1)}{\frac{1}{8}/(s+1)^3} = \frac{-1}{5s+1} \qquad (13\text{-}8)$$

The feedforward controller is a first-order lag with a steady-state gain of -1. The feedforward control system is shown in Fig. 13-4c. Figure 13-5 shows the response of the system to a step load disturbance in C_{AL} of 0.2 mole of A/ft^3. The feedforward controller gives perfect control of C_{A3}. The response with a PI feedback controller (tuned for LM = +2 db) is shown for comparison.

Also shown is the response with an imperfect feedforward controller. All the dynamics of the feedforward controller have been removed, so a step change in C_{AL} produces an instantaneous step change in the manipulative variable C_{AM}. This gain-only controller overcorrects initially and causes C_{A3} to deviate in the opposite direction. Eventually C_{A3} returns to its set-point value. This illustrates the need for dynamic elements to achieve good feedforward control.

The other curve shown in Fig. 13-5 is for a combined gain-only feedforward-feedback control system. The imperfect feedforward controller produces an error and causes the feedback controller to start changing C_{AM} initially in the wrong direction.

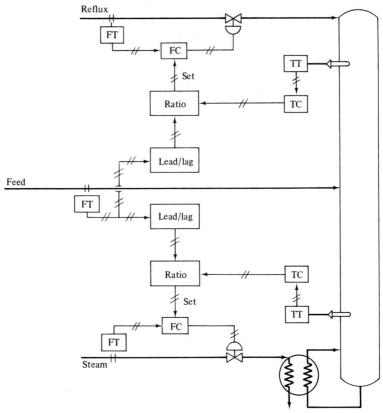

FIGURE 13-3
Combined feedforward-feedback system with two controlled variables.

13-3.2 Nonisothermal CSTR

The linearized equations describing the nonisothermal CSTR of Example 7-6 were

$$\frac{dC_A}{dt} = a_{11}C_A + a_{12}T + a_{13}C_{A0} + a_{15}F$$

$$\frac{dT}{dt} = a_{21}C_A + a_{22}T + a_{24}T_0 + a_{25}F + a_{26}T_J \qquad (13\text{-}9)$$

Laplace-transforming and rearranging to get the open-loop process transfer functions gave

$$C_{A(s)} = G_{11(s)}C_{A0(s)} + G_{12(s)}T_{0(s)} + G_{13(s)}F_{(s)} + G_{14(s)}T_{J(s)}$$

$$T_{(s)} = G_{21(s)}C_{A0(s)} + G_{22(s)}T_{0(s)} + G_{23(s)}F_{(s)} + G_{24(s)}T_{J(s)} \qquad (13\text{-}10)$$

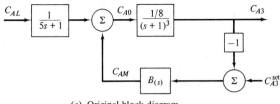

(a) Original block diagram

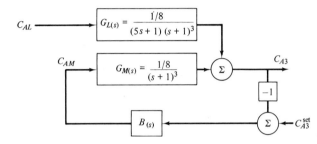

(b) Modified block diagram

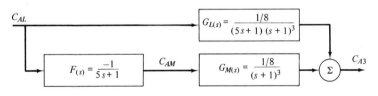

(c) Feed-forward control system

FIGURE 13-4
Three-CSTR system.

We will now consider several feedforward control systems with different controlled variables and different manipulative variables.

Control C_A with F   In the first system, reactor concentration C_A is to be held constant by manipulation of feed flow rate F. Disturbances occur in inlet temperature T_0 and feed concentration C_{A0}. We need two feedforward controllers that will change F as C_{A0} and T_0 change.

$$F_{1(s)} = \left(\frac{F}{C_{A0}}\right)_{(s)}$$

$$F_{2(s)} = \left(\frac{F}{T_0}\right)_{(s)} \qquad (13\text{-}11)$$

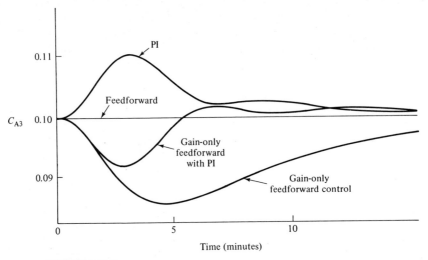

FIGURE 13-5
Step load response of a three-CSTR system with feedforward and feedback control.

The system is shown in Fig. 13-6a. Setting $C_{A(s)}$ to zero in Eqs. (13-10) gives these two feedforward controllers. Temperature is not controlled. T_J is also set equal to zero since jacket-cooling-water temperature is assumed to be constant.

$$C_{A(s)} = 0 = G_{11(s)} C_{A0} + G_{12(s)} T_0 + G_{13(s)} F$$

$$F_{(s)} = \frac{-G_{11}}{G_{13}} C_{A0(s)} + \frac{-G_{12}}{G_{13}} T_{0(s)}$$

$$= F_{1(s)} C_{A0(s)} + F_{2(s)} T_{0(s)} \qquad (13\text{-}12)$$

Substituting for the G_{ij}'s from Eq. (7-84) gives

$$F_{1(s)} = \left(\frac{-G_{11}}{G_{13}}\right)_{(s)} = \frac{-a_{13}(s - a_{22})}{a_{12}a_{25} + a_{15}(s - a_{22})}$$

$$F_{2(s)} = \left(\frac{-G_{12}}{G_{13}}\right)_{(s)} = \frac{-a_{12}a_{24}}{a_{12}a_{25} + a_{15}(s - a_{22})} \qquad (13\text{-}13)$$

The two feedforward controllers turn out to be a lead-lag and a lag.

Control of T with T_J   In the second system, reactor temperature T is to be held constant by manipulating cooling-jacket temperature T_J in the face of disturbances in feed concentration C_{A0}, feed temperature T_0, and feed rate F. We now need three feedforward controllers to handle all three disturbances, as shown in Fig. 13-6b. Setting T equal to zero in Eqs. (13-10) gives

$$0 = G_{21(s)} C_{A0} + G_{22(s)} T_0 + G_{23(s)} F + G_{24(s)} T_J$$

$$T_{J(s)} = \left(\frac{-G_{21}}{G_{24}}\right)_{(s)} C_{A0} + \left(\frac{-G_{22}}{G_{24}}\right)_{(s)} T_0 + \left(\frac{-G_{23}}{G_{24}}\right)_{(s)} F \qquad \text{(13-14)}$$

$$T_{J(s)} = F_{1(s)} C_{A0} + F_{2(s)} T_0 + F_{3(s)} F \qquad \text{(13-15)}$$

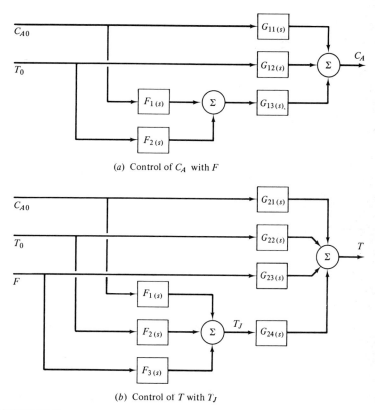

(a) Control of C_A with F

(b) Control of T with T_J

FIGURE 13-6
Nonisothermal CSTR linear feedforward control systems.

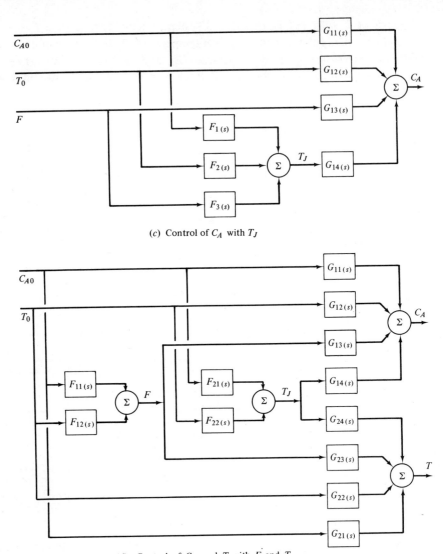

(c) Control of C_A with T_J

(d) Control of C_A and T with F and T_J

FIGURE 13-6 (c and d)

Substituting for the G_{ij}'s from Eq. (7-85) gives

$$F_{1(s)} = \frac{-a_{13}\,a_{21}}{a_{26}(s - a_{11})}$$

$$F_{2(s)} = \frac{-a_{24}}{a_{26}}$$

$$F_{3(s)} = \frac{-a_{15}\,a_{21} - a_{25}\,(s - a_{11})}{a_{26}(s - a_{11})} \qquad (13\text{-}16)$$

The three feedforward controllers are a lag, a gain, and a lead-lag.

Control of C_A with T_J   In the third system, reactor concentration C_A is to be held constant by manipulation of cooling-jacket temperature T_J. Disturbances are C_{A0}, T_0, and F. Three feedforward controllers are again needed (Fig. 13-6c).

$$0 = G_{11(s)}\,C_{A0} + G_{12(s)}\,T_0 + G_{13(s)}\,F + G_{14(s)}\,T_J$$

$$T_{J(s)} = \left(\frac{-G_{11}}{G_{14}}\right)_{(s)} C_{A0} + \left(\frac{-G_{12}}{G_{14}}\right)_{(s)} T_0 + \left(\frac{-G_{13}}{G_{14}}\right)_{(s)} F \qquad (13\text{-}17)$$

$$= F_{1(s)}\,C_{A0} + F_{2(s)}\,T_0 + F_{3(s)}\,F$$

$$F_{1(s)} = \frac{-a_{13}}{a_{12}\,a_{26}}(s - a_{22})$$

$$F_{2(s)} = \frac{-a_{24}}{a_{26}}$$

$$F_{3(s)} = \frac{-a_{12}\,a_{25} - a_{15}(s - a_{22})}{a_{12}\,a_{26}} \qquad (13\text{-}18)$$

One of the feedforward controllers, $F_{2(s)}$, is a gain element. It is exactly the same as the one found in the previous section. Thus T_J must be changed exactly the same to hold T or C_A constant when T_0 changes.

Two of the feedforward controllers, $F_{1(s)}$ and $F_{3(s)}$, are first-order leads. We know that a perfect lead element is physically unrealizable. This means that perfect feedforward compensation is impossible in this system.

When a desired feedforward control performance is specified, there is no guarantee that the required feedforward controller will be physically realizable. We may have specified an impossible performance. The mathematics tell us this quantitatively by yielding feedforward-controller transfer functions that have higher orders of s in the numerator than in the denominator or that have positive dead times.

Qualitatively, it is easy to see when a simple, single-variable feedforward control system will be workable. If the manipulative variable affects the controlled variable faster than the disturbance variable affects the controlled variable, the feedforward system should work well. If the reverse is true, feedforward control will probably be imperfect.

However, even imperfect feedforward control is often an improvement over feedback control alone. A derivative unit is used to approximate the lead action or the positive dead time.

Control of C_A and T with T_J and F Both reactor concentration C_A and temperature T are to be held constant. With two controlled variables we need two manipulative variables. We will choose feed flow rate F and cooling-jacket temperature T_J. Disturbances are C_{A0} and T_0.

Four feedforward controllers are needed, as shown in Fig. 13-6d.

$$F_{(s)} = F_{11(s)} C_{A0(s)} + F_{12(s)} T_{0(s)}$$

$$T_{J(s)} = F_{21(s)} C_{A0(s)} + F_{22(s)} T_{0(s)} \qquad (13\text{-}19)$$

Setting C_A and T equal to zero in Eqs. (13-10) gives, after considerable algebraic manipulation,

$$F_{11(s)} = \frac{G_{11} G_{24} - G_{14} G_{21}}{G_{14} G_{23} - G_{13} G_{24}} \qquad F_{12(s)} = \frac{G_{12} G_{24} - G_{14} G_{22}}{G_{14} G_{23} - G_{13} G_{24}}$$

$$F_{21(s)} = \frac{G_{13} G_{21} - G_{11} G_{23}}{G_{14} G_{23} - G_{13} G_{24}} \qquad F_{22(s)} = \frac{G_{13} G_{22} - G_{12} G_{23}}{G_{14} G_{23} - G_{13} G_{24}} \qquad (13\text{-}20)$$

Substituting for the G_{ij}'s gives

$$F_{11(s)} = \frac{-\bar{F}}{\bar{C}_{A0} - \bar{C}_A} \qquad\qquad F_{12(s)} = 0$$

$$F_{21(s)} = \frac{-C_p \bar{F}(\bar{T} - \bar{T}_0)}{UA(\bar{C}_{A0} - \bar{C}_A)} \qquad F_{22(s)} = \frac{-C_p \bar{F}}{UA} \qquad (13\text{-}21)$$

The four feedforward controllers are all gains with no dynamics. A step change in one of the disturbances requires an immediate change in the manipulative variables. The $F_{12(s)}$ feedforward controller is an interesting one. It tells us that throughput should not be changed when inlet temperature changes. Only cooling-jacket temperature T_J is changed. The negative gain in $F_{22(s)}$ makes sense; an increase in T_0 requires a decrease in T_J to remove the additional sensible heat.

In this case, and in many other systems, it is easier to solve for the feedforward controllers directly from the original linearized ordinary differential equations describing the system, instead of using the system transfer functions. C_A and T in Eqs. (13-9) are set equal to zero.

$$0 = 0 + 0 + a_{13} C_{A0} + a_{15} F$$

$$0 = 0 + 0 + a_{24} T_0 + a_{25} F + a_{26} T_J \qquad (13\text{-}22)$$

Solving for F and T_J gives

$$F_{(s)} = \frac{-a_{13}}{a_{15}} C_{A0(s)} + (0)T_{0(s)}$$

$$T_{J(s)} = \frac{a_{13}a_{25}}{a_{15}a_{26}} C_{A0(s)} + \frac{-a_{24}}{a_{26}} T_{0(s)} \qquad (13\text{-}23)$$

Substituting for the a_{ij}'s gives

$$F_{(s)} = \frac{-\bar{F}}{\bar{C}_{A0} - \bar{C}_A} C_{A0(s)} + (0)T_{0(s)}$$

$$T_{J(s)} = \frac{-\bar{F}C_p(\bar{T} - \bar{T}_0)}{UA(\bar{C}_{A0} - \bar{C}_A)} C_{A0(s)} + \frac{-C_p\bar{F}}{UA} T_{0(s)} \qquad (13\text{-}24)$$

13-3.3 Distillation Column

In Chap. 8 frequency-domain techniques were used to find the dynamics of a binary distillation column. The eight open-loop process transfer functions P_{ij} were found as eight Bode plots.

Feedforward transfer functions can be found for this system from the P_{ij}'s or from the intermediate g equations that are used in the stepping technique [Eqs. (8-69)]. These transfer functions are obtained in terms of the frequency-response curves of the feedforward controllers.

Various feedforward control systems could be considered. We could control x_D with R, or we could control x_B with V. Let us consider here the case where we want to control both x_D and x_B by manipulation of R and V. Disturbances are feed rate F and feed composition x_F. There are four feedforward transfer functions:

$$R_{(s)} = F_{11(s)}x_F + F_{12(s)}F$$
$$V_{(s)} = F_{21(s)}x_F + F_{22(s)}F \qquad (13\text{-}25)$$

The F_{ij}'s expressed in terms of the open-loop process transfer functions look like Eqs. (13-20). The F_{ij}'s expressed in terms of the g_{ij}'s of the stepping technique are given in the program of Fig. 8-27. Figure 13-7 gives the feedforward-controller Bode plots of $F_{12(i\omega)}$ and $F_{22(i\omega)}$ for the numerical case presented in Figs. 5-24 and 8-27.

The curves can be crudely approximated by first-order lags.

$$F_{12(s)} = \left(\frac{R}{F}\right)_{(s)} \simeq \frac{1.28}{2s + 1}$$

$$F_{22(s)} = \left(\frac{V}{F}\right)_{(s)} \simeq \frac{1.78}{2s + 1} \qquad (13\text{-}26)$$

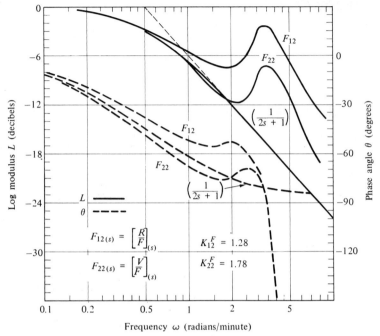

FIGURE 13-7
Bode plots of feedforward controllers $F_{12(s)}$ and $F_{22(s)}$.

The effectiveness of these approximate feedforward controllers is shown in Fig. 13-8. A step feed rate change is made at time zero from 100 to 110 moles/minute. The digital simulation of the rigorous nonlinear model of the column, as presented in Chap. 5, was used. We are testing on a nonlinear model of the process the approximate feedforward controllers that have been derived from a linear model of the process.

The feedforward control is not perfect because of the approximation and the nonlinearity. But the combined feedback-feedforward system is a great improvement over the feedback control alone. The feedforward control is improved somewhat by increasing the time constant τ^F of the feedforward controllers to 3 min.

13-4   NONLINEAR FEEDFORWARD SYSTEMS

All the feedforward controllers that we have designed up to this point have been based on linear systems, using transfer-function notation. There are, however, no inherent linear limitations in feedforward control. Nonlinear feedforward controllers can be designed for nonlinear systems.[1] The concepts are illustrated in the following example.

[1] W. L. Luyben, *A.I.Ch.E. J.*, vol. 14, p. 37, 1968.

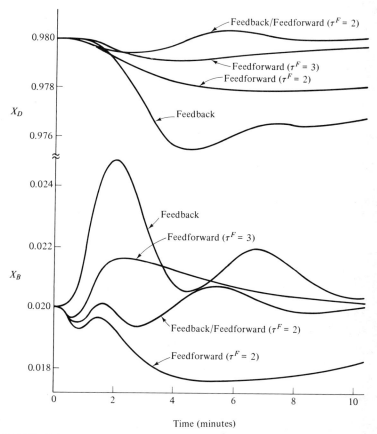

FIGURE 13-8
Performance of a feedforward controller on a nonlinear distillation column for a feed-rate disturbance.

EXAMPLE 13-2 The nonlinear ordinary differential equations describing the constant holdup, nonisothermal CSTR system in their original form before linearization are

$$\frac{dC_A}{dt} = \frac{F}{V}(C_{A0} - C_A) - C_A \alpha e^{-E/RT}$$

$$\frac{dT}{dt} = \frac{F}{V}(T_0 - T) - \left(\frac{\lambda}{C_p \rho}\right) C_A \alpha e^{-E/RT} - \left(\frac{UA}{C_p V \rho}\right)(T - T_J) \quad (13\text{-}27)$$

Let us choose a feedforward control system of Sec. 13-3.2. Both reactor concentration C_A and temperature T are to be held constant at their steady-state

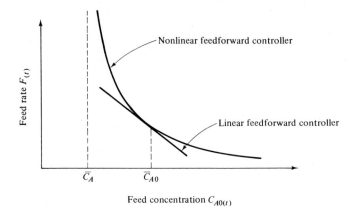

FIGURE 13-9
Nonlinear relationship between feed rate and feed concentration.

values $\bar{C}_A$ and $\bar{T}$. Remember Eqs. (13-27) are nonlinear and are in terms of total variables, *not* perturbations. Feed flow rate F and cooling-jacket temperature T_J are the manipulative variables. Disturbances are feed concentration C_{A0} and feed temperature T_0.

The feedforward control objectives are

$$C_{A(t)} = \bar{C}_A$$
$$T_{(t)} = \bar{T} \qquad (13\text{-}28)$$

Substituting these into Eqs. (13-27) gives

$$\frac{d\bar{C}_A}{dt} = 0 = \frac{F_{(t)}}{V}(C_{A0(t)} - \bar{C}_A) - \bar{C}_A k \qquad (13\text{-}29)$$

$$\frac{d\bar{T}}{dt} = 0 = \frac{F_{(t)}}{V}(T_{0(t)} - \bar{T}) - \frac{\lambda}{C_p \rho}\bar{C}_A k - \frac{UA}{C_p V \rho}(\bar{T} - T_{J(t)}) \qquad (13\text{-}30)$$

Rearranging Eq. (13-29) to find $F_{(t)}$, the manipulative variable, in terms of the disturbance $C_{A0(t)}$ gives

$$F_{(t)} = \frac{\bar{C}_A k V}{C_{A0(t)} - \bar{C}_A} \qquad (13\text{-}31)$$

This is a nonlinear feedforward relationship that shows how feed rate $F_{(t)}$ must be changed as feed concentration $C_{A0(t)}$ varies. The relationship is hyperbolic, as shown in Fig. 13-9, not linear as was the one we derived from the linearized system in Sec. 13-3.2. Feed rate must be decreased as feed concentration increases. This increases holdup time, with constant volume, so that the additional reactant is consumed. Equation (13-31) also tells us that, just as in the linearized system, F should not be varied as feed temperature T_0 changes.

Substituting Eq. (13-31) into Eq. (13-30) and solving for the other manipulative variable T_J give

$$T_{J(t)} = \bar{T} + \frac{\bar{C}_A \bar{k} V}{UA} \left[\lambda + \frac{C_p(\bar{T} - T_{0(t)})}{C_{A0(t)} - \bar{C}_A} \right] \quad (13\text{-}32)$$

This is a second nonlinear feedforward relationship that shows how cooling-jacket temperature $T_{J(t)}$ must be changed as both feed concentration $C_{A0(t)}$ and feed temperature $T_{0(t)}$ change. Notice that the relationship between T_J and C_{A0} is nonlinear, but the relationship between T_J and T_0 is linear.   ////

The design of the nonlinear feedforward controllers in the above example was done in the time domain. Laplace-domain techniques could not be used because the equations are nonlinear.

The above feedforward controller equations were found analytically. In more complex systems, analytical methods become too complex, and numerical techniques must be used to find the required nonlinear changes in manipulative variables. The nonlinear steady-state changes can usually be easily found numerically by using the nonlinear steady-state equations of the process.[1] The nonlinear dynamic portion is probably most easily found by linearization around various steady-states.

PROBLEMS

13-1 The load and manipulative-variable transfer functions of a process are

$$\frac{X_{(s)}}{M_{(s)}} = G_{M(s)} = \frac{1}{(s+1)(5s+1)}$$

$$\frac{X_{(s)}}{L_{(s)}} = G_{L(s)} = \frac{2}{(s+1)(5s+1)(\frac{1}{2}s+1)}$$

Derive the feedforward-controller transfer function that will keep the process output $X_{(s)}$ constant with load changes $L_{(s)}$.

13-2 Repeat Prob. 13-1 with

$$G_{M(s)} = \frac{\frac{1}{2}s+1}{(s+1)(5s+1)}$$

13-3 Design a feedforward controller for the heat exchanger of Fig. 10-9 and Prob. 10-4. The inlet process temperature T_1 is detected by a temperature transmitter and sensor with a combined transfer function:

$$\frac{P_{T1}}{T_1} = \frac{0.12}{0.024s+1} \quad \text{psi/}^\circ\text{F}$$

[1] W. L. Luyben, *Chem. Eng. Prog.*, vol. 61, p. 74, 1965.

The feedforward controller's job is to change the signal to the steam control valve to keep the outlet temperature T_2 constant. The transfer function relating inlet and outlet process temperatures has been found by pulse testing to be approximately

$$\frac{T_{2(s)}}{T_{1(s)}} \simeq \frac{0.2e^{-0.1s}}{(0.8s+1)(0.4s+1)^2}$$

(a) Find $F_{(s)}$. Is it physically realizable?

(b) Simulate this system and test the effectiveness of various approximations of $F_{(s)}$. Compare feedback control alone with feedforward control alone and with combined feedback-feedforward control.

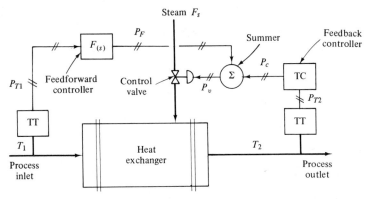

13-4 Develop the equations for calculating feedforward controllers for the binary distillation column of Sec. 13-3.3 from the process open-loop transfer functions P_{ij} and from the g_{ij}'s of the stepping technique when:

(a) x_D is to be held constant by R (with V constant).

(b) x_B is to be held constant by V (with R constant).

13-5 The transfer functions of a binary distillation column between distillate composition x_D and feed rate F, reflux rate R, and feed composition x_F are

$$\frac{x_D}{F} = \frac{K_F e^{-D_F S}}{(\tau_F s + 1)^2} \qquad \frac{x_D}{x_F} = \frac{K_x e^{-D_x S}}{(\tau_x s + 1)^2}$$

$$\frac{x_D}{R} = \frac{K_R e^{-D_R S}}{\tau_R s + 1}$$

Find the feedforward-controller transfer functions that will keep x_D constant, by manipulating R, despite changes in x_F and F. For what values of parameters are these feedforward controllers physically realizable?

13-6 Derive the equations for a nonlinear feedforward controller that is designed to maintain both composition C_A and temperature T constant in a CSTR with the first-order irreversible reaction A $\xrightarrow{k}$ B. Disturbances in inlet concentration C_{A0} and inlet temperature T_0 are experienced. Cooling-jacket temperature T_J and outlet-product withdrawal rate F are the manipulative variables. Assume constant density ρ, specific heat C_p, heat of reaction λ, heat transfer coefficient U, area A_H, and feed rate F_0.

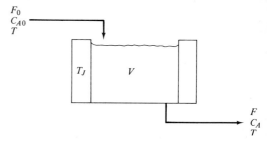

13-7 Find the nonlinear feedforward controller that will keep C_A constant in the nonlinear nonisothermal CSTR of Sec. 13-4 by manipulation of T_J despite disturbances in F, T_0, and C_{A0}.

13-8 Repeat Prob. 13-1 with

$$G_{M(S)} = \frac{-3s + 1}{(s + 1)(5s + 1)}$$

Is this feedforward controller physically realizable?

13-9 Greg Shinskey[1] has suggested that the steady-state distillate and bottoms compositions in a binary distillation column can be approximately related by

$$\frac{x_D/(1 - x_D)}{x_B/(1 - x_B)} = S$$

where S is a separation factor. At total reflux it is equal to α^{N_T+1} where α is the relative volatility and N_T is the number of theoretical trays. Assuming S is a constant, derive the nonlinear steady-state relationship showing how distillate drawoff rate D must be manipulated, as feed rate F and feed composition x_F vary, in order to hold distillate composition x_D constant. Sketch this relationship for several values of S and x_D.

[1] " Process-control Systems," chap. 11, McGraw-Hill, 1967.

PART SIX

Sampled-data Systems

All the control systems that we studied in the previous parts of this book were continuous analog devices. All control signals were continuously generated by transmitters, computing relays, controllers, etc., and continuously fed to control valves, controllers, or other devices.

In recent years, the development of digital control computers and of chromatographs has resulted in a rapidly increasing number of control systems that have discontinuous, intermittent components. The nature of operation of both these devices is such that their input and output signals are discrete.

A chromatograph injects a sample into a chromatographic column every few minutes. The sample works its way through the column and is detected as it emerges a few minutes later. Thus a composition signal is produced only once every few minutes. The time between composition signals is called the sampling period T_s.

Digital computers are used in process control systems on a "time-shared" basis. A single digital computer services a number of control loops. At a given instant in time, the computer looks at one control loop, checking the value of the controlled variable and computing a new signal to send to the control valve (in direct digital control, DDC) or to the set point of a continuous analog controller (in supervisory control). The computer then moves on to another loop. The control signal is changed only at discrete moments in time.

To analyze systems with discontinuous control elements we will use a new mathematical tool called the z transformation. z transforms are to sampled-data systems what Laplace transforms are to continuous systems. In Chap. 14 we will define mathematically the sampling process, derive the z transforms of common functions, and develop transfer functions in the z domain. These fundamentals will then be applied to controller design in Chap. 15. We will find that practically all the stability-analysis and controller-design techniques that we used in the Laplace and frequency domains for continuous systems can be directly applied in the z domain for sampled-data systems. Thus the mathematics in the z domain and in the Laplace domain are very similar.

It has been a difficult job to condense sampled-data control into two chapters. Several excellent texts are devoted entirely to this subject.[1] The treatment is of necessity limited to those aspects that I have found to be most useful and practical in real industrial systems.

[1] J. R. Ragazzini and G. F. Franklin, "Sampled-data Control Systems," McGraw-Hill, 1958.
J. T. Tou, "Digital and Sampled-data Control Systems," McGraw-Hill, 1959.

SAMPLING AND z TRANSFORMS

14-1 INTRODUCTION

14-1.1 Definition

Sampled-data systems are systems in which signals are discontinuous or discrete. Figure 14-1 shows a continuous analog signal or function $f_{(t)}$ being fed into a sampler. Every T_s minutes the sampler closes for a very brief instant. The output of the sampler $f_{s(t)}$ is, therefore, an intermittent series of pulses. Between sampling times the sampler output is zero. At the instant of sampling the output of the sampler is equal to the input function.

$$f_{s(t)} = f_{(nT_s)} \qquad \text{for } t = nT_s$$
$$f_{s(t)} = 0 \qquad \text{for } t \neq nT_s \qquad (14\text{-}1)$$

14-1.2 Occurrence of Sampled-data Systems in Chemical Engineering

As mentioned in the introduction to Part 6, chromatographs and digital control computers are the principal gadgets that produce sampled-data systems.

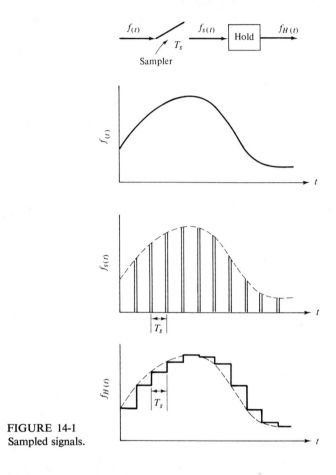

FIGURE 14-1
Sampled signals.

Figure 14-2 sketches a typical chromatograph system. The process output variable $x_{(t)}$ is sampled every T_s minutes. The sample is injected into a chromatographic column that has a retention time of D_c minutes, which is essentially a pure time delay or dead time. The sampling period T_s is usually set equal to the chromatograph cycle time D_c. The detector on the output of the column produces a signal that can be related to composition. The "peak picker" converts the detector signal into a composition signal. The maximum value or peak on the chromatograph curve is often used directly, but sometimes the areas under the curves are integrated and converted into a composition signal.

This signal is generated only every T_s minutes. It is fed into a device called a *hold* that clamps the signal until the next sample comes along; i.e., the output of the hold is maintained at a constant value over the sampling period. The hold converts

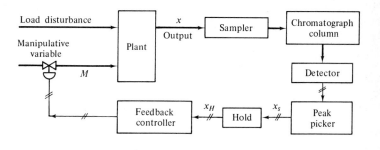

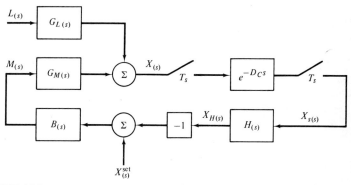

FIGURE 14-2
Chromatograph loop.

the sampled-data, discrete $x_{s(t)}$ signal, which is a series of pulses, into a continuous signal $x_{H(t)}$ that is a stair-step function. See Fig. 14-1. This continuous signal is the input to a conventional continuous analog feedback controller. The equivalent block diagram of this system is shown in Fig. 14-2 at the bottom. $H_{(s)}$ is the transfer function of the hold.

Figure 14-3*a* shows a "supervisory" digital control computer. Output variables $x_1, x_2, \ldots, x_N$ are sensed and converted into signals by transmitters $T_1, T_2, \ldots, T_N$. Continuous analog feedback controllers $B_1, B_2, \ldots, B_N$ send signals to control valves on the manipulative variables $M_1, M_2, \ldots, M_N$. The set points of the analog controllers come from the digital computer and are clamped between sampling times by holds $H_1, H_2, \ldots, H_N$. Data enter the digital computer through a multiplexed analog-to-digital (A/D) converter. Set-point signals are sent to the holds through a multiplexed digital-to-analog (D/A) converter. A block diagram of one loop is shown in the bottom of Fig. 14-3*a*. The digital computer is designated as $D^*_{(s)}$.

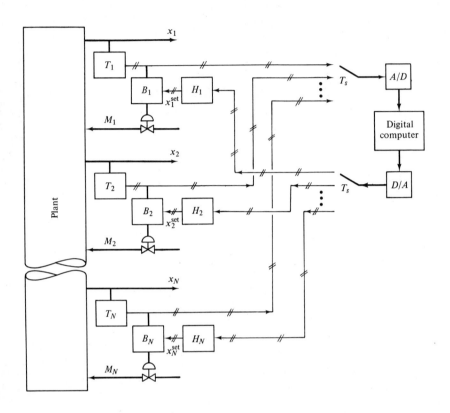

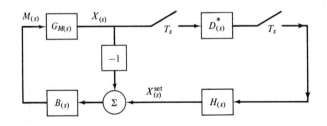

(a) Supervisory

FIGURE 14-3a
Digital control computers.

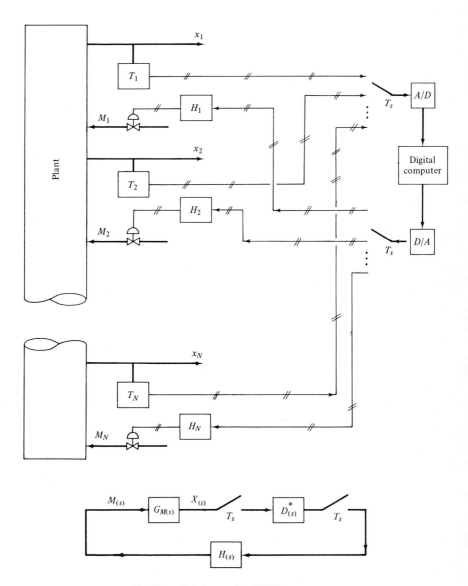

(b)   Direct digital control — "DDC"

FIGURE 14-3b

Figure 14-3*b* shows a DDC (direct digital control) computer. All the control calculations are done in the digital computer. The computer output goes, through holds, directly to the control valves.

The sampling rate of these digital control computers can vary from several times a second to only several times an hour. The dynamics of the process dictates the sampling time required. The faster the process, the smaller the sampling period T_s must be. One of the important questions that we will explore in these two chapters is what should the sampling rate be for a given process. For a given number of loops, the smaller the value of T_s specified the faster the computer and the input-output equipment must be. This increases the cost of the digital hardware.

14-2   IMPULSE SAMPLER

A real sampler, as shown in Fig. 14-1, is closed for a finite period of time. This time of closure is usually small compared with the sampling period T_s. Therefore the real sampler can be closely approximated by an *impulse sampler*. An impulse sampler is a device that converts a continuous input signal into a sequence of impulses or delta functions. Remember, these are impulses, not pulses. The height of each of these impulses is infinite. The width of each is zero. The area of the impulse or the "strength" of the impulse is equal to the magnitude of the input function at the sampling instant.

$$\int_{nT_s^-}^{nT_s^+} f_{(t)}^* \, dt = f_{(nT_s)} \qquad (14\text{-}2)$$

If the units of $f_{(t)}$ are, for example, psig, the units of $f_{(t)}^*$ are psig/min.

The impulse function is, of course, a mathematical fiction; an impulse sampler is, rigorously, not physically realizable. But the behavior of a real sampler and hold circuit is practically identical to that of the idealized impulse sampler and hold circuit. The impulse sampler is used in the analysis of sampled-data systems and in the design of sampled-data controllers because it greatly simplifies these calculations.

Let us now define an infinite sequence of unit impulses $\delta_{(t)}$ or Dirac delta functions whose strengths are all equal to unity. One unit impulse occurs at every sampling time. We will call this series of unit impulses, shown in Fig. 14-4, the function $I_{(t)}$.

$$I_{(t)} = \delta_{(t)} + \delta_{(t-T_s)} + \delta_{(t-2T_s)} + \delta_{(t-3T_s)} + \cdots$$

$$I_{(t)} = \sum_{n=0}^{\infty} \delta_{(t-nT_s)} \qquad (14\text{-}3)$$

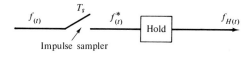

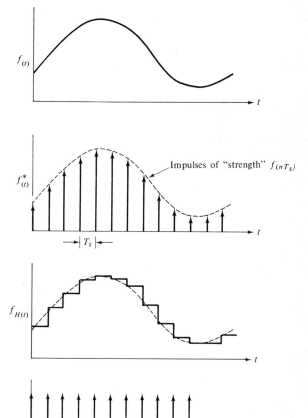

FIGURE 14-4
Impulse sampler.

Thus the sequence of impulses $f^*_{(t)}$ that comes out of an impulse sampler can be expressed:

$$f^*_{(t)} = f_{(t)}I_{(t)} = f_{(0)}\delta_{(t)} + f_{(T_s)}\delta_{(t-T_s)} + f_{(2T_s)}\delta_{(t-2T_s)} + \cdots$$

$$f^*_{(t)} = \sum_{n=0}^{\infty} f_{(nT_s)}\delta_{(t-nT_s)} \tag{14-4}$$

Laplace-transforming Eq. (14-4) gives

$$\mathscr{L}[f^*_{(t)}] = \mathscr{L}\left[\sum_{n=0}^{\infty} f_{(nT_s)}\delta_{(t-nT_s)}\right]$$

$$= \sum_{n=0}^{\infty} f_{(nT_s)}\mathscr{L}[\delta_{(t-nT_s)}]$$

$$= \sum_{n=0}^{\infty} f_{(nT_s)}e^{-nT_s s}\mathscr{L}[\delta_{(t)}]$$

$$F^*_{(s)} = \sum_{n=0}^{\infty} f_{(nT_s)}e^{-nT_s s} \tag{14-5}$$

Equation (14-4) expresses the sequence of impulses that comes out of an impulse sampler in the time domain. Equation (14-5) gives the sequence in the Laplace domain. Substituting $i\omega$ for s gives the impulse sequence in the frequency domain.

$$F^*_{(i\omega)} = \sum_{n=0}^{\infty} f_{(nT_s)}e^{-inT_s\omega} \tag{14-6}$$

The sequence of impulses $f^*_{(t)}$ can also be represented in an alternative manner. The $I_{(t)}$ function is a periodic function (see Fig. 14-4) with a period T_s and a frequency ω_s in radians per minute.

$$\omega_s = \frac{2\pi}{T_s} \tag{14-7}$$

Since $I_{(t)}$ is periodic, it can be represented as a complex Fourier series:

$$I_{(t)} = \sum_{n=-\infty}^{+\infty} C_n e^{in\omega_s t} \tag{14-8}$$

where

$$C_n = \frac{1}{T_s}\int_{-T_s/2}^{+T_s/2} I_{(t)}e^{-in\omega_s t}\,dt \tag{14-9}$$

Over the interval from $-T_s/2$ to $+T_s/2$ the $I_{(t)}$ is just $\delta_{(t)}$. Therefore Eq. (14-9) becomes

$$C_n = \frac{1}{T_s}\int_{-T_s/2}^{+T_s/2} \delta_{(t)}e^{-in\omega_s t}\,dt = \frac{1}{T_s}(e^{-in\omega_s t})_{t=0} = \frac{1}{T_s} \tag{14-10}$$

Remember, multiplying a function $f_{(t)}$ by the Dirac delta function and integrating give $f_{(0)}$. Therefore $I_{(t)}$ becomes

$$I_{(t)} = \frac{1}{T_s} \sum_{n=-\infty}^{+\infty} e^{in\omega_s t}$$

The sequence of impulses $f_{(t)}^*$ can be expressed as a doubly infinite series:

$$f_{(t)}^* = f_{(t)} I_{(t)} = \frac{1}{T_s} \sum_{n=-\infty}^{+\infty} f_{(t)} e^{in\omega_s t} \qquad (14\text{-}11)$$

Laplace-transforming gives [1]

$$F_{(s)}^* = \frac{1}{T_s} \sum_{n=-\infty}^{+\infty} F_{(s-in\omega_s)} = \frac{1}{T_s} \sum_{n=-\infty}^{+\infty} F_{(s+in\omega_s)} \qquad (14\text{-}12)$$

Substituting $i\omega$ for s gives

$$F_{(i\omega)}^* = \frac{1}{T_s} \sum_{n=-\infty}^{+\infty} F_{(i(\omega+n\omega_s))} \qquad (14\text{-}13)$$

Equation (14-4) is completely equivalent to Eq. (14-11) in the time domain. Equation (14-5) is equivalent to Eq. (14-12) in the Laplace domain. Equation (14-6) is equivalent to Eq. (14-13) in the frequency domain. Table 14-1 summarizes these alternative representations.

[1] $\mathcal{L}[f_{(t)} e^{at}] = \int_0^\infty f_{(t)} e^{at} e^{-st} \, dt = \int_0^\infty f_{(t)} e^{-(s-a)t} \, dt \equiv F_{(s-a)}$

Table 14-1   REPRESENTATIONS OF THE SEQUENCE OF IMPULSES $f_{(t)}^*$

Domain	Infinite series	Double infinite series
Time	$f_{(t)}^* = \sum_{n=0}^{\infty} f_{(nT_s)} \delta_{(t-nT_s)}$	$f_{(t)}^* = \frac{1}{T_s} \sum_{n=-\infty}^{+\infty} f_{(t)} e^{in\omega_s t}$
Laplace	$F_{(s)}^* = \sum_{n=0}^{\infty} f_{n(T_s)} e^{-nT_s s}$	$F_{(s)}^* = \frac{1}{T_s} \sum_{n=-\infty}^{+\infty} F_{(s+in\omega_s)}$
Frequency	$F_{(i\omega)}^* = \sum_{n=0}^{\infty} f_{(nT_s)} e^{-inT_s \omega}$	$F_{(i\omega)}^* = \frac{1}{T_s} \sum_{n=-\infty}^{+\infty} F_{(i(\omega+n\omega_s))}$
z	$F_{(z)} = \sum_{n=0}^{\infty} f_{(nT_s)} z^{-n}$	

14-3 BASIC SAMPLING THEOREM

A very important theorem of sampled-data systems is:

To obtain dynamic information about a plant that is meaningful out to some frequency ω_{max}, the sampling frequency ω_s must be set at a rate greater than twice ω_{max}.

$$\omega_s > 2\omega_{max} \qquad (14\text{-}14)$$

EXAMPLE 14-1 Suppose we want dynamic information that is good out to 100 radians/minute. We must set the sampling frequency at a rate greater than 200 radians/minute.

$$\omega_s > 200 \text{ radians/minute}$$

$$T_s = \frac{2\pi}{\omega_s} = \frac{2\pi}{200} = 0.0314 \text{ min} \qquad ////$$

To prove the sampling theorem let us consider a continuous $f_{(t)}$ that is a sine wave with a frequency ω_0 and an amplitude A_0.

$$f_{(t)} = A_0 \sin \omega_0 t \qquad (14\text{-}15)$$

$$f_{(t)} = A_0 \frac{e^{i\omega_0 t} - e^{-i\omega_0 t}}{2i} \qquad (14\text{-}16)$$

Suppose we sample this $f_{(t)}$ with an impulse sampler. The sequence of impulses $f_{(t)}^*$ coming out of the impulse sampler will be, according to Eq. (14-11),

$$f_{(t)}^* = \frac{1}{T_s} \sum_{n=-\infty}^{+\infty} f_{(t)} e^{in\omega_s t} = \frac{1}{T_s} \sum_{n=-\infty}^{+\infty} \frac{A_0}{2i} (e^{i\omega_0 t} - e^{-i\omega_0 t}) e^{in\omega_s t}$$

$$= \frac{A_0}{2iT_s} \sum_{n=-\infty}^{+\infty} (e^{i(\omega_0 + n\omega_s)t} - e^{-i(\omega_0 - n\omega_s)t})$$

$$= \frac{A_0}{T_s} \left(\frac{e^{i\omega_0 t} - e^{-i\omega_0 t}}{2i} + \frac{e^{i(\omega_0 + \omega_s)t} - e^{-i(\omega_0 + \omega_s)t}}{2i} \right.$$

$$+ \frac{e^{i(\omega_0 - \omega_s)t} - e^{-i(\omega_0 - \omega_s)t}}{2i} + \frac{e^{i(\omega_0 + 2\omega_s)t} - e^{-i(\omega_0 + 2\omega_s)t}}{2i}$$

$$\left. + \frac{e^{i(\omega_0 - 2\omega_s)t} - e^{-i(\omega_0 - 2\omega_s)t}}{2i} + \cdots \right)$$

$$f_{(t)}^* = \frac{A_0}{T_s} [\sin \omega_0 t + \sin(\omega_0 + \omega_s)t + \sin(\omega_0 - \omega_s)t$$

$$+ \sin(\omega_0 + 2\omega_s)t + \sin(\omega_0 - 2\omega_s)t + \cdots] \qquad (14\text{-}17)$$

Thus the sampled function $f^*_{(t)}$ contains a primary component at frequency ω_0 plus an infinite number of complementary components at frequencies $\omega_0 + \omega_s$, $\omega_0 - \omega_s$, $\omega_0 + 2\omega_s$, $\omega_0 - 2\omega_s$, ... The amplitude of each component is the amplitude of the original sine wave $f_{(t)}$ attenuated by $1/T_s$. The sampling process produces a signal that has components at frequencies that are multiples of the sampling frequency plus the original frequency of the continuous signal before sampling. Figure 14-5a illustrates this in terms of the frequency spectrum of the signal.

Now suppose we have a continuous function $f_{(t)}$ that contains components over a range of frequencies. Figure 14-5b shows its frequency spectrum $f_{(\omega)}$. If this signal is sent through an impulse sampler, the output $f^*_{(t)}$ will have a frequency spectrum $f^*_{(\omega)}$, as shown in Fig. 14-5b. If the sampling rate or sampling frequency ω_s is high, there will be no overlap between the primary and complementary components. Therefore $f^*_{(t)}$ can be filtered to remove all the high-frequency complementary components, leaving just the primary component. This can then be related to the original continuous function. Therefore, if the sampling frequency is greater than twice the highest frequency in the original signal, the original signal can be determined from the sampled signal.

If, however, the sampling frequency is less than twice the highest frequency in the original signal, the primary and complementary components will overlap. Then the sampled signal cannot be filtered to recover the original signal.

Figure 14-5b shows that $f^*_{(\omega)}$ is a periodic function of frequency ω. Its period is ω_s.

$$f^*_{(\omega)} = f^*_{(\omega + \omega_s)} = f^*_{(\omega + 2\omega_s)} = \cdots \quad (14\text{-}18)$$

This equation can also be written

$$f^*_{(i\omega)} = f^*_{(i\omega + i\omega_s)} = f^*_{(i\omega + i2\omega_s)} = \cdots \quad (14\text{-}19)$$

Going into the Laplace domain by substituting s for $i\omega$ gives

$$F^*_{(s)} = F^*_{(s + i\omega_s)} = F^*_{(s + i2\omega_s)} = \cdots \quad (14\text{-}20)$$

Thus $F^*_{(s)}$ is a periodic function of s with a period $i\omega_s$. We will use this periodicity property later.

14-4   z TRANSFORMATION

14-4.1   Definition

Sequences of impulses, such as the output of an impulse sampler, can be z-transformed. For a specified sampling period T_s, the z transform of an impulse sampled signal $f^*_{(t)}$ is defined by the equation

$$\mathscr{Z}[f^*_{(t)}] \equiv f_{(0)} + f_{(T_s)}z^{-1} + f_{(2T_s)}z^{-2} + f_{(3T_s)}z^{-3} + \cdots + f_{(nT_s)}z^{-n} + \cdots \quad (14\text{-}21)$$

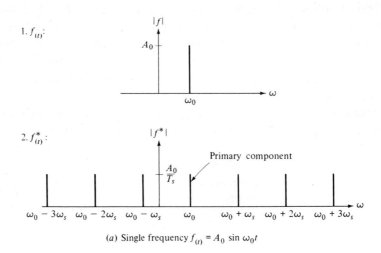

(a) Single frequency $f_{(t)} = A_0 \sin \omega_0 t$

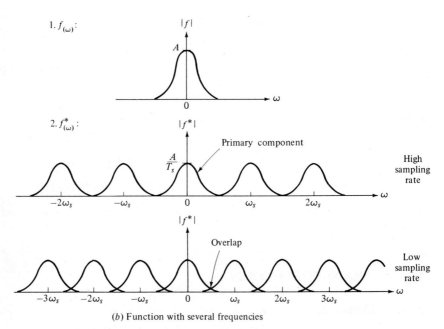

(b) Function with several frequencies

FIGURE 14-5
Frequency spectrum of continuous and sampled signals.

The $\mathscr{L}[\ ]$ notation means the z-transformation operation. $f_{(nT_s)}$ is the value of the continuous function before sampling at $t = nT_s$. We will use the notation that the z transform of $f_{(t)}^*$ is $F_{(z)}$.

$$F_{(z)} = \sum_{n=0}^{\infty} f_{(nT_s)} z^{-n} \qquad (14\text{-}22)$$

The z variable can be considered an "ordering" variable whose exponent represents the position of the impulse in the infinite sequence $f_{(t)}^*$.

Comparing Eqs. (14-5) and (14-22), we can see that the s and z variables are related by

$$z = e^{T_s s} \qquad (14\text{-}23)$$

We will make frequent use of this very important relationship between these two complex variables.

Keep in mind the concept that we always take z transforms of impulse sampled signals, not continuous functions. We will also use the notation

$$\mathscr{L}[F_{(s)}^*] = F_{(z)} \qquad (14\text{-}24)$$

This means exactly the same thing that is shown in Eqs. (14-21) and (14-22). We can go directly from the time domain $f_{(t)}^*$ to the z domain $F_{(z)}$. Or we can go from the time domain $f_{(t)}^*$ to the Laplace domain $F_{(s)}^*$ and on to the z domain $F_{(z)}$.

14-4.2 Derivation of z Transforms of Common Functions

Step function

$$f_{(t)} = K u_{(t)}$$

If we run the step function through an impulse sampler we get

$$f_{(t)}^* = K u_{(t)} I_{(t)}$$

where $I_{(t)}$ is the sequence of unit impulses defined in Eq. (14-3). Using the definition of z transformation [Eq. (14-22)] gives

$$
\begin{aligned}
F_{(z)} &= \sum_{n=0}^{\infty} f_{(nT_s)} z^{-n} \\
&= f_{(0)} + f_{(T_s)} z^{-1} + f_{(2T_s)} z^{-2} + f_{(3T_s)} z^{-3} + \cdots \\
&= K + K z^{-1} + K z^{-2} + K z^{-3} + \cdots \\
&= K(1 + z^{-1} + z^{-2} + z^{-3} + \cdots) \\
&= K \frac{1}{1 - z^{-1}}
\end{aligned}
$$

provided $|z^{-1}| < 1$

This requirement is analogous to the requirement in Laplace transformation that s be large enough so that the integral converges.

$$z^{-1} = e^{-T_s s}$$

s must be large enough to keep $e^{-T_s s}$ less than 1.

The z transform of the impulse sampled step function is

$$\mathscr{L}[Ku_{(t)} I_{(t)}] = K\frac{z}{z-1} \qquad (14\text{-}25)$$

Ramp function

$$f_{(t)} = Kt$$
$$f^*_{(t)} = KtI_{(t)}$$
$$F_{(z)} = \sum_{n=0}^{\infty} f_{(nT_s)} z^{-n} = 0 + KT_s z^{-1} + 2KT_s z^{-2} + 3KT_s z^{-3} + \cdots$$
$$= KT_s(1 + 2z^{-1} + 3z^{-2} + \cdots)z^{-1} = \frac{KT_s z^{-1}}{(1 - z^{-1})^2}$$

for $|z^{-1}| < 1$.

The z transform of the impulse sampled ramp function is

$$\mathscr{L}[KtI_{(t)}] = \frac{KT_s z}{(z-1)^2} \qquad (14\text{-}26)$$

Exponential

$$f_{(t)} = Ke^{-at}$$

$$F_{(z)} = \sum_{n=0}^{\infty} (Ke^{-anT_s})z^{-n}$$
$$= K[1 + (e^{-aT_s}z^{-1}) + (e^{-aT_s}z^{-1})^2 + (e^{-aT_s}z^{-1})^3 + \cdots]$$
$$= K\frac{1}{1 - e^{-aT_s}z^{-1}}$$

$$\text{for } |e^{-aT_s}z^{-1}| < 1.$$

The z transform of the impulse sampled exponential function is

$$\mathscr{L}[Ke^{-at} I_{(t)}] = \frac{Kz}{z - e^{-aT_s}} \qquad (14\text{-}27)$$

Sine

$$f_{(t)} = \sin \omega t$$

$$F_{(z)} = \sum_{n=0}^{\infty} \left(\frac{e^{in\omega T_s} - e^{-in\omega T_s}}{2i} \right) z^{-n} = \frac{1}{2i} \left(\frac{1}{1 - e^{i\omega T_s} z^{-1}} - \frac{1}{1 - e^{-i\omega T_s} z^{-1}} \right)$$

$$= \frac{1}{2i} \frac{e^{i\omega T_s} z^{-1} - e^{-i\omega T_s} z^{-1}}{1 + z^{-2} - e^{i\omega T_s} z^{-1} - e^{-i\omega T_s} z^{-1}}$$

$$= \frac{1}{2i} \frac{z^{-1}(2i) \sin \omega T_s}{1 + z^{-2} - z^{-1}(2 \cos \omega T_s)}$$

The z transform of an impulse sampled sine wave is

$$\mathscr{L}[I_{(t)} \sin \omega t] = \frac{z \sin \omega T_s}{z^2 + 1 - 2z \cos \omega T_s} \qquad (14\text{-}28)$$

Exponential multiplied by time to the pth power

$$f_{(t)} = \frac{K}{p!} t^p e^{-at} \qquad (14\text{-}29)$$

This function can be expressed in the alternative form:

$$f_{(t)} = (-1)^p \frac{K}{p!} \frac{\partial^p}{\partial a^p} (e^{-at}) \qquad (14\text{-}30)$$

$$F_{(z)} = \sum_{n=0}^{\infty} (-1)^p \frac{K}{p!} \frac{\partial^p}{\partial a^p} (e^{-anT_s}) z^{-n}$$

$$= \frac{(-1)^p K}{p!} \frac{\partial^p}{\partial a^p} \left[\sum_{n=0}^{\infty} (z^{-1} e^{-aT_s})^n \right]$$

$$\mathscr{L} \left[\frac{K}{p!} t^p e^{-at} I_{(t)} \right] = (-1)^p \frac{K}{p!} \frac{\partial^p}{\partial a^p} \left(\frac{z}{z - e^{-aT_s}} \right) \qquad (14\text{-}31)$$

EXAMPLE 14-2   Take the case where $p = 1$.

$$\mathscr{L}[Kte^{-at} I_{(t)}] = -K \frac{\partial}{\partial a} \left(\frac{z}{z - e^{-aT_s}} \right) = \frac{K T_s e^{aT_s} z}{(z e^{aT_s} - 1)^2} \qquad (14\text{-}32) \qquad ////$$

Unit impulse function

$$f_{(t)} = \delta_{(t)}$$

By definition, the z transform of an impulse sampled function is

$$F_{(z)} = f_{(0)} + f_{(T_s)} z^{-1} + f_{(2T_s)} z^{-2} + \cdots$$

If $f_{(t)}$ is a unit impulse, putting it through an impulse sampler should give an $f^*_{(t)}$ that is still just a unit impulse $\delta_{(t)}$. But Eq. (14-4) says that

$$f^*_{(t)} = f_{(0)}\,\delta_{(t)} + f_{(T_s)}\,\delta_{(t-T_s)} + f_{(2T_s)}\,\delta_{(t-2T_s)} + \cdots$$

But if $f^*_{(t)}$ must be equal to $\delta_{(t)}$, $f_{(0)}$ must be equal to 1 and $f_{(T_s)}, f_{(2T_s)}, \ldots$ must all be equal to zero. Therefore the z transform of the unit impulse is unity.

$$\mathscr{L}\left[\delta_{(t)}\right] = 1 \qquad (14\text{-}33)$$

14-4.3 Effect of Dead Time

Dead time in a sampled-data system is very easily handled if the dead time D is an integer multiple[1] of the sampling period T_s. Let us assume that

$$D = kT_s \qquad (14\text{-}34)$$

where k is an integer. Consider the function $f_{(t-D)}$. The original function $f_{(t)}$ before the time delay is assumed to be zero for time less than zero.

Running the delayed function through an impulse sampler and z-transforming give

$$\mathscr{L}\left[f^*_{(t-D)}\right] = \sum_{n=0}^{\infty} f_{(nT_s-kT_s)} z^{-n}$$

Let

$$x = n - k$$

$$\mathscr{L}\left[f^*_{(t-D)}\right] = \sum_{x=-k}^{\infty} f_{(xT_s)} z^{-x-k} = \left[\sum_{x=0}^{\infty} f_{(xT_s)} z^{-x}\right] z^{-k}$$

since $f_{(xT_s)} = 0$ for $x < 0$. The term in the brackets is just the z transform of $f^*_{(t)}$ since x is a dummy variable of summation.

$$\mathscr{L}\left[f^*_{(t-D)}\right] = F_{(z)} z^{-k} \qquad (14\text{-}35)$$

Therefore the dead-time transfer function in the z domain is a z^{-k}.

Time domain:

$$\xrightarrow{\;f^*_{(t)}\;} \boxed{\begin{array}{c} Dead\ time \\ D = kT_s \end{array}} \xrightarrow{\;f^*_{(t-D)}\;}$$

z domain:

$$\xrightarrow{\;F_{(z)}\;} \boxed{z^{-k}} \xrightarrow{\;z^{-k}F_{(z)}\;}$$

14-4.4   z-transform Theorems

Just as in Laplace transforms, there are several useful theorems in z transforms that are given below.

---

[1] Noninteger values can be handled by the so-called "modified z transforms." See J. T. Tou, "Digital and Sampled-data Control Systems," p. 255, McGraw-Hill, 1959.

Linearity

$$\mathscr{L}[f^*_{1(t)} + f^*_{2(t)}] = \mathscr{L}[f^*_{1(t)}] + \mathscr{L}[f^*_{2(t)}] \qquad (14\text{-}36)$$

The linearity property is easily proved from the definition of z transformation.

Scale change

$$\mathscr{L}[e^{-at}f^*_{(t)}] = F_{(z\,e^{aT_s})} = F_{(z_1)} = \mathscr{L}_1[f^*_{(t)}] \qquad (14\text{-}37)$$

The notation $\mathscr{L}_1[\ ]$ means z-transforming using the z_1 variable where $z_1 = ze^{aT_s}$. This theorem is proved by going back to the definition of z transformation.

$$\mathscr{L}[e^{-at}f^*_{(t)}] = \sum_{n=0}^{\infty} e^{-anT_s} f_{(nT_s)} z^{-n} = \sum_{n=0}^{\infty} f_{(nT_s)}(ze^{aT_s})^{-n}$$

Now substitute $z_1 = ze^{aT_s}$ into the above equation.

$$\mathscr{L}[e^{-at}f^*_{(t)}] = \sum_{n=0}^{\infty} f_{(nT_s)} z_1^{-n} = F_{(z_1)} = F_{(z\,e^{aT_s})}$$

EXAMPLE 14-3   Suppose we want to take the z transform of $KtI_{(t)}e^{-at}$. Using Eqs. (14-26) and (14-37) gives

$$\mathscr{L}[KtI_{(t)}e^{-at}] = \mathscr{L}_1[KtI_{(t)}] = \frac{KT_s z_1}{(z_1 - 1)^2}$$

Substituting $z_1 = e^{aT_s}z$ gives

$$\mathscr{L}[tKI_{(t)}e^{-at}] = \frac{KT_s e^{aT_s}z}{(e^{aT_s}z - 1)^2} \qquad (14\text{-}38)$$

This is exactly what we found in Example 14-2.   ////

Final-value theorem

$$\lim_{t \to \infty} f_{(t)} = \lim_{z \to 1}\left(\frac{z-1}{z} F_{(z)}\right) \qquad (14\text{-}39)$$

To prove this theorem, let $f_{(t)}$ be the step response of an arbitrary Nth-order system:

$$f_{(t)} = Ku_{(t)} + \sum_{i=1}^{N} K_i e^{-a_i t}$$

The steady-state value of $f_{(t)}$ or the limit of $f_{(t)}$ as time t goes to infinity is K. Running $f_{(t)}$ through an impulse sampler and z-transforming give

$$\mathscr{L}[f_{(t)}^*] = \mathscr{L}[Ku_{(t)}I_{(t)}] + \mathscr{L}\left[\sum_{i=1}^{N} K_i e^{-a_i t} I_{(t)}\right]$$

$$F_{(z)} = \frac{Kz}{z-1} + \sum_{i=1}^{N} K_i \frac{z}{z - e^{-a_i T_s}}$$

Multiplying both sides by $(z - 1)/z$ and letting $z \to 1$ give

$$\lim_{z \to 1} \left(\frac{z-1}{z} F_{(z)}\right) = K = \lim_{t \to \infty} f_{(t)}$$

Initial-value theorem

$$\lim_{t \to 0} f_{(t)} = \lim_{z \to \infty} F_{(z)} \qquad (14\text{-}40)$$

The definition of the z transform of $f_{(t)}^*$ is

$$F_{(z)} = f_{(0)} + f_{(T_s)} z^{-1} + f_{(2T_s)} z^{-2} + \cdots$$

Letting z go to infinity (for $|z^{-1}| < 1$) in this equation gives $f_{(0)}$, which is the limit of $f_{(t)}$ as $t \to 0$.

14-4.5 Inversion

We sometimes want to invert from the z domain back into the time domain. The inversion will give the values of the function $f_{(t)}$ only at the sampling instants.

$$\mathscr{L}^{-1}[F_{(z)}] = f_{(nT_s)} \qquad \text{for} \quad n = 0, 1, 2, \ldots \qquad (14\text{-}41)$$

The z transformation of an impulse sampled function is unique; i.e., there is only one $F_{(z)}$ that is the z transform of a given $f_{(t)}^*$. The inverse z transform of an $F_{(z)}$ is also unique; i.e., there is only one $f_{(t)}^*$ that corresponds to a given $F_{(z)}$.

However, keep in mind the fact that there are more than one continuous function $f_{(t)}$ that will give the same impulse sampled function $f_{(t)}^*$. The sampled function $f_{(t)}^*$ contains information about the original continuous function $f_{(t)}$ only at the sampling times. This nonuniqueness between $f_{(t)}^*$ (and $F_{(z)}$) and $f_{(t)}$ is illustrated in Fig. 14-6. There are several ways to invert z transforms.

Complex integration   The inversion formula of this seldom used method is[1]

$$f_{(nT_s)} = \frac{1}{2\pi i} \oint F_{(z)} z^{n-1} \, dz \qquad (14\text{-}42)$$

[1] Tou, *op. cit.*, p. 177.

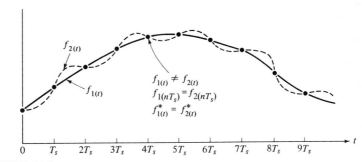

FIGURE 14-6
Continuous functions with identical values at sampling time.

Partial fractions expansion   The linearity theorem [Eq. (14-36)] permits us to expand the function $F_{(z)}$ into a sum of simple terms and invert each individually. This is completely analogous to Laplace-transformation inversion. Let $F_{(z)}$ be a ratio of polynomials in z:

$$F_{(z)} = \frac{Z_{(z)}}{P_{(z)}} \qquad (14\text{-}43)$$

where $Z_{(z)}$ = Mth-order polynomial in z
$\qquad P_{(z)}$ = Nth-order polynomial in z

The denominator is factored into its N poles $p_1, p_2, p_3, \ldots, p_N$. Each pole can be expressed in terms of the sampling period T_s.

$$
\begin{aligned}
F_{(z)} &= \frac{Z_{(z)}}{(z - p_1)(z - p_2)(z - p_3)\cdots(z - p_N)} \\[2mm]
&= \frac{Az}{z - p_1} + \frac{Bz}{z - p_2} + \frac{Cz}{z - p_3} + \cdots + \frac{Wz}{z - p_N} \\[2mm]
&= \frac{Az}{z - e^{-a_1 T_s}} + \frac{Bz}{z - e^{-a_2 T_s}} + \frac{Cz}{z - e^{-a_3 T_s}} + \cdots + \frac{Wz}{z - e^{-a_N T_s}} \qquad (14\text{-}44)
\end{aligned}
$$

where

$$a_1 = -\frac{1}{T_s} \ln p_1$$

$$a_2 = -\frac{1}{T_s} \ln p_2$$

$$\cdots\cdots\cdots\cdots\cdots$$

$$a_N = -\frac{1}{T_s} \ln p_N \qquad (14\text{-}45)$$

The coefficients $A, B, C, \ldots, W$ are found and $F_{(z)}$ is inverted term by term to give

$$\mathscr{L}^{-1}[F_{(z)}] = f_{(nT_s)} = Ae^{-a_1 nT_s} + Be^{-a_2 nT_s} + \cdots + We^{-a_N nT_s} \quad (14\text{-}46)$$

EXAMPLE 14-4 We will show later that the closed-loop response to a unit step change in load with a sampled-data proportional controller and a first-order process is

$$X_{(z)} = \frac{K_p(1-b)z}{z^2 + z[K_c K_p(1-b) - (1+b)] + [b - K_c K_p(1-b)]} \quad (14\text{-}47)$$

where $b \equiv e^{-T_s/\tau_p}$

K_c = feedback-controller gain

K_p = process steady-state gain

τ_p = process time constant

For the numerical values $K_p = \tau_p = K_c = 1$ and $T_s = 0.2$, $X_{(z)}$ becomes

$$X_{(z)} = \frac{0.181z}{z^2 - 1.638z + 0.638}$$

$$= \frac{0.181z}{(z-1)(z-0.638)} = \frac{0.5z}{z-1} - \frac{0.5z}{z-0.638} \quad (14\text{-}48)$$

The pole at 0.638 can be expressed:

$$0.638 = e^{-aT_s} = e^{-0.451}$$

$$X_{(z)} = \frac{0.5z}{z-1} - \frac{0.5z}{z - e^{-0.451}}$$

Inverting,

$$x_{(nT_s)} = 0.5(1 - e^{-anT_s})$$

$$x_{(0.2n)} = 0.5(1 - e^{-0.451n}) \quad (14\text{-}49)$$

Table 14-2 and Fig. 14-7 give the calculated results of $x_{(nT_s)}$ as a function of time.

////

Table 14-2 VALUES OF $x_{(nT_s)}$
FROM EXAMPLE 14-4

t	n	$x_{(nT_s)}$
0	0	0
0.2	1	0.181
0.4	2	0.297
0.6	3	0.372
0.8	4	0.421
1.0	5	0.451

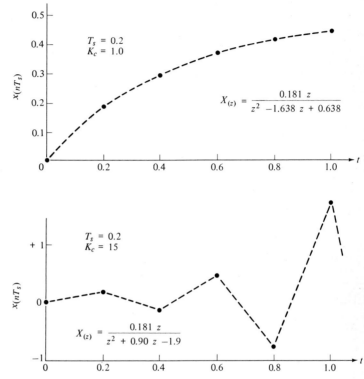

FIGURE 14-7

$f_{(nT_s)}$ from inversion of $F_{(z)}$.

Long division The most interesting and probably the most useful z-transform inversion technique is simple long division of the numerator by the denominator of $F_{(z)}$. The ease with which z transforms can be inverted by this technique is one of the reasons why z transforms are being used more and more.

By definition,

$$F_{(z)} = f_{(0)} + f_{(T_s)}z^{-1} + f_{(2T_s)}z^{-2} + \cdots$$

If we can get $F_{(z)}$ in terms of an infinite series of powers of z^{-1}, the coefficients in front of all the terms give the values of $f_{(nT_s)}$. The infinite series is obtained by merely dividing the numerator of $F_{(z)}$ by the denominator of $F_{(z)}$.

$$F_{(z)} = \frac{Z_{(z)}}{P_{(z)}} = f_{(0)} + f_{(T_s)}z^{-1} + f_{(2T_s)}z^{-2} + \cdots \qquad (14\text{-}50)$$

EXAMPLE 14-5   The function of Example 14-4 was

$$X_{(z)} = \frac{0.181z}{z^2 - 1.638z + 0.638}$$

Long division gives

$$
\begin{array}{r}
0.181z^{-1} + 0.297z^{-2} + 0.372z^{-3} + \cdots \\
z^2 - 1.638z + 0.638 \overline{)0.181z} \\
\underline{0.181z - 0.297 + 0.115z^{-1}} \\
0.297 - 0.115z^{-1} \\
\underline{0.297 - 0.487z^{-1} + 0.19z^{-2}} \\
0.372z^{-1} - 0.19z^{-2} \\
\end{array}
$$

. . . .

$$\text{Therefore} \quad f_{(0)} = 0$$

$$f_{(T_s)} = f_{(0.2)} = 0.181$$

$$f_{(2T_s)} = f_{(0.4)} = 0.297$$

$$f_{(3T_s)} = f_{(0.6)} = 0.372$$

. . . .

These are the same results we found by partial fractions expansion in Example 14-4.

////

EXAMPLE 14-6   If the value of K_c in Example 14-4 is changed to 15, $X_{(z)}$ becomes

$$X_{(z)} = \frac{0.181z}{z^2 + 0.90z - 1.9}$$

Inverting by long division gives

$$
\begin{array}{r}
0.181z^{-1} - 0.163z^{-2} + 0.491z^{-3} - 0.751z^{-4} + 1.61z^{-5} + \cdots \\
z^2 + 0.90z - 1.9 \overline{)0.181z} \\
\underline{0.181z + 0.163 - 0.344z^{-1}} \\
-0.163 + 0.344z^{-1} \\
\underline{-0.163 - 0.147z^{-1} + 0.31z^{-2}} \\
0.491z^{-1} - 0.31z^{-2} \\
\underline{0.491z^{-1} + 0.441z^{-2} - 0.932z^{-3}} \\
-0.751z^{-2} + 0.932z^{-3} \\
\underline{-0.751z^{-2} - 0.676z^{-3} + 1.42z^{-4}} \\
1.61z^{-3} - 1.42z^{-4} \\
\end{array}
$$

. . . .

The results are plotted in Fig. 14-7. The system is unstable with this value of gain ($K_c = 15$).

////

```
SUBROUTINE LONGD (A0,A,B,X0,X,N,M,NT)
DIMENSION A(10),B(10),X(100),D(10)
NMAX=N
IF(M.GT.N) NMAX=M
DO 10 I=1,NMAX
D(I)=A(I)
IF(I.GT.N) B(I)=0.
10 IF(I.GT.M) D(I)=0.
D(NMAX+1)=0.
IF(A0 .EQ.0.) GO TO 30
X0=A0
DO 20 K=1,NMAX
20 D(K)=D(K )-X0 *B(K)
X(1)=D(1)
GO TO 40
30 X0=0.
X(1)=A(1)
40 DO 100 J=2,NT
DO 50 K=1,NMAX
50 D(K)=D(K+1)-X(J-1)*B(K)
100 X(J)=D(1)
RETURN
END
```

FIGURE 14-8

Subroutine for inversion of z transforms by long division.

Inversion of z transforms by long division is very easily accomplished numerically by a digital computer. The FORTRAN subroutine LONGD given in Fig. 14-8 performs this long division. The output variable X is calculated for N_T sampling times, given the coefficients $A0$, $A(1)$, $A(2)$, ..., $A(M)$ of the numerator and the co-efficients $B(1)$, $B(2)$, ..., $B(N)$ of the denominator.

$$X_{(z)} = X0 + X(1)z^{-1} + X(2)z^{-2} + X(3)z^{-3} + \cdots$$

$$= \frac{A0 + A(1)z^{-1} + A(2)z^{-2} + \cdots + A(M)z^{-M}}{1 + B(1)z^{-1} + B(2)z^{-2} + \cdots + B(N)z^{-N}} \quad (14\text{-}51)$$

14-5 PULSE TRANSFER FUNCTIONS

We know how to find the z transforms of functions. Let us now turn to the problem of expressing input-output transfer-function relationships in the z domain. Figure 14-9a shows a system with samplers on the input and on the output of the process. Time-, Laplace-, and z-domain representations are shown. $G_{(z)}$ is called a *pulse transfer function*. It will be defined below.

A sequence of impulses $Q^*_{(t)}$ comes out of the impulse sampler on the input of the process. Each of these impulses will produce a response from the process.

Time domain:

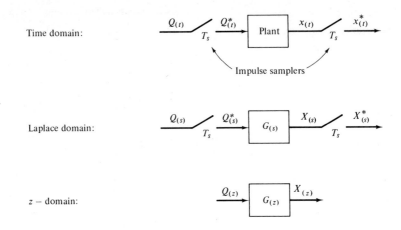

(a) Representation of process

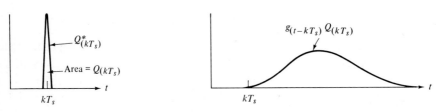

(b) Effect of kth impulse

FIGURE 14-9
Pulse transfer functions.

Consider the kth impulse $Q^*_{(kT_s)}$. Its area or strength is equal to $Q_{(kT_s)}$. Its effect on the continuous output of the plant $x_{(t)}$ will be

$$x_{k(t)} = g_{(t-kT_s)}Q_{(kT_s)} \qquad (14\text{-}52)$$

where $x_{k(t)}$ = response of process to kth impulse
  $g_{(t)}$ = unit impulse response of process = $\mathcal{L}^{-1}[G_{(s)}]$

Figure 14-9b shows these functions.

The system is linear, so the total output $x_{(t)}$ is the sum of all the x_k's.

$$x_{(t)} = \sum_{k=0}^{\infty} x_{k(t)} = \sum_{k=0}^{\infty} g_{(t-kT_s)}Q_{(kT_s)} \qquad (14\text{-}53)$$

At the sampling times, the value of $x_{(t)}$ is $x_{(nT_s)}$:

$$x_{(nT_s)} = \sum_{k=0}^{\infty} g_{(nT_s - kT_s)}Q_{(kT_s)} \qquad (14\text{-}54)$$

The continuous function $x_{(t)}$ coming out of the process is then impulse-sampled, producing a sequence of impulses $x_{(t)}^*$. If we z-transform $x_{(t)}^*$ we get

$$\mathscr{Z}[x_{(t)}^*] = \sum_{n=0}^{\infty} x_{(nT_s)} z^{-n} = X_{(z)}$$

$$X_{(z)} = \sum_{n=0}^{\infty} \left(\sum_{k=0}^{\infty} g_{(nT_s - kT_s)} Q_{(kT_s)} \right) z^{-n} \qquad (14\text{-}55)$$

Letting $m = n - k$ and remembering that $g_{(t)} = 0$ for $t < 0$ give

$$X_{(z)} = \sum_{m=0}^{\infty} \sum_{k=0}^{\infty} g_{(mT_s)} Q_{(kT_s)} z^{-(m+k)}$$

$$= \left(\sum_{m=0}^{\infty} g_{(mT_s)} z^{-m} \right) \left(\sum_{k=0}^{\infty} Q_{(kT_s)} z^{-k} \right) \qquad (14\text{-}56)$$

$$X_{(z)} = G_{(z)} Q_{(z)} \qquad (14\text{-}57)$$

The pulse transfer function $G_{(z)}$ is defined as the first term in Eq. (14-56).

$$G_{(z)} \equiv \sum_{m=0}^{\infty} g_{(mT_s)} z^{-m} \qquad (14\text{-}58)$$

Defining $G_{(z)}$ in this way permits us to use transfer functions in the z domain [Eq. (14-57)] just as we use transfer functions in the Laplace domain. $G_{(z)}$ is the z transform of the impulse sampled response $g_{(t)}^*$ of the system to a unit impulse function $\delta_{(t)}$. In z-transforming functions, we used the notation

$$\mathscr{Z}[f_{(t)}^*] = \mathscr{Z}[F_{(s)}^*] = F_{(z)}$$

In handling pulse transfer functions, we will use similar notation.

$$\mathscr{Z}[g_{(t)}^*] = \mathscr{Z}[G_{(s)}^*] = G_{(z)} \qquad (14\text{-}59)$$

where $G_{(s)}^*$ is the Laplace transform of the impulse sampled response $g_{(t)}^*$ of the system to a unit impulse function.

$$G_{(s)}^* = \mathscr{L}[g_{(t)}^*] \qquad (14\text{-}60)$$

$G_{(s)}^*$ can also be expressed, using Eq. (14-12), as

$$G_{(s)}^* = \frac{1}{T_s} \sum_{n=-\infty}^{+\infty} G_{(s+in\omega_s)} \qquad (14\text{-}61)$$

We will show how these pulse transfer functions are applied to open-loop and closed-loop systems in Sec. 14-7.

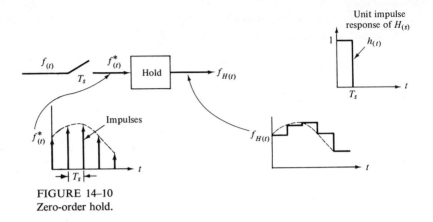

FIGURE 14–10
Zero-order hold.

14-6   HOLD DEVICES

A hold device is always needed in a sampled-data process control system. The hold converts the sequence of impulses of an impulse sampled function $f^*_{(t)}$ into a continuous staircase function $f_{H(t)}$. There are several types of mathematical holds. The one that is used in practically all real systems is called a *zero-order* hold. This type of hold generates the stair-step function described above.

The hold must convert an impulse $f^*_{(t)}$ of area or strength $f_{(nT_s)}$ at time $t = nT_s$ into a *pulse* of height $f_{(nT_s)}$ and width T_s. See Fig. 14-10. Let the unit impulse response of the hold be defined as $h_{(t)}$. If the hold is to do what we want it to do, its unit impulse response must be

$$h_{(t)} = u_{(t)} - u_{(t-T_s)} \qquad (14\text{-}62)$$

where $u_{(t)}$ is the unit step function.

Therefore the Laplace-domain transfer function $H_{(s)}$ of a zero-order hold is

$$H_{(s)} = \mathscr{L}[h_{(t)}] = \mathscr{L}[u_{(t)} - u_{(t-T_s)}] = \frac{1}{s} - \frac{e^{-T_s s}}{s}$$

$$H_{(s)} = \frac{1 - e^{-T_s s}}{s} \qquad (14\text{-}63)$$

14-7   OPEN-LOOP AND CLOSED-LOOP SYSTEMS

We are now ready to use the concepts of impulse sampled functions, pulse transfer functions, and holds to study the dynamics of sampled-data systems.

14-7.1 Open-loop Systems

Consider the sampled-data system shown in Fig. 14-11a in the Laplace domain. The input enters through an impulse sampler. The continuous output of the process $X_{(s)}$ is

$$X_{(s)} = G_{(s)}Q^*_{(s)} \qquad (14\text{-}64)$$

$X_{(s)}$ is then impulse-sampled to give $X^*_{(s)}$. Equation (14-12) says that $X^*_{(s)}$ is

$$X^*_{(s)} = \frac{1}{T_s} \sum_{n=-\infty}^{+\infty} X_{(s+in\omega_s)}$$

Substituting for $X_{(s+in\omega_s)}$, using Eq. (14-64), gives

$$X^*_{(s)} = \frac{1}{T_s} \sum_{n=-\infty}^{+\infty} G_{(s+in\omega_s)}Q^*_{(s+in\omega_s)} \qquad (14\text{-}65)$$

We showed [Eq. (14-20)] that the Laplace transform of an impulse sampled function is periodic.

$$Q^*_{(s)} = Q^*_{(s+i\omega_s)} = Q^*_{(s-i\omega_s)} = Q^*_{(s+i2\omega_s)} = \cdots \qquad (14\text{-}66)$$

Therefore the $Q^*_{(s+in\omega_s)}$ terms can be factored out of the summation in Eq. (14-65) to give

$$X^*_{(s)} = \left(\frac{1}{T_s} \sum_{n=-\infty}^{+\infty} G_{(s+in\omega_s)} \right) Q^*_{(s)}$$

The term in the parentheses is $G^*_{(s)}$ according to Eq. (14-61), and therefore the output of the process in the Laplace domain is

$$X^*_{(s)} = G^*_{(s)}Q^*_{(s)} \qquad (14\text{-}67)$$

By z-transforming this equation, using Eq. (14-59), the output in the z domain is

$$X_{(z)} = G_{(z)}Q_{(z)} \qquad (14\text{-}68)$$

Now consider the system shown in Fig. 14-11b where there are two elements separated by a sampler. The continuous output $X_{1(s)}$ is

$$X_{1(s)} = G_{1(s)}Q^*_{(s)}$$

When $X_{1(s)}$ goes through the impulse sampler it becomes $X^*_{1(s)}$, which can be expressed [see Eq. (14-67)]:

$$X^*_{1(s)} = \frac{1}{T_s} \sum_{n=-\infty}^{+\infty} G_{1(s+in\omega_s)}Q^*_{(s+in\omega_s)}$$

$$= G^*_{1(s)}Q^*_{(s)} \qquad (14\text{-}69)$$

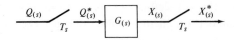

(a) Single Element

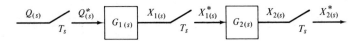

(b) Series Elements with Intermediate Sampler

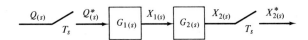

(c) Series Elements that are Continuous

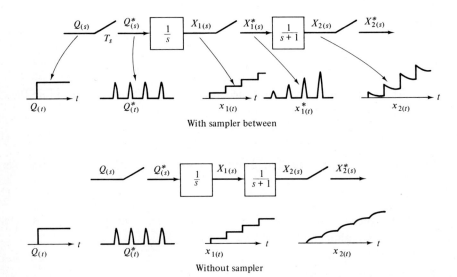

(d) System of Example 14-7

FIGURE 14-11
Open-loop sampled-data systems.

The continuous function $X_{2(s)}$ is

$$X_{2(s)} = G_{2(s)}X_{1(s)}^*$$

The impulse sampled function $X_{2(s)}^*$ is

$$X_{2(s)}^* = G_{2(s)}^*X_{1(s)}^* = G_{2(s)}^*(G_{1(s)}^*Q_{(s)}^*)$$
$$X_{2(s)}^* = G_{1(s)}^*G_{2(s)}^*Q_{(s)}^* \qquad (14\text{-}70)$$

In the z domain, the equation above becomes

$$X_{2(z)} = G_{1(z)}G_{2(z)}Q_{(z)} \qquad (14\text{-}71)$$

Thus the overall transfer function of the process can be expressed as a product of the two individual pulse transfer functions if there is an impulse sampler between the elements.

Consider the system shown in Fig. 14-11c where the two continuous elements $G_{1(s)}$ and $G_{2(s)}$ do not have a sampler between them. The continuous output $X_{2(s)}$ is

$$X_{2(s)} = G_{2(s)} X_{1(s)} = G_{2(s)} G_{1(s)} Q_{(s)}^* \qquad (14\text{-}72)$$

Sampling the output gives

$$X_{2(s)}^* = \frac{1}{T_s} \sum_{n=-\infty}^{+\infty} G_{1(s+in\omega_s)}G_{2(s+in\omega_s)}Q_{(s+in\omega_s)}^*$$

$$= \left[\frac{1}{T_s} \sum_{n=-\infty}^{+\infty} G_{1(s+in\omega_s)}G_{2(s+in\omega_s)}\right]Q_{(s)}^* \qquad (14\text{-}73)$$

The term in brackets is the Laplace transformation of the impulse sampled response of the combined continuous system to a unit impulse function. We will call this $(G_1G_2)_{(s)}^*$ in the Laplace domain and $(G_1G_2)_{(z)}$ in the z domain.

$$X_{2(s)}^* = [G_1G_2]_{(s)}^*Q_{(s)}^* \qquad (14\text{-}74)$$
$$X_{2(z)} = (G_1G_2)_{(z)} Q_{(z)} \qquad (14\text{-}75)$$

Equations (14-70) and (14-71) and Eqs. (14-74) and (14-75) look somewhat similar, but they are not at all the same.

$$G_{1(s)}^*G_{2(s)}^* \neq [G_1G_2]_{(s)}^*$$
$$G_{1(z)}G_{2(z)} \neq (G_1G_2)_{(z)} \qquad (14\text{-}76)$$

Let us take a specific example to illustrate the difference between these two systems.

EXAMPLE 14-7   Suppose the system has two elements shown in Fig. 14-11d.

$$G_{1(s)} = \frac{1}{s}$$

$$G_{2(s)} = \frac{1}{s+1} \qquad (14\text{-}77)$$

With an impulse sampler between the elements, the overall system transfer function is, from Eq. (14-71),

$$G_{1(z)}G_{2(z)} = \mathscr{L}[g^*_{1(t)}]\,\mathscr{L}[g^*_{2(t)}]$$

$$= \mathscr{L}\left[I_{(t)}\mathscr{L}^{-1}\left[\frac{1}{s}\right]\right]\mathscr{L}\left[I_{(t)}\mathscr{L}^{-1}\left[\frac{1}{s+1}\right]\right] \qquad (14\text{-}78)$$

$$G_{1(z)}G_{2(z)} = \mathscr{L}[I_{(t)}u_{(t)}]\mathscr{L}[I_{(t)}e^{-t}]$$

$$= \frac{z}{z-1}\frac{z}{z-e^{-T_s}} \qquad (14\text{-}79)$$

In the calculation above, we went through the time domain, getting $g_{(t)}$ by inverting $G_{(s)}$, and then z-transforming $g^*_{(t)}$. The operation can be represented more concisely by going directly from the Laplace domain to the z domain.

$$G_{1(z)}G_{2(z)} = \mathscr{L}[G^*_{1(s)}]\mathscr{L}[G^*_{2(s)}] = \mathscr{L}\left[\frac{1}{s}\right]\mathscr{L}\left[\frac{1}{s+1}\right] \qquad (14\text{-}80)$$

This equation is a shorthand expression for Eq. (14-78). The inversion to the impulse response $g_{(t)}$ and the impulse sampling to get $g^*_{(t)}$ is implied in the notation $\mathscr{L}[1/s]$ and $\mathscr{L}[1/(s+1)]$.

$$G_{1(z)}G_{2(z)} = \mathscr{L}\left[\frac{1}{s}\right]\mathscr{L}\left[\frac{1}{s+1}\right] = \frac{z}{z-1}\frac{z}{z-e^{-T_s}} \qquad (14\text{-}81)$$

The responses of $x^*_{1(t)}$, $x_{1(t)}$, and $x_{2(t)}$ to a unit step change in $Q_{(t)}$ are sketched in Fig. 14-11d.

Without a sampler between the elements, the overall system transfer function is [Eq. (14-75)]

$$[G_1G_2]_{(z)} = \mathscr{L}\left[I_{(t)}\mathscr{L}^{-1}\left[\frac{1}{s(s+1)}\right]\right] = \mathscr{L}\left[I_{(t)}\mathscr{L}^{-1}\left[\frac{1}{s}-\frac{1}{s+1}\right]\right]$$

$$= \mathscr{L}[I_{(t)}u_{(t)} - I_{(t)}e^{-t}] = \frac{z}{z-1} - \frac{z}{z-e^{-T_s}}$$

$$= \frac{z(1-e^{-T_s})}{(z-1)(z-e^{-T_s})} \qquad (14\text{-}82)$$

Using the short-hand notation,

$$[G_1 G_2]_{(z)} = \mathscr{L}\left[\frac{1}{s(s+1)}\right] = \mathscr{L}\left[\frac{1}{s} - \frac{1}{s+1}\right]$$

$$= \frac{z}{z-1} - \frac{z}{z-e^{-T_s}} = \frac{z(1-e^{-T_s})}{(z-1)(z-e^{-T_s})}$$

From now on we will use the short-hand, Laplace-domain notation, but keep in mind what is implied in its use.

Notice that Eq. (14-79) is not equal to Eq. (14-82). The responses of the two systems $x_{2(t)}$'s are not the same, as shown in Fig. 14-11d, because the systems are physically different.   ////

14-7.2   Closed-loop Systems

The methods used in the previous section can be easily extended to closed-loop sampled-data systems. Let us first consider a chromatograph control loop, as shown in Fig. 14-12a. The output of the process $X_{(s)}$ is

$$X_{(s)} = G_{L(s)}L_{(s)} + B_{(s)} G_{M(s)}(X_{(s)}^{\text{set}} - X_{H(s)}) \qquad (14\text{-}83)$$

The output of the hold $X_{H(s)}$ is

$$X_{H(s)} = H_{(s)} X_{c(s)}^* \qquad (14\text{-}84)$$

The output of the chromatograph column (the dead-time element) is

$$X_{c(s)} = e^{-D_c s} X_{(s)}^* \qquad (14\text{-}85)$$

Substituting Eq. (14-84) into Eq. (14-83) and sampling $X_{(s)}$ give

$$X_{(s)}^* = [G_L L]_{(s)}^* + [BG_M X^{\text{set}}]_{(s)}^* - [BG_M H]_{(s)}^* X_{c(s)}^* \qquad (14\text{-}86)$$

z-transforming gives

$$X_{(z)} = (G_L L)_{(z)} + (BG_M X^{\text{set}})_{(z)} - (BG_M H)_{(z)} X_{c(z)} \qquad (14\text{-}87)$$

Let us assume that the chromatograph dead time is an integer multiple of the sampling period.

$$D_c = kT_s$$
$$X_{c(s)} = e^{-kT_s s} X_{(s)}^*$$

z-transforming $X_{c(s)}^*$ gives [using Eq. (14-35)]

$$X_{c(z)} = \mathscr{L}[e^{-kT_s s} X_{(s)}^*] = z^{-k} \mathscr{L}[X_{(s)}^*] = z^{-k} X_{(z)} \qquad (14\text{-}88)$$

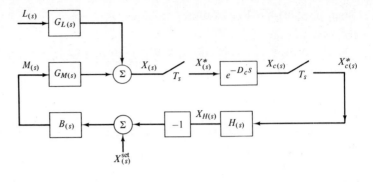

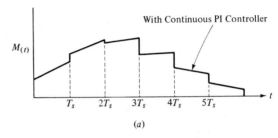

(a)

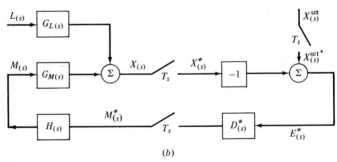

(b)

FIGURE 14-12
Closed-loop systems. (a) Chromatograph loop; (b) DDC loop.

Combining this with Eq. (14-87) gives

$$X_{(z)} = (G_L L)_{(z)} + (BG_M X^{\text{set}})_{(z)} - (BG_M H)_{(z)} z^{-k} X_{(z)}$$

$$X_{(z)} = \frac{(G_L L)_{(z)} + (BG_M X^{\text{set}})_{(z)}}{1 + z^{-k}(BG_M H)_{(z)}} \qquad (14\text{-}89)$$

In this system explicit input-output transfer-function relationships are not obtained. The $(G_L L)_{(z)}$ and $(BG_M X^{\text{set}})_{(z)}$ terms in the numerator of Eq. (14-89) are z transforms of functions. The inputs L and X^{set} cannot be separated out because they are directly connected to the output $X_{(s)}$ by continuous elements.

A specific example will illustrate how the output of the closed-loop system can be obtained in the z domain.

EXAMPLE 14-8 Consider a first-order process with the transfer functions of Fig. 14-12a:

$$G_{M(s)} = G_{L(s)} = \frac{K_p}{\tau_p s + 1} \qquad (14\text{-}90)$$

A zero-order hold and a proportional controller are used.

$$B_{(s)} = K_c \qquad (14\text{-}91)$$

$$H_{(s)} = \frac{1 - e^{-T_s s}}{s} \qquad (14\text{-}92)$$

We want to find the response of the closed-loop system to a unit step change in load.

$$L_{(s)} = \frac{1}{s} \qquad (14\text{-}93)$$

There is no change in set point, so $X_{(s)}^{set}$ is zero. We need to find $(G_L L)_{(z)}$ and $(BG_M H)_{(z)}$ to plug into Eq. (14-89).

$$\mathscr{L}[G_L L] = \mathscr{L}\left[\frac{K_p}{\tau_p s + 1}\frac{1}{s}\right] = \mathscr{L}\left[\frac{K_p}{s} - \frac{K_p}{s + 1/\tau_p}\right]$$

$$= K_p\left(\frac{z}{z - 1} - \frac{z}{z - b}\right) = \frac{K_p(1 - b)z}{(z - 1)(z - b)} \qquad (14\text{-}94)$$

where b is defined

$$b \equiv e^{-T_s/\tau_p} \qquad (14\text{-}95)$$

$$\mathscr{L}[BG_M H] = \mathscr{L}\left[K_c\frac{K_p}{\tau_p s + 1}\frac{1 - e^{-T_s s}}{s}\right]$$

$$= K_c K_p\mathscr{L}\left[\frac{1 - e^{-T_s s}}{s(\tau_p s + 1)}\right] = K_c K_p(1 - z^{-1})\mathscr{L}\left[\frac{1}{s(\tau_p s + 1)}\right]$$

since

$$\mathscr{L}[(1 - e^{-T_s s})F_{(s)}^*] = \mathscr{L}[F_{(s)}^*] - \mathscr{L}[e^{-T_s s}F_{(s)}^*]$$

$$= F_{(z)} - z^{-1}F_{(z)} = (1 - z^{-1})F_{(z)}$$

$$\mathscr{L}[BG_M H] = K_c K_p\left(1 - \frac{1}{z}\right)\frac{(1 - b)z}{(z - 1)(z - b)} = \frac{K_c K_p(1 - b)}{z - b} \qquad (14\text{-}96)$$

Therefore $X_{(z)}$ becomes

$$X_{(z)} = \frac{(G_L L)_{(z)}}{1 + z^{-k}(BG_M H)_{(z)}} = \frac{\dfrac{K_p(1-b)z}{(z-1)(z-b)}}{1 + z^{-k}\dfrac{K_c K_p(1-b)}{z-b}}$$

$$= \frac{K_p(1-b)z}{(z-b)(z-1) + z^{-k} K_c K_p (1-b)(z-1)}$$

$$= \frac{K_p(1-b)z}{z^2 + z[K_c K_p(1-b)z^{-k} - (1+b)] + [b - K_c K_p(1-b)z^{-k}]} \qquad (14\text{-}97)$$

When there is no dead time ($k = 0$), this equation reduces to Eq. (14-47) used in Example 14-4. When the dead time is equal to the sampling period ($k = 1$), Eq. (14-97) becomes

$$X_{(z)} = \frac{K_p(1-b)z^2}{z^3 - (1+b)z^2 + [K_c K_p(1-b) + b]z - K_c K_p(1-b)} \qquad (14\text{-}98)$$

When the dead time is equal to two sampling periods ($k = 2$), $X_{(z)}$ becomes

$$X_{(z)} = \frac{K_p(1-b)z^3}{z^4 - (1+b)z^3 + [K_c K_p(1-b) + b]z^2 - K_c K_p(1-b)} \qquad (14\text{-}99)$$

The order of the system in the z domain (the highest power of z in the denominator) increases with increasing dead time or k.   ////

EXAMPLE 14-9   Let us take the same system as above but use a PI controller. The chromatograph dead time is assumed equal to the sampling period, so $D_c = T_s$ and $k = 1$. The disturbance is again a unit step change in load.

$$B_{(s)} = K_c\left(1 + \frac{1}{\tau_I s}\right) \qquad (14\text{-}100)$$

$$(BG_M H)_{(z)} = \mathscr{L}\left[K_c \frac{s + 1/\tau_I}{s} \frac{K_p}{\tau_p s + 1} \frac{1 - e^{-T_s s}}{s}\right]$$

$$= K_c K_p(1 - z^{-1})\mathscr{L}\left[\frac{(s + 1/\tau_I)(1/\tau_p)}{s^2(s + 1/\tau_p)}\right]$$

$$= K_c K_p \frac{z-1}{z} \mathscr{L}\left[\frac{1/\tau_I}{s^2} + \frac{1 - \tau_p/\tau_I}{s} - \frac{1 - \tau_p/\tau_I}{s + 1/\tau_p}\right]$$

$$= K_c K_p \frac{z-1}{z}\left[\frac{(T_s/\tau_I)z}{(z-1)^2} - \frac{(\tau_p/\tau_I - 1)z}{z-1} + \frac{(\tau_p/\tau_I - 1)z}{z - e^{-T_s/\tau_p}}\right]$$

$$= K_c K_p \frac{(T_s/\tau_I)(z-b) + (\tau_p/\tau_I - 1)(b-1)(z-1)}{(z-1)(z-b)} \qquad (14\text{-}101)$$

$$X_{(z)} = \frac{(G_L L)_{(z)}}{1 + z^{-1}(BG_M H)_{(z)}} = \frac{\dfrac{K_p(1-b)z}{(z-1)(z-b)}}{1 + z^{-1}K_c K_p \dfrac{(T_s/\tau_I)(z-b)+(\tau_p/\tau_I-1)(b-1)(z-1)}{(z-1)(z-b)}}$$

$$X_{(z)} = \frac{K_p(1-b)z^2}{z^3 - (1+b)z^2 + z[b - K_c K_p(\tau_p/\tau_I - 1)(1-b)}$$
$$+ K_c K_p(T_s/\tau_I)] + [(-T_s/\tau_I)b + (\tau_p/\tau_I - 1)(1-b)]K_c K_p \quad (14\text{-}102)$$

The order of the system is increased by 1 when a PI controller is used instead of a proportional controller.

The feedback controller is continuous, and it sees a constant error between samples. Therefore the manipulative variable $m_{(t)}$ is ramped up or down during the sampling period by the integral action, as sketched in Fig. 14-12a. $////$

For our second sampled-data closed-loop system, let us consider the direct digital control (DDC) loop sketched in Fig. 14-12b. The equations describing the system are

$$X_{(s)} = G_{L(s)}L_{(s)} + H_{(s)}G_{M(s)}M_{(s)}^* \quad (14\text{-}103)$$
$$M_{(s)} = D_{(s)}^*(X_{(s)}^{\text{set}*} - X_{(s)}^*) \quad (14\text{-}104)$$

Sampling $X_{(s)}$ and $M_{(s)}$ gives

$$X_{(s)}^* = [G_L L]_{(s)}^* + [HG_M]_{(s)}^* M_{(s)}^*$$
$$M_{(s)}^* = D_{(s)}^* X_{(s)}^{\text{set}*} - D_{(s)}^* X_{(s)}^*$$

z-transforming and combining give

$$X_{(z)} = (G_L L)_{(z)} + (HG_M)_{(z)}(D_{(z)}X_{(z)}^{\text{set}} - D_{(z)}X_{(z)})$$
$$X_{(z)} = \frac{(G_L L)_{(z)} + (HG_M)_{(z)}D_{(z)}X_{(z)}^{\text{set}}}{1 + (HG_M)_{(z)}D_{(z)}} \quad (14\text{-}105)$$

In this system we obtain an explicit input-output transfer-function relationship between $X_{(z)}$ and $X_{(z)}^{\text{set}}$:

$$\frac{X_{(z)}}{X_{(z)}^{\text{set}}} = \frac{(HG_M)_{(z)}D_{(z)}}{1 + (HG_M)_{(z)}D_{(z)}} \quad (14\text{-}106)$$

For proportional controllers, the continuous $B_{(s)}$ and the sampled-data $D_{(z)}$ give the same results since

$$(BG_M H)_{(z)} = K_c(G_M H)_{(z)}$$
$$(HG_M)_{(z)}D_{(z)} = K_c(HG_M)_{(z)} \quad (14\text{-}107)$$

EXAMPLE 14-10 One form of $D_{(z)}$ that gives approximately the same response as a continuous PI controller is (as we will show in Chap. 15)

$$D_{(z)} = K_c \frac{1}{\alpha} \frac{z - \alpha}{z - 1} \qquad (14\text{-}108)$$

where

$$\alpha \equiv \frac{\tau_I}{T_s + \tau_I} \qquad (14\text{-}109)$$

For the same process and disturbance of Example 14-8 with no dead time the output $X_{(z)}$ becomes

$$X_{(z)} = \frac{\dfrac{K_p(1 - b)z}{(z - 1)(z - b)}}{1 + \dfrac{K_p(1 - b)}{z - b} \dfrac{K_c}{\alpha} \left(\dfrac{z - \alpha}{z - 1} \right)}$$

$$= \frac{K_p(1 - b)z}{z^2 + z\left[\dfrac{K_p K_c(1 - b)}{\alpha} - (1 + b) \right] + [b - K_p K_c(1 - b)]} \qquad (14\text{-}110)$$

$$////$$

PROBLEMS

14-1 Derive the z transforms of the functions:

(a) $f^*_{(t)} = I_{(t)}t^2$

(b) $f^*_{(t)} = I_{(t)}t^2 e^{-at}$

(c) $f^*_{(t)} = I_{(t)} \cos \omega t$

(d) $f^*_{(t)} = I_{(t)}e^{-\zeta t/\tau_p}\left[\cos\left(\dfrac{\sqrt{1 - \zeta^2}}{\tau_p} t \right) + \dfrac{\zeta}{\sqrt{1 - \zeta^2}} \sin\left(\dfrac{\sqrt{1 - \zeta^2}}{\tau_p} t \right) \right]$

(e) $f^*_{(t)} = I_{(t)}K_p K\tau_p\left(\dfrac{t}{\tau_p} - 1 + e^{-t/\tau_p} \right)$

(f) $f^*_{(t)} = I_{(t)}e^{-a(t - kT_s)}$ where k is an integer

(g) $f^*_{(t)} = I_{(t)} \dfrac{K}{\tau_{p1} - \tau_{p2}} (e^{-t/\tau_{p1}} - e^{-t/\tau_{p2}})$

14-2 Find the pulse transfer functions in the z domain $(HBG_M)_{(z)}$ for the systems ($H_{(s)}$ is a zero-order hold):

(a) $G_{M(s)} = \dfrac{K_p}{(\tau_{p1}s + 1)(\tau_{p2}s + 1)} \qquad B_{(s)} = K_c$

(b) $G_{M(s)} = \dfrac{K_p e^{-kT_s s}}{(\tau_{p1}s + 1)(\tau_{p2}s + 1)} \qquad B_{(s)} = K_c$

(c) $G_{M(s)} = \dfrac{K_p e^{-kT_s s}}{(\tau_{p1}s + 1)(\tau_{p2}s + 1)} \qquad B_{(s)} = K_c\left(1 + \dfrac{1}{\tau_I s} \right)$

14-3 Find $x_{(nT_s)}$ for a unit step input in $Q_{(t)}$ for the system in part (*a*) of Prob. 14-2 by partial fractions expansion and by long division. Use the numerical values of parameters given below:

$$K_p = \tau_{p2} = K_c = 1 \qquad \tau_{p1} = 5 \qquad T_s = 0.5$$

14-4 Repeat Prob. 14-3 for part *c* of Prob. 14-2. Use $\tau_I = 2$ and $k = 3$.

14-5 Use the subroutine LONGD given in Fig. 14-8 to find the response of the closed-loop system of Example 14-4 to a unit step load disturbance. Use values of $\tau_p = K_p = 1$.
(*a*) With $T_s = 0.2$ and $K_c = 2, 4, 6, 8, 10, 12$
(*b*) With $T_s = 0.4$ and $K_c = 2, 4, 6, 8, 10, 12$
(*c*) With $T_s = 0.6$ and $K_c = 2, 4, 6, 8, 10, 12$
     What do you conclude about the effect of sampling time on stability from these results?

14-6 Find the outputs $x_{2(nT_s)}$ of the two systems of Example 14-7 for a unit step input in $Q_{(t)}$. Use partial fractions expansion and long division.

14-7 Repeat Prob. 14-6 for a ramp input in $Q_{(t)}$.

14-8 Find the output $x_{(nT_s)}$ of the chromatograph closed-loop system described by Eq. (14-98). The sampling time is equal to the chromatograph dead time. Use the values of parameters, sampling times, and gains given in Prob. 14-5.

14-9 Find the output $x_{(nT_s)}$ of the system of Example 14-9 with a continuous PI controller for values of integral time given below. Use $\tau_p = K_p = 1$ and $K_c = 4$ and $T_s = 0.2$.
(*a*) $\tau_I = 2$ (*c*) $\tau_I = 0.5$
(*b*) $\tau_I = 1$ (*d*) $\tau_I = 0.25$

14-10 Repeat Prob. 14-9 for the system of Example 14-10 with a sampled-data PI controller.

14-11 A distillation column has an approximate transfer function between overhead composition x_D and reflux flow rate R of

$$G_{M(s)} = \frac{x_{D(s)}}{R_{(s)}} = \frac{0.0092}{(5s+1)^2} \diamond \frac{\text{mole fraction}}{\text{moles/min}}$$

A chromatograph must be used to detect x_D. A continuous PI controller is used with a gain of 1,000 and an integral time of 5 min. Calculate the response of x_D to a unit step change in set point for different chromatograph cycle times $D_c = 5, 10,$ and 20 min. The sampling period T_s is set equal to the chromatograph cycle time.

14-12 A tubular chemical reactor's response to a change in feed concentration is found to be essentially a pure dead time D with attenuation K_p. A DDC computer monitors the outlet concentration $C_{AL(t)}$ and changes the feed concentration $C_{A0(t)}$, through a zero-order hold, using proportional action. The sampling period T_s can be adjusted to an integer multiple of D. Calculate the response of C_{AL} for a unit step change in set point C_{AL}^{set} for $D/T_s = 1$ and $D/T_s = 2$ (*a*) with $K_c = 1/K_p$; (*b*) with $K_c = 1/2K_p$.

14-13 Derive the closed-loop transfer functions between $X_{2(z)}$ and the two inputs L and X_2^{set} for the DDC cascade control system sketched below. The hold is zero order.

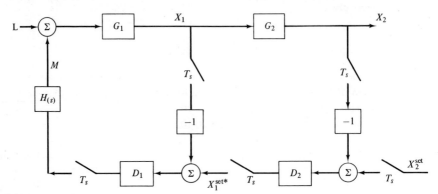

ANALYSIS AND SYNTHESIS OF SAMPLED-DATA CONTROL SYSTEMS

15-1   STABILITY IN THE z PLANE

In Parts 3 and 4 we learned that the stability of a linear continuous system is determined by the location of the roots of its characteristic equation. The characteristic equation is a polynomial in the complex variable s. If all the roots of this polynomial are in the left-half of the s plane, the system is stable. For a continuous closed-loop system, all the roots of $1 + B_{(s)} G_{M(s)}$ must lie in the left-half of the s plane. Thus the region of stability in continuous systems is the left-half of the s plane.

The stability of a sampled-data system is determined by the location of the roots of a characteristic equation that is a polynomial in the complex variable z. The roots of this polynomial are plotted in the z plane. The ordinate is the imaginary part of z, and the abscissa is the real part of z.

The region of stability in the z plane can be found directly from the region of stability in the s plane by using the basic relationship between the complex variables s and z [Eq. (14-23)]:

$$z = e^{T_s S} \qquad (15\text{-}1)$$

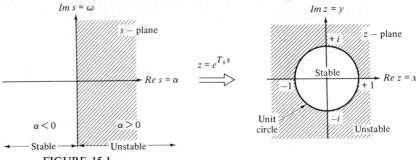

FIGURE 15-1
Stability regions in the s plane and in the z plane.

Figure 15-1 shows the s plane. Let the real part of s be α and the imaginary part of s be ω.

$$s = \alpha + i\omega \qquad (15\text{-}2)$$

The stability region in the s plane is where α, the real part of s, is negative. Substituting Eq. (15-2) into Eq. (15-1) gives

$$z = e^{T_s(\alpha + i\omega)} = (e^{\alpha T_s})\, e^{i\omega T_s} \qquad (15\text{-}3)$$

The absolute magnitude of z, $|z|$, is $e^{\alpha T_s}$. When α is negative, $|z|$ is less than 1. When α is positive, $|z|$ is greater than 1. Therefore the left-half of the s plane maps into the inside of the unit circle in the z plane, as shown in Fig. 15-1.

A sampled-data system is stable if all the roots of its characteristic equation lie inside the unit circle in the z plane.

The equation describing the closed-loop chromatograph system of Sec. 14-7.2 was [Eq. (14-89)]

$$X_{(z)} = \frac{(G_L L)_{(z)} + (BG_M X^{\text{set}})_{(z)}}{1 + z^{-k}(BG_M H)_{(z)}} \qquad (15\text{-}4)$$

The closed-loop stability of this system depends on the location of the roots of the characteristic equation:

$$1 + z^{-k}(BG_M H)_{(z)} = 0 \qquad (15\text{-}5)$$

If all the roots lie inside the unit circle, the system is closed-loop stable.

The equation describing the closed-loop digital-computer control system of Sec. 14-7.2 was [Eq. (14-105)]

$$X_{(z)} = \frac{(G_L L)_{(z)} + (HG_M)_{(z)}\, D_{(z)} X^{\text{set}}_{(z)}}{1 + (HG_M)_{(z)}\, D_{(z)}} \qquad (15\text{-}6)$$

The closed-loop stability of this system depends on the location of the roots of the characteristic equation:

$$1 + (HG_M)_{(z)} D_{(z)} = 0 \qquad (15\text{-}7)$$

If all the roots lie inside the unit circle, the system is closed-loop stable.

We will write the closed-loop characteristic equation of a general sampled-data system as

$$1 + A_{(z)} = 0 \qquad (15\text{-}8)$$

where $A_{(z)}$ is either $(HG_M)_{(z)}D_{(z)}$ or $z^{-k}(BG_M H)_{(z)}$.

A sampled-data system is *open-loop* stable if the roots of its open-loop characteristic equation are all inside the unit circle, i.e., if the poles of $A_{(z)}$ lie inside the unit circle.

EXAMPLE 15-1   The system of Example 14-8 is a first-order process, a zero-order hold, and a proportional controller. See Eq. (14-96).

$$A_{(z)} = z^{-k}(BG_M H)_{(z)} = z^{-k}\mathscr{L}\left[K_c \frac{K_p}{\tau_p s + 1} \frac{1 - e^{-T_s s}}{s} \right] = \frac{z^{-k}K_c K_p(1 - b)}{z - b} \qquad (15\text{-}9)$$

where K_c = feedback controller gain

K_p = process gain

$b = e^{-T_s/\tau_p}$

Let us consider the case where there is no dead time and $k = 0$. The closed-loop characteristic equation of the system is

$$1 + \frac{K_c K_p(1 - b)}{z - b} = 0$$

$$z = b - K_c K_p(1 - b) \qquad (15\text{-}10)$$

There is a single root. It lies on the real axis in the z plane. When the feedback-controller gain is zero, the root lies at $z = b = e^{-T_s/\tau_p}$, which is inside the unit circle. The system is therefore open-loop stable. As K_c is increased, the root moves toward the left in the z plane, as shown in Fig. 15-2, along the real axis.

The system reaches the limit of closed-loop stability when the root crosses the unit circle at $z = -1$. The value of controller gain $(K_c)_{\max}$ at this limit is found from Eq. (15-10).

$$z = -1 = b - (K_c)_{\max} K_p(1 - b)$$

$$(K_c)_{\max} = K_u = \frac{1 + b}{K_p(1 - b)} \qquad (15\text{-}11)$$

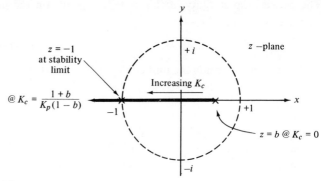

FIGURE 15-2
z-plane location of roots (Example 15-1).

K_u is the ultimate gain. For the system of Example 14-4, $T_s = 0.2$ and $K_p = \tau_p = 1$, giving a value of $b = 0.819$.

$$K_u = \frac{1 + 0.819}{1 - 0.819} = 10 \qquad (15\text{-}12)$$

Remember, we found in Example 14-6 that a K_c of 15 gave an unstable response.

Thus this system is closed-loop stable for values of gain K_c up to 10, since the roots of the closed-loop characteristic equation lie inside the unit circle.

It is worth noting, before we leave this example, that the above results show that the gain can be increased to a point where the closed-loop system is unstable. In a continuous first-order system, increasing the gain to infinity (in theory) will not make the system closed-loop unstable. Thus the addition of the sampler and hold has made the system more unstable. ////

15-2 FREQUENCY-DOMAIN DESIGN TECHNIQUES

Sampled-data control systems can be designed in the frequency domain by using the same techniques that we employed for continuous control systems.

15-2.1 Nyquist Stability Criterion

The closed-loop characteristic equation of a sampled-data system is

$$1 + A_{(z)} = 0$$

We want to find out if $1 + A_{(z)}$ has any zeros or roots outside the unit circle in the z plane. If it does, the system is closed-loop unstable.

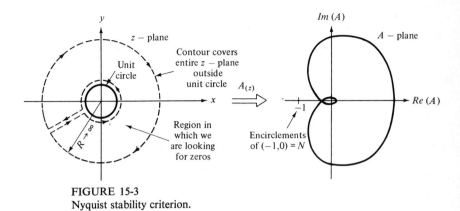

FIGURE 15-3
Nyquist stability criterion.

We can apply the $Z - P = N$ theorem of Chap. 12 to this new problem. We pick a contour that goes completely around the area in the z plane that is outside the unit circle, as shown in Fig. 15-3. We then plot $A_{(z)}$ in the A plane and look at the encirclements of the $(-1,0)$ point to find N.

If the number of poles of $A_{(z)}$ outside the unit circle is known, the number of zeros outside the unit circle can be calculated from

$$Z = N + P \qquad (15\text{-}13)$$

If the system is open-loop stable there are no poles of $A_{(z)}$ outside the unit circle and $P = 0$.

Thus the Nyquist stability criterion can be applied directly to sampled-data systems.

15-2.2   Rigorous Method

Going from the Laplace domain to the frequency domain by substituting $s = i\omega$ in Eq. (15-1) gives

$$z = e^{i\omega T_s} \qquad (15\text{-}14)$$

To make a Nyquist plot, we merely substitute $e^{i\omega T_s}$ for z in the $A_{(z)}$ function of Eq. (15-8) and make a polar plot of $A^*_{(i\omega)}$ as frequency ω goes from 0 to $\omega_s/2$, where

$$\omega_s = \frac{2\pi}{T_s} \qquad (15\text{-}15)$$

The reason why we only have to vary ω from 0 to $\omega_s/2$ will be demonstrated in the example below.

EXAMPLE 15-2 Let us consider the chromatograph system of Example 14-9, which has a PI controller and a sampling rate equal to the chromatograph dead time. The closed-loop characteristic equation was found [Eq. (14-101)] to be

$$1 + z^{-1}(BG_M H)_{(z)} = 1 + K_c K_p \frac{(T_s/\tau_I)(z - b) - (\tau_p/\tau_I - 1)(1 - b)(z - 1)}{z(z - 1)(z - b)}$$

Therefore the $A_{(z)}$ for this system is

$$A_{(z)} = \frac{K_c K_p[(T_s/\tau_I)(z - b) - (\tau_p/\tau_I - 1)(1 - b)(z - 1)]}{z(z - 1)(z - b)} \qquad (15\text{-}16)$$

The following numerical values of parameters are assumed.

$$K_c = K_p = \tau_p = 1 \qquad \tau_I = 2 \qquad T_s = 0.2 \text{ min}$$

The parameter b becomes

$$b = e^{-T_s/\tau_p} = 0.819$$

The sampling frequency is

$$\omega_s = \frac{2\pi}{T_s} = \frac{2\pi}{0.2} = 31.4 \text{ radians/minute}$$

Substituting into Eq. (15-16) gives

$$A_{(z)} = \frac{(0.2/2)(z - 0.819) - (0.5 - 1)(1 - 0.819)(z - 1)}{z(z - 1)(z - 0.819)}$$

$$A_{(z)} = \frac{0.19(z - 0.905)}{z(z - 1)(z - 0.819)} \qquad (15\text{-}17)$$

This system has three poles: $z = 0$, $z = +1$, and $z = 0.819$. All of them are inside the unit circle. Thus we can say immediately that the number of poles of $A_{(z)}$ outside the unit circle is zero; that is, $P = 0$.

We now select a contour that goes completely around the area in the z plane outside the unit circle. The contour, as shown in Fig. 15-4a, is broken up into several pieces. The contour C_+ goes counterclockwise around the unit circle from $z = +1$ to $z = -1$ (angles θ from 0 to π radians). The contour C_- goes from $z = -1$ back to $z = +1$ (angles θ from π to 2π or from $-\pi$ to 0). The contour C_R is an infinite circle $(R \to \infty)$ that goes completely around the z plane. The C_{out} and C_{in} contours go out to and back from the C_R contour on a radial line where the angle θ is equal to π radians. The contour C_o is a little semicircle around the $z = +1$ point so that we exclude the pole at $z = +1$ from the area enclosed by the contours. Let us examine each of these contours in detail.

(a) On C_+ contour: We are on the unit circle, so the magnitude of z is unity

$$z = e^{i\theta} \qquad (15\text{-}18)$$

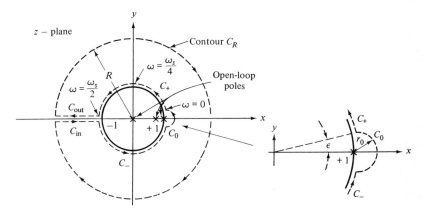

(a) z − plane contours

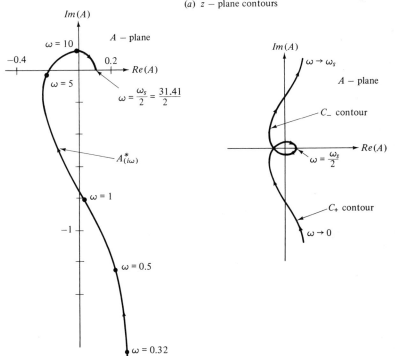

(b) C_+ contour in the A − plane

(c) C_+ and C_- contours

FIGURE 15-4
Nyquist plots of Example 15-2.

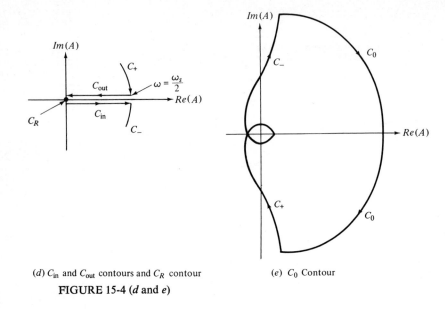

(d) C_{in} and C_{out} contours and C_R contour   (e) C_0 Contour

FIGURE 15-4 (d and e)

The angle θ goes from ϵ to π (from 0 to π as we take the limit $r_o \to 0$). Comparing Eqs. (15-14) and (15-18) shows that $\theta = \omega T_s$ on this contour. Expressing T_s in terms of the sampling frequency gives

$$\theta = \omega \frac{2\pi}{\omega_s}$$

As θ goes from 0 to π on the C_+ contour, ω goes from 0 to $\omega_s/2$.

We will designate the frequency-domain representation of the $A_{(z)}$ transfer function as $A^*_{(i\omega)}$. The asterisk is to remind us that this is a pulse transfer function.

$$A^*_{(i\omega)} = \frac{0.19(e^{i\omega T_s} - 0.905)}{e^{i\omega T_s}(e^{i\omega T_s} - 1)(e^{i\omega T_s} - 0.819)} \qquad (15\text{-}19)$$

The polar plot of $A^*_{(i\omega)}$ is shown in Fig. 15-4b as ω is varied from 0 to $\omega_s/2$. The value of $A^*_{(i\omega)}$ at the end of the contour where $\omega = \omega_s/2$ or where $z = -1$ is

$$A^*_{(15.7\,i)} = \frac{0.19(-1 - 0.905)}{(-1)(-1 - 1)(-1 - 0.819)} = +0.062$$

The contour crosses the negative real axis at about -0.18.

(b) On the C_- contour: $z = e^{i\theta}$ as θ goes from π to 2π or from $-\pi$ to 0. This means that frequency ω goes from $\omega_s/2$ to ω_s or from $-\omega_s/2$ to 0. Each point on the C_- contour in the A plane is the complex conjugate of a point on the C_+ contour in the A plane.

The C_- contour is just the reflection of the C_+ contour over the real axis, as shown in Fig. 15-4c.

(c) *On the C_{out} and C_{in} contours:* On these lines $z = re^{i\theta}$ where r goes from 1 out to infinity as $R \to \infty$. The phase angle is π radians.

$$z = r(\cos\pi + i\sin\pi) = -r$$

$A_{(z)}$ on these contours becomes (using Eq. (15-17)]

$$A_{(z=-r)} = \frac{0.19(-r-0.905)}{-r(-r-1)(-r-0.819)} \qquad (15\text{-}20)$$

When $r = 1$, $A_{(z)} = +0.062$. As $r \to \infty$, $A_{(z)} \to 0$. Therefore the C_{out} and C_{in} contours follow the positive real axis in the A plane from Re $A = 0.062$ into the origin and back out again, as shown in Fig. 15-4d.

(d) *On the C_R contour:* $z = Re^{i\theta}$ as $R \to \infty$. The phase angle θ goes from $+\pi$ through 0 to $-\pi$ radians.

$$A_{(z=Re^{i\theta})} = \frac{0.190(Re^{i\theta} - 0.905)}{Re^{i\theta}(Re^{i\theta} - 1)(Re^{i\theta} - 0.819)}$$

As R becomes large, we can neglect the smaller terms in the parentheses.

$$\lim_{R\to\infty} A_{(z)} = \lim_{R\to\infty} \frac{0.19Re^{i\theta}}{Re^{i\theta}Re^{i\theta}Re^{i\theta}} = \lim_{R\to\infty}\left(\frac{0.19}{R^2}e^{-i2\theta}\right) = 0 \qquad (15\text{-}21)$$

Thus the infinite circle of the C_R contour in the z plane maps into the origin in the A plane.

(e) *On the C_o contour:* On this bypass around the $z = +1$ point the variable z is given by

$$z = 1 + r_o e^{i\theta}$$

r_o goes to zero and θ goes from $-\pi/2$ through 0 to $+\pi/2$ radians.

$$A_{(z=1+r_o e^{i\theta})} = \frac{0.19(1 + r_o e^{i\theta} - 0.905)}{(1 + r_o e^{i\theta})(1 + r_o e^{i\theta} - 1)(1 + r_o e^{i\theta} - 0.819)}$$

As r_o becomes small, the $r_o e^{i\theta}$ can be neglected in some of the terms.

$$\lim_{r_o\to 0} A_{(z)} = \lim_{r_o\to 0} \frac{0.19(0.095)}{r_o e^{i\theta}(0.181)} = \lim_{r_o\to 0}\left[\frac{0.19(0.095)}{0.181 r_o}e^{-i\theta}\right] \qquad (15\text{-}22)$$

Thus the C_o contour in the A plane is an infinite semicircle, going from $+\pi/2$ through 0 to $-\pi/2$. The complete Nyquist plot is shown in Fig. 15-4e.

The encirclements of the $(-1,0)$ point in the A plane are determined by the C_+ contour. Therefore we usually make only a polar plot of $A^*_{(i\omega)}$ as ω goes from 0 to $\omega_s/2$. This is the contour around the upper half of the unit circle in the z plane.

The system is closed-loop stable since $(-1,0)$ is not encircled. N is zero and P is zero, and therefore Z must be zero. The $A^*_{(i\omega)}$ curve crosses the negative real axis at -0.18. The ultimate gain is 5.5. A gain of 3.2 will give a phase margin of 45°. Figure 15-5 shows the effects on the $A^*_{(i\omega)}$ curves of changing sampling period T_s and integral time τ_I. Increasing T_s or decreasing τ_I moves the curves closer to the $(-1,0)$ point and therefore reduces closed-loop stability.   ////

15-2.3   Approximate Method

To generate the $A^*_{(i\omega)}$ Nyquist plots discussed above, the z transform of the appropriate transfer functions must first be obtained. Then $e^{i\omega T_s}$ is substituted for z, and ω is varied from 0 to $\omega_s/2$.

There is an alternative way to generate the $A^*_{(i\omega)}$ Nyquist plots that is often more convenient to use, particularly in high-order systems. Equation (14-13) gives a doubly infinite series representation of $A^*_{(i\omega)}$.

$$A^*_{(i\omega)} = \frac{1}{T_s} \sum_{n=-\infty}^{+\infty} A_{(i\omega + in\omega_s)} \qquad (15\text{-}23)$$

where $A_{(s)}$ is the transfer function of the original continuous elements before z-transforming. Remember $A^*_{(s)}$ is a pulse transfer function. $A_{(s)}$ is a continuous transfer function. For example, the chromatograph system has an $A_{(s)}$ that is $B_{(s)} G_{M(s)} H_{(s)}$. The dead time is included in the $G_{M(s)}$ term for convenience. If this series converges in a reasonable number of terms, we can approximate $A^*_{(i\omega)}$ with a few terms in the series. Usually two or three are all that are required.

$$A^*_{(i\omega)} = [BG_MH]^*_{(i\omega)} = \frac{1}{T_s} \sum_{n=-\infty}^{+\infty} B_{(i\omega + in\omega_s)}G_{M(i\omega + in\omega_s)}H_{(i\omega + in\omega_s)} \qquad (15\text{-}24)$$

$$A^*_{(i\omega)} \simeq \frac{1}{T_s} (B_{(i\omega)}G_{M(i\omega)}H_{(i\omega)} + B_{(i\omega + i\omega_s)}G_{M(i\omega + i\omega_s)}H_{(i\omega + i\omega_s)}$$

$$+ B_{(i\omega - i\omega_s)}G_{M(i\omega - i\omega_s)}H_{(i\omega - i\omega_s)}) \qquad (15\text{-}25)$$

This will give an approximate $A^*_{(i\omega)}$ curve, but we have eliminated the step of z transformation. For complex systems this can be a considerable savings. The series approximation of $A^*_{(i\omega)}$ can be conveniently generated on a digital computer.

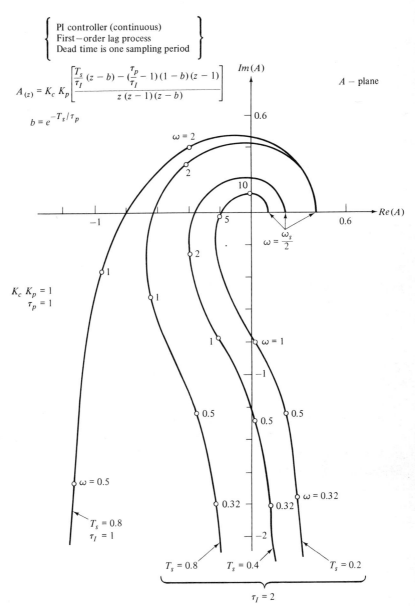

FIGURE 15-5
Nyquist plots of $A^*_{(i\omega)}$ for various sampling periods and integral times.

EXAMPLE 15-3 The system of Example 15-2 had the original continuous transfer functions

$$G_{M(s)} = \frac{K_p e^{-T_s s}}{\tau_p s + 1} = \frac{e^{-0.2s}}{s + 1} \qquad (15\text{-}26)$$

$$B_{(s)} = K_c\left(1 + \frac{1}{\tau_I s}\right) = \frac{2s + 1}{2s} \qquad (15\text{-}27)$$

$$H_{(s)} = \frac{1 - e^{-T_s s}}{s} = \frac{1 - e^{-0.2s}}{s} \qquad (15\text{-}28)$$

The sampling frequency ω_s is $2\pi/T_s = 2\pi/0.2 = 31.4$ radians/minute.

$$A_{(i\omega)} = B_{(i\omega)}G_{M(i\omega)}H_{(i\omega)} = \frac{1 + i2\omega}{i2\omega}\frac{e^{-i0.2\omega}}{1 + i\omega}\frac{1 - e^{-i0.2\omega}}{i\omega} \qquad (15\text{-}29)$$

$$A^*_{(i\omega)} \simeq \frac{1}{0.2}\left(A_{(i\omega)} + A_{(i\omega+i31.4)} + A_{(i\omega-i31.4)}\right) \qquad (15\text{-}30)$$

The approximate $A^*_{(i\omega)}$ curve using three terms in the series is essentially the same as the rigorous curve shown in Fig. 15-5. ////

15-3 z-DOMAIN ROOT LOCUS DESIGN METHODS

With continuous systems we made root locus plots in the s plane. Controller gain was varied from zero to infinity, and the roots of the closed-loop characteristic equation were plotted. Time constants, damping, and stability could be determined from the position of the roots in the s plane. The limit of stability was the imaginary axis.

With sampled-data systems, root locus plots can be made in the z plane. Controller gain is varied from zero to infinity, and the roots of the closed-loop characteristic equation are plotted.

$$1 + A_{(z)} = 0 \qquad (15\text{-}31)$$

When the roots lie inside the unit circle, the system is closed-loop stable. When the roots lie outside the unit circle, the system is closed-loop unstable.

In Example 15-1 we drew a root locus plot for a first-order process, proportional controller, and zero-order hold. As shown in Fig. 15-2, there is only one path. It starts ($K_c = 0$) at the open-loop pole ($z = b$) of the transfer function $A_{(z)}$.

$$A_{(z)} = \frac{K_c K_p(1 - b)}{z - b}$$

The system is stable for controller gains up to $K_c = K_u = (1 + b)/K_p(1 - b)$. At this point the path crosses the unit circle at $z = -1$ and the system goes closed-loop un-

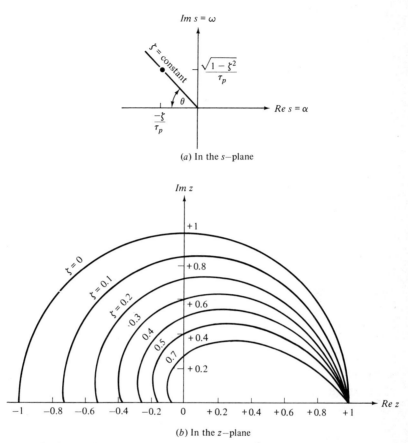

(a) In the s–plane

(b) In the z–plane

FIGURE 15-6
Lines of constant damping coefficient.

stable. Notice that K_u decreases as the sampling period T_s is increased, since $b = e^{-T_s/\tau_p}$ decreases.

We will give root locus plots of some other systems in the examples below. The roots of the higher-order systems were found by using the POLRT subroutine given in the Appendix.

Lines of constant damping coefficient ζ in the s plane are radial lines from the origin.

$$\zeta = \cos\theta \qquad (15\text{-}32)$$

where θ is the angle between the radial line and the negative real axis. See Fig. 15-6a.

These lines can be mapped into the z plane. Along a line of constant ζ in the s plane, the tangent of θ is

$$\tan \theta = \frac{\omega}{\alpha} = \frac{\sqrt{1 - \zeta^2}/\tau_p}{-\zeta/\tau_p}$$

The real part of s, α, can be expressed in terms of the imaginary part of s, ω, and the damping coefficient ζ.

$$\alpha = \frac{-\zeta\omega}{\sqrt{1 - \zeta^2}} \qquad (15\text{-}33)$$

Then the z variable along a line of constant damping is

$$z = e^{T_s s} = e^{T_s(\alpha + i\omega)} = e^{\alpha T_s} e^{i\omega T_s}$$

$$z = \exp\left(-\frac{\zeta\omega T_s}{\sqrt{1 - \zeta^2}}\right) e^{i\omega T_s} \qquad (15\text{-}34)$$

Lines of constant damping coefficient in the z plane can be generated by picking a value of ζ and varying ω in Eq. (15-34) from 0 to $\omega_s/2$. Figure 15-6b shows these curves. The system of Example 15-1 has a closed-loop damping coefficient of 0.3 when the controller gain K_c is 6.6. Notice that this occurs on the negative real axis in the z plane. The system is underdamped even though there is only one root.

Root locus plots of sampled-data systems are even more simply plotted in the ln z plane.[1] In this coordinate system lines of the constant damping coefficient are again straight radial lines.

EXAMPLE 15-4   Consider the process of Example 15-1 with a dead time of one sampling period added ($k = 1$ in Example 14-8). The closed-loop characteristic equation is

$$1 + A_{(z)} = 1 + \frac{K_c K_p(1 - b)}{z(z - b)} = 0$$

$$z^2 - bz + K_c K_p(1 - b) = 0 \qquad (15\text{-}35)$$

There are two root loci, as shown in Fig. 15-7a for the numerical values $K_p = \tau_p = 1$, $T_s = 0.2$, and $b = 0.819$.

$$z = \frac{b \pm \sqrt{b^2 - 4K_c K_p(1 - b)}}{2} \qquad (15\text{-}36)$$

The paths start ($K_c = 0$) at $z = 0$ and $z = b$. They come together on the positive real

---

[1] G. Marroguin and W. L. Luyben, *Instrum. Technol.*, September, 1971, p. 69.

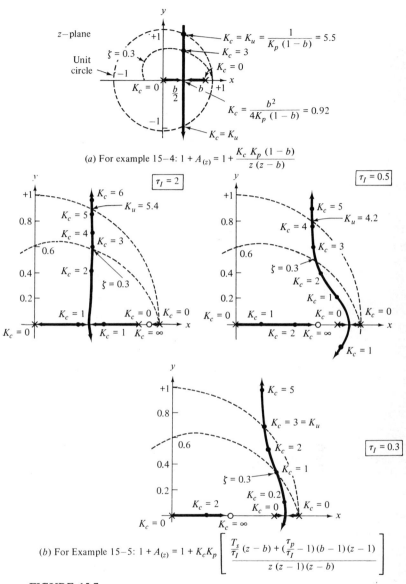

(a) For example 15–4: $1 + A_{(z)} = 1 + \dfrac{K_c K_p (1 - b)}{z (z - b)}$

(b) For Example 15–5: $1 + A_{(z)} = 1 + K_c K_p \left[\dfrac{\frac{T_s}{\tau_I} (z - b) + (\frac{\tau_p}{\tau_I} - 1)(b - 1)(z - 1)}{z (z - 1)(z - b)} \right]$

FIGURE 15-7
Root locus plots.

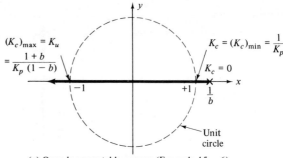

(c) Open-loop unstable process (Example 15 — 6)

FIGURE 15-7c

axis at $z = b/2$ when $K_c = b^2/4K_p(1 - b) = 0.925$. For controller gains greater than this, the system is underdamped. The roots are

$$z = \frac{b}{2} \pm i\tfrac{1}{2}\sqrt{4K_c K_p(1 - b) - b^2} \qquad (15\text{-}37)$$

The maximum K_c for which the closed-loop system is stable occurs when the paths cross the unit circle. At that point the magnitude of z, $|z|$ is unity.

$$|z| = \sqrt{\left(\frac{b}{2}\right)^2 + \left[\frac{\sqrt{4K_c K_p(1 - b) - b^2}}{2}\right]^2} = \frac{1}{2}\sqrt{4K_c K_p(1 - b)} = 1$$

$$K_c = K_u = \frac{1}{K_p(1 - b)} = 5.5 \qquad (15\text{-}38)$$

Comparison of this result with Example 15-1 shows that the addition of the dead time reduces the maximum gain by $1/(1 + b)$. A gain of $K_c = 3$ gives a damping coefficient of 0.3. ////

EXAMPLE 15-5   Let us now use a PI controller with the same system considered above. The closed-loop characteristic equation is [see Eq. (14-102)]

$$1 + A_{(z)} = 1 + z^{-1}(BG_M H)_{(z)} =$$

$$1 + \frac{K_c K_p[(T_s/\tau_I)(z - b) + (\tau_p/\tau_I - 1)(b - 1)(z - 1)]}{z(z - 1)(z - b)}$$

$$z^3 - (1 + b)z^2 + z\left[b - K_c K_p\left(\frac{\tau_p}{\tau_I} - 1\right)(1 - b) + K_c K_p\frac{T_s}{\tau_I}\right]$$

$$+ \left[\frac{-T_s}{\tau_I}b + \left(\frac{\tau_p}{\tau_I} - 1\right)(1 - b)\right]K_c K_p = 0 \qquad (15\text{-}39)$$

There are three loci (when $\tau_I \neq \tau_p$). They begin at $z = 0$, $z = +1$, and $z = b$. One path ends at the zero of $A_{(z)}$. The root loci for several values of τ_I are shown in Fig. 15-7b. Decreasing τ_I decreases stability and ultimate gain K_u. ////

EXAMPLE 15-6   Suppose we have a first-order open-loop *unstable*[1] process with a transfer function (Sec. 11-4)

$$G_{M(s)} = \frac{K_p}{\tau_p s - 1} \quad (15\text{-}40)$$

This process is controlled by a sampled-data proportional controller with a zero-order hold. The closed-loop characteristic equation is

$$1 + A_{(z)} = 1 + \mathscr{L}\left[K_c \frac{K_p}{\tau_p s - 1} \frac{1 - e^{-T_s s}}{s} \right] = 1 + K_c K_p \frac{b^{-1} - 1}{z - b^{-1}} = 0 \quad (15\text{-}41)$$

There is a single root.

$$z = b^{-1} - K_c K_p (b^{-1} - 1) \quad (15\text{-}42)$$

The root locus plot is given in Fig. 15-7c. The path begins ($K_c = 0$) at $z = b^{-1} = (e^{-T_s/\tau_p})^{-1} = e^{T_s/\tau_p}$. This is greater than 1 and is located outside the unit circle. Thus the system is unstable. As K_c is increased, the path moves toward the left in the z plane, entering the unit circle at $(K_c)_{min}$ when $z = +1$. Substituting $z = +1$ into Eq. (15-42) gives

$$z = +1 = b^{-1} - K_c K_p (b^{-1} - 1)$$

$$(K_c)_{min} = \frac{1}{K_p} \quad (15\text{-}43)$$

The path along the real axis passes through the unit circle again as K_c is increased at $z = -1$ when $K_c = (K_c)_{max} = K_u$.

$$(K_c)_{max} = K_u = \frac{b^{-1} + 1}{K_p(b^{-1} - 1)} = \frac{1 + b}{K_p(1 - b)} \quad (15\text{-}44)$$

For values of gain greater than K_u, the system is again closed-loop unstable. Therefore this system is conditionally stable.

In Sec. 11-4.1 we found the same minimum gain for stability but there was no maximum gain. Sampling has made the system more unstable. ////

[1] L. B. Koppel, *Ind. Eng. Chem., Fundamentals*, vol. 5, p. 396, 1966.

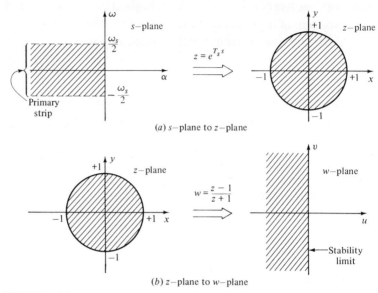

(a) s–plane to z–plane

(b) z–plane to w–plane

FIGURE 15-8
Bilinear transformation.

15-4   BILINEAR-TRANSFORMATION DESIGN METHODS

The bilinear transformation is a change of variables from z to a new complex variable w. The transformation maps the unit circle of the z plane into the left-half of the w plane. This mapping converts the stability region back to the familiar LHP region. The Routh criterion can then be used. The conversion to the frequency domain is a simple matter of substituting iv for w in the system transfer function $A_{(w)}$. Likewise, root locus plots can be made in the w plane with the system going closed-loop unstable when the loci cross over into the RHP.

The transformation $z = e^{T_s s}$ maps the left-half of the s plane into the unit circle. Actually, a number of horizontal strips in the s plane are each mapped into the unit circle, one on top of the other. The mapping is, therefore, not unique. The "primary strip" from $\omega = -\omega_s/2$ to $+\omega_s/2$, sketched in Fig. 15-8a, is the only one that we are interested in since $A^*_{(s)}$ is periodic.

The bilinear transformation is defined in two ways:

$$w = \frac{z - 1}{z + 1} \qquad (15\text{-}45)$$

$$w = \frac{z + 1}{z - 1} \qquad (15\text{-}46)$$

These equations differ only in the sign of z. Since we are interested in the interior and exterior of the unit circle, switching signs or quadrants in the z plane does not matter.

To prove that this transformation maps the unit circle in the z plane into the left-half of the w plane, let us express the complex variables w and z in the following rectangular and polar form, respectively:

$$w = u + iv \qquad (15\text{-}47)$$

$$z = re^{i\theta} \qquad (15\text{-}48)$$

where u is the real part of w, v is the imaginary part of w, r is the magnitude of z, and θ is the argument or phase angle of z.

Substituting these into Eq. (15-45) gives

$$w = \frac{z-1}{z+1} = \frac{-1 + r\cos\theta + ir\sin\theta}{1 + r\cos\theta + ir\sin\theta}$$

$$u + iv = \frac{r^2 - 1}{1 + r^2 + 2r\cos\theta} + i\frac{2r\sin\theta}{1 + r^2 + 2r\cos\theta} \qquad (15\text{-}49)$$

When r is less than 1, u is negative. Thus a point inside the unit circle in the z plane maps into a point in the left-half of the w plane.

On the stability boundary in the z plane, r is equal to 1 and θ goes from 0 to π and then from $-\pi$ to 0 radians. When $r = 1$, u is zero. This is the imaginary axis in the w plane. Also when $r = 1$, v is equal to $(\sin\theta)/(1 + \cos\theta)$. At $\theta = 0$, $v = 0$. At $\theta = \pi/2$, $v = 1$. As θ goes to π, we must take the limit of $(\sin\theta)/(1 + \cos\theta)$ using L'Hôpital's rule.

$$\lim_{\theta \to \pi} v = \lim_{\theta \to \pi} \frac{\sin\theta}{1 + \cos\theta} = \lim_{\theta \to \pi} \frac{\cos\theta}{-\sin\theta} = +\infty$$

Thus the path along the upper half of the unit circle in the z plane maps into the positive real axis in the w plane. As θ goes from $-\pi$ to 0, v goes from $-\infty$ to 0, which is the negative real axis in the w plane.

The examples below illustrate the use of the bilinear transformation to analyze the stability of sampled-data systems. We can use all the classic methods: root locus, Routh stability criterion, direct substitution, and Nyquist stability criterion.

EXAMPLE 15-7   The first-order process, zero-order hold, and proportional controller of Example 15-1 gave the system transfer function [Eq. (15-9)]

$$A_{(z)} = \frac{K_c K_p (1 - b)}{z - b} \qquad (15\text{-}50)$$

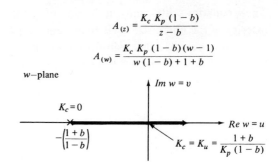

$$A_{(z)} = \frac{K_c\,K_p\,(1-b)}{z-b}$$

$$A_{(w)} = \frac{K_c\,K_p\,(1-b)(w-1)}{w\,(1-b)+1+b}$$

FIGURE 15-9
w-plane root locus plot (Example 15-7).

Equation (15-46) can be solved for z to give

$$z = \frac{w+1}{w-1} \qquad (15\text{-}51)$$

Substituting for z in Eq. (15-50) gives

$$A_{(w)} = \frac{K_c\,K_p(1-b)}{(w+1)/(w-1)-b} = \frac{K_c\,K_p(1-b)(w-1)}{w(1-b)+1+b} \qquad (15\text{-}52)$$

To make a frequency-response plot and use the Nyquist stability criterion, we merely substitute iv for w in $A_{(w)}$ and let v take on values from 0 to $+\infty$.

The closed-loop characteristic equation for this system is

$$1 + A_{(w)} = 1 + \frac{K_c\,K_p(1-b)(w-1)}{w(1-b)+1+b} = 0$$

$$w = -\frac{(1+b)/(1-b) - K_c\,K_p}{1 + K_c\,K_p} \qquad (15\text{-}53)$$

Varying K_c from 0 to ∞ and plotting the location of this single root in the w plane give a root locus plot of the closed-loop system. Figure 15-9 shows that the path starts at $u = -(1+b)/(1-b)$ in the left-half of the w plane when $K_c = 0$. The path moves along the negative real axis toward the origin. As long as it is in the LHP, the system is closed-loop stable. The limit of stability occurs when the root passes through the origin ($w = 0$). The value of controller gain at this limit is

$$(K_c)_{max} = K_u = \frac{1+b}{K_p(1-b)}$$

This is the same value we found in Example 15-1.   ////

EXAMPLE 15-8   Let us consider the system of Example 15-2. We will pick a τ_I that is equal to τ_p. This simplifies the closed-loop characteristic equation to

$$1 + A_{(z)} = 1 + \frac{K_c K_p T_s/\tau_p}{z(z-1)} \qquad (15\text{-}54)$$

Substituting for z gives

$$1 + \frac{K_c K_p T_s/\tau_p}{\dfrac{w+1}{w-1}\left(\dfrac{w+1}{w-1}-1\right)} = 0$$

$$w^2 + \left(\frac{2\tau_p}{K_c K_p T_s} - 2\right)w + \left(1 + \frac{2\tau_p}{K_c K_p T_s}\right) = 0 \qquad (15\text{-}55)$$

We could make a root locus plot in the w plane. Or we could use the direct-substitution method (let $w = iv$) to find the maximum stable value of K_c. Let us use the Routh stability criterion. This criterion cannot be applied in the z plane because it gives the number of positive roots, not the number of roots outside the unit circle. There is a stability-analysis technique, the Schur-Cohn criterion, that can be used in the z plane, but it is fairly complex.[1] The Routh criterion can be applied in the w plane.

The Routh array is

$$\begin{bmatrix} 1 & 1 + \dfrac{2\tau_p}{K_c K_p T_s} \\[2ex] \dfrac{2\tau_p}{K_c K_p T_s} - 2 & \cdots \\[2ex] 1 + \dfrac{2\tau_p}{K_c K_p T_s} & \cdots \end{bmatrix}$$

All the terms in the first column must have the same sign for the system to have no zeros in the RHP of the w plane. Therefore, the two requirements are

$$\frac{\tau_p}{K_c K_p T_s} - 1 > 0$$

$$1 + \frac{2\tau_p}{K_c K_p T_s} > 0$$

The first establishes the upper limit on K_c.

$$(K_c)_{\max} = K_u = \frac{\tau_p}{K_p T_s} \qquad (15\text{-}56) \qquad ////$$

---

[1] J. T. Tou, "Digital and Sampled-data Control Systems," p. 238, McGraw-Hill, 1959.

15-5   SAMPLED-DATA CONTROLLERS

Sampled-data systems have two types of feedback controllers. In the chromatograph system, the controller is a conventional continuous analog device. It has the usual continuous transfer functions $B_{(s)}$ of P, PI, and PID analog controllers.

In the digital-computer control system, the feedback controller $D_{(z)}$ or $D_{(s)}^*$ is a pulse transfer function. This controller is called a *sampled-data controller*. The analysis and design of these elements are discussed below.

What we are seeking is an equation or algorithm that can be programmed into the digital computer. At the sampling time for a given loop, the computer looks at the current process output $x_{(t)}$, compares it to a set point, and calculates a current value of the error $e_{(t)}$. This error plus some old values of error and old values of the controller output or manipulative variable $m_{(t)}$ that have been stored in computer memory are then used to calculate a new value of the controller output.

These algorithms are basically finite-difference equations that relate the current value of m to the current value of e and old values of m and e. These finite-difference equations can be derived from the pulse transfer functions $D_{(z)}$.

Suppose the current moment in time is the nth sampling period $t = nT_s$. The current value of the error $e_{(t)}$ is $e_{(nT_s)}$. We will call this e_n. The value of $e_{(t)}$ at the previous sampling time was $e_{[(n-1)T_s]}$ or e_{n-1}. Other old values are e_{n-2}, e_{n-3}, etc.

The value of the controller output $m_{(t)}$ that is computed at the current instant in time $t = nT_s$ is $m_{(nTs)}$ or m_n. Old values of $m_{(t)}$ are m_{n-1}, m_{n-2}, etc.

Suppose we have the following finite-difference equation or algorithm:

$$m_n = a_0 e_n + a_1 e_{n-1} + a_2 e_{n-2} + \cdots + a_M e_{n-M} - b_1 m_{n-1} - b_2 m_{n-2}$$
$$- b_3 m_{n-3} - \cdots - b_N m_{n-N} \quad (15\text{-}57)$$

$$m_{(nT_s)} = a_0 e_{(nT_s)} + a_1 e_{(nT_s-T_s)} + a_2 e_{(nT_s-2T_s)} + \cdots + a_M e_{(nT_s-MT_s)}$$
$$- b_1 m_{(nT_s-T_s)} - b_2 m_{(nT_s-2T_s)} - \cdots - b_N m_{(nT_s-NT_s)} \quad (15\text{-}58)$$

Limiting t to some multiple of T_s,

$$m_{(t)} = a_0 e_{(t)} + a_1 e_{(t-T_s)} + a_2 e_{(t-2T_s)} + \cdots + a_M e_{(t-MT_s)}$$
$$- b_1 m_{(t-T_s)} - b_2 m_{(t-2T_s)} - \cdots - b_N m_{(t-NT_s)} \quad (15\text{-}59)$$

If each of the functions $m_{(t)}, m_{(t-T_s)}, m_{(t-2T_s)}, \ldots, e_{(t)}, e_{(t-T_s)}, e_{(t-2T_s)}, \ldots$ is impulse-sampled and z-transformed, Eq. (15-59) becomes

$$M_{(z)} = a_0 E_{(z)} + a_1 z^{-1} E_{(z)} + a_2 z^{-2} E_{(z)} + \cdots + a_M z^{-M} E_{(z)}$$
$$- b_1 z^{-1} M_{(z)} - b_2 z^{-2} M_{(z)} - \cdots - b_N z^{-N} M_{(z)} \quad (15\text{-}60)$$

Putting this in terms of a pulse transfer function gives

$$D_{(z)} = \frac{M_{(z)}}{E_{(z)}} = \frac{a_0 + a_1 z^{-1} + a_2 z^{-2} + \cdots + a_M z^{-M}}{1 + b_1 z^{-1} + b_2 z^{-2} + \cdots + b_N z^{-N}} \quad (15\text{-}61)$$

A sampled-data controller is a ratio of polynomials in either positive or negative powers of z. It can be directly converted into a finite-difference equation or algorithm [Eq. (15-57)] for programming into the computer.

15-5.1 Physical Realizability

Continuous transfer functions are physically realizable if the order of the polynomial in s of their numerator is less than or equal to the order of the polynomial in s of their denominator.

The physical realizability of pulsed transfer functions uses the basic criterion that the current output of a device (digital computer) cannot depend upon future information about the input. We cannot build a gadget that can predict the future.

If $D_{(z)}$ is expressed as a polynomial in negative powers of z, as in Eq. (15-61), the requirement for physical realizability is that there must be 1 term in the denominator. If $D_{(z)}$ is expressed as a polynomial in positive powers of z, as shown in the equation below, the requirement for physical realizability is that the order of the numerator polynomial in z must be less than or equal to the order of the denominator polynomial in z. These two ways of expressing physical realizability are completely equivalent.

Suppose $D_{(z)}$ is expressed in positive powers of z.

$$D_{(z)} = \frac{a_0 z^M + a_1 z^{M-1} + a_2 z^{M-2} + \cdots + a_M}{z^N + b_1 z^{N-1} + b_2 z^{N-2} + \cdots + b_N} = \frac{M_{(z)}}{E_{(z)}} \qquad (15\text{-}62)$$

Multiplying top and bottom by z^{-N} and converting into difference-equation form gives the current value of the output m_n:

$$m_n = a_0 e_{n+M-N} + a_1 e_{n+M-N-1} + \cdots + a_M e_{n-N} - b_1 m_{n-1}$$
$$- b_2 m_{n-2} - \cdots - b_N m_{n-N} \qquad (15\text{-}63)$$

If the order of the numerator M is greater than the order of the denominator N in Eq. (15-62), the calculation of m_n will require future values of error. For example, if $M - N = 1$, Eq. (15-63) tells us that we need to know e_{n+1} or $e_{(t+T_s)}$ in order to calculate m_n or $m_{(t)}$. Since we do not know $e_{(t+T_s)}$ at time t, this calculation is physically impossible.

15-5.2 Controller Design

Sampled-data controllers can, in principle, be designed in the same way continuous controllers are designed. Root locus plots in the z plane or frequency-response plots are made with various types of $D_{(z)}$'s (different orders of M and N and different values of the a_i and b_i coefficients). These parameters are varied to achieve some desired performance criteria. In the z-plane root locus plots, the specifications of time constant

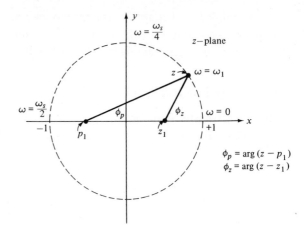

(a) Location of poles and zeros in the z plane

FIGURE 15-10a
Sampled-data controller $D_{(z)}$.

and damping coefficient can be used. The roots of the closed-loop characteristic equation $1 + D_{(z)}(G_M H)_{(z)}$ are modified by changing $D_{(z)}$.

In the frequency domain, the conventional criteria of phase margin, gain margin, or maximum closed-loop log modulus can be used. The shape of the $A^*_{(i\omega)}$ or $D^*_{(i\omega)}[G_M H]^*_{(i\omega)}$ curve is modified by changing $D^*_{(i\omega)}$.

The simplest form of a $D_{(z)}$ sampled-data controller is

$$D_{(z)} = \frac{z - z_1}{z - p_1} \qquad (15\text{-}64)$$

where z_1 is the zero of $D_{(z)}$ and p_1 is the pole of $D_{(z)}$. Selecting different values of z_1 and p_1 gives different compensation. If lead action (positive phase-angle advance) is required in the frequency domain, the pole must be chosen to lie to the left of the zero, as shown in Fig. 15-10a.

$$\text{arg } D_{(z)} = \text{arg } (z - z_1) - \text{arg } (z - p_1) \qquad (15\text{-}65)$$

At some frequency ω_1, the arg $D_{(z)} = \phi_z - \phi_p$. As long as p_1 is located to the left of z_1, the arg $D_{(z)}$ will be positive. Tou[1] presents curves showing how the selection of z_1 and p_1 changes the magnitude and phase angle of $D_{(z)}$.

In practice, most algorithms that are used in process control are finite-difference approximations of conventional controllers. We will cover their derivation in the next section. The next most popular kind of sampled-data controllers are the so-called

---

[1] *Ibid.*, p. 440.

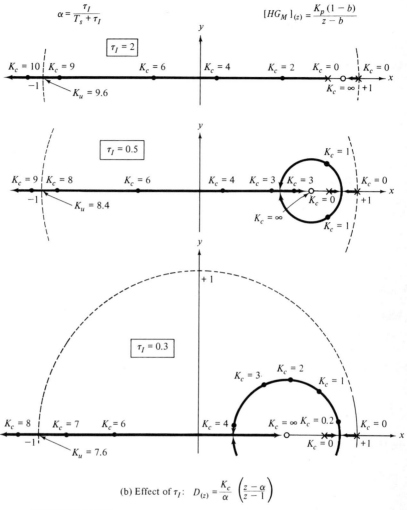

(b) Effect of τ_I: $D_{(z)} = \dfrac{K_c}{\alpha}\left(\dfrac{z-\alpha}{z-1}\right)$

FIGURE 15-10b

"minimal prototype" controllers, which will be discussed in Sec. 15-6. Only rarely does a process control engineer juggle the poles and zeros of a $D_{(z)}$ to derive his control algorithm.

EXAMPLE 15-9   The first-order process and zero-order hold of Example 15-1 have a $(G_M H)_{(z)}$ equal to $K_c K_p(1 - b)/(z - b)$. Suppose we are controlling this process with a sampled-data controller. We choose a $D_{(z)}$ that approximates a continuous PI controller (to be derived later).

$$D_{(z)} = \frac{K_c}{\alpha} \frac{z - \alpha}{z - 1} \qquad (15\text{-}66)$$

where

$$\alpha = \frac{\tau_I}{T_s + \tau_I}$$

This pulse transfer function has a zero at $z = \alpha$ and a pole at $z = +1$. It cannot produce any phase-angle advance since the pole lies to the right of the zero (α is less than 1). The pole at $z = +1$ is equivalent to integration (pole at $s = 0$) in continuous systems. It drives the system to zero steady-state error with a step disturbance.

Varying τ_I is equivalent to varying the location of the zero α. Figure 15-10b shows the effect of changing τ_I on the root locus plot of the system. Stability decreases as τ_I is decreased. Ultimate gains and damping coefficients at a given gain decrease with τ_I.

15-5.3 Approximating Continuous Elements

Discrete approximations for integration There are numerous finite-difference approximations for the continuous operation of integration. Rectangular integration uses the present value of the input times the sampling period to approximate the integral of the input.

$$x_{(nT_s)} = \int_0^{nT_s} Q_{(t)}dt = x_{[(n-1)T_s]} + \int_{(n-1)T_s}^{nT_s} Q_{(t)}dt$$

$$\simeq x_{[(n-1)T_s]} + Q_{(nT_s)}T_s$$

In the z domain,

$$X_{(z)} \simeq z^{-1}X_{(z)} + T_s Q_{(z)}$$

$$\frac{X_{(z)}}{Q_{(z)}} = \frac{T_s}{1 - z^{-1}} \qquad (15\text{-}67)$$

Trapezoidal integration draws a straight line between the values of the input.

$$x_{(nT_s)} \simeq x_{[(n-1)T_s]} + (Q_{(nT_s)} + Q_{[(n-1)T_s]})\frac{T_s}{2}$$

$$X_{(z)} = z^{-1}X_{(z)} + \frac{T_s}{2}(Q_{(z)} + z^{-1}Q_{(z)})$$

$$\frac{X_{(z)}}{Q_{(z)}} = \frac{T_s}{2}\frac{1 + z^{-1}}{1 - z^{-1}} \qquad (15\text{-}68)$$

Both Eqs. (15-67) and (15-68) are pulse transfer functions that approximate the continuous transfer function s^{-1}. There are functions, called *z forms*, that are similar to these approximations; z forms can be used to invert Laplace transforms.[1]

Digital computer algorithms   To obtain finite-difference equations that approximate a continuous device, we rearrange the continuous transfer function $G_{(s)}$ to put it in terms of s^{-1}. Then we substitute one of the approximations for s^{-1} [Eqs. (15-67) or (15-68)].

EXAMPLE 15-10   We want to derive a finite-difference equation that approximates the action of a continuous PI controller.

$$B_{(s)} = \frac{M_{(s)}}{E_{(s)}} = K_c\left(1 + \frac{1}{\tau_I s}\right) = K_c\left(1 + \frac{1}{\tau_I}s^{-1}\right) \qquad (15\text{-}69)$$

Let us use the simple rectangular approximation for s^{-1}.

$$D_{(z)} = \frac{M_{(z)}}{E_{(z)}} = K_c\left(1 + \frac{1}{\tau_I}\frac{T_s}{1 - z^{-1}}\right) = K_c\frac{1 - z^{-1} + T_s/\tau_I}{1 - z^{-1}}$$

$$= K_c\frac{z(1 + T_s/\tau_I) - 1}{z - 1} = \frac{K_c}{\tau_I/(\tau_I + T_s)}\left[\frac{z - \tau_I/(\tau_I + T_s)}{z - 1}\right]$$

$$D_{(z)} = \frac{K_c}{\alpha}\frac{z - \alpha}{z - 1} \qquad (15\text{-}70)$$

where

$$\alpha = \frac{\tau_I}{\tau_I + T_s}$$

Converting to finite-difference form gives

$$M_{(z)}(z - 1) = \frac{K_c}{\alpha}(z - \alpha)E_{(z)}$$

$$M_{(z)} - z^{-1}M_{(z)} = \frac{K_c}{\alpha}(E_{(z)} - \alpha z^{-1}E_{(z)})$$

$$m_n = m_{n-1} + \frac{K_c}{\alpha}e_n - K_c e_{n-1} \qquad (15\text{-}71)$$

Equation (15-71) is a digital-computer control algorithm.   ////

EXAMPLE 15-11   We want to find a finite-difference equation that approximates a first-order lag. This is eloquently called a *digital filter*.

$$G_{(s)} = \frac{X_{(s)}}{Q_{(s)}} = \frac{1}{\tau s + 1} = \frac{s^{-1}}{\tau + s^{-1}} \qquad (15\text{-}72)$$

[1] R. Boxer and S. Thaler, *Proc. IRE*, vol. 44, p. 89, 1956.

We will use the trapezoidal approximation for s^{-1} and will label the digital filter $D_{F(z)}$.

$$D_{F(z)} = \frac{X_{(z)}}{Q_{(z)}} = \frac{(T_s/2)(1 + z^{-1})/(1 - z^{-1})}{\tau + (T_s/2)(1 + z^{-1})/(1 - z^{-1})} = \frac{(T_s/2)(1 + z^{-1})}{\tau(1 - z^{-1}) + (T_s/2)(1 + z^{-1})}$$

$$= \frac{T_s/(2\tau + T_s) + T_s/(2\tau + T_s)z^{-1}}{1 + (T_s - 2\tau)/(2\tau + T_s)z^{-1}} \quad (15\text{-}73)$$

The digital filter has the standard form:

$$D_{F(z)} = \frac{a_0 + a_1 z^{-1}}{1 + b_1 z^{-1}} \qquad ////$$

15-6   MINIMAL-PROTOTYPE SAMPLED-DATA CONTROLLERS

Minimal-prototype control is a type of optimal control applied to sampled-data systems. The basic idea is to specify the desired response of a system to a specific type of disturbance and then back-calculate the controller required. This is analogous to determining feedforward controllers. And just as with feedforward controllers, there is no guarantee that the minimal-prototype controller will be physically realizable. Therefore, the specified response may have to be modified to make the controller realizable.

Many people think of minimal-prototype controllers whenever the term "sampled-data controller" is mentioned.[1] Keep in mind that the minimal-prototype controller is only one type of $D_{(z)}$. We can use the methods discussed in this chapter to design $D_{(z)}$'s for specified damping coefficients, gain margins, phase margins, etc.

Let us consider the closed-loop set-point response of an arbitrary system with a sampled-data controller [Eq. (14-106)]:

$$\frac{X_{(z)}}{X_{(z)}^{\text{set}}} = \frac{(HG_M)_{(z)}D_{(z)}}{1 + (HG_M)_{(z)}D_{(z)}} \quad (15\text{-}74)$$

If we specify the form of the input $X_{(z)}^{\text{set}}$ and the desired form of the output $X_{(z)}$ and if the process and hold transfer functions are known, we can rearrange Eq. (15-74) to give the required controller $D_{MP(z)}$.

$$D_{MP(z)} = \frac{X_{(z)}}{(HG_M)_{(z)}(X_{(z)}^{\text{set}} - X_{(z)})} \quad (15\text{-}75)$$

Consider a step change in set point:

$$X_{(z)}^{\text{set}} = \frac{1}{1 - z^{-1}} = \frac{z}{z - 1} \quad (15\text{-}76)$$

---

[1] H. A. Mosler et al., *A.I.Ch.E. J.*, vol. 13, p. 768, 1967.

Let us assume that we want the output of this closed-loop system to come up to the set point in one sampling period, as sketched in Fig. 15-11a. Remember, we are specifying only the values of the variables at the sampling times. The output at $t = 0$ is zero. At $t = T_s$, the output should be 1 and should stay at 1 at all subsequent sampling times.

$$X_{(z)} = x_{(0)} + x_{(T_s)}z^{-1} + x_{(2T_s)}z^{-2} + x_{(3T_s)}z^{-3} + \cdots$$

$$X_{(z)} = 0 + z^{-1} + z^{-2} + z^{-3} + \cdots \qquad (15\text{-}77)$$

$$X_{(z)} = \frac{z^{-1}}{1 - z^{-1}} = \frac{1}{z - 1} \qquad (15\text{-}78)$$

Plugging these specified functions for $X_{(z)}$ and $X_{(z)}^{\text{set}}$ into Eq. (15-75) gives

$$D_{MP(z)} = \frac{1/(z - 1)}{(HG_M)_{(z)}[z/(z - 1) - 1/(z - 1)]}$$

$$D_{MP(z)} = \frac{1}{(z - 1)(HG_M)_{(z)}} \qquad (15\text{-}79)$$

EXAMPLE 15-12   The first-order system of Example 15-1 has an

$$(HG_M)_{(z)} = \frac{K_p(1 - b)}{z - b}$$

The minimal-prototype controller for a step set-point change would be

$$D_{MP(z)} = \frac{1}{(z - 1)(HG_M)_{(z)}} = \frac{z - b}{(z - 1)K_p(1 - b)} \qquad (15\text{-}80)$$

This sampled-data controller is physically realizable since the order of the polynomial in the numerator is equal to the order of the polynomial in the denominator.   ////

EXAMPLE 15-13   If we add a dead time of one sampling period to the above system, the system transfer function is

$$(HG_M)_{(z)} = \frac{K_p(1 - b)}{z(z - b)}$$

The minimal-prototype controller must be

$$D_{MP(z)} = \frac{1}{(z - 1)(HG_M)_{(z)}} = \frac{z(z - b)}{(z - 1)K_p(1 - b)} \qquad (15\text{-}81)$$

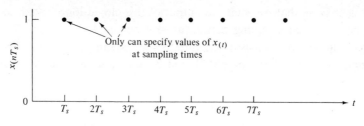

(a) Desired response to unit step change in set point

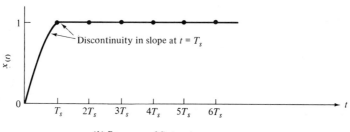

(b) Response of first-order process

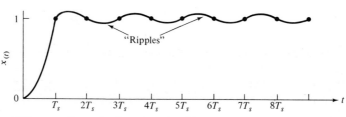

(c) Response of second-order system when driven to set point in one sampling period

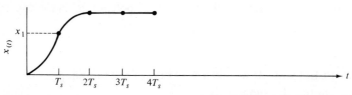

(d) Modified response of second-order system to take two sampling periods to reach set point without rippling

FIGURE 15-11
Minimal-prototype responses.

This controller is physically unrealizable because the order of the numerator is higher than the order of the denominator. Therefore we cannot achieve the response specified. This result should really not be unexpected. The dead time will not let the output change during the first sampling period, and we cannot drive the output up to its set point instantaneously.

Let us back off on the specified output and say we want the output to come up to the set point in two sampling periods:

$$X_{(z)} = 0 + 0z^{-1} + z^{-2} + z^{-3} + \cdots = \frac{z^{-2}}{1 - z^{-1}} = \frac{1}{z^2 - z} \qquad (15\text{-}82)$$

Now the minimal-prototype controller becomes

$$D_{MP(z)} = \frac{X_{(z)}}{(HG_M)_{(z)}(X_{(z)}^{\text{set}} - X_{(z)})} = \frac{1/(z^2 - z)}{[K_p(1 - b)/z(z - b)][z/(z - 1) - 1/(z^2 - z)]}$$

$$D_{MP(z)} = \frac{z(z - b)}{K_p(1 - b)(z^2 - 1)} \qquad (15\text{-}83)$$

The controller is now physically realizable and stable. ////

Minimal-prototype controllers are designed for specific types of inputs. A controller designed for a step input will not perform well with a ramp input, and vice versa.

The required $D_{MP(z)}$ also depends on the process $(HG_M)_{(z)}$. If the process is first-order we should be able to drive it to the new set point in one sampling period and hold its output right on the set point even between the sampling periods. This is possible because we can change the slope of a first-order-process response curve, as shown in Fig. 15-11b.

If the process is second or higher order, we will not be able to make a discontinuous change in the slope of the response curve. Consequently we would expect a second-order process to overshoot the set point and oscillate between sampling times. This is called *ripple* and is illustrated in Fig. 15-11c.

Ripple is usually undesirable since we do not want to keep wiggling the control valve. We may want to modify the specified output response in order to eliminate ripple. Allowing two sampling periods for the process to come up to the set point gives us two switches of the manipulative variable and should let us bring up a second-order process without rippling. This is illustrated in Example 15-14 below. In general, an Nth-order process must be given N sampling periods to come up to the set point if the response is to be completely ripple-free.

Since we know only the values of $x_{(t)}$ at the sampling times, we cannot use it to see if there are ripples. We can see what the manipulative variable $m_{(t)}$ is doing at each sampling period. If $m_{(nT_s)}$ is changing value at each sampling time, it means the system is rippling.

$$M_{(z)} = D_{(z)}E_{(z)} = D_{(z)}(X^{set}_{(z)} - X_{(z)}) \qquad (15\text{-}84)$$

Substituting for $D_{(z)}$ from Eq. (15-75) gives

$$M_{(z)} = \frac{X_{(z)}}{(HG_M)_{(z)}} \qquad (15\text{-}85)$$

Let us check the system of Example 15-12 for ripples.

$$M_{(z)} = \frac{1/(z-1)}{K_p(1-b)/(z-b)} = \frac{z-b}{K_p(1-b)(z-1)}$$

$$M_{(z)} = \frac{1}{K_p}\left(\frac{1}{1-b} + z^{-1} + z^{-2} + z^{-3} + z^{-4} + \cdots\right) \qquad (15\text{-}86)$$

The manipulative variable holds constant after the first sampling period, indicating no rippling.

EXAMPLE 15-14   A second-order system is controlled by a sampled-data controller with a zero-order hold.

$$(HG_M)_{(z)} = \mathscr{L}\left[\frac{1-e^{-T_s s}}{s}\frac{K_p}{(\tau_{p1}s+1)(\tau_{p2}s+1)}\right]$$

$$= (1-z^{-1})K_p\mathscr{L}\left[\frac{1}{s(\tau_{p1}s+1)(\tau_{p2}s+1)}\right]$$

$$= \frac{z-1}{z}K_p\left(\frac{z}{z-1} - \frac{\tau_{p1}}{\tau_{p1}-\tau_{p2}}\frac{z}{z-b_1} + \frac{\tau_{p2}}{\tau_{p1}-\tau_{p2}}\frac{z}{z-b_2}\right) \qquad (15\text{-}87)$$

where

$$b_1 = e^{-T_s/\tau_{p1}}$$

$$b_2 = e^{-T_s/\tau_{p2}} \qquad (15\text{-}88)$$

$$(HG_M)_{(z)} = K_p\left(1 + \frac{b_2\tau_{p2} - b_1\tau_{p1}}{\tau_{p1}-\tau_{p2}}\right)\frac{z + \left(\dfrac{b_1b_2(\tau_{p1}-\tau_{p2}) + \tau_{p2}b_1 - \tau_{p1}b_2}{\tau_{p1}-\tau_{p2} + b_2\tau_{p2} - b_1\tau_{p1}}\right)}{(z-b_1)(z-b_1)} \qquad (15\text{-}89)$$

This equation has the form

$$(HG_M)_{(z)} = a_0\frac{(z+a_1)}{(z-b_1)(z-b_2)} \qquad (15\text{-}90)$$

where the a_0 and a_1 terms are defined in Eq. (15-89).

We now want to design a minimal-prototype controller for a unit step set-point disturbance. The output is supposed to come up to the new set point in one sampling period. Substituting Eq. (15-90) into Eq. (15-79) gives

$$D_{MP(z)} = \frac{(z - b_1)(z - b_2)}{(z - 1)a_0(z + a_1)} \qquad (15\text{-}91)$$

This controller is physically realizable. Therefore minimal-prototype control should be attainable.

But what about intersample ripples? Let us check the manipulative variable. According to Eq. (15-85),

$$M_{(z)} = \frac{X_{(z)}}{(HG_M)_{(z)}} = \frac{1/(z - 1)}{a_0(z + a_1)/(z - b_1)(z - b_2)} = \frac{(z - b_1)(z - b_2)}{a_0(z - 1)(z + a_1)} \qquad (15\text{-}92)$$

Let us take a specific numerical case; $K_p = \tau_{p1} = 1$; $\tau_{p2} = 5$; $T_s = 0.2$. These values make $b_1 = 0.8187$, $b_2 = 0.9608$, $a_0 = 0.0037$, and $a_1 = 0.923$. Long division gives

$$M_{(z)} = 270 - 460z^{-1} + 427z^{-2} - 392z^{-3} + 364z^{-4} - 334z^{-5} + 310z^{-6}$$
$$- 285z^{-7} + 265z^{-8} - 242z^{-9} + 256z^{-10} + \cdots \qquad (15\text{-}93)$$

This system will exhibit intersample rippling.

To prevent rippling we will modify our desired output response to give the system two sampling periods to come up to the set point. The value of $x_{(t)}$ at the first sampling period, the x_1 shown in Fig. 15-11d, is unspecified at this point. The output $X_{(z)}$ is now

$$X_{(z)} = x_1 z^{-1} + z^{-2} + z^{-3} + z^{-4} + \cdots \qquad (15\text{-}94)$$
$$= x_1 z^{-1} + z^{-2}(1 + z^{-1} + z^{-2} + \cdots)$$
$$= x_1 z^{-1} + z^{-2} \frac{1}{1 - z^{-1}}$$
$$X_{(z)} = \frac{x_1 z + 1 - x_1}{z(z - 1)} \qquad (15\text{-}95)$$

The set point is still a unit step disturbance:

$$X_{(z)}^{\text{set}} = \frac{z}{z - 1}$$

The new controller is

$$D_{MP(z)} = \frac{X_{(z)}}{(HG_M)_{(z)}(X_{(z)}^{\text{set}} - X_{(z)})}$$

$$= \frac{\dfrac{x_1 z + 1 - x_1}{z(z - 1)}}{\dfrac{a_0(z + a_1)}{(z - b_1)(z - b_2)}\left[\dfrac{z}{z - 1} - \dfrac{x_1 z + 1 - x_1}{z(z - 1)}\right]}$$

$$D_{(z)} = \frac{(z - b_1)(z - b_2)(x_1 z + 1 - x_1)}{a_0(z + a_1)(z - 1)(z + 1 - x_1)} \qquad (15\text{-}96)$$

The manipulative variable is

$$M_{(z)} = \frac{X_{(z)}}{(HG_M)_{(z)}} = \frac{(x_1 z + 1 - x_1)(z - b_1)(z - b_2)}{a_0(z + a_1)z(z - 1)} \qquad (15\text{-}97)$$

Rippling will occur whenever the denominator of $M_{(z)}$ contains any terms other than z or $z - 1$. Therefore, the $z + a_1$ term must be eliminated. This is done by picking x_1 such that the $z + a_1$ term is canceled out.

$$\frac{1 - x_1}{x_1} = a_1 \qquad (15\text{-}98)$$

$$x_1 = \frac{1}{1 + a_1} = 0.52 \qquad (15\text{-}99)$$

Then $M_{(z)}$ becomes

$$M_{(z)} = \frac{x_1(z - b_1)(z - b_2)}{a_0 z(z - 1)}$$

$$= \frac{\dfrac{x_1}{a_0} - \dfrac{(b_1 + b_2)x_1}{a_0} z^{-1} + \dfrac{b_1 b_2 x_1}{a_0} z^{-2}}{1 - z^{-1}}$$

$$M_{(z)} = \frac{x_1}{a_0} + \frac{(1 - b_1 - b_2)x_1}{a_0} z^{-1} + z^{-2} + z^{-3} + z^{-4} + \cdots$$

$$= 140.7 - 109.67z^{-1} + z^{-2} + z^{-3} + z^{-4} + \cdots \qquad (15\text{-}100)$$

Thus there is no rippling.   ////

PROBLEMS

15-1 Find the maximum value of K_c for which the digital-computer control system shown below is closed-loop stable for sampling periods T_s of 0.2 and 0.4 min.

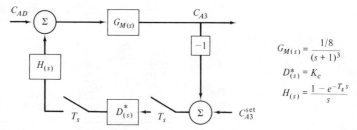

$$G_{M(s)} = \frac{1/8}{(s + 1)^3}$$

$$D^*_{(s)} = K_c$$

$$H_{(s)} = \frac{1 - e^{-T_s s}}{s}$$

15-2 Repeat Prob. 15-1 for

$$D_{(z)} = \frac{K_c}{\alpha} \frac{z - \alpha}{z - 1}$$

where $\alpha = \tau_I/(\tau_I + T_s)$. Use values of τ_I of 0.5, 1, and 2 min.

15-3　Make Nyquist plots of $A^*_{(i\omega)}$ for the systems of Prob. 15-1 and find the value of gain that gives the following frequency-domain specifications:

(a) Gain margin of 2

(b) Phase margin of 45°

(c) Maximum closed-loop log modulus of +2 db

15-4　Using a value of $\tau_I = \tau_p$ in the system of Example 15-2, show that the ultimate gain of the closed-loop system is $K_u = \tau_p/(K_p T_s)$ by:

(a) Direct substitution in the w plane

(b) A root locus plot in the z plane

(c) A Nyquist plot of $A^*_{(i\omega)}$

15-5　Repeat Prob. 15-3 for the systems of Examples 15-1 and 15-4.

15-6　Make a root locus plot in the z plane of the system of Prob. 15-1 and find the value of gain that gives a closed-loop damping coefficient ζ equal to 0.3.

15-7　Repeat Prob. 15-6 for the system of Example 15-4.

15-8　Use the bilinear transformation and the Nyquist stability criterion to find the ultimate gain of the open-loop unstable system of Example 15-6.

15-9　Draw a z-plane root locus plot for a second-order open-loop unstable process in a sampled-data control system. The controller is proportional and the hold is zero-order.

$$G_{(s)} = \frac{K_p}{(\tau_{p1}s + 1)(\tau_{p2}s - 1)}$$

15-10　Make Nyquist plots of the second-order system of Example 15-14 with the two minimal-prototype sampled-data controllers, one with ripples and one without ripples [Eqs. (15-91) and (15-96)]. Compare phase margins, gain margins, and maximum closed-loop log moduli.

15-11　What closed-loop damping coefficients do the two sampled-data controllers of Example 15-14 give?

15-12　Prove that the Nyquist plots of $A^*_{(i\omega)}$ found by setting $z = e^{i\omega T_s}$ in $A_{(z)}$ are identical to those found by setting $w = iv$ in $A_{(w)}$ after using the bilinear transformation.

15-13　Generate lines of constant damping coefficients in the w plane and in the $\ln z$ plane.

15-14　A distillation column has an approximate transfer function between distillate composition x_D and reflux flow rate R of

$$G_{M(s)} = \frac{0.0092}{(5s + 1)^2} \quad \diamond \quad \frac{\text{mole fraction}}{\text{moles/min}}$$

x_D is controlled by manipulation of R in a proportional sampled-data control loop. x_D is measured by a chromatograph with a dead time that is equal to the sampling period T_s.

(a) Find the ultimate gain of the system for values of $T_s = 2, 5, 10,$ and 20 min.

(b) Find the values of K_c that give a closed-loop damping coefficient of 0.3 with each T_s of part a.

15-15　Repeat Prob. 15-14 when a continuous PI controller is used with τ_I set at 5 min.

15-16   Develop the finite-difference equations and the z-domain pulse transfer functions that approximate the following continuous elements.

(a) Using the rectangular approximation for s^{-1}:

$$G_{(s)} = \frac{\tau s + 1}{\alpha \tau s + 1} \qquad G_{(s)} = \frac{1}{\tau^2 s^2 + 2\tau \zeta s + 1}$$

$$G_{(s)} = \frac{\tau s}{\alpha \tau s + 1} \qquad G_{(s)} = K_c \frac{\tau_I s + 1}{\tau_I s} \frac{\tau_D s + 1}{\alpha \tau_D s + 1}$$

(b) Using the trapezoidal approximation for s^{-1}:

$$G_{(s)} = K_c \frac{\tau_I s + 1}{\tau_I s}$$

15-17   Design a minimal-prototype sampled-data controller for a first-order system with a dead time that is three sampling periods. The input is a unit step change in set point. Your controller must be physically realizable.

15-18   Show that the equation for a minimal-prototype sampled-data controller depends on the type of input but not on the magnitude of the input disturbance.

15-19   Design a minimal-prototype sampled-data controller for the first-order process of Example 15-12 for a ramp input in set point: $x_{(t)}^{set} = t$. We want the output to come up to and follow the ramp after one sampling period: $X_{(z)} = 0 + z^{-1} + 2z^{-2} + 3z^{-3} + 4z^{-4} + \cdots$.

15-20   Calculate what $X_{(z)}$ does in the system and controller of Prob. 15-19 when the disturbance is not what the controller was designed for, a ramp, but is a step input.

15-21   Design a minimal-prototype sampled-data controller for the first-order open-loop unstable process of Example 15-6. The input is a step disturbance in set point. Is this controller stable?

15-22   Design a minimal-prototype sampled-data controller that will handle a step change in load $L_{(s)}$ to the system shown in Fig. 14-12b.

$$G_{M(s)} = G_{L(s)} = \frac{K_p}{\tau_p s + 1}$$

The hold is zero order. The desired response of the output $x_{(t)}$ to the load change is that $x_{(t)}$ return to zero after two sampling periods: $X_{(z)} = 0 + x_1 z^{-1} + 0 + 0 + \cdots$. The disturbance enters the system at time $t = 0$, but the controller does not see anything until $t = T_s$, when $x_{(t)}$ has climbed to x_1. The best that the controller can do is to bring $x_{(t)}$ back to zero at $t = 2T_s$.

15-23   Find the response of the system of Prob. 15-22 when the minimal-prototype controller derived for a load change is used but a step change in set point occurs.

15-24   Grandpa McCoy has decided to open up a new Liquid Lightning plant in the California gold fields. He plans to stay in Kentucky, and he must direct the operation of the plant via the available communications facilities. Telegraph can be used from his home to Denver. From there, the pony express is the only available link to his new plant. It takes two days for the mail to go between Denver and San Francisco, and a rider arrives at each end every day.

The new Liquid Lightning reactor is a single, isothermal, constant-holdup CSTR in which the concentration of ethanol, C, is controlled by manual changes in the feed concentration, C_0. Ethanol undergoes an irreversible first-order reaction at a specific rate $k = 0.25$/day. The volume of the reactor is 100 barrels, and the throughput, designed for the anticipated consumption, is 25 barrels/day.

Grandpa will receive information from the plant every day telling him what the concentration C was 2 days earlier. He will then immediately send back instructions to the operator in San Francisco of how to change C_0. What is the largest change Grandpa can make in C_0 as a percentage of C without causing the concentration in the reactor to begin oscillating with increasing amplitude?

POLYNOMIAL ROOT-SOLVING SUBROUTINE

(Courtesy of International Business Machines Corporation)

```
C
C
C     ••••••••••••••••••••••••••••••••••••••••••••••••••••••••••••
C
C     SUBROUTINE POLRT
C
C     PURPOSE
C       COMPUTES THE REAL AND COMPLEX ROOTS OF A REAL POLYNOMIAL
C
C     USAGE
C       CALL POLRT(XCOF,COF,M,ROOTR,ROOTI,IER)
C
C     DESCRIPTION OF PARAMETERS
C       XCOF -VECTOR OF M+1 COEFFICIENTS OF THE POLYNOMIAL
C             ORDERED FROM SMALLEST TO LARGEST POWER
C       COF  -WORKING VECTOR OF LENGTH M+1
C       M    -ORDER OF POLYNOMIAL
C       ROOTR-RESULTANT VECTOR OF LENGTH M CONTAINING REAL ROOTS
C             OF THE POLYNOMIAL
C       ROOTI-RESULTANT VECTOR OF LENGTH M CONTAINING THE
C             CORRESPONDING IMAGINARY ROOTS OF THE POLYNOMIAL
C       IER  -ERROR CODE WHERE
C             IER 0   NO ERROR
C             IER 1   M LESS THAN ONE
C             IER 2   M GREATER THAN 36
C             IER 3   UNABLE TO DETERMINE ROOT WITH 500 INTERATIONS
C                     ON 5 STARTING VALUES
C             IER 4   HIGH ORDER COEFFICIENT IS ZERO
C
C     REMARKS
C       LIMITED TO 36TH ORDER POLYNOMIAL OR LESS.
C       FLOATING POINT OVERFLOW MAY OCCUR FOR HIGH ORDER
C       POLYNOMTALS BUT WILL NOT AFFECT THE ACCURACY OF THE RESULTS.
C
C     SUBROUTINES AND FUNCTION SUBPROGRAMS REQUIRED
C       NONE
C
C     METHOD
C       NEWTON-RAPHSON ITERATIVE TECHNIQUE.  THE FINAL ITERATIONS
C       ON EACH ROOT ARE PERFORMED USING THE ORIGINAL POLYNOMIAL
C       RATHER THAN THE REDUCED POLYNOMTAL TO AVOID ACCUMULATED
C       ERRORS IN THE REDUCED POLYNOMIAL.
C
C     ••••••••••••••••••••••••••••••••••••••••••••••••••••••••••••
C
      SUBROUTINE POLRT(XCOF,COF,M,ROOTR,ROOTI,IER)
      DIMENSION XCOF(1),COF(1),ROOTR(1),ROOTI(1)
      DOUBLE PRECISION XO,YO,X,Y,XPR,YPR,UX,UY,V,YT,XT,U,XT2,YT2,SUMSQ,
     1 DX,DY,TEMP,ALPHA
C
C
C     ••••••••••••••••••••••••••••••••••••••••••••••••••••••••••••
C
C     IF A DOUBLE PRECISION VERSION OF THIS ROUTINE IS DESIRED, THE
C     C IN COLUMN 1 SHOULD BE REMOVED FROM THE DOUBLE PRECISION
C     STATEMENT WHICH FOLLOWS.
C
C     DOUBLE PRECISION XCOF,COF,ROOTR,ROOTI
C
C     THE C MUST ALSO BE REMOVED FROM DOUBLE PRECISION STATEMENTS
C     APPEARING IN OTHER ROUTINES USED IN CONJUNCTION WITH THIS
C     ROUTINE.
C     THE DOUBLE PRECISION VERSION MAY BE MODIFIED BY CHANGING THE
C     CONSTANT IN STATEMENT 78 TO 1.0D-12 AND TN STATEMENT 122 TO
C     1.0D-10.  THIS WILL PROVIDE HIGHER PRECISION RESULTS AT THE
C     COST OF EXECUTION TIME
C
C     ••••••••••••••••••••••••••••••••••••••••••••••••••••••••••••
C
      IFIT=0
```

```
      N=M
      IER=0
      IF(XCOF(N+1))10,25,10
   10 IF(N) 15,15,32
C
C          SET ERROR CODE TO 1
C
   15 IER=1
   20 RETURN
C
C          SET ERROR CODE TO 4
C
   25 IER=4
      GO TO 20
C
C          SET ERROR CODE TO 2
C
   30 IER=2
      GO TO 20
   32 IF(N-36) 35,35,30
   35 NX=N
      NXX=N+1
      N2=1
      KJ1=   N+1
      DO 40 L=1,KJ1
      MT=KJ1-L+1
   40 COF(MT)=XCOF(L)
C
C          SET INITIAL VALUES
C
   45 XO=.00500101
      YO=0.01000101
C
C          ZERO INITIAL VALUE COUNTER
C
      IN=0
   50 X=XO
C
C          INCREMENT INITIAL VALUES AND COUNTER
C
      XO=-10.0*YO
      YO=-10.0*X
C
C          SET X AND Y TO CURRENT VALUE
C
      X=XO
      Y=YO
      IN=IN+1
      GO TO 59
   55 IFIT=1
      XPR=X
      YPR=Y
C
C          EVALUATE POLYNOMIAL AND DERIVATIVES
C
   59 ICT=0
   60 UX=0.0
      UY=0.0
      V= 0.0
      YT=0.0
      XT=1.0
      U=COF(N+1)
      IF(U) 65,130,65
   65 DO 70 I=1,N
      L= N-I+1
      TEMP=COF(L)
      XT2=X*XT-Y*YT
      YT2=X*YT+Y*XT
```

```
                    U=U+TEMP*XT2
                    V=V+TEMP*YT2
                    FI=I
                    UX=UX+FI*XT*TEMP
                    UY=UY-FI*YT*TEMP
                    XT=XT2
                70  YT=YT2
                    SUMSQ=UX*UX+UY*UY
                    IF(SUMSQ) 75,110,75
                75  DX=(V*UY-U*UX)/SUMSQ
                    X=X+DX
                    DY=-(U*UY+V*UX)/SUMSQ
                    Y=Y+DY
                78  IF(DABS(DY)+DABS(DX)-1.0D-05) 100,80,80
       C
       C            STEP ITERATION COUNTER
       C
                80  ICT=ICT+1
                    IF(ICT-500) 60,85,85
                85  IF(IFIT)100,90,100
                90  IF(IN-5) 50,35,95
       C
       C            SET ERROR CODE TO 3
       C
                95  IER=3
                    GO TO 20
               100  DO 105 L=1,NXX
                    MT=KJ1-L+1
                    TEMP=XCOF(MT)
                    XCOF(MT)=COF(L)
               105  COF(L)=TEMP
                    ITEMP=N
                    N=NX
                    NX=ITEMP
                    IF(IFIT) 120,55,120
               110  IF(IFIT) 115,50,115
               115  X=XPR
                    Y=YPR
               120  IFIT=0
               122  IF(DABS(Y)-1.0D-4*DABS(X)) 135,125,125
               125  ALPHA=X+X
                    SUMSQ=X*X+Y*Y
                    N=N-2
                    GO TO 140
               130  X=0.0
                    NX=NX-1
                    NXX=NXX-1
               135  Y=0.0
                    SUMSQ=0.0
                    ALPHA=X
                    N=N-1
               140  COF(2)=COF(2)+ALPHA*COF(1)
               145  DO 150 L=2,N
               150  COF(L+1)=COF(L+1)+ALPHA*COF(L)-SUMSQ*COF(L-1)
               155  ROOTI(N2)=Y
                    ROOTR(N2)=X
                    N2=N2+1
                    IF(SUMSQ) 160,165,160
               160  Y=-Y
                    SUMSQ=0.0
                    GO TO 155
               165  IF(N) 20,20,45
                    END
```

INSTRUMENTATION HARDWARE

A.2.1 SENSORS

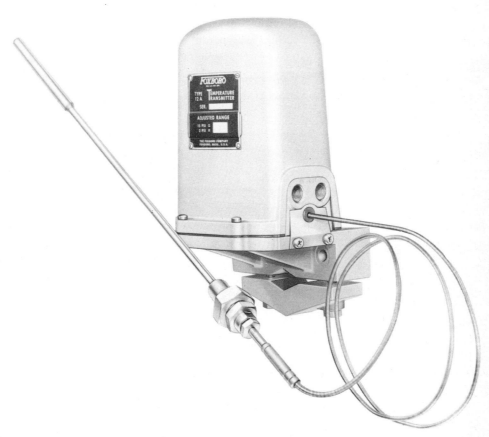

FIGURE A-1
Filled-bulb pneumatic temperature transmitter. (Courtesy of The Foxboro
Company.)

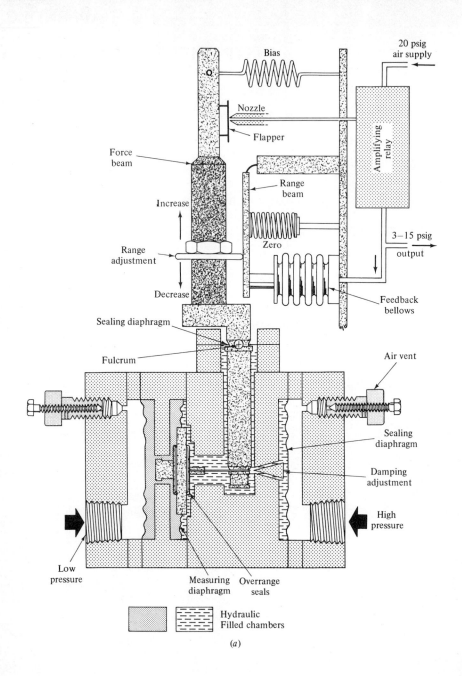

(a)

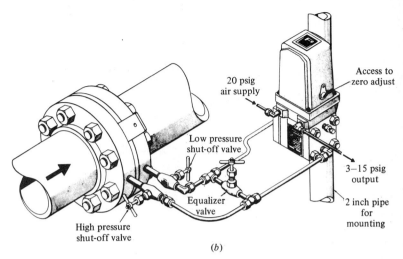

20 psig
air supply

Access to
zero adjust

Low pressure
shut-off valve

3–15 psig
output

Equalizer
valve

2 inch pipe
for
mounting

High pressure
shut-off valve

(b)

FIGURE A-2
Pneumatic differential pressure transmitter. (a) Details of operation; (b) typical
installation with orifice plate to sense flow rate. (Courtesy of Fischer and Porter
Company.)

FIGURE A-3
Electronic temperature transmitter. (Courtesy of Honeywell Industrial Division.)

A.2.2   CONTROL VALVES

FIG. A-4 (*a*)

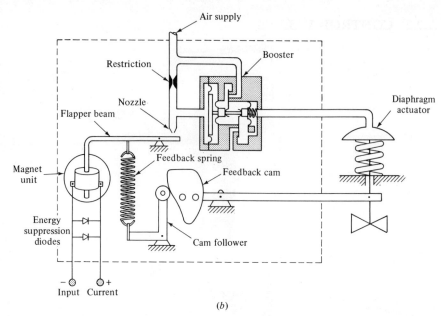

(b)

FIGURE A-4
Electronic control valve (current input-air actuated). (a) Electropneumatic valve
positioner mounted on a Honeywell diaphragm-actuated control valve; (b)
schematic diagram of electropneumatic valve positioner. (Courtesy of Honeywell
Industrial Division.)

A.2.3   CONTROLLERS

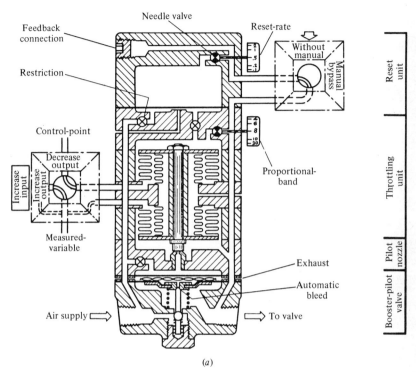

(a)

FIG. A-5

FIGURE A-5
Pneumatic " stack " controller. (a) Schematic of internals; (b) external appearance. (Courtesy of Moore Products Company.)

(b)

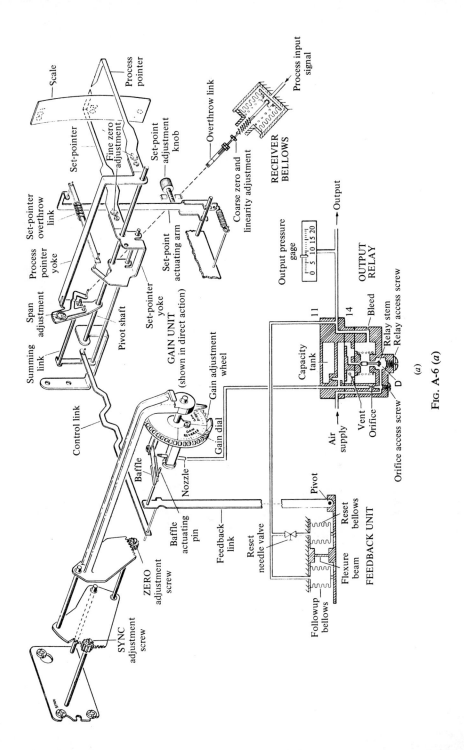

Scale
Process pointer
Fine zero adjustment
Set-pointer
Set-point adjustment knob
Set-point adjustment
Overthrow link
Coarse zero and linearity adjustment
RECEIVER BELLOWS
Process input signal

Set-pointer overthrow link
Process pointer yoke
Set-point actuating arm
Set-pointer yoke

Span adjustment
Summing link
Pivot shaft
GAIN UNIT (shown in direct action)

Control link
Gain adjustment wheel
Gain dial

Baffle
Nozzle
Baffle actuating pin
Feedback link

ZERO adjustment screw

SYNC adjustment screw

Reset needle valve
Followup bellows
Reset bellows
Flexure beam
Pivot
FEEDBACK UNIT

Output pressure gage
0 5 10 15 20
Output
OUTPUT RELAY

Capacity tank
11
14
Bleed
Relay stem
Relay access screw
Air supply
Vent
Orifice
D
Orifice access screw

Fig. A-6 (a)

(a)

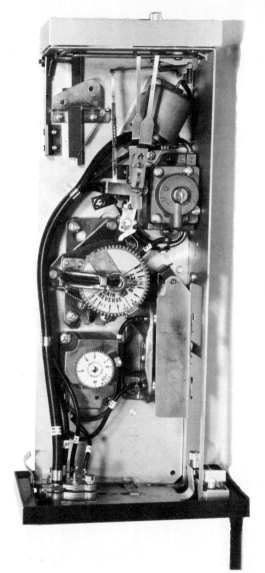

(b)

FIGURE A-6
Pneumatic controller. (a) Schematic of internals; (b) view of controller internals. (Courtesy of Taylor Instrument Companies.)

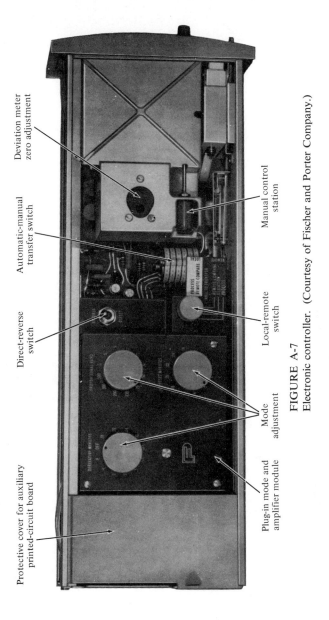

Deviation meter
zero adjustment

Automatic-manual
transfer switch

Direct-reverse
switch

Protective cover for auxiliary
printed-circuit board

Manual control
station

Local-remote
switch

Mode
adjustment

Plug-in mode and
amplifier module

FIGURE A-7
Electronic controller.   (Courtesy of Fischer and Porter Company.)

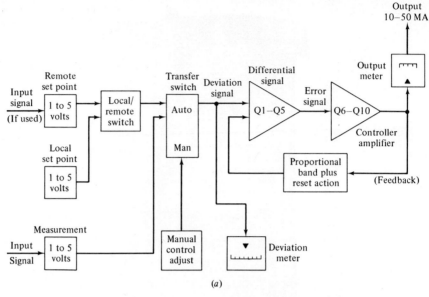

(a)

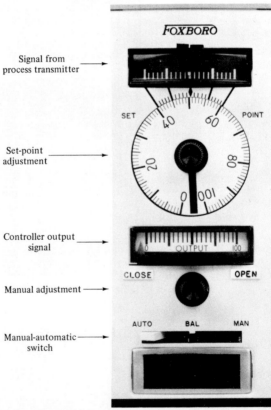

(b)

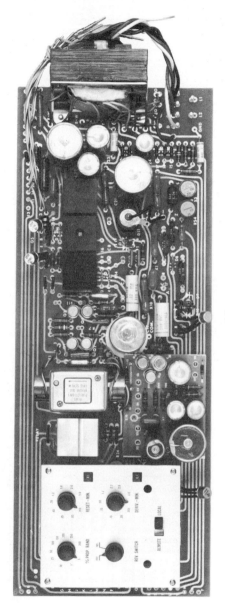

(c)

FIGURE A-8

Electronic controller. (a) Circuit diagram; (b) front view; (c) view of controller internals. (Courtesy of The Foxboro Company.)

A.2.4   COMPUTING RELAYS

(a)

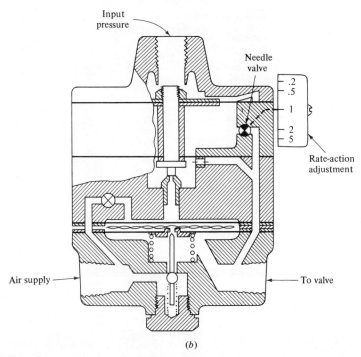

(b)

FIGURE A-9
Pneumatic derivative unit. (a) External appearance; (b) schematic of internals.
(Courtesy of Moore Products Company.)

FIG. A-10 (*a*)   (*a*)

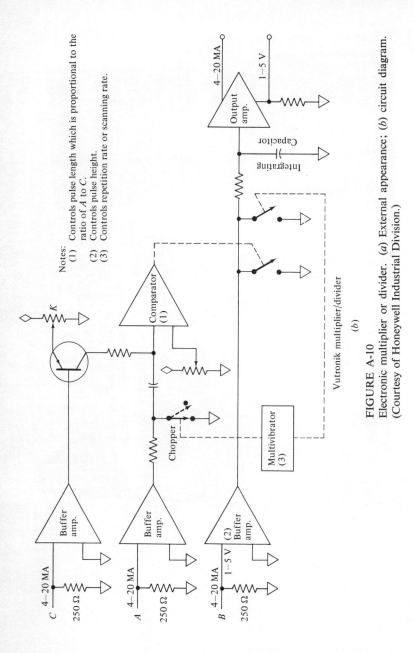

Notes: (1) Controls pulse length which is proportional to the ratio of A to C.
(2) Controls pulse height.
(3) Controls repetition rate or scanning rate.

FIGURE A-10

Electronic multiplier or divider. (*a*) External appearance; (*b*) circuit diagram. (Courtesy of Honeywell Industrial Division.)

FIGURE A-11
Pneumatic low limiter. (Courtesy of
Moore Products Company.)

FIGURE A-12
Pneumatic high selector. (Courtesy of
Moore Products Company.)

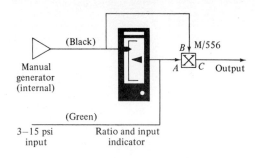

Function: (input) (ratio) = output

(a)

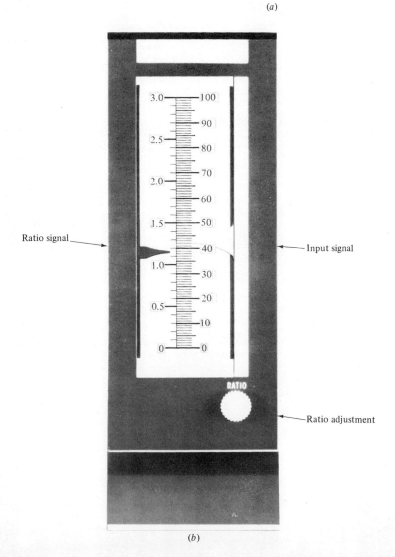

(b)

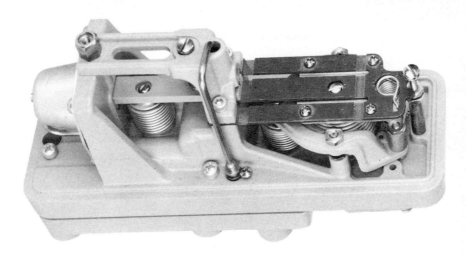

(*c*)

FIGURE A-13
Pneumatic ratio control station. (*a*) Schematic diagram of operation; (*b*) front
view of ratio station; (*c*) pneumatic multiplier (M/556). (Courtesy of The Foxboro Company.)

FIGURE A-14
Typical back-of-the-panel-board installation. (Courtesy of Moore Products Company.)

Activation energy, 39
Amplifier, high-gain, 94
Analog computers, 93-117
Arrhenius temperature dependence, 39

Batch reactors:
    digital simulation, 160-167
    model, 62-67
Bilinear transformation, 510-513
Bode plots, 250-261
Breakpoint frequency, 254
Buckley, P. S., 307, 315, 333, 342, 421

Capacitor, 94
Carnahan, Brice, 90
Cascade control, 326-328
Ceaglske, N. H., 376
Characteristic equation:
    definition, 189
    nth order system, 199
    in z domain, 494

Chromatographic control systems, 456
Complementary solution of ODE, 188
Complex variables, digital computer, 262
Computing relays, 321
Continuity equations, 18-24
Controllers, commercial hardware, 317-321
Convergence, implicit functions, 123-130
Critical damping, 190
CSTR models, 44-54
CSTR simulation:
    analog computer, 99-117
    digital computer, 139-148
CSTR transfer functions, 221-228
C_y of control values, 313

Damping coefficient, 175, 189
D'Azzo, J. J., 413
Deadtime:
    Laplace transformation, 219
    frequency response, 247, 254
    z domain, 476
Decibels, 251

Decoupling, 383
Degrees of freedom, 17
Derivative:
    frequency response, 256
    transfer function, 217
Derivative action in feedback controllers, 320,
    326
Digital control algorithms, 519
Digital control computers, 457-460
Diode, 94
Distillation columns:
    analog simulation, 107-109
    digital simulation, 148-159
    feed forward control, 445
    frequency domain solution, 267-276
    models, 69-81
Distinct roots, 189

Efficiency, tray, 75
Energy equation, 24-29
Equilibrium:
    chemical, 36
    phase, 37-39
    vapor-liquid, 37-39
Euler integration algorithm, 132-135
Explicit convergence, 128
Exponential:
    Laplace transformation, 211
    z transformation, 468

False position convergence, 128
Feed forward control, 431-449
Final-value theorem:
    Laplace transforms, 231
    z transforms, 471
First-order ODE, analytical solution, 182-187
Flash drum model, 58-61
Force balances, 29-33
Forcing functions, 45
Fourier transforms, digital evaluation, 285-288
Francis weir formula, 71
Franks, R. G. E., 60, 122
Frequency domain solution techniques, 264-
    276
Frequency response, definition, 238

Gain transfer function, 216
Gain margin, 407
Gravity-flow tank, 2, 104

Himmelblau, D. M., 280, 295
Hold, zero-order, 480
Hougen, J. O., 283, 333

Impulse function:
    definition, 175
    Laplace transform, 212
    z transform, 469
Impulse sampler, 460-463
Integral action in feedback controllers, 319,
    326
Integration, numerical, 130-139
    accuracy and stability, 137-139
Integrator:
    analog computer, 96
    frequency response, 248, 256
    transfer function, 218
Interaction, 380-384
Interval-halving convergence, 124-126
Inverse response, 377-380
Inversion:
    Laplace transforms, 213-216
    z transforms, 472-477

Jacket, cooling, 50-54

Kinetics, 39
Koppel, L. B., 509

Lag:
    first-order: definition, 221
        frequency response, 245, 253
    second-order underdamped frequency re-
        sponse, 249, 256
Lamb, D. E., 266, 267
Lapidus, L., 90
Laplace transforms, 209-220
Lead, frequency response, 245, 254
Lead-lag, 230
Limiter, high and low, 322, 344
Linear ODE, 177
Linearization, 177-180
Log modulus:
    definition, 250
    maximum closed-loop specification, 407-
        413
Luyben, W. L., 268, 307, 377, 384, 446, 506

McCracken, D. D., 91
Magnitude ratio, 239
Manipulative variables, 9
Marroquin, G., 506
Mass transfer in reactor model, 67-69
Messa, C. J., 288
Minimal-prototype sampled-data controllers, 520-526
Momentum, 30
Mosler, H. A., 520
Motion, equations of, 29-33
Multipliers, analog computers, 97
Murrill, P. W., 331

Nested control loops, 336
Newton-Raphson convergence, 126
Nichols chart, 410-413
Nichols plots, 261
Nonlinear controllers:
    feedback, 339-341
    feedforward, 446-449
Nyquist plots, 244
Nyquist stability criterion, 390-402, 496

Open-loop unstable process, 372-377, 423-426, 509
Order of differential equations, 174

Pade approximation of deadtime, 366
Partial fractions expansions, 213, 473
Particular solution of ODE, 194-198
Perturbation variables, 180-182
Phase angle, definition, 239
Phase margin, 404
Physical realizability, 229, 514
Pigford, R. L., 188
Poles of transfer function, 221, 230
POLRT, 368
Positive zero, 378
Pot (potentiometer), 94
Proportional action in feedback controllers, 318, 324
Proportional band, 318
Pulse function, 175
Pulse testing, 282-292
Pulse transfer function, 477-479

Ragazzini, J. R., 454

Ramp function:
    definition, 175
    Laplace transform, 210
    z transform, 468
Ratio control, 344
Regulator response, 177
Relative volatility, 38,69
Repeated roots, 190
Reset (*see* Integral action)
Reset windup, 341-344
Rippin, D. W. T., 267
Rippling, 523-526
Root locus analysis:
    in s plane, 363-372
    in z plane, 504-509
Routh stability criterion, 355-359, 513
Runge-Kutta numerical integration algorithm, 135-137

Sampled-data controllers, 514-526
Sampling theorem, 464
Second-order ODE analytical solution, 187-198
Selective control loops, 342-344
Selectors, high and low, 322
Sensors, 308-310
Servo response, 177
Shinskey, F. G., 333, 341, 451
Shunta, J. P., 268
Sine, Laplace transform, 211
Sine wave testing, 280
Specifications for control performance:
    frequency domain, 404-410
    Laplace domain, 360-363
    time domain, 323
Stability, 10, 174
Steady-state gain, 185, 221, 231
Steady-state techniques, 201-204
Step function:
    definition, 175
    Laplace transform, 210
    z transform, 467
Step testing, 280, 294
Stepping technique, 267-276
Summer, analog computer, 95
Switching, manual-automatic, 307

Taylor series expansion, 178, 221
Time constant, 175, 185
Time scaling, 102

Tou, J. T., 454, 470, 513
Transfer functions:
    definition, 216-220
    properties, 229-232
Transmission lag in pneumatic tubing, 307
Transmitters, 310
Transport law, 34
Tuning controllers, 328-332

Ultimate frequency, 330-360
Ultimate gain, 330-358, 360
Ultimate period, 330-360
Underdamped system, 191
Undetermined coefficients, 194-198

Valves, control: design and performance, 313-
    317
    flow characteristics, 314-316
    split-ranged, 65
Van Heerden, C., 201
Vaporizer model, 54
Viscosity, 32
Voltage scaling, 100

z transforms, 465-477
Zeros of transfer function, 230
Ziegler-Nichols tuning, 331
Zoss, L. M., 341